ENGINEERING ELECTROMAGNETICS

MCGRAW-HILL ELECTRICAL AND ELECTRONIC ENGINEERING SERIES

LEY, LUTZ, AND REHBERG Linear Circuit Analysis
LINVILL AND GIBBONS Transistors and Active Circuits
LITTAUER Pulse Electronics
LYNCH AND TRUXAL Introductory System Analysis
LYNCH AND TRUXAL Principles of Electronic Instrumentation
LYNCH AND TRUXAL Signals and Systems in Electrical Engineering
MANNING Electrical Circuits
MCCLUSKEY Introduction to the Theory of Switching Circuits
MEISEL Principles of Electromechanical-energy Conversion
MILLMAN Vacuum-tube and Semiconductor Electronics
MILLMAN AND SEELY Electronics
MILLMAN AND TAUB Pulse and Digital Circuits
MILLMAN AND TAUB Pulse, Digital, and Switching Waveforms
MISHKIN AND BRAUN Adaptive Control Systems
MOORE Traveling-wave Engineering
NANAVATI An Introduction to Semiconductor Electronics
PETTIT Electronic Switching, Timing, and Pulse Circuits
PETTIT AND MCWHORTER Electronic Amplifier Circuits
PFEIFFER Concepts of Probability Theory
REZA An Introduction to Information Theory
REZA AND SEELY Modern Network Analysis
ROGERS Introduction to Electric Fields
RUSTON AND BORDOGNA Electric Networks: Functions, Filters, Analysis
RYDER Engineering Electronics
SCHWARTZ Information Transmission, Modulation, and Noise
SCHWARZ AND FRIEDLAND Linear Systems
SEELY Electromechanical Energy Conversion
SEELY Electron-tube Circuits
SEELY Electronic Engineering
SEELY Introduction to Electromagnetic Fields
SEELY Radio Electronics
SEIFERT AND STEEG Control Systems Engineering
SISKIND Direct-current Machinery
SKILLING Electric Transmission Lines
SKILLING Transient Electric Currents
SPANGENBERG Fundamentals of Electron Devices
SPANGENBERG Vacuum Tubes
STEVENSON Elements of Power System Analysis
STEWART Fundamentals of Signal Theory
STORER Passive Network Synthesis
STRAUSS Wave Generation and Shaping
SU Active Network Synthesis
TERMAN Electronic and Radio Engineering
TERMAN AND PETTIT Electronic Measurements
THALER Elements of Servomechanism Theory
THALER AND BROWN Analysis and Design of Feedback Control Systems
THALER AND PASTEL Analysis and Design of Nonlinear Feedback Control Systems
THOMPSON Alternating-current and Transient Circuit Analysis
TOU Digital and Sampled-data Control Systems
TOU Modern Control Theory
TRUXAL Automatic Feedback Control System Synthesis
TUTTLE Electric Networks: Analysis and Synthesis
VALDES The Physical Theory of Transistors
VAN BLADEL Electromagnetic Fields
WEINBERG Network Analysis and Synthesis
WILLIAMS AND YOUNG Electrical Engineering Problems

ENGINEERING ELECTROMAGNETICS

Second Edition

WILLIAM H. HAYT, Jr.

Professor of Electrical Engineering, Purdue University

McGRAW-HILL BOOK COMPANY

New York, St. Louis, San Francisco, Toronto, London, Sydney

PREFACE

Although most electrical engineering curricula begin with a study of electric and magnetic circuits, it is now recognized that the more basic theory of the electric and magnetic fields deserves subsequent attention in the curriculum. Some familiarity with circuit concepts as well as a knowledge of calculus allows a treatment of field theory in the junior year, which proceeds through Maxwell's equations and justifies the approximations which lead to circuit theory.

This textbook uses Maxwell's equations as the central theme. These equations are developed from the historical approach in which the several experimental laws are gradually introduced and manipulated with the help of a gradually increasing knowledge of vector calculus. Maxwell's equations are identified as they occur, even as they apply to static fields, and a certain sense of accomplishment should be felt when the theory is finally completed. Several applications of these equations are described in the subsequent sections, including wave motion, skin effect, transmission-line phenomena, circuit theory, and radiation.

The material is more than adequate for a one-semester course. Depending on the instructional level, it may be desirable to omit portions of the chapters on experimental mapping methods, the solution of Laplace's equation, the application of Maxwell's equations, and transmission lines.

This book has been written with the goal of making it as easy as possible for the student to teach himself. This has been done by applying a carefully graduated scale of difficulty within each chapter and among the chapters themselves, by providing numerous examples interpreting and applying every basic result and also numerical examples where possible, by including a large number of drill problems to which numerical answers are given, and by avoiding an excessive involvement with analytic geometry and its detailed use in interpreting fields.

The more difficult material has been placed near the ends of the chapters or at the end of the study of some definite phase of the subject. The poorer student, who admittedly cannot assimilate the same amount of material as the better one, will thus be attracted to the more basic material at the beginning of each chapter. Since the subject matter of the following chapter is not usually built on the most advanced material of the previous chapter, he can then make a fresh start from his poorer but adequate background.

The more advanced material does, however, offer a needed challenge to the better students.

Drill problems are placed at the ends of most sections in which a formula or law is introduced which is capable of expression in problem form. Each drill problem has three parts of a generally similar nature. The problems appearing at the ends of the chapters are more difficult, more interesting, and are given without answers. With the exception of one or two problems in each chapter that refer the student to technical articles and other books in order to promote at least a casual acquaintance with the library, the problem order corresponds to the order of the corresponding text material.

Most of the goals of the first edition continue to be valid in this newer edition. However, nine years of usage have prompted many students and colleagues to suggest additions, deletions, and changes; even the author has contributed a few suggestions.

All of the problems in the second edition are new, and there are more of them for the sake of variety. The units and abbreviations used are those of the International System of Units, adopted by the National Bureau of Standards in 1964. More standard symbols have also been adopted for current density ($\mathbf{J}$) and surface current density ($\mathbf{K}$).

The important vector-calculus relationships in the several co-ordinate systems have been printed inside the back cover for easy reference, and the bibliographies at the end of each chapter have been augmented and updated.

The increasing importance of materials has necessitated complete revision and expansion of the discussion of conductors, dielectrics, and magnetic materials in Chapters 5 and 9. The initial discussion of both electric and magnetic fields has been modified so that it is restricted to free-space conditions.

New material is also included on streamlines, the line integral, the application of Poisson's equation to solid-state devices, the scalar magnetic potential, magnetic circuits, inductance, Faraday's law for moving conductors, the uniform plane wave, reflection and voltage-standing-wave ratio, transmission lines, the circuit equivalent of a resonant cavity, and the International System of Units in Appendix B.

Topics which have been deleted include the relaxation method in Chapter 6 and the chapter on charged particles in electromagnetic fields. Several of the repetitious and less important examples in Chapters 2 and 3 have also been omitted in acknowledgment of the improved preparation of today's electrical engineering undergraduates.

The author gratefully acknowledges the thorough reviewing of the entire manuscript by Prof. W. L. Weeks of Purdue University.

Professors R. J. Schwartz and L. F. Silva made valuable suggestions with respect to Chapters 5 and 9, respectively. Many anonymous reviewers have suggested a number of the changes in this edition (as well as many more that could not be incorporated in what is nominally a one-semester text). Finally, letters from many students across the country have pointed out errors and inadequate expositions. These are greatly appreciated, and the author also invites comment from the new generation of readers.

William H. Hayt, Jr.

CONTENTS

1 VECTOR ANALYSIS

Vector analysis is a mathematical subject which is much better taught by mathematicians than by engineers. Most junior and senior engineering students, however, have not had the time (or perhaps the inclination) to take a course in vector analysis, although it is likely that elementary vector concepts and operations were introduced in early mathematics courses. These fundamental concepts and operations are covered in this chapter, and the time devoted to them should depend on past exposure.

The viewpoint here is also that of the engineer or physicist and not that of the mathematician in that proofs are indicated rather than rigorously expounded and the physical interpretation is stressed. It is easier for an engineer to take a more rigorous and complete course in the mathematics department after he has been presented with a few physical pictures and applications.

It is possible to study electricity and magnetism without the use of vector analysis, and some engineering students have probably done so in a previous electrical engineering or basic physics course. Carrying this elementary work a bit further, however, soon leads to line-filling equations often composed of terms which all look about the same. A quick glance at one of these long equations discloses little of the physical nature of the equation and may even lead to slighting an old friend.

Vector analysis is a mathematical shorthand. It has some new symbols, some new rules, a pitfall here and there like most new fields, and it demands concentration, attention, and practice. The drill problems, first met at the end of Sec. 1.4, should be considered an integral part of the text and should all be worked. They should not prove to be difficult if the material in the accompanying section of the text has been thoroughly understood. It takes a little longer to "read" the chapter this way, but the investment in time will produce a surprising interest.

1.1 SCALARS AND VECTORS

The term *scalar* refers to a quantity which has only a magnitude. The x, y, and z we used in basic algebra are scalars, and the quantities they represent are scalars. If we speak of a body falling a distance L in a time t, or the temperature T at any point in a bowl of soup whose coordinates are x, y, and z, then L, t, T, x, y, and z are all scalars. Other scalar quantities are mass, density, pressure

1

(but not force), volume, and volume resistivity. Voltage is also a scalar quantity, although the complex representation of a sinusoidal voltage, an artificial procedure, produces a *complex scalar* or *phasor*.

A *vector* quantity has both a magnitude and a direction in space. We shall be concerned with two- and three-dimensional spaces only, but vectors may be defined in n-dimensional space in more advanced applications. Force, velocity, acceleration, and a line from the positive to the negative terminal of a storage battery are examples of vectors. Each quantity is characterized by both a magnitude and a direction.

We shall be mostly concerned with scalar and vector *fields*. A field (scalar or vector) may be defined mathematically as some function of the vector connecting an arbitrary origin to a general point in space. We usually find it possible to associate some physical effect with a field, such as the force on a compass needle in the earth's magnetic field, or the movement of smoke particles in the field defined by the vector velocity of air in some region of space. Note that the field concept invariably is related to a region. Some quantity is defined at every point in a region. Both *scalar fields* and *vector fields* exist. The temperature throughout the bowl of soup and the density at any point in the earth are examples of scalar fields, for a scalar quantity has some specific value at every point in the given region, a value in general varying with both position and time. The gravitational and magnetic fields of the earth, the voltage gradient in a cable, and the temperature gradient in a soldering-iron tip are examples of vector fields.

In this book, as in most others using vector notation, vectors will be indicated by boldface type, for example, **A**. Scalars are printed in italic type, for example, A, and have no special symbol. When writing longhand or using a typewriter, it is customary to draw a line or an arrow over a vector quantity to show its vector character. (CAUTION: This is the first pitfall. Sloppy notation, such as the omission of the line or arrow symbol for a vector, is the major cause of errors in vector analysis.)

1.2 VECTOR ALGEBRA

With the definitions of vectors and vector fields now accomplished, we may proceed to define the rules of vector arithmetic, vector algebra, and (later) of vector calculus. Some of the rules will be similar to those of scalar algebra, some will differ slightly, and some will be entirely new and strange. This is to be expected, for a vector represents more information than does a scalar, and the multiplication of two vectors, for example, will be more involved than the multiplication of two scalars.

FIG. 1.1 Two vectors may be added graphically either by drawing both vectors from a common origin and completing the parallelogram or by beginning the second vector from the head of the first and completing the triangle; either method is easily extended to three or more vectors.

The rules are those of a branch of mathematics which is firmly established. Everyone "plays by the same rules," and we, of course, are merely going to look at and interpret these rules. However, it is enlightening to consider ourselves pioneers in the field. We are making our own rules, and we can make any rules we wish. The only requirement is that the rules be self-consistent. Of course, it would be nice if the rules agreed with those of scalar algebra where possible, and it would be even nicer if the rules enabled us to solve a few practical problems.

One should not fall into the trap of "algebra worship" and believe that the rules of college algebra were delivered unto man at the Creation. These rules are merely self-consistent and extremely useful. There are other less familiar algebras, however, with very different rules. In Boolean algebra the product AB can be only unity or zero. Vector algebra has its own set of rules, and we must be constantly on guard against the mental forces exerted by the more familiar rules of scalar algebra.

Vectorial addition follows the parallelogram law, and this is easily, if inaccurately, accomplished graphically. Figure 1.1 shows the sum of two vectors, **A** and **B**. It is easily seen that $\mathbf{A} + \mathbf{B} = \mathbf{B} + \mathbf{A}$, or that vector addition obeys the commutative law. Vector addition also obeys the associative law,

$$\mathbf{A} + (\mathbf{B} + \mathbf{C}) = (\mathbf{A} + \mathbf{B}) + \mathbf{C}$$

Coplanar vectors, or vectors lying in a common plane, such as those of Fig. 1.1, which both lie in the plane of the paper, may also be added by expressing each vector in terms of "horizontal" and "vertical" components and adding the corresponding components.

Vectors in three dimensions may likewise be added by expressing the vectors in terms of three components and adding the corresponding components. Examples of this process of addition will be given after vector components are discussed in Sec. 1.4.

The rule for the subtraction of vectors follows easily from that for addition, for we may always express $\mathbf{A} - \mathbf{B}$ as $\mathbf{A} + (-\mathbf{B})$; the sign and direction of the second vector are reversed, and this vector is then added to the first by the rule for vector addition.

Vectors may be multiplied by scalars. The magnitude of the vector changes, but its direction does not when the scalar is positive, although it reverses direction when multiplied by a negative scalar. Multiplication of a vector by a scalar also obeys the associative and distributive laws of algebra, leading to

$$(r + s)(\mathbf{A} + \mathbf{B}) = r(\mathbf{A} + \mathbf{B}) + s(\mathbf{A} + \mathbf{B}) = r\mathbf{A} + r\mathbf{B} + s\mathbf{A} + s\mathbf{B}$$

Division of a vector by a scalar is merely multiplication by the reciprocal of that scalar.

The multiplication of a vector by a vector is discussed in Secs. 1.6 and 1.7 below.

Two vectors are said to be equal if their difference is zero, or $\mathbf{A} = \mathbf{B}$ if $\mathbf{A} - \mathbf{B} = 0$.

In our use of vector fields we shall always add and subtract vectors which are defined at the same point. For example, the *total* magnetic field about a small horseshoe magnet will be shown to be the sum of the fields produced by the earth and the permanent magnet; the total field at any point is the sum of the individual fields at that point.

If we are not considering a vector *field*, however, we may add or subtract vectors which are not defined at the same point. For example, the sum of the gravitational force acting on a 150-lbf (pound-force) man at the North Pole and that acting on a 175-lbf man at the South Pole may be obtained by shifting each force vector to the South Pole before addition. The resultant is a force of 25 lbf directed toward the center of the earth at the South Pole; if we wanted to be difficult, we could just as well describe the force as 25 lbf directed *away* from the center of the earth (or "upward") at the North Pole.[1]

1.3 THE CARTESIAN COORDINATE SYSTEM

In order to describe a vector accurately, some specific lengths, directions, angles, projections, or components must be given. There are three simple methods of doing this, and about eight or ten other methods which are useful in very special cases. We are going to use only the three simple methods, and the simplest of these is the *cartesian*, or *rectangular*, *coordinate system*.

In the cartesian coordinate system we set up three coordinate axes, mutually at right angles to each other, and call them the x, y, and z axes. It is customary to choose a *right-handed* coordinate system, in which a rotation (through the smaller angle) of the x axis into

---

[1] Someone has also pointed out that the force might be described at the equator as being in a "northerly" direction. He is right, but enough is enough.

FIG. 1.2 (*a*) A right-handed cartesian coordinate system. If the curved fingers of the right hand indicate the direction through which the *x* axis is turned into coincidence with the *y* axis, the thumb shows the direction of the *z* axis. (*b*) The location of points *P* (1,2,3) and *Q* (2,−2,1). (*c*) The differential volume element in cartesian coordinates; dx, dy, and dz are in general independent differentials.

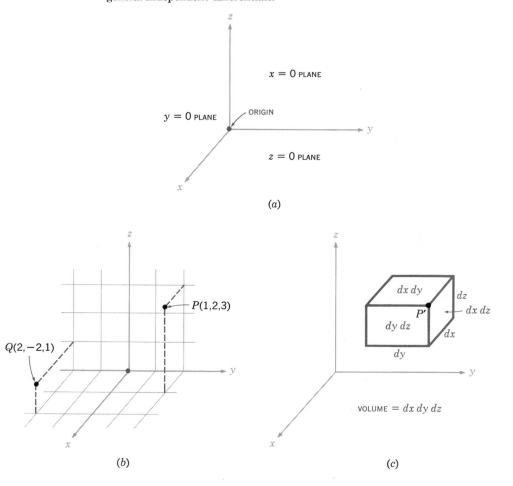

(*a*)

(*b*)

(*c*)

the *y* axis would cause a right-handed screw to progress in the direction of the *z* axis.   Using the right hand, the thumb, forefinger, and middle finger may then be identified, respectively, as the *x*, *y*, and *z* axes.   Figure 1.2*a* shows a right-handed cartesian coordinate system.

A point is located by giving its *x*, *y*, and *z* coordinates.   These are, respectively, the distances from the origin to the intersection of a perpendicular dropped from the point to the *x*, *y*, and *z* axes. An alternative method of interpreting coordinate values, and a method corresponding to that which *must* be used in all other coordinate systems, is to consider the point as being at the common intersection of three planes, given by x = constant, y = constant, and z = constant, the constants being the coordinate values of the point.

Figure 1.2b shows the points P and Q whose coordinates are (1,2,3) and (2,−2,1), respectively. Point P is therefore located at the common point of intersection of the planes x = 1, y = 2, and z = 3, while point Q is located at the intersection of the planes x = 2, y = −2, z = 1.

As we encounter other coordinate systems in Secs. 1.8 and 1.9, we should expect points to be located by the common intersection of three surfaces, not necessarily planes, but still mutually perpendicular at the point of intersection.

If we visualize three planes intersecting at the general point P, whose coordinates are x, y, and z, we may increase each coordinate value by a differential amount and obtain three slightly displaced planes intersecting at point P', whose coordinates are $x + dx$, $y + dy$, and $z + dz$. The six planes define a rectangular parallelepiped whose volume is $dv = dx\,dy\,dz$; the surfaces have differential areas dS of $dx\,dy$, $dy\,dz$, and $dz\,dx$. Finally, the distance dL from P to P' is the diagonal of the parallelepiped and has a length of $\sqrt{(dx)^2 + (dy)^2 + (dz)^2}$. The volume element is shown in Fig. 1.2c; point P' is indicated, but point P is located at the only invisible corner.

All this is familiar from trigonometry or solid geometry and as yet involves only scalar quantities. We shall begin to describe vectors in terms of a coordinate system in the next section.

1.4 VECTOR COMPONENTS AND UNIT VECTORS

To describe a vector in the cartesian coordinate system let us first consider a vector $\mathbf{r}$ extending outward from the origin. A logical way to identify this vector is by giving the three *component vectors*, lying along the three coordinate axes, whose vector sum must be the given vector. If the component vectors of the vector $\mathbf{r}$ are $\mathbf{x}, \mathbf{y}$, and $\mathbf{z}$, then $\mathbf{r} = \mathbf{x} + \mathbf{y} + \mathbf{z}$. The component vectors are shown in Fig. 1.3a. Instead of one vector, we now have three, but this is a step forward, because the three vectors are of a very simple nature; each is always directed along one of the coordinate axes.

In other words, the component vectors have a magnitude which depends on the given vector (such as $\mathbf{r}$ above), but they each have a known and constant direction. This suggests the use of *unit vectors* having unit magnitude, by definition, and directed along the coordinate axes in the direction of the increasing coordinate values. We shall reserve the symbol $\mathbf{a}$ for a unit vector and identify the direction of the unit vector by an appropriate subscript.

FIG. 1.3 (*a*) The component vectors **x**, **y**, and **z** of vector **r**. (*b*) The unit vectors of the cartesian coordinate system have unit magnitude and are directed toward increasing values of their respective variables.

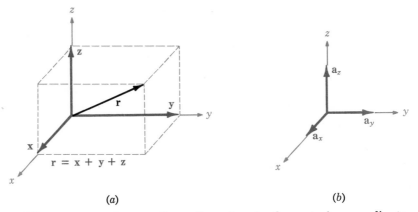

(*a*)   (*b*)

Thus $\mathbf{a}_x$, $\mathbf{a}_y$, and $\mathbf{a}_z$ are the unit vectors in the cartesian coordinate system.[1] They are directed along the x, y, and z axes, respectively, as shown in Fig. 1.3*b*.

If the component vector **y** happens to be 2 units in magnitude and directed toward increasing values of y, we should then write $\mathbf{y} = 2\mathbf{a}_y$. A vector $\mathbf{r}_P$ pointing from the origin to point P (1,2,3) is written $\mathbf{r}_P = \mathbf{a}_x + 2\mathbf{a}_y + 3\mathbf{a}_z$. The vector from P to Q may be obtained by applying the rule of vector addition. This rule shows that the vector from the origin to P plus the vector from P to Q is equal to the vector from the origin to Q. The desired vector from P (1,2,3) to Q (2,$-$2,1) is therefore

$$\mathbf{r}_Q - \mathbf{r}_P = (2 - 1)\mathbf{a}_x + (-2 - 2)\mathbf{a}_y + (1 - 3)\mathbf{a}_z = \mathbf{a}_x - 4\mathbf{a}_y - 2\mathbf{a}_z$$

This last vector does not extend outward from the origin, as did the vector **r** we initially considered. However, we have already learned that vectors having the same magnitude and pointing in the same direction are equal, so we see that to help our visualization processes we are at liberty to slide any vector over to the origin before determining its component vectors. Parallelism must, of course, be maintained during the sliding process.

If we are discussing a force vector **F**, or indeed any vector other than a displacement-type vector such as **r**, the problem arises of providing suitable letters for the three component vectors. It would not do to call them **x**, **y**, and **z**, for these are displacements, or directed distances, and are measured in meters (abbreviated m) or some other unit of length. The problem is most often avoided by using *component scalars*, simply called *components*, F_x, F_y, and F_z. The components are the signed magnitudes of the component

---

[1] The symbols **i**, **j**, and **k** are also commonly used for the unit vectors in cartesian coordinates.

vectors. We may then write $\mathbf{F} = F_x\mathbf{a}_x + F_y\mathbf{a}_y + F_z\mathbf{a}_z$. The component vectors are $F_x\mathbf{a}_x$, $F_y\mathbf{a}_y$, and $F_z\mathbf{a}_z$. These expressions are sufficiently simple that no other nomenclature is commonly used.

Any vector $\mathbf{B}$ then may be described by $\mathbf{B} = B_x\mathbf{a}_x + B_y\mathbf{a}_y + B_z\mathbf{a}_z$. The magnitude of $\mathbf{B}$, written $|\mathbf{B}|$, or simply B, is given by

$$|\mathbf{B}| = \sqrt{B_x{}^2 + B_y{}^2 + B_z{}^2}$$

Each of the three coordinate systems we discuss will have its three fundamental and mutually perpendicular unit vectors which are used to resolve any vector into its component vectors. However, unit vectors are not limited to this application. It is often helpful to be able to write a unit vector having a specified direction. This is simply done, for a unit vector in a given direction is merely a vector in that direction divided by its magnitude. A unit vector in the $\mathbf{r}$ direction is $\mathbf{r}/\sqrt{x^2 + y^2 + z^2}$, and a unit vector in the direction of the vector $\mathbf{B}$ is

$$\mathbf{a}_B = \frac{\mathbf{B}}{\sqrt{B_x{}^2 + B_y{}^2 + B_z{}^2}} = \frac{\mathbf{B}}{|\mathbf{B}|}$$

A special identifying symbol is desirable for a unit vector so that its character is immediately apparent. Symbols which have been used are $\mathbf{u}_B$, $\mathbf{a}_B$, $\mathbf{1}_B$, or even $\mathbf{b}$. We shall consistently use the lowercase $\mathbf{a}$ with an appropriate subscript.

[NOTE: Throughout the text, drill problems appear following sections in which a new principle is introduced in order to allow the student to test his understanding of the basic fact itself. The problems are useful in gaining familiarization with new terms and ideas and should all be worked. More general problems appear at the ends of the chapters. The answers to the drill problems are given in random order. For example, in Prob. D1.1 the answers are (a) $-\mathbf{a}_x - 5\mathbf{a}_y + 3\mathbf{a}_z$; (b) $4\mathbf{a}_x - \mathbf{a}_z$; and (c) $-3\mathbf{a}_x + 4\mathbf{a}_y + 12\mathbf{a}_z$.]

D 1.1 Write in component form the expression for the vector which extends from

(a) The origin to C $(-1,-5,3)$
(b) C $(-1,-5,3)$ to D $(3,-5,2)$
(c) E $(2,-2,-6)$ to F $(-1,2,6)$

Ans. $4\mathbf{a}_x - \mathbf{a}_z$; $-3\mathbf{a}_x + 4\mathbf{a}_y + 12\mathbf{a}_z$; $-\mathbf{a}_x - 5\mathbf{a}_y + 3\mathbf{a}_z$

D 1.2 Find the magnitude of the vector

(a) $3\mathbf{a}_x + 4\mathbf{a}_y - 5\mathbf{a}_z$
(b) $-4\mathbf{a}_y + 6\mathbf{a}_z$
(c) $2\cos\alpha\,\mathbf{a}_x + 2\sin\alpha\,\mathbf{a}_y + 7\mathbf{a}_z$

Ans. 7.07; 7.28; 7.21

D 1.3   Determine the component form of the unit vector

    (*a*) Which is directed along a line from the origin to $(-2,1,2)$
    (*b*) Which lies in the direction of the vector $6\mathbf{a}_x - 3\mathbf{a}_y + 6\mathbf{a}_z$
    (*c*) Which is directed from $(3,1,-2)$ toward $(4,-1,0)$

Ans. $-\tfrac{2}{3}\mathbf{a}_x + \tfrac{1}{3}\mathbf{a}_y + \tfrac{2}{3}\mathbf{a}_z;\ \tfrac{1}{3}\mathbf{a}_x - \tfrac{2}{3}\mathbf{a}_y + \tfrac{2}{3}\mathbf{a}_z;\ \tfrac{2}{3}\mathbf{a}_x - \tfrac{1}{3}\mathbf{a}_y + \tfrac{2}{3}\mathbf{a}_z$

1.5   THE VECTOR FIELD

We have already defined a vector field as a vector function of a position vector. In general, the magnitude and direction of the function will change as we move throughout the region, and its value must be determined from the coordinate values of the point in question. Since we have considered only the cartesian coordinate system, we should expect the vector to be a function of the variables x, y, and z.

If we consider the velocity of the water in the ocean in some region near the surface where tides and currents are important, we may obtain a velocity vector which is in any direction, even up or down. If the z axis is taken as upward, the x axis in a northerly direction, and the y axis to the west, we have a right-handed coordinate system and may write the velocity vector as $\mathbf{U} = U_x\mathbf{a}_x + U_y\mathbf{a}_y + U_z\mathbf{a}_z$, where each of the components U_x, U_y, and U_z may be a function of the three variables x, y, and z. If the problem is simplified by assuming that we are in some portion of the Gulf Stream where the water is moving only to the north, then U_y and U_z are zero. Further simplifying assumptions may be made, for the velocity usually falls off with depth and changes very slowly as we move north, south, east, or west. A suitable expression might be $\mathbf{U} = 2e^{z/100}\mathbf{a}_x$. We have a velocity of 2 meters per second (m/s) at the surface, a velocity of 0.368×2, or 0.736 m/s, at a depth of 100 m ($z = -100$), and the velocity continues to decrease with depth; in this example the vector velocity has a constant direction.

While the example given above is fairly simple and only a rough approximation to a physical situation, a more exact expression would be correspondingly more complex and difficult to interpret. We shall come across many fields in our study of electricity and magnetism which are simpler than the velocity example, an example in which only one component and one variable were involved (the x component and the variable z). We shall also study more complicated fields, and methods of interpreting these expressions physically will be discussed then.

1.6   THE DOT PRODUCT

We now consider the first of two types of vector multiplication. The second type will be discussed in the following section.

Given two vectors **A** and **B**, the *dot product*, or *scalar product*, is defined as the product of the magnitude of **A**, the magnitude of **B**, and the cosine of the smaller angle between them,

$$\mathbf{A} \cdot \mathbf{B} = |\mathbf{A}|\,|\mathbf{B}|\,\cos\theta_{AB}$$

The dot appears between the two vectors and should be made heavy for emphasis. The dot, or scalar, product is a scalar, as one of the names implies, and it obeys the commutative law,

$$\mathbf{A} \cdot \mathbf{B} = \mathbf{B} \cdot \mathbf{A}$$

for the sign of the angle does not affect the cosine term. The expression **A·B** is read "**A** dot **B**."

Perhaps the most common application of the dot product is in mechanics, where a constant force **F** applied over a straight displacement **L** does an amount of work $FL \cos\theta$, which is more easily written **F·L**. We might anticipate one of the results of Chap. 4 by pointing out that if the force varies along the path, integration is necessary to find the total work, and the result becomes

$$\text{Work} = \int \mathbf{F} \cdot d\mathbf{L}$$

Another example might be taken from magnetic fields, a subject about which we shall have a lot more to say later. The total flux Φ crossing a surface of area S is given by BS if the magnetic flux density B is perpendicular to the surface and uniform over it. If we define a vector surface **S** as having the usual area for its magnitude and having a direction *normal* to the surface (avoiding for the moment the problem of which of the two possible normals to take), then the flux becomes **B·S**. This expression is valid for any direction of the uniform magnetic flux density. However, if the flux density is not constant over the surface, the total flux is $\Phi = \int \mathbf{B} \cdot d\mathbf{S}$. Integrals of this general form appear in Chap. 3.

Finding the angle between two vectors in three-dimensional space is often a job we would prefer to avoid, and for that reason the definition of the dot product is usually not used in its basic form. A more helpful result is obtained by considering two vectors whose cartesian components are given, such as $\mathbf{A} = A_x\mathbf{a}_x + A_y\mathbf{a}_y + A_z\mathbf{a}_z$ and $\mathbf{B} = B_x\mathbf{a}_x + B_y\mathbf{a}_y + B_z\mathbf{a}_z$. As one of the problems indicates, the dot product obeys the distributive law, or

$$\mathbf{C} \cdot (\mathbf{D} + \mathbf{E}) = \mathbf{C} \cdot \mathbf{D} + \mathbf{C} \cdot \mathbf{E}$$

and therefore **A·B** yields the sum of nine scalar terms, each involving the dot product of two unit vectors. Since the angle between two different unit vectors of the cartesian coordinate system is 90°, we then have

$$\mathbf{a}_x \cdot \mathbf{a}_y = \mathbf{a}_y \cdot \mathbf{a}_x = \mathbf{a}_x \cdot \mathbf{a}_z = \mathbf{a}_z \cdot \mathbf{a}_x = \mathbf{a}_y \cdot \mathbf{a}_z = \mathbf{a}_z \cdot \mathbf{a}_y = 0$$

The remaining three terms involve the dot product of a unit vector with itself, which is unity, giving finally

$$\boxed{\mathbf{A} \cdot \mathbf{B} = A_x B_x + A_y B_y + A_z B_z}$$

which is an expression involving no angles.

A vector dotted with itself yields the magnitude squared, or

$$\boxed{\mathbf{A} \cdot \mathbf{A} = A^2 = |\mathbf{A}|^2}$$

Probably the most important application of the dot product is that of finding the component of a vector in a given direction. If **a** represents a unit vector in any direction, then

$$\mathbf{A} \cdot \mathbf{a} = |\mathbf{A}| \, |\mathbf{a}| \cos \theta_{Aa} = |\mathbf{A}| \cos \theta_{Aa}$$

is the component of **A** in the direction of the unit vector **a**. As a simple example, we note that $\mathbf{A} \cdot \mathbf{a}_x$ is the component of **A** in the direction of $\mathbf{a}_x$, or $\mathbf{A} \cdot \mathbf{a}_x = A_x$. Hence the problem of finding the component of a vector in any desired direction becomes the problem of finding a unit vector in that direction, and this has been done (see Sec. 1.4 and Prob. D1.3).

D 1.4   Find the dot product of the vectors **A** and **B** if

     (a) $\mathbf{A} = 2\mathbf{a}_x - 3\mathbf{a}_y + 4\mathbf{a}_z$ and $\mathbf{B} = -\mathbf{a}_x + 2\mathbf{a}_y + 2\mathbf{a}_z$
     (b) $\mathbf{A} = 1.2\mathbf{a}_x + 0.4\mathbf{a}_y + 2\mathbf{a}_z$ and $\mathbf{B} = 0.8\mathbf{a}_x + 2.1\mathbf{a}_y + 0.1\mathbf{a}_z$
     (c) $\mathbf{A} = 3\mathbf{a}_y - 2\mathbf{a}_z$ and $\mathbf{B} = 2\mathbf{A}$

Ans.   26; 2; 0

D 1.5   Use the dot product to find the angle between the two vectors

     (a) $3\mathbf{a}_x - 2\mathbf{a}_y + \mathbf{a}_z$ and $-\mathbf{a}_x + 2\mathbf{a}_y + 7\mathbf{a}_z$
     (b) $-4\mathbf{a}_x + 2\mathbf{a}_y$ and $3\mathbf{a}_y - \mathbf{a}_z$
     (c) $2\mathbf{a}_x$ and $-\mathbf{a}_x + 2\mathbf{a}_y + 7\mathbf{a}_z$

Ans.   64.9°; 90°; 97.8°

1.7   THE CROSS PRODUCT

Given two vectors **A** and **B**, we shall now define the *cross product*, or *vector product*, of **A** and **B**, written with a cross between the two vectors as **A** × **B** and read "A cross B." - The cross product **A** × **B** is a vector; the magnitude of **A** × **B** is equal to the product of the magnitudes of **A**, **B**, and the sine of the smaller angle between **A**

FIG. 1.4
The direction of **A** × **B** is in the direction of advance of a right-handed screw as **A** is turned into **B**.

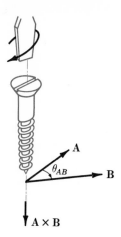

and **B**; the direction of **A** × **B** is perpendicular to the plane containing **A** and **B** and is along that one of the two possible perpendiculars which is in the direction of advance of a right-handed screw as **A** is turned into **B**. This direction is illustrated in Fig. 1.4. Remember that either vector may be moved about at will, maintaining its direction constant, until the two vectors have a "common origin." This determines the plane containing both. However, in most of our applications we shall be concerned with vectors defined at the same point.

As an equation we can write

$$\mathbf{A} \times \mathbf{B} = \mathbf{a}_N \, |\mathbf{A}| \, |\mathbf{B}| \sin \theta_{AB}$$

where an additional statement, such as that given above, is still required to explain the direction of the unit vector $\mathbf{a}_N$. The subscript stands for "normal."

Reversing the order of the vectors **A** and **B** results in a unit vector in the opposite direction, and we see that the cross product is not commutative, for $\mathbf{B} \times \mathbf{A} = -(\mathbf{A} \times \mathbf{B})$.

If the definition of the cross product is applied to the unit vectors $\mathbf{a}_x$ and $\mathbf{a}_y$, we find $\mathbf{a}_x \times \mathbf{a}_y = \mathbf{a}_z$, for each vector has unit magnitude, the two vectors are perpendicular, and the rotation of $\mathbf{a}_x$ into $\mathbf{a}_y$ indicates the positive z direction by the definition of a right-handed coordinate system. In a similar way, $\mathbf{a}_y \times \mathbf{a}_z = \mathbf{a}_x$ and $\mathbf{a}_z \times \mathbf{a}_x = \mathbf{a}_y$. Note the alphabetic symmetry. As long as the three vectors $\mathbf{a}_x$, $\mathbf{a}_y$, and $\mathbf{a}_z$ are written in order (and assuming that $\mathbf{a}_x$ follows $\mathbf{a}_z$, like three elephants in a circle holding tails, so that we could also write $\mathbf{a}_y$, $\mathbf{a}_z$, $\mathbf{a}_x$ or $\mathbf{a}_z$, $\mathbf{a}_x$, $\mathbf{a}_y$), then the cross and equal sign may be placed in either of the two vacant spaces. As a matter of fact, it is now simpler to define a right-handed cartesian coordinate system by saying that $\mathbf{a}_x \times \mathbf{a}_y = \mathbf{a}_z$.

A simple example of the use of the cross product may be taken from geometry or trigonometry. To find the area of a parallelogram the product of the lengths of two adjacent sides is multiplied by the sine of the angle between them. Using vector notation for the two sides, we then may express the (scalar) area as the *magnitude* of $\mathbf{A} \times \mathbf{B}$, or $|\mathbf{A} \times \mathbf{B}|$.

The cross product may be used to replace the right-hand rule familiar to all electrical engineers. Consider the force on a straight conductor of length $\mathbf{L}$, where the direction assigned to $\mathbf{L}$ corresponds to the direction of the steady current I, and a uniform magnetic field of flux density $\mathbf{B}$ is present. Using vector notation, we may write the result neatly as $\mathbf{F} = I\mathbf{L} \times \mathbf{B}$. This relationship will be obtained later in Chap. 9.

The evaluation of a cross product by means of its definition turns out to be more work than the evaluation of the dot product from its definition, for not only must we find the angle between the vectors, but we must find an expression for the unit vector $\mathbf{a}_N$. This work may be avoided by using cartesian components for the two vectors $\mathbf{A}$ and $\mathbf{B}$ and expanding the cross product as a sum of nine simpler cross products, each involving two unit vectors,

$$\begin{aligned}
\mathbf{A} \times \mathbf{B} = \quad & A_x B_x \mathbf{a}_x \times \mathbf{a}_x + A_x B_y \mathbf{a}_x \times \mathbf{a}_y + A_x B_z \mathbf{a}_x \times \mathbf{a}_z \\
+ & A_y B_x \mathbf{a}_y \times \mathbf{a}_x + A_y B_y \mathbf{a}_y \times \mathbf{a}_y + A_y B_z \mathbf{a}_y \times \mathbf{a}_z \\
+ & A_z B_x \mathbf{a}_z \times \mathbf{a}_x + A_z B_y \mathbf{a}_z \times \mathbf{a}_y + A_z B_z \mathbf{a}_z \times \mathbf{a}_z
\end{aligned}$$

We have already found that $\mathbf{a}_x \times \mathbf{a}_y = \mathbf{a}_z$, $\mathbf{a}_y \times \mathbf{a}_z = \mathbf{a}_x$, and $\mathbf{a}_z \times \mathbf{a}_x = \mathbf{a}_y$, and it follows that $\mathbf{a}_y \times \mathbf{a}_x = -\mathbf{a}_z$, $\mathbf{a}_z \times \mathbf{a}_y = -\mathbf{a}_x$, and $\mathbf{a}_x \times \mathbf{a}_z = -\mathbf{a}_y$. The three remaining terms are zero, for the cross product of any vector with itself is zero, since the included angle is zero. These results may be combined to give

$$\mathbf{A} \times \mathbf{B} = (A_y B_z - A_z B_y)\mathbf{a}_x + (A_z B_x - A_x B_z)\mathbf{a}_y + (A_x B_y - A_y B_x)\mathbf{a}_z$$

or written as a determinant in a more easily remembered form,

$$\mathbf{A} \times \mathbf{B} = \begin{vmatrix} \mathbf{a}_x & \mathbf{a}_y & \mathbf{a}_z \\ A_x & A_y & A_z \\ B_x & B_y & B_z \end{vmatrix}$$

D 1.6 Find the cross product $\mathbf{A} \times \mathbf{B}$ if

(a) $\mathbf{A} = -2\mathbf{a}_x + 3\mathbf{a}_y - 4\mathbf{a}_z$ and $\mathbf{B} = 4\mathbf{a}_x - \mathbf{a}_y + 2\mathbf{a}_z$
(b) $\mathbf{A} = \mathbf{a}_x \cos \beta - \mathbf{a}_y \sin \beta + \mathbf{a}_z \cos \beta$ and $\mathbf{B} = \mathbf{a}_x \sin \beta + \mathbf{a}_y \cos \beta + \mathbf{a}_z \sin \beta$
(c) $\mathbf{A} = 3\mathbf{a}_x - 2\mathbf{a}_y + 2\mathbf{a}_z$ and $\mathbf{B} = -6\mathbf{a}_x + 4\mathbf{a}_y - 4\mathbf{a}_z$

Ans. 0; $-\mathbf{a}_x + \mathbf{a}_z$; $2\mathbf{a}_x - 12\mathbf{a}_y - 10\mathbf{a}_z$

D 1.7 Use the definition of the cross product to find the angle between the two vectors

(a) $\mathbf{a}_x$ and $4\mathbf{a}_y - 3\mathbf{a}_z$
(b) $\mathbf{a}_x - \mathbf{a}_y$ and $-\mathbf{a}_x + \mathbf{a}_y$
(c) $\mathbf{a}_x - 2\mathbf{a}_y + 2\mathbf{a}_z$ and $2\mathbf{a}_x - \mathbf{a}_y - 2\mathbf{a}_z$

Ans. $90°$; $90°$; $180°$

1.8   OTHER COORDINATE SYSTEMS: CIRCULAR CYLINDRICAL COORDINATES

The cartesian coordinate system is in general the one in which students prefer to work every problem. This often means a lot more work for the student, because many problems possess a type of symmetry which pleads for a more logical treatment. It is easier to do now, once and for all, the work required to become familiar with cylindrical and spherical coordinates, instead of applying an equal or greater effort to every problem involving cylindrical or spherical symmetry later. With this future saving of labor in mind, we shall take a careful and unhurried look at cylindrical and spherical coordinates.

The circular cylindrical coordinate system is the three-dimensional version of the polar coordinates of analytic geometry. In the two-dimensional polar coordinates, a point was located in a plane by giving its distance r from the origin, and the angle ϕ between the line from the point to the origin and an arbitrary radial line taken as $\phi = 0$.[1]   A three-dimensional coordinate system, circular cylindrical coordinates, is obtained by also specifying the distance z of the point from an arbitrary $z = 0$ reference plane which is perpendicular to the line $r = 0$.   For simplicity, we usually refer to circular cylindrical coordinates simply as cylindrical coordinates. This will not be confusing in this course, but it is only fair to point out that there are such systems as elliptic cylindrical coordinates, hyperbolic cylindrical coordinates, parabolic cylindrical coordinates, and others.

We no longer set up three axes as in cartesian coordinates, but must instead consider any point as the intersection of three mu-

---

[1] In polar coordinates this angle is commonly called θ, but we will use ϕ instead; this will make the transition between circular cylindrical and spherical coordinates smoother.

FIG. 1.5 (a) The three mutually perpendicular surfaces of the circular cylindrical coordinate system. (b) The three unit vectors of the circular cylindrical coordinate system. (c) The differential volume unit in the circular cylindrical coordinate system; dr, $r\, d\phi$, and dz are all elements of length.

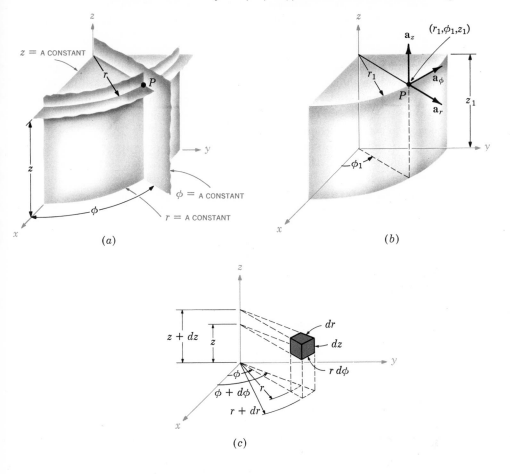

tually perpendicular surfaces. These surfaces are a circular cylinder (r = constant), a plane (ϕ = constant), and another plane (z = constant). This corresponds to the location of a point in a cartesian coordinate system by the intersection of three planes (x = constant, y = constant, and z = constant). The three surfaces of circular cylindrical coordinates are shown in Fig. 1.5a. Note that three such surfaces may be passed through any point.

Three unit vectors must also be defined, but we may no longer direct them along the "coordinate axes," for such axes exist only in cartesian coordinates. Instead, we take a broader view of the unit vectors in cartesian coordinates and realize that they are directed toward increasing coordinate values and are perpendicular to the surface on which that coordinate value is constant; i.e., the unit vector $\mathbf{a}_x$ is normal to the plane $x = $ constant and points toward larger values of x. In a corresponding way we may now define three unit vectors in cylindrical coordinates, $\mathbf{a}_r$, $\mathbf{a}_\phi$, and $\mathbf{a}_z$.

The unit vector $\mathbf{a}_r$ *at any point* (r_1,ϕ_1,z_1) is directed radially out-ward, normal to the cylindrical surface $r = r_1$. It lies in the planes $\phi = \phi_1$ and $z = z_1$. The unit vector $\mathbf{a}_\phi$ is normal to the plane $\phi = \phi_1$, points in the direction of increasing ϕ, lies in the plane $z = z_1$, and is tangent to the cylindrical surface $r = r_1$. The unit vector $\mathbf{a}_z$ is the same as the unit vector $\mathbf{a}_z$ of the cartesian coordinate system. Figure 1.5b shows the three unit vectors in cylindrical coordinates. Two of these unit vectors change in direction (but not in magnitude, of course) as we construct them at various points; this is not the case in cartesian coordinates.

The unit vectors are again mutually perpendicular, for each is normal to one of the three mutually perpendicular surfaces, and we may define a right-handed cylindrical coordinate system as one in which $\mathbf{a}_r \times \mathbf{a}_\phi = \mathbf{a}_z$, or for those who have flexible fingers, as one in which the thumb, forefinger, and middle finger point in the direction of increasing r, ϕ, and z, respectively.

A differential volume element in cylindrical coordinates may be obtained by increasing r, ϕ, and z by the differential increments dr, $d\phi$, and dz. The two cylinders of radius r and $r + dr$, the two radial planes at angles ϕ and $\phi + d\phi$, and the two "horizontal" planes at "elevations" z and $z + dz$ now enclose a small volume, shown in Fig. 1.5c, having the shape of a truncated wedge. As the volume element becomes very small, its shape approaches that of a rectangular parallelepiped having sides of length dr, $r\,d\phi$, and dz. Note that dr and dz are dimensionally lengths, but $d\phi$ is not; $r\,d\phi$ is the length. The surfaces have areas of $r\,dr\,d\phi$, $dr\,dz$, and $r\,d\phi\,dz$, and the volume becomes $r\,dr\,d\phi\,dz$.

1.9 THE SPHERICAL COORDINATE SYSTEM

We have no two-dimensional coordinate system to help us under-stand the three-dimensional spherical coordinate system, as we have for the circular cylindrical coordinate system. In certain respects we can draw on our knowledge of the latitude-and-longitude system of locating a place on the surface of the earth, but usually we consider only points on the surface and not those below or above ground.

Let us start by building a spherical coordinate system on the three cartesian axes (Fig. 1.6a). We first define the distance from the origin to any point as r, the same letter we used in cylindrical coordinates to designate the distance from a line, but definitely not the same meaning. This is a fault of the nomenclature, for which everyone apologizes but can do little. When the small letter r is seen, it must be immediately determined whether it is a coordi-

(a)   (b)

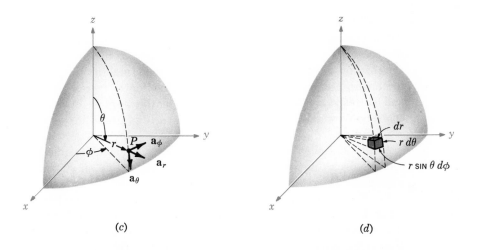

(c)   (d)

nate in the cylindrical or spherical system. In spherical coordinates, the surface r = constant is a sphere.

The second coordinate is an angle θ between the z axis and the line drawn from the origin to the point in question. The surface θ = constant is a cone, and the two surfaces, cone and sphere, are everywhere perpendicular. The intersection of the cone and sphere is a circle of radius $r \sin \theta$. The coordinate θ corresponds to latitude, except that latitude is measured from the equator and θ is measured from the "North Pole."

The third coordinate ϕ is also an angle and in this case is exactly the same as the angle ϕ of cylindrical coordinates. It is the angle

The Spherical Coordinate System   17

between the x axis and the projection in the $z = 0$ plane of the line drawn from the origin to the point. It corresponds to the angle of longitude, but the angle ϕ increases to the "east." The surface $\phi = $ constant is a plane passing through the $\theta = 0$ line (or the z axis).

We should again consider any point as the intersection of three mutually perpendicular surfaces, a sphere, a cone, and a plane, each oriented in the manner described above. The three surfaces are shown in Fig. 1.6b.

Three unit vectors may again be defined at any point. Each unit vector is perpendicular to one of the three mutually perpendicular surfaces and oriented in that direction in which the coordinate increases. The unit vector $\mathbf{a}_r$ is directed radially outward, normal to the sphere $r = $ constant, and lies in the cone $\theta = $ constant and the plane $\phi = $ constant. The unit vector $\mathbf{a}_\theta$ is normal to the conical surface, lies in the plane, and is tangent to the sphere. It is directed along a line of "longitude" and points "south." The third unit vector $\mathbf{a}_\phi$ is the same as in cylindrical coordinates, being normal to the plane and tangent to both the cone and sphere. It is directed to the "east."

The three unit vectors are shown in Fig. 1.6c. They are, of course, mutually perpendicular, and a right-handed coordinate system is defined by causing $\mathbf{a}_r \times \mathbf{a}_\theta = \mathbf{a}_\phi$. Our system is right-handed, as an inspection of Fig. 1.6c will show, on application of the definition of the cross product. The right-hand rule serves to identify the thumb, forefinger, and middle finger with the direction of increasing r, θ, and ϕ, respectively. (Note that the identification in cylindrical coordinates was with r, ϕ, and z, and in cartesian coordinates with x, y, and z.)

A differential volume element may be constructed in spherical coordinates by increasing r, θ, and ϕ by dr, $d\theta$, and $d\phi$, as shown in Fig. 1.6d. The distance between the two spherical surfaces of radius r and $r + dr$ is dr; the distance between the two cones having generating angles of θ and $\theta + d\theta$ is $r\,d\theta$; and the distance between the two radial planes at angles ϕ and $\phi + d\phi$ is found to be $r \sin \theta\, d\phi$, after a few moments of trigonometric thought. The surfaces have areas of $r\,dr\,d\theta$, $r \sin \theta\, dr\, d\phi$, and $r^2 \sin \theta\, d\theta\, d\phi$, and the volume is

$$r^2 \sin \theta\, dr\, d\theta\, d\phi$$

Appendix A describes the general curvilinear coordinate system of which the cartesian, circular cylindrical, and spherical coordinate systems are special cases. The first section of this appendix could well be scanned now.

1.10 TRANSFORMATIONS BETWEEN COORDINATE SYSTEMS

After we have begun to use vector analysis as a tool in solving electric and magnetic field problems, we shall meet several of the more difficult problems in which it is easier to carry out a first step using cartesian coordinates but desirable to have an answer expressed in cylindrical or spherical coordinates. Sometimes the transformation between coordinate systems in the reverse direction is wanted. There are even cases here and there in which it is advantageous to use a mixed coordinate system for a special problem in which the transformation between coordinate systems essentially occurs from line to line. The transformations between coordinate systems which are discussed in this section will only be used occasionally in the remainder of this book, and it cannot be said that they are vitally important; they do, however, serve to illustrate the vector concepts we have been studying.

First let us consider specifically the transformation of a vector in cartesian coordinates into one in cylindrical coordinates. This is fundamentally a two-step problem, that of changing variables and that of changing components. A vector in cartesian coordinates $\mathbf{A} = A_x\mathbf{a}_x + A_y\mathbf{a}_y + A_z\mathbf{a}_z$, where A_x, A_y, and A_z are functions of x, y, and z, must be changed to a vector in cylindrical coordinates, $\mathbf{A} = A_r\mathbf{a}_r + A_\phi\mathbf{a}_\phi + A_z\mathbf{a}_z$, where A_r, A_ϕ, and A_z are functions of r, ϕ, and z.

The order of the two steps makes little difference, so we may consider the change of variables first. If we set up our two coordinate systems as shown in Fig. 1.7, so that the $z = 0$ planes coincide and

FIG. 1.7 The relationship between the cartesian variables x, y, z and the cylindrical coordinate variables r, ϕ, z. There is no change in the variable z between the two systems.

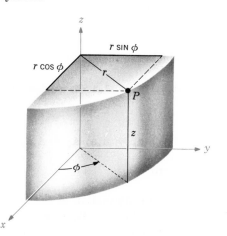

it includes the results for a transformation in the reverse direction, for expressions are given for the components in cartesian coordinates in terms of those in cylindrical coordinates. These are obtained by the same method used in arriving at (1) and again make use of the expressions for the dot products of the unit vectors which we developed then.

The transformation of a vector from cartesian coordinates to spherical coordinates, or the reverse, is accomplished by following the same general procedure. The relationships between the variables are somewhat more involved but are obtained readily with the aid of Fig. 1.6a:

$$x = r \sin \theta \cos \phi \qquad y = r \sin \theta \sin \phi \qquad z = r \cos \theta$$

$$r^2 = x^2 + y^2 + z^2 \qquad \cos \theta = \frac{z}{\sqrt{x^2 + y^2 + z^2}} \qquad \tan \phi = \frac{y}{x}$$

The dot products of the unit vectors in the two coordinate systems are determined from Fig. 1.6c and a little trigonometry. Since the dot product of any spherical unit vector with any cartesian unit vector is the component of the spherical vector in the direction of the cartesian vector, the dot products with $\mathbf{a}_z$ are found to be

$$\mathbf{a}_r \cdot \mathbf{a}_z = \mathbf{a}_z \cdot \mathbf{a}_r = \cos \theta$$

$$\mathbf{a}_\theta \cdot \mathbf{a}_z = \mathbf{a}_z \cdot \mathbf{a}_\theta = - \sin \theta$$

$$\mathbf{a}_\phi \cdot \mathbf{a}_z = \mathbf{a}_z \cdot \mathbf{a}_\phi = 0$$

The dot products involving $\mathbf{a}_x$ and $\mathbf{a}_y$ require first the projection of the spherical unit vector on the xy plane and then the projection onto the desired axis. For example, $\mathbf{a}_r \cdot \mathbf{a}_x$ is obtained by projecting $\mathbf{a}_r$ on the xy plane, giving $\sin \theta$, and then projecting $\sin \theta$ on the x axis, which yields $\sin \theta \cos \phi$. The remaining dot products are

$$\mathbf{a}_r \cdot \mathbf{a}_x = \sin \theta \cos \phi$$

$$\mathbf{a}_\theta \cdot \mathbf{a}_x = \cos \theta \cos \phi$$

$$\mathbf{a}_\phi \cdot \mathbf{a}_x = - \sin \phi$$

$$\mathbf{a}_r \cdot \mathbf{a}_y = \sin \theta \sin \phi$$

$$\mathbf{a}_\theta \cdot \mathbf{a}_y = \cos \theta \sin \phi$$

$$\mathbf{a}_\phi \cdot \mathbf{a}_y = \cos \phi$$

With this information we are now able to write the components A_r, A_θ, and A_ϕ in terms of A_x, A_y, and A_z, or vice versa. This information is tabulated in Table 1.2, which should be referred to when the need arises to make a transformation between cartesian and spherical coordinates.

TABLE 1.2   **Relation between the Variables and Components of the Cartesian and Spherical Coordinate Systems**

Cartesian to spherical	*Spherical to cartesian*
$x = r \sin \theta \cos \phi$	$r = \sqrt{x^2 + y^2 + z^2}$
$y = r \sin \theta \sin \phi$	$\theta = \cos^{-1} \dfrac{z}{\sqrt{x^2 + y^2 + z^2}}$
$z = r \cos \theta$	$\phi = \tan^{-1} \dfrac{y}{x}$
$\begin{aligned} A_r = &A_x \sin \theta \cos \phi \\ &+ A_y \sin \theta \sin \phi \\ &+ A_z \cos \theta \end{aligned}$	$\begin{aligned} A_x = &\dfrac{A_r x}{\sqrt{x^2 + y^2 + z^2}} \\ &+ \dfrac{A_\theta x z}{\sqrt{(x^2 + y^2)(x^2 + y^2 + z^2)}} \\ &- \dfrac{A_\phi y}{\sqrt{x^2 + y^2}} \end{aligned}$
$\begin{aligned} A_\theta = &A_x \cos \theta \cos \phi \\ &+ A_y \cos \theta \sin \phi \\ &- A_z \sin \theta \end{aligned}$	$\begin{aligned} A_y = &\dfrac{A_r y}{\sqrt{x^2 + y^2 + z^2}} \\ &+ \dfrac{A_\theta y z}{\sqrt{(x^2 + y^2)(x^2 + y^2 + z^2)}} \\ &+ \dfrac{A_\phi x}{\sqrt{x^2 + y^2}} \end{aligned}$
$\begin{aligned} A_\phi = &-A_x \sin \phi \\ &+ A_y \cos \phi \end{aligned}$	$\begin{aligned} A_z = &\dfrac{A_r z}{\sqrt{x^2 + y^2 + z^2}} \\ &- \dfrac{A_\theta \sqrt{x^2 + y^2}}{\sqrt{x^2 + y^2 + z^2}} \end{aligned}$

D 1.8 Locate on a sketch and give the cylindrical coordinates of the point whose cartesian coordinates are

(a) $x = 1, y = 2, z = 3$
(b) $x = -1, y = -2, z = 3$
(c) $x = 1, y = -2, z = 3$

Ans. $(2.24,63.4°,3)$; $(2.24,243.4°,3)$; $(2.24,296.6°,3)$

D 1.9 Locate on a sketch and give the spherical coordinates of the point whose cartesian coordinates are

(a) $x = 1, y = 2, z = 3$
(b) $x = -1, y = -2, z = -3$
(c) $x = 1, y = -2, z = 3$

Ans. $(3.74,36.7°,296.6°)$; $(3.74,36.7°,63.4°)$; $(3.74,143.3°,243.4°)$

D 1.10 Transform the following vectors to cylindrical coordinates:

(a) $\dfrac{x}{y}\, \mathbf{a}_x$

(b) $\dfrac{x}{\sqrt{x^2 + y^2}}\, \mathbf{a}_x + \dfrac{y}{\sqrt{x^2 + y^2}}\, \mathbf{a}_y$

(c) $\dfrac{x}{\sqrt{x^2 + y^2 + z^2}}\, \mathbf{a}_x + \dfrac{y}{\sqrt{x^2 + y^2 + z^2}}\, \mathbf{a}_y + \dfrac{z}{\sqrt{x^2 + y^2 + z^2}}\, \mathbf{a}_z$

Ans. $\dfrac{r}{\sqrt{r^2 + z^2}}\, \mathbf{a}_r + \dfrac{z}{\sqrt{r^2 + z^2}}\, \mathbf{a}_z$; $\cos \phi \cot \phi\, \mathbf{a}_r - \cos \phi\, \mathbf{a}_\phi$; $\mathbf{a}_r$

D 1.11 Transform the following vectors from cylindrical coordinates to cartesian coordinates:

(a) $\dfrac{1}{r}\, \mathbf{a}_r$

(b) $r\mathbf{a}_r + r\mathbf{a}_\phi$
(c) $\mathbf{a}_\phi \sec \phi$

Ans. $(x - y)\mathbf{a}_x + (x + y)\mathbf{a}_y$; $-\dfrac{y}{x}\, \mathbf{a}_x + \mathbf{a}_y$; $\dfrac{x}{x^2 + y^2}\, \mathbf{a}_x + \dfrac{y}{x^2 + y^2}\, \mathbf{a}_y$

D 1.12 Transform the following vectors to spherical coordinates:

(a) $y\mathbf{a}_x$
(b) $x\mathbf{a}_x + y\mathbf{a}_y + z\mathbf{a}_z$

(c) $\dfrac{yz}{x}\, \mathbf{a}_z$

Ans. $r\mathbf{a}_r$; $r \tan \phi \cos^2 \theta\, \mathbf{a}_r - r \tan \phi \sin \theta \cos \theta\, \mathbf{a}_\theta$; $r \sin \theta \sin \phi\, (\sin \theta \cos \phi\, \mathbf{a}_r + \cos \theta \cos \phi\, \mathbf{a}_\theta - \sin \phi\, \mathbf{a}_\phi)$

D 1.13 Transform the following vectors from spherical coordinates to cartesian coordinates:

(a) $\dfrac{1}{r}\,\mathbf{a}_r$

(b) $\dfrac{1}{r\sin\theta}\,\mathbf{a}_\phi$

(c) $\dfrac{1}{r\sin\theta\cos\phi}\,\mathbf{a}_\theta$

Ans. $\dfrac{x\mathbf{a}_x + y\mathbf{a}_y + z\mathbf{a}_z}{x^2 + y^2 + z^2}$; $\dfrac{-y\mathbf{a}_x + x\mathbf{a}_y}{x^2 + y^2}$; $\dfrac{xz\mathbf{a}_x + yz\mathbf{a}_y - (x^2 + y^2)\mathbf{a}_z}{x\sqrt{(x^2 + y^2)\,(x^2 + y^2 + z^2)}}$

SUGGESTED REFERENCES

1 Apostol, T. M.: "Calculus," vols. I and II, Blaisdell Publishing Company, New York, 1961. This introductory calculus set contains all the vector analysis and calculus which we shall use. Answers are given for a number of problems.

2 Fisher, R. C., and A. D. Ziebur: "Calculus and Analytic Geometry," Prentice-Hall, Inc., Englewood Cliffs, N.J., 1961. The material of this chapter is discussed in chaps. 8 and 9 of this first calculus text.

3 Spiegel, M. R.: "Vector Analysis," Schaum Publishing Company, New York, 1959. A large number of examples and problems with answers are provided in this concise, inexpensive member of an outline series.

PROBLEMS

1 If $\mathbf{A}$ represents a vector one unit in length directed due east, $\mathbf{B}$ represents a vector three units in length directed due north, and $\mathbf{A} + \mathbf{B} = 2\mathbf{C} - \mathbf{D}$ and $2\mathbf{A} - \mathbf{B} = \mathbf{C} + 2\mathbf{D}$, determine the length and direction of $\mathbf{C}$.

2 Given that $\mathbf{A} + \mathbf{B} + \mathbf{C} = 0$, which of the four following equations *must* be true and which *might* be true for certain special cases? (a) $|\mathbf{A} + \mathbf{B}| = |\mathbf{C}|$; (b) $|\mathbf{A}| + |\mathbf{B}| = |\mathbf{C}|$; (c) $|\mathbf{A}| + |\mathbf{B}| > |\mathbf{C}|$; (d) $|\mathbf{A}| + |\mathbf{B}| < |\mathbf{C}|$.

3 Given that $\mathbf{A} + \mathbf{B} + \mathbf{C} = 0$, where the three vectors represent directed line segments and extend from a common origin, must the three vectors be coplanar? If $\mathbf{A} + \mathbf{B} + \mathbf{C} + \mathbf{D} = 0$, are the four vectors coplanar?

4 Write an expression in cartesian components for the vector which extends from (x_1,y_1,z_1) to (x_2,y_2,z_2) and determine the magnitude of this vector.

5 A circle, centered at the origin with a radius of two units, lies in the xy plane. Determine the unit vector in cartesian components which lies in the xy plane, is tangent to the circle at $(\sqrt{3},1,0)$, and is in the general direction of increasing values of y.

6 Given the vector **A** from the origin to the point $(4,0,0)$ and the vector **B** from the origin to $(3,4,0)$, determine the component form of the unit vector in the direction of the bisector of the angle formed by **A** and **B**.

7 A certain vector field is given as $\mathbf{E} = (y+1)\mathbf{a}_x + x\mathbf{a}_y$. (a) Determine **E** at the point $(3,-2,4)$. (b) Obtain a unit vector defining the direction of **E** at $(3,-2,4)$.

8 Given the vector field $\mathbf{E} = y\mathbf{a}_x + x\mathbf{a}_y$, make a sketch using short directed line segments to indicate the magnitude and direction of **E** at the 16 points for which $0 \leq x \leq 3$, $0 \leq y \leq 3$, and $z = 0$, where x and y are integers.

9 Consider a problem analogous to the varying wind velocities encountered by transcontinental jet aircraft. We assume a constant altitude, a plane earth, a flight along the x axis from 0 to 10 units, no vertical velocity component, and no change in wind velocity with time. Assume $\mathbf{a}_x$ directed to the east and $\mathbf{a}_y$ to the north. The wind velocity at this altitude is assumed to be

$$\mathbf{U} = \frac{(0.01x^2 - 0.08x + 0.66)\mathbf{a}_x - (0.05x - 0.4)\mathbf{a}_y}{1 + 0.5y^2}$$

(a) Determine the location and magnitude of the maximum tailwind encountered. (b) Repeat for headwind. (c) Repeat for crosswind. (d) Would more favorable tailwinds be available at some other latitude? If so, where?

10 By expressing the diagonals as vectors and using the definition of the dot product, find the smaller angle between any two diagonals of a cube, where each diagonal connects diametrically opposite corners and passes through the center of the cube.

11 If the three sides of a triangle are represented by the vectors **A**, **B**, and **C**, all directed counterclockwise, show that $|\mathbf{C}|^2 = (\mathbf{A} + \mathbf{B}) \cdot (\mathbf{A} + \mathbf{B})$ and expand the dot product to obtain the law of cosines.

12 The force field $\mathbf{F} = -2\mathbf{a}_x + 4\mathbf{a}_y + 5\mathbf{a}_z$ is encountered by an object moving about the plane $z = 0$. (a) How much work is done on the object as it moves from $x = 0$ to $x = 3$ along the x axis? (b) How much work is done on the object as it moves from $y = 0$ to $y = 3$ along the y axis?

13 What is the component of field $\mathbf{E} = -y\mathbf{a}_x - x\mathbf{a}_y$ at the point $(3,-2,6)$ which is directed toward the point $(4,0,1)$?

14 Find the ratio of the radial component (directed away from the origin) of the force field $\mathbf{F} = 3x^2\mathbf{a}_x - 2yz\mathbf{a}_y + z^2\mathbf{a}_z$ at $(2,1,0)$ to that at $(0,1,2)$.

15 If $\mathbf{E}_1 = 2y\mathbf{a}_x + 2x\mathbf{a}_y + \mathbf{a}_z$ and $\mathbf{E}_2 = -(z+1)\mathbf{a}_x + \mathbf{a}_y - x\mathbf{a}_z$, find (a) the component of $\mathbf{E}_1$ in the direction of $\mathbf{E}_2$ at $(1,2,3)$; (b) the component of $\mathbf{E}_2$ in the direction of $\mathbf{E}_1$ at $(1,2,3)$.

16 Describe a simple method for showing that two vectors are (a) perpendicular to each other; (b) parallel.

17 Write the (scalar) equation of the line in the $z = 0$ plane which is perpendicular to the vector $\mathbf{A} = 3\mathbf{a}_x - 4\mathbf{a}_y$ and passes through (a) the origin; (b) the point $(1,5,0)$.

18 Demonstrate the ambiguity which results when the cross product is used to find the angle between two vectors by finding the angle between $\mathbf{A} = 3\mathbf{a}_x - 2\mathbf{a}_y + 4\mathbf{a}_z$ and $\mathbf{B} = 2\mathbf{a}_x + \mathbf{a}_y - 2\mathbf{a}_z$. Does this ambiguity exist when the dot product is used?

19 For any $\mathbf{A}$ and $\mathbf{B}$, show that (a) $\mathbf{A} \times \mathbf{A} = \mathbf{B} \times \mathbf{B}$; (b) $\mathbf{A} \cdot (\mathbf{A} \times \mathbf{B}) = \mathbf{B} \cdot (\mathbf{A} \times \mathbf{B})$.

20 If $\mathbf{A} = 2\mathbf{a}_x - 2\mathbf{a}_y + 3\mathbf{a}_z$, $\mathbf{B} = -\mathbf{a}_x + 3\mathbf{a}_y - \mathbf{a}_z$, and $\mathbf{C} = 3\mathbf{a}_x - \mathbf{a}_y + 2\mathbf{a}_z$, find (a) $\mathbf{A} \cdot (\mathbf{B} \times \mathbf{C})$; (b) $(\mathbf{A} \times \mathbf{B}) \cdot \mathbf{C}$.

21 Show that $|\mathbf{A} \times \mathbf{B}|^2 + |\mathbf{A} \cdot \mathbf{B}|^2 = |\mathbf{A}|^2 |\mathbf{B}|^2$.

22 Describe the families of surfaces to which these fields in cylindrical coordinates are everywhere perpendicular: (a) $(1/r)\mathbf{a}_r$; (b) $(1/r)\mathbf{a}_\phi$.

23 Given the vector field $\mathbf{E} = (1/r)(\mathbf{a}_r - \mathbf{a}_\phi)$ in cylindrical coordinates, determine the unit vector at $r = 1$, $\phi = 90°$, $z = 0$ which is in the direction of $\mathbf{E}$. Express the answer in (a) cylindrical coordinates; (b) cartesian coordinates.

24 Determine the component of the field $\mathbf{F} = (y - 1)\mathbf{a}_x + (x + 1)\mathbf{a}_y + 2\mathbf{a}_z$ which is (a) perpendicular (outward) to the cylinder $r = 2$ at $\phi = 0°$, $z = 0$; (b) perpendicular (outward) to the sphere $r = 3$ at $\theta = 90°$, $\phi = 90°$.

25 Determine the cartesian components at $(1,1,1)$ of the vector field $\mathbf{C} = (1/r)\mathbf{a}_r$ if the field is expressed in (a) cylindrical coordinates; (b) spherical coordinates.

26 Given the vector field $\mathbf{A} = \mathbf{a}_r \cos \phi \sin \theta + \mathbf{a}_\theta \cos \phi \cos \theta + \mathbf{a}_\phi \sin \phi$; (a) show that the magnitude of $\mathbf{A}$ is everywhere the same; (b) show that $\mathbf{A} = \mathbf{a}_x \cos 2\phi + \mathbf{a}_y \sin 2\phi$.

27 Transform the vector field $\mathbf{E} = (1/r)\mathbf{a}_\phi$, given in cylindrical coordinates, to spherical coordinates.

28 What systems of variables and what unit vectors are used for the cartesian, cylindrical, and spherical coordinate systems in (a) R. Plonsey and R. E. Collin, "Principles and Applications of Electromagnetic Fields," McGraw-Hill Book Company, New York, 1961; (b) J. A. Stratton, "Electromagnetic Theory," McGraw-Hill Book Company, New York, 1941; (c) W. L. Weeks, "Electromagnetic Theory for Engineering Applications," John Wiley & Sons, Inc., New York, 1964?

29 In *Telecommunications*, the English edition of the Russian journal *Elektrosyaz'*, no. 3, 1963, p. 7, the article Design of an Electronically Scanned Antenna Array by L. G. Sodin and I. L. Verbitskiy introduces a spherical coordinate system. Express the three Russian variables r, ϵ, and ϕ in terms of our spherical coordinate variables r_A, θ_A, and ϕ_A.

30 What two different methods of indicating vector quantities are used in the following articles? (a) S. A. Schelkunoff, Generalized Telegraphist's Equations for Waveguides, *Bell System Tech. J.*, vol. 31, no. 4, p. 784, July, 1952; (b) S. P. Morgan, Jr., Mathematical Theory of Laminated Transmission Lines: Part I, *Bell System Tech. J.*, vol. 31, no. 5, p. 883, September, 1952.

2 COULOMB'S LAW AND ELECTRIC FIELD INTENSITY

Now that we have formulated a new language in the first chapter, we shall establish a few basic principles of electricity and attempt to describe them in terms of it. If we had used vector calculus for several years and already had a few correct ideas about electricity and magnetism, we might jump in now with both feet and present a handful of equations, including Maxwell's equations and a few other auxiliary equations, and proceed to describe them physically by virtue of our knowledge of vector analysis. This is perhaps the ideal way, starting with the most general results and then showing that Ohm's, Gauss's, Coulomb's, Faraday's, Ampère's, Biot-Savart's, Kirchhoff's, and a few less familiar laws are all special cases of these equations. It is philosophically satisfying to have the most general result and to feel that we are able to obtain the results for any special case at will. However, such a jump would lead to many frantic cries of "Help" and not a few drowned students.

Instead we shall present at decent intervals the experimental laws mentioned above, expressing each in vector notation, and use these laws to solve a number of simple problems. In this way our familiarity with vector analysis and electric and magnetic fields will both gradually increase, and by the time we have finally reached our handful of general equations, little additional explanation will be required. The entire field of electromagnetic theory is then open to us, and we may use Maxwell's equations to describe wave propagation, radiation from antennas, skin effect, waveguides and transmission lines, and traveling-wave tubes, and even to obtain a new insight into the ordinary power transformer.

In this chapter we shall restrict our attention to static electric fields in vacuum or free space. For all practical purposes, our results will also be applicable to air and other gases. Other materials will be introduced in Chap. 5, and time-varying fields will be introduced in Chap. 10.

We shall begin by describing a quantitative experiment performed in the seventeenth century.

2.1 THE EXPERIMENTAL LAW OF COULOMB

Records from at least 600 B.C. show the knowledge of static electricity. The Greeks were responsible for the term "electricity," derived from their word for amber, and they spent many a leisure hour rubbing a small piece of amber on their sleeves and observing how it would then attract pieces of lint and fluff. However, their main interest lay in philosophy and logic, not in experimental science, and it was many centuries before the attracting effect was considered to be anything other than magic or a "life force."

Dr. Gilbert, physician to Her Majesty the Queen of England, was the first to do any true experimental work with this effect and in 1600 stated that glass, sulfur, amber, and other materials which he named would "not only draw to themselves straws and chaff, but all metals, wood, leaves, stone, earths, even water and oil."

Shortly thereafter a colonel in the French Army Engineers, Col. Charles Coulomb, a precise and orderly-minded officer, performed an elaborate series of experiments using a delicate torsion balance, invented by himself, to determine quantitatively the force exerted between two objects each having a static charge of electricity. His published result is now known to many high school students and bears a great similarity to Newton's gravitational law (discovered about a hundred years earlier). Coulomb stated that the force between two very small objects separated in a vacuum or free space by a distance which is large compared to their size is proportional to the charge on each and inversely proportional to the square of the distance between them, or

(1)
$$F = k\frac{Q_1 Q_2}{R^2}$$

Q_1 and Q_2 are the positive or negative quantities of charge, R is the separation, and k is a proportionality constant. If the International System of units[1] is used, Q is measured in coulombs (C), R is in meters, and the force should be in newtons (N). This will be achieved if the constant of proportionality in (1) is written as

$$k = \frac{1}{4\pi\epsilon_0}$$

where the factor 4π will now appear in the denominator of Coulomb's law but will not appear in the more useful equations (including Maxwell's equations) which we shall obtain with the help of Coulomb's law. The new constant ϵ_0 is called the *permittivity of free space* and has the magnitude, measured in farads per meter (F/m),

(2)
$$\epsilon_0 = 8.854 \times 10^{-12} \doteq \frac{1}{36\pi} 10^{-9} \quad \text{F/m}$$

[1] The International System (an mks system) is described in Appendix B. Abbreviations for the units are given in Table B.1.

The quantity ϵ_0 is not dimensionless, for Coulomb's law shows that it has the label $C^2/N\text{-}m^2$. We shall later define the farad and show that it has the dimensions $C^2/N\text{-}m$; we anticipate this definition by using the unit F/m in (2) above.

Coulomb's law is now

$$(3) \qquad F = \frac{Q_1 Q_2}{4\pi\epsilon_0 R^2}$$

Not all units of the International System are as familiar as the English units we use daily, but they are now standard in electrical engineering and physics. The newton is a unit of force that is equal to 0.2248 lbf, and is the force required to give a one-kilogram mass an acceleration of one meter per second per second (m/s^2). The coulomb is an extremely large unit of charge, for the smallest known quantity of charge is that of the electron (negative) or proton (positive), given in mks units as $(1.60210 \pm 0.00007) \times 10^{-19}$ C, and hence a negative charge of one coulomb represents about 6×10^{18} electrons. Coulomb's law shows that the force between two charges of one coulomb each, separated by one meter, is 9×10^9 N, or about one million tons. The electron has a rest mass of $(9.1091 \pm 0.0004) \times 10^{-31}$ kg and has a radius of the order of magnitude of 3.8×10^{-15} m. This does not mean that the electron is spherical in shape, but merely serves to describe the size of the region in which a slowly moving electron has the greatest probability of being found. All other known charged particles, including the proton, have larger masses, larger radii, and occupy a probabilistic volume larger than does the electron.

In order to write the vector form of (3) we need the additional fact (furnished also by Col. Coulomb) that the force acts along the line joining the two charges and is repulsive if the charges are alike in sign and attractive if they are of opposite sign. Let the vector $\mathbf{R}_{12}$ represent the directed line segment from Q_1 to Q_2, and let $\mathbf{F}_2$ be the force on Q_2. Then

$$(4) \qquad \mathbf{F}_2 = \frac{Q_1 Q_2}{4\pi\epsilon_0 R_{12}^2} \mathbf{a}_{R_{12}}$$

where $\mathbf{a}_{R_{12}} = $ a unit vector in the direction of $\mathbf{R}_{12}$, or

$$(5) \qquad \mathbf{a}_{R_{12}} = \frac{\mathbf{R}_{12}}{|\mathbf{R}_{12}|} = \frac{\mathbf{R}_{12}}{R_{12}}$$

As an example of the use of the vector form of Coulomb's law, consider a charge of 3×10^{-4} C at P (1,2,3) and a charge of -10^{-4}

C at Q (2,0,5) in a vacuum. Then

$$Q_1 = 3 \times 10^{-4} \qquad Q_2 = -10^{-4}$$

$$\mathbf{R}_{12} = (2 - 1)\mathbf{a}_x + (0 - 2)\mathbf{a}_y + (5 - 3)\mathbf{a}_z = \mathbf{a}_x - 2\mathbf{a}_y + 2\mathbf{a}_z$$

$$\mathbf{a}_{R_{12}} = \frac{\mathbf{a}_x - 2\mathbf{a}_y + 2\mathbf{a}_z}{3}$$

$$\mathbf{F}_2 = \frac{3 \times 10^{-4}(-10^{-4})}{4\pi(1/36\pi)10^{-9} \times 9}\left(\frac{\mathbf{a}_x - 2\mathbf{a}_y + 2\mathbf{a}_z}{3}\right)$$

$$= -30\left(\frac{\mathbf{a}_x - 2\mathbf{a}_y + 2\mathbf{a}_z}{3}\right) \qquad \text{N}$$

The magnitude of the force is 30 N (or about 7 lbf), and the direction is specified by the unit vector, which has been left in parentheses to display the magnitude of the force. The force on Q_2 may also be considered as three component forces,

$$\mathbf{F}_2 = -10\mathbf{a}_x + 20\mathbf{a}_y - 20\mathbf{a}_z$$

The force expressed by Coulomb's law is a mutual force, for each of the two charges experiences a force of the same magnitude, although of opposite direction. We might equally well have written

$$\mathbf{F}_1 = -\mathbf{F}_2 = \frac{Q_1Q_2}{4\pi\epsilon_0 R_{12}{}^2}\mathbf{a}_{R_{21}} = -\frac{Q_1Q_2}{4\pi\epsilon_0 R_{12}{}^2}\mathbf{a}_{R_{12}}$$

Coulomb's law is linear, for if we multiply Q_1 by a factor n the force on Q_2 is also multiplied by the same factor n. It is also true that the force on a charge in the presence of several other charges is the sum of the forces on that charge due to each of the other charges acting alone.

D 2.1 A charge $Q_2 = 121 \times 10^{-9}$ C is located in a vacuum at P_2 $(-0.03,0.01, 0.04)$. Find the force on Q_2 due to

(a) $Q_1 = 110$ microcoulombs (μC) at P_1 (0.03,0.08,-0.02)
(b) $Q_3 = 110\ \mu$C at P_3 ($-0.09,-0.06,0.10$)
(c) Q_1 and Q_3

Ans. $5.4\mathbf{a}_x + 6.3\mathbf{a}_y - 5.4\mathbf{a}_z; -5.4\mathbf{a}_x - 6.3\mathbf{a}_y + 5.4\mathbf{a}_z; 0 \qquad$ N

2.2 ELECTRIC FIELD INTENSITY

If we now consider one charge fixed in position, say Q_1, and move a second charge slowly around, we note that there exists everywhere a force on this second charge; in other words, this second charge is displaying the existence of a force *field*. Calling this second charge a test charge, Q_t, the force on it is given by Coulomb's law,

$$\mathbf{F}_t = \frac{Q_1 Q_t}{4\pi\epsilon_0 R_{1t}^2} \mathbf{a}_{R_{1t}}$$

Writing this force as a force per unit charge,

(1)
$$\boxed{\frac{\mathbf{F}_t}{Q_t} = \frac{Q_1}{4\pi\epsilon_0 R_{1t}^2} \mathbf{a}_{R_{1t}}}$$

We now have an expression which does not involve the size or sign of the test charge, for as the test charge increases or decreases in magnitude, so does the force on it. As the test charge changes sign, the force obediently changes direction, and their ratio is still constant. The quantity on the right side of (1) is a function only of Q_1 and the directed line segment from Q_1 to the position of the test charge. This describes a vector field and is called the *electric field intensity*.

We define the electric field intensity as the vector force on a unit positive test charge. We would not *measure* it experimentally by finding the force on a 1-C test charge, however, for this would probably cause such a force on Q_1 as to change the position of that charge.

Electric field intensity must be measured by the unit newtons per coulomb, force per unit charge. Again anticipating a new dimensional quantity, the *volt*, to be presented in Chap. 4 and having the label of joules per coulomb (J/C) or newton-meters per coulomb (N-m/C), we shall at once measure electric field intensity in the practical units of volts per meter (V/m). Using a capital letter $\mathbf{E}$ for electric field intensity, we have finally

(2)
$$\boxed{\mathbf{E} = \frac{\mathbf{F}_t}{Q_t}}$$

(3)
$$\mathbf{E} = \frac{Q_1}{4\pi\epsilon_0 R_{1t}^2} \mathbf{a}_{R_{1t}}$$

Equation (2) is the defining expression for electric field intensity, and (3) is the expression for the electric field intensity due to a single point charge Q_1 in a vacuum. In the succeeding sections we shall obtain and interpret expressions for the electric field intensity due to more complicated arrangements of charge, but now let us see what information we can obtain from (3), the field of a single point charge.

First, let us dispense with the subscripts in (3), reserving the right to use them again any time there is a possibility of misunderstanding:

(4) $$\boxed{\mathbf{E} = \frac{Q}{4\pi\epsilon_0 R^2}\,\mathbf{a}_R}$$

We should remember that R is the magnitude of the vector $\mathbf{R}$, the directed line segment from the point at which the point charge Q is located to the point at which $\mathbf{E}$ is desired, and $\mathbf{a}_R$ is a unit vector in the $\mathbf{R}$ direction.[1]

Let us arbitrarily locate Q_1 at the center of a spherical coordinate system. The unit vector $\mathbf{a}_R$ then becomes the radial unit vector $\mathbf{a}_r$, and R is r. Hence

(5) $$\mathbf{E} = \frac{Q_1}{4\pi\epsilon_0 r^2}\,\mathbf{a}_r$$

or

$$E_r = \frac{Q_1}{4\pi\epsilon_0 r^2}$$

The field has a single radial component, and its inverse-square-law relationship is quite obvious.

In cartesian coordinates we should write $\mathbf{R} = x\mathbf{a}_x + y\mathbf{a}_y + z\mathbf{a}_z$, $\mathbf{a}_R = (x\mathbf{a}_x + y\mathbf{a}_y + z\mathbf{a}_z)/\sqrt{x^2 + y^2 + z^2}$, and then

(6) $$\mathbf{E} = \frac{Q}{4\pi\epsilon_0 (x^2 + y^2 + z^2)}\left(\frac{x}{\sqrt{x^2 + y^2 + z^2}}\,\mathbf{a}_x \right.$$

$$\left. + \frac{y}{\sqrt{x^2 + y^2 + z^2}}\,\mathbf{a}_y + \frac{z}{\sqrt{x^2 + y^2 + z^2}}\,\mathbf{a}_z\right)$$

This expression no longer shows immediately the simple nature of the field, and its complexity is the price we pay for solving a problem having spherical symmetry in a coordinate system with which we may (temporarily) have more familiarity.

Without using vector analysis, the information contained in (6) would have to be expressed in three equations, one for each component, and in order to obtain the equations we should have to break up the magnitude of the electric field intensity into the three components by finding the projection on each coordinate axis. Using vector notation, this is done automatically when we write the unit vector.

[1] We firmly intend to avoid confusing r and $\mathbf{a}_r$ with R and $\mathbf{a}_R$. The first two refer specifically to the spherical or cylindrical coordinate systems, whereas R and $\mathbf{a}_R$ do not refer to any coordinate system—the choice is still available to us.

If we consider a charge which is *not* at the origin of our coordinate system, the field no longer possesses spherical symmetry (nor cylindrical symmetry, unless the charge lies on the z axis), and we might as well use cartesian coordinates. For a charge Q located at $\mathbf{R'} = a\mathbf{a}_x + b\mathbf{a}_y + c\mathbf{a}_z$ the field at $\mathbf{R} = x\mathbf{a}_x + y\mathbf{a}_y + z\mathbf{a}_z$ is

$$(7) \quad \mathbf{E} = \frac{Q(\mathbf{R} - \mathbf{R'})}{4\pi\epsilon_0 |\mathbf{R} - \mathbf{R'}|^3}$$

$$= \frac{Q}{4\pi\epsilon_0} \frac{(x-a)\mathbf{a}_x + (y-b)\mathbf{a}_y + (z-c)\mathbf{a}_z}{[(x-a)^2 + (y-b)^2 + (z-c)^2]^{3/2}}$$

Equation (6) is merely a special case of (7), where $a = b = c = 0$.

2.3 FIELD OF n POINT CHARGES

Since the coulomb forces are linear, the electric field intensity due to two point charges Q_1 and Q_2 is the sum of the forces on Q_t caused by Q_1 and Q_2 acting alone, or

$$\mathbf{E} = \frac{Q_1}{4\pi\epsilon_0 R_1^2} \mathbf{a}_{R_1} + \frac{Q_2}{4\pi\epsilon_0 R_2^2} \mathbf{a}_{R_2}$$

The distances R_1 and R_2 and the unit vectors $\mathbf{a}_{R_1}$ and $\mathbf{a}_{R_2}$ are, of course, different. The linear combination of the two fields is illustrated in Fig. 2.1.

As soon as we add this second charge, the spherical symmetry disappears and it becomes simplest to solve the problem in cartesian coordinates. The field due to each charge is obtained in terms

FIG. 2.1   The vector addition of the total electric field intensity at P due to Q_1 and Q_2 is made possible by the linearity of Coulomb's law.

of cartesian components, and these may be added to find the total field. This is the same procedure as is used in Prob. D2.1c to find the force on a charge due to two other charges.

If we add more charges at other positions the field due to n point charges is

$$(1) \quad \mathbf{E} = \frac{Q_1}{4\pi\epsilon_0 R_1{}^2}\mathbf{a}_{R_1} + \frac{Q_2}{4\pi\epsilon_0 R_2{}^2}\mathbf{a}_{R_2} + \cdots + \frac{Q_n}{4\pi\epsilon_0 R_n{}^2}\mathbf{a}_{R_n}$$

This expression takes up less space when we use a summation sign Σ and a summing integer m which takes on all integral values between 1 and n,

$$(2) \quad \mathbf{E} = \sum_{m=1}^{n} \frac{Q_m}{4\pi\epsilon_0 R_m{}^2}\mathbf{a}_{R_m}$$

When expanded, (2) is identical with (1), and those unfamiliar with summation signs and series should check that result.

D 2.2   Point charges of 3×10^{-9}, 1×10^{-9}, and -1×10^{-9} C are located at the three corners of an equilateral triangle 1 m on a side in air. Find the total magnitude of $\mathbf{E}$ at each corner which is produced by the charges at the other two corners.

Ans.   9; 23.8; 32.4 V/m

D 2.3   Evaluate the following sums:

(a) $\displaystyle\sum_{m=1}^{5} \frac{m}{m+1}\mathbf{a}_x$

(b) $\displaystyle\sum_{m=1}^{6} \left[\sin\frac{(m-1)\pi}{2}\right]\mathbf{a}_x$

(c) $\displaystyle\sum_{m=1}^{4} \mathbf{a}_{R_m}$, where $\mathbf{a}_{R_m}$ is directed from the origin to point m, and the four points m are located at 90° intervals on a unit circle centered at the origin and lying in the plane $y = 0$

Ans.   0; $\mathbf{a}_x$; $3.55\mathbf{a}_x$

2.4   FIELD DUE TO A CONTINUOUS VOLUME CHARGE DISTRIBUTION

If we now visualize a region of space filled with a tremendous number of charges separated by minute distances, such as the space between grid and cathode in a vacuum tube operating with space charge, we see that we can replace this distribution of very small particles with a smooth continuous distribution described by a *volume charge density,* just as we describe water as having a density of one gram per cubic centimeter even though it consists of atomic- and molecular-sized particles. We are able to do this only if we are uninterested in the small irregularities (or ripples) in the field as we move from electron to electron, or if we care little that the mass of the water actually increases in small but finite steps as each new molecule is added.

This is really no limitation at all, for our end results are almost always in terms of a current in a receiving antenna, a voltage in an electronic circuit, a charge on a capacitor, or in general in some large-scale *macroscopic* result. It is very seldom that we must know a current electron by electron.

We denote volume charge density by the Greek letter *rho* (ρ), and it is, of course, measured in coulombs per cubic meter (C/m³).

The small amount of charge ΔQ in a small volume Δv is

(1) $\quad \Delta Q = \rho \, \Delta v$

and we may define ρ mathematically by using a limiting process on (1),

(2) $\quad \boxed{\rho = \lim_{\Delta v \to 0} \frac{\Delta Q}{\Delta v}}$

The total charge within some finite volume is obtained by integrating throughout that volume,

(3) $\quad \boxed{Q = \int_{\text{vol}} dQ = \int_{\text{vol}} \rho \, dv}$

Only one integral sign is customarily indicated, but the differential dv signifies integration throughout a volume, and hence a triple integration. Fortunately, we may content ourselves for the most part with no more than the indicated integration, for multiple integrals are very difficult to evaluate in all but the most symmetrical problems.

As an example of the evaluation of a volume integral, let us find the total charge contained in the cylinder shown in Fig. 2.2 if the volume charge density is

$\rho = 100e^{-z}(x^2 + y^2)^{-1/4} \quad$ C/m³

Since the volume is most easily described in cylindrical coordinates, we should express the charge density in cylindrical coordinates and integrate in cylindrical coordinates. Using the information in Table 1.1, if necessary, we have

$\rho = 100e^{-z}r^{-1/2}$

FIG. 2.2 The total charge contained within the right circular cylinder may be obtained by evaluating $Q = \int_{\text{vol}} \rho \, dv$.

$$\rho = \frac{100 \, e^{-z}}{(x^2 + y^2)^{1/4}}$$

$h = 30$ cm

$r = 10$ cm

The volume differential in cylindrical coordinates is given in Sec. 1.8; therefore

$$Q = \int_0^{0.3} \int_0^{2\pi} \int_0^{0.1} 100 e^{-z} r^{-1/2} r \, dr \, d\phi \, dz$$

$$= \int_0^{0.3} \int_0^{2\pi} 100 e^{-z} \tfrac{2}{3} r^{3/2} \Big]_0^{0.1} d\phi \, dz$$

$$= \int_0^{0.3} \int_0^{2\pi} 2.11 e^{-z} \, d\phi \, dz$$

$$= \int_0^{0.3} 13.25 e^{-z} \, dz$$

$$= 3.43 \text{ C}$$

The incremental contribution to the electric field intensity produced by the incremental charge ΔQ is

$$\Delta \mathbf{E} = \frac{\Delta Q}{4 \pi \epsilon_0 R^2} \mathbf{a}_R = \frac{\rho \, \Delta v}{4 \pi \epsilon_0 R^2} \mathbf{a}_R$$

If we sum the contributions of all the volume charge in a given region,

$$\mathbf{E} = \sum_{m=1}^{n} \frac{\rho \, \Delta v}{4 \pi \epsilon_0 R^2} \mathbf{a}_R$$

and then let the volume element Δv approach zero as the number of these elements n becomes infinite, the summation becomes an integral,

(4)
$$\mathbf{E} = \int_{\text{vol}} \frac{\rho\, dv}{4\pi\epsilon_0 R^2} \mathbf{a}_R$$

This is again a triple integral, and we shall do our best to avoid actually performing the integration.

The significance of the various quantities under the integral sign of (4) has not changed from their interpretation in Sec. 2.2, Eq. (4). The unit vector $\mathbf{a}_R$ is in the direction of $\mathbf{R}$, which extends from the position of the element of charge $\rho\, dv$ to the point at which we are determining the electric field intensity. In general, we must expect that ρ, $\mathbf{a}_R$, and R are functions of the variables of integration, say x, y, and z.

D 2.4 Find the total charge in the specified volume:

 (a) A cube with edges 2 m long and parallel to axes, lying in the first octant (x, y, $z \geq 0$) with one corner at the origin; $\rho = 2xy/(z + 1)$

 (b) Cylindrical wedge bounded by surfaces $z = -1$, $z = 2$, $\phi = 30°$, $\phi = 60°$, $r = 3$; $\rho = r \sin 2\phi$

 (c) A sphere with a radius of 2 m and center at the origin; $\rho = 2r(1 + \cos\theta) \sin \frac{1}{2}\phi$

Ans.   8.80; 13.5; 64 C

2.5 FIELD OF A LINE CHARGE

Up to this point we have considered two types of charge distribution, the point charge and charge distributed throughout a volume with a density of $\rho\, \text{C/m}^3$. If we now consider a filamentlike distribution of volume charge density, such as a very fine, sharp beam in a cathode-ray tube or a charged conductor of very small radius, we find it convenient to treat the charge as a line charge of density $\rho_L\, \text{C/m}$. In the case of the electron beam the charges are in motion and it is true that we do not have an electrostatic problem. However, if the electron motion is steady and uniform (a d-c beam) and if we ignore for the moment the magnetic field which is produced, the electron beam may be considered as composed of stationary electrons, for snapshots taken at any time will show the same charge distribution.

Let us assume a straight line charge extending along the z axis in a cylindrical coordinate system from $-\infty$ to ∞, as shown in Fig. 2.3. We desire the electric field intensity $\mathbf{E}$ at any and every point resulting from a *uniform* line charge density ρ_L.

Symmetry should always be considered first in order to determine two specific factors: (1) with which coordinates the field does *not*

FIG. 2.3 The contribution $d\mathbf{E} = dE_r\, \mathbf{a}_r + dE_z\, \mathbf{a}_z$
to the electric field intensity produced by an
element of charge $dQ = \rho_L\, dL$ located a
distance L from the origin. The linear
charge density is uniform and extends along
the entire z axis.

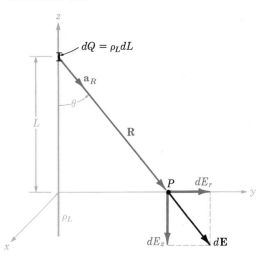

vary, and (2) which components of the field are *not* present. The
answers to these questions then tell us which components are present
and with which coordinates they do vary.

Referring to Fig. 2.3, we realize that as we move around the line
charge, varying ϕ while keeping r and z constant, the line charge
appears the same from every angle. In other words, azimuthal
symmetry is present and no field component may vary with ϕ.

Again, if we maintain r and ϕ constant while moving up and down
the line charge by changing z, the line charge still recedes into infinite distance in both directions and the problem is unchanged.
This is axial symmetry and leads to fields which are not functions
of z.

If we maintain ϕ and z constant and vary r the problem changes,
and Coulomb's law leads us to expect the field to become weaker
as r increases. Hence, by a process of elimination we are led to the
fact that the field varies only with r.

Now, which components are present? Each incremental length
of line charge acts as a point charge and produces an incremental
contribution to the electric field intensity which is directed away
from the bit of charge (assuming a positive line charge). No element of charge produces a ϕ component of electric field intensity;
E_ϕ is zero. However, each element does produce an E_r and E_z
component, but the contribution to E_z by elements of charge which

are equal distances above and below the point at which we are determining the field will cancel.

We therefore have found that we have only an E_r component and it varies only with r. Now to find this component.

We choose a point P on the y axis at which to determine the field. This is a perfectly general point in view of the lack of variation of the field with ϕ and z. Applying Sec. 2.2, Eq. (4), to find the incremental field at P due to the incremental charge $dQ = \rho_L \, dL$, we have

$$(1) \qquad d\mathbf{E} = \frac{\rho_L \, dL}{4\pi\epsilon_0 R^2} \, \mathbf{a}_R$$

or

$$dE_r = \frac{\rho_L \, dL \sin \theta}{4\pi\epsilon_0 R^2} = \frac{\rho_L \, dL}{4\pi\epsilon_0 R^2} \frac{y}{R} = \frac{\rho_L \, dL \, r}{4\pi\epsilon_0 R^3}$$

Replacing R^2 by $L^2 + r^2$ and summing the contributions from every element of charge,

$$E_r = \int_{-\infty}^{\infty} \frac{\rho_L r \, dL}{4\pi\epsilon_0 (L^2 + r^2)^{3/2}}$$

Integrating by integral tables or change of variable, $L = r \cot \theta$, we have

$$E_r = \frac{\rho_L}{4\pi\epsilon_0} r \left[\frac{1}{r^2} \frac{L}{\sqrt{L^2 + r^2}} \right]_{-\infty}^{\infty}$$

and

$$(2) \qquad \boxed{E_r = \frac{\rho_L}{2\pi\epsilon_0 r}}$$

This is the desired answer, but there are many other ways of obtaining it. We might have used the angle θ as our variable of integration, for $L = r \cot \theta$ from Fig. 2.3 and $dL = -r \csc^2 \theta \, d\theta$. Since $R = r \csc \theta$, our integral becomes, simply,

$$dE_r = \frac{\rho_L \, dL}{4\pi\epsilon_0 R^2} \sin \theta = -\frac{\rho_L \sin \theta \, d\theta}{4\pi\epsilon_0 r}$$

$$E_r = -\frac{\rho_L}{4\pi\epsilon_0 r} \int_{180°}^{0°} \sin \theta \, d\theta = \frac{\rho_L}{4\pi\epsilon_0 r} \cos \theta \Big]_{180°}^{0°}$$

$$= \frac{\rho_L}{2\pi\epsilon_0 r}$$

Coulomb's Law and Electric Field Intensity 40

FIG. 2.4   The geometry of the problem for the field about an infinite line charge leads to more difficult integrations when symmetry is ignored.

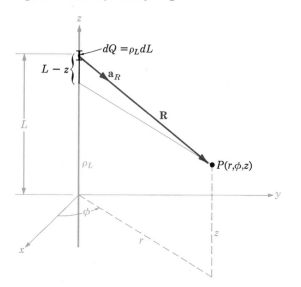

Here the integration was simpler, but some experience with problems of this type is necessary before we can unerringly choose the simplest variable of integration at the beginning of the problem.

We might also have considered Sec. 2.4, Eq. (4), as our starting point,

$$\mathbf{E} = \int_{\text{vol}} \frac{\rho \, dv}{4\pi\epsilon_0 R^2} \mathbf{a}_R$$

letting $\rho \, dv = \rho_L \, dL$ and integrating along the line which is now our "volume" containing all the charge. Suppose we do this and forget everything we have learned from the symmetry of the problem. Choose point P now at a general location (r,ϕ,z) (Fig. 2.4) and write

$$\mathbf{R} = r\mathbf{a}_r - (L - z)\mathbf{a}_z$$

$$R = \sqrt{r^2 + (L - z)^2}$$

$$\mathbf{a}_R = \frac{r\mathbf{a}_r - (L - z)\mathbf{a}_z}{\sqrt{r^2 + (L - z)^2}}$$

$$\mathbf{E} = \int_{-\infty}^{\infty} \frac{\rho_L \, dL[r\mathbf{a}_r - (L - z)\mathbf{a}_z]}{4\pi\epsilon_0[r^2 + (L - z)^2]^{3/2}}$$

$$= \frac{\rho_L}{4\pi\epsilon_0} \left\{ \int_{-\infty}^{\infty} \frac{r \, dL \, \mathbf{a}_r}{[r^2 + (L - z)^2]^{3/2}} - \int_{-\infty}^{\infty} \frac{(L - z) \, dL \, \mathbf{a}_z}{[r^2 + (L - z)^2]^{3/2}} \right\}$$

Before integrating a vector expression we must know whether or not the vector under the integral sign (here the unit vectors $\mathbf{a}_r$ and $\mathbf{a}_z$) varies with the variable of integration (here dL). If it does not, then it is a constant and may be removed from within the integral, leaving a scalar which may be integrated by normal methods. Our unit vectors, of course, cannot change in magnitude, but a change in direction is just as troublesome. Fortunately, the direction of $\mathbf{a}_r$ does not change with L (nor with r, but it does change with ϕ), and $\mathbf{a}_z$ is constant always.

Hence we remove the unit vectors from the integrals and again integrate with tables or by changing variables,

$$\mathbf{E} = \frac{\rho_L}{4\pi\epsilon_0}\left\{\mathbf{a}_r\int_{-\infty}^{\infty}\frac{r\,dL}{[r^2+(L-z)^2]^{3/2}} - \mathbf{a}_z\int_{-\infty}^{\infty}\frac{(L-z)\,dL}{[r^2+(L-z)^2]^{3/2}}\right\}$$

$$= \frac{\rho_L}{4\pi\epsilon_0}\left\{\left[\mathbf{a}_r\frac{1}{r^2}\frac{L-z}{\sqrt{r^2+(L-z)^2}}\right]_{-\infty}^{\infty} - \left[\mathbf{a}_z\frac{1}{\sqrt{r^2+(L-z)^2}}\right]_{-\infty}^{\infty}\right\}$$

$$= \frac{\rho_L}{4\pi\epsilon_0}\left[\mathbf{a}_r\frac{2}{r} + \mathbf{a}_z(0)\right] = \frac{\rho_L}{2\pi\epsilon_0 r}\mathbf{a}_r$$

Again we obtain the same answer, as we should, for there is nothing wrong with the method except that the integration was harder and there were two integrations to perform. This is the price we pay for neglecting the consideration of symmetry and plunging doggedly ahead with mathematics. Look before you integrate.

Other methods for solving this basic problem will be discussed later after we introduce Gauss's law and the concept of potential.

Now let us consider the answer itself,

$$E_r = \frac{\rho_L}{2\pi\epsilon_0 r}$$

We note that the field falls off inversely with the distance to the charged line, as compared with the point charge, where the field decreased with the square of the distance. Moving ten times as far from a point charge leads to a field only 1 per cent the previous strength, but moving ten times as far from a line charge only reduces the field to 10 per cent of its former value. An analogy can be drawn with a source of illumination, for the light intensity from a point source of light also falls off inversely as the square of the distance to the source. The field of an infinitely long fluorescent tube thus decays inversely as the first power of the radial distance to the tube, and we should expect the light intensity about a finite-length tube to obey this law near the tube. As our point recedes farther and farther from a finite-length tube, however, it eventually looks like a point source and the field obeys the inverse-square relationship.

In Sec. 2.7 we shall describe how fields may be sketched and use the field of the line charge as one example.

D 2.5 Find **E** in cartesian coordinates at (1,2,3) in free space if the source of the field is

(a) A line charge $\rho_L = 0.5 \times 10^{-9}$ C/m along the z axis
(b) A line charge $\rho_L = 0.5 \times 10^{-9}$ C/m along the y axis
(c) A line charge $\rho_L = 0.5 \times 10^{-9}$ C/m along the line $\phi = 0, r = 1$

Ans. $0.9\mathbf{a}_x + 2.7\mathbf{a}_z;\; 1.8\mathbf{a}_x + 3.6\mathbf{a}_y;\; 4.5\mathbf{a}_y$ V/m

2.6   FIELD OF A SHEET OF CHARGE

Another basic charge configuration is the infinite sheet of charge having a uniform density of ρ_s C/m². The charge-distribution family now is complete—point, line, sheet, and volume, or Q, ρ_L, ρ_s, ρ.

Let us place this sheet in the yz plane and again consider symmetry (Fig. 2.5). We see first that the field cannot vary with y or with z, and then that the y and z components arising from differential elements of charge symmetrically located with respect to the point at which we wish the field will cancel. Hence only E_x is present, and this component is a function of x alone. We are again faced with a choice of many methods by which to evaluate this component, and this time we shall use but one method and leave the others as exercises for a quiet Sunday afternoon.

Let us use the field of the infinite line charge [Sec. 2.5, Eq. (2)]

FIG. 2.5   An infinite sheet of charge in the yz plane, a general point P on the x axis, and the differential-width line charge used as the element in determining the field at P by $d\mathbf{E} = \rho_s\, dy\, \mathbf{a}_R/2\pi\epsilon_0 R$.

by dividing the infinite sheet into differential-width strips. One such strip is shown in Fig. 2.5. The line charge density, or charge per unit length, is $\rho_L = \rho_s\, dy$, and the distance to our general point P on the x axis from this line charge is $r = \sqrt{x^2 + y^2}$. The contribution to E_x at P from this differential-width strip is then

$$dE_x = \frac{\rho_s\, dy}{2\pi\epsilon_0 \sqrt{x^2 + y^2}} \cos\theta = \frac{\rho_s}{2\pi\epsilon_0}\frac{x\, dy}{x^2 + y^2}$$

Adding the effects of all the strips,

$$(1) \quad E_x = \frac{\rho_s}{2\pi\epsilon_0}\int_{-\infty}^{\infty}\frac{x\, dy}{x^2 + y^2} = \frac{\rho_s}{2\pi\epsilon_0}\tan^{-1}\frac{y}{x}\bigg]_{-\infty}^{\infty}$$

$$= \frac{\rho_s}{2\epsilon_0}$$

If the point P were chosen on the negative x axis, then

$$E_x = -\frac{\rho_s}{2\epsilon_0}$$

for the field is always directed away from the positive charge. This difficulty in sign is usually overcome by specifying a unit vector $\mathbf{a}_n$, which is normal to the sheet and directed outward, or away from it. Then

$$(2) \quad \boxed{\mathbf{E} = \frac{\rho_s}{2\epsilon_0}\mathbf{a}_n}$$

This is a startling answer, for the field is constant in magnitude and direction. It is just as strong a million miles away from the sheet as it is right off the surface. Returning to our light analogy, we see that a uniform source of light on the ceiling of a very large room leads to just as much illumination on a square foot on the floor as it does on a square foot 1 in. below the ceiling. If you desire greater illumination on this subject, it will do you no good to hold the book closer to this light source.

If a second infinite sheet of charge, having a *negative* charge density $-\rho_s$, is located in the plane $x = a$, we may find the total field by adding the contribution of each sheet. In the region $x > a$,

$$\mathbf{E}_+ = \frac{\rho_s}{2\epsilon_0}\mathbf{a}_x \qquad \mathbf{E}_- = -\frac{\rho_s}{2\epsilon_0}\mathbf{a}_x \qquad \mathbf{E} = \mathbf{E}_+ + \mathbf{E}_- = 0$$

and for $x < 0$,

$$\mathbf{E}_+ = -\frac{\rho_s}{2\epsilon_0}\mathbf{a}_x \qquad \mathbf{E}_- = \frac{\rho_s}{2\epsilon_0}\mathbf{a}_x \qquad \mathbf{E} = \mathbf{E}_+ + \mathbf{E}_- = 0$$

and when $0 < x < a$,

$$\mathbf{E}_+ = \frac{\rho_s}{2\epsilon_0}\,\mathbf{a}_x \qquad \mathbf{E}_- = \frac{\rho_s}{2\epsilon_0}\,\mathbf{a}_x$$

and

(3)
$$\boxed{\mathbf{E} = \mathbf{E}_+ + \mathbf{E}_- = \frac{\rho_s}{\epsilon_0}\,\mathbf{a}_x}$$

This is an important practical answer, for it is the field between the parallel plates of an air capacitor, provided the linear dimensions of the plates are very much greater than their separation and provided also that we are considering a point well removed from the edges. The field outside the capacitor, while not zero, as we found for the ideal case above, is usually negligible.

D 2.6 Charge is distributed uniformly in a finite-sized rectangular sheet perpendicular to and centered upon the z axis; the edges are parallel to the x or y axis. The dimensions of the sheet are 1 millimeter (mm) by 1 m, and $\rho_s = 10^{-9}/18\pi$ C/m². Use common-sense approximations to estimate $\mathbf{E}$ at points on the z axis for which

(a) $z = 0.001$ mm
(b) $z = 1$ centimeter (cm)
(c) $z = 100$ m

Ans. $\mathbf{a}_z$; $0.1\mathbf{a}_z/\pi$; $10^{-7}\mathbf{a}_z/2\pi$ V/m (by more exact methods, answers are $0.99873\mathbf{a}_z$; $0.099897\mathbf{a}_z/\pi$; $0.9999875 \times 10^{-7}\mathbf{a}_z/2\pi$ V/m)

2.7 STREAMLINES AND SKETCHES OF FIELDS

We now have vector equations for the electric field intensity resulting from several different charge configurations, and we have had little difficulty in interpreting the magnitude and direction of the field from the equations. Unfortunately, this simplicity cannot last much longer, for we have solved most of the simple cases and our new charge distributions now must lead to more complicated expressions for the fields and more difficulty in visualizing the fields through the equations. However, it is true that one picture is worth about a thousand words if we just know what picture to draw.

Consider the field about the line charge,

$$\mathbf{E} = \frac{\rho_L}{2\pi\epsilon_0 r}\,\mathbf{a}_r$$

Figure 2.6a shows a cross-sectional view of the line charge, and on it is shown what might be our first effort at picturing the field, short line segments drawn here and there having a length proportional

FIG. 2.6   (a) One very poor, (b) and (c) two fair, and (d) the usual form of streamline sketch.   In the last form the arrows show the direction of the field at every point, and the spacing of the lines is inversely proportional to the strength of the field.

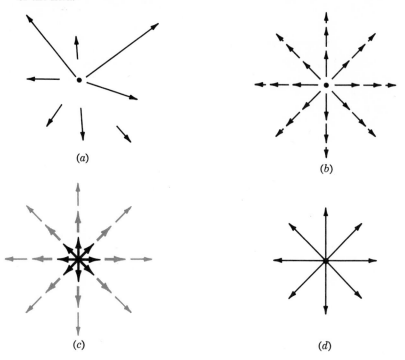

(a)

(b)

(c)

(d)

to the magnitude of **E** and pointing in the direction of **E**.   The figure fails to show the symmetry with respect to ϕ, so we try again in Fig. 2.6*b* with a symmetrical location of the line segments.   The real trouble now appears—the longest lines must be drawn in the most crowded region, and this also plagues us if we use line segments of equal length but of a thickness which is proportional to *E* (Fig. 2.6*c*).   Other schemes which have been suggested include drawing shorter lines to represent stronger fields (inherently misleading) and using intensity of color to represent stronger fields (difficult and uneconomical).

For the present, then, let us be content to show only the *direction* of **E** by drawing continuous lines from the charge which are everywhere tangent to **E**.   Figure 2.6*d* shows this compromise.   A symmetrical distribution of lines (one every 45°) indicates azimuthal symmetry, and arrowheads should be used to show direction.

These lines are usually called *streamlines*, although other terms such as flux lines and direction lines are also used.   A small positive test charge placed at any point in this field and free to move would accelerate in the direction of the streamline passing through that point. If the field represented the velocity of a liquid or a gas (which, incidentally, would have to have a source at $r = 0$), small suspended particles in the liquid or gas would trace out the streamlines.

We shall find out later that a bonus accompanies this streamline sketch, for the magnitude of the field can be shown to be inversely proportional to the spacing of the streamlines for some important special cases. The closer they are together, the stronger is the field. At that time we shall also find an easier, more accurate method of making the streamline sketch.

If we attempted to sketch the field of the point charge the variation of the field into and away from the page would cause essentially unsurmountable difficulties; for this reason sketching is usually limited to two-dimensional fields.

In the case of the two-dimensional field let us arbitrarily set $E_z = 0$. The streamlines are thus confined to planes for which z is constant, and the sketch is the same for any such plane. Several streamlines are shown in Fig. 2.7, and the E_x and E_y components are indicated at a general point. Since it is apparent that

(1)
$$\frac{E_y}{E_x} = \frac{dy}{dx}$$

a knowledge of the functional form of E_x and E_y (and the ability to solve the resultant differential equation) will enable us to obtain the equations of the streamlines.

FIG. 2.7   The equation of a streamline is obtained by solving the differential equation, $E_y/E_x = dy/dx$.

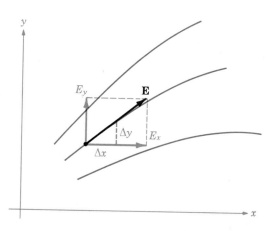

As an illustration of this method, consider the field of the uniform line charge with $\rho_L = 2\pi\epsilon_0$,

$$\mathbf{E} = \frac{1}{r}\,\mathbf{a}_r$$

In cartesian coordinates,

$$\mathbf{E} = \frac{x}{x^2 + y^2}\,\mathbf{a}_x + \frac{y}{x^2 + y^2}\,\mathbf{a}_y$$

Thus we form the differential equation

$$\frac{dy}{dx} = \frac{E_y}{E_x} = \frac{y}{x}$$

or

$$\frac{dy}{y} = \frac{dx}{x}$$

Therefore

$$\ln y = \ln x + C_1$$

or

$$\ln y = \ln x + \ln C$$

from which the equations of the streamlines are obtained,

$$y = Cx$$

These are obviously the radial lines shown in Fig. 2.6d if $C = 0, 1, -1$ and if $1/C = 0$.

SUGGESTED REFERENCES

1 Boast, W. B.: "Vector Fields," Harper and Row, Publishers, Incorporated, New York, 1964. This book contains numerous examples and sketches of fields.

2 Moore, A. D.: Fields from Fluid Flow Mappers, *J. Appl. Phys.*, vol. 20, pp. 790–804, August, 1949. This paper contains many photographs of flow fields which are analogous to electric fields.

3 Schelkunoff, S. A.: "Electromagnetic Fields," Blaisdell Publishing Company, New York, 1963. Many of the physical aspects of fields are discussed early in this text without advanced mathematics.

PROBLEMS

1 Newton's law of gravity may be written $F = Gm_1m_2/R^2$, where m_1 and m_2 are point masses separated a distance R, and G is the gravitational constant, $6.664 \times 10^{-11}\,\text{m}^3/\text{kg-s}^2$. If the masses of the earth and moon are 5.98×10^{24} kg and 7.35×10^{22} kg, respectively, and the average separation is 239,000 miles, (a) find the gravitational force of attraction; (b) find the values of the equal and opposite charges which, when placed on the earth and moon, would cause the same force. (c) If $Q = It$ for a direct current, how long would a current of 100 amperes (A) have to flow to transfer this charge?

2 Point charges of 2×10^{-9} and -10^{-9} C are located at $(0,0,0)$ and $(0,1,0)$, respectively, in free space. Determine the force exerted on each charge.

3 Two pith balls, each having a mass of 0.1 gram (g), are free to slide up and down on a nylon thread. The lower ball rests on a knot. If each ball is given a positive charge of 10^{-8} C, determine their separation.

4 Three point charges, each 5×10^{-9} C, are located on the x axis at $x = -1, 0$, and 1 in free space. (a) Find $\mathbf{E}$ at $x = 5$. (b) Determine the value and location of the equivalent single point charge which would produce the same field at very large distances. (c) Determine $\mathbf{E}$ at $x = 5$, using the simplifying approximation of (b).

5 A charge of -10^{-9} C is located at the origin in free space. What charge must be located at $(2,0,0)$ to cause E_x to be zero at $(3,1,1)$?

6 A charge Q ($Q > 0$) is located at the origin. At what point on the line defined by $x = 1, z = 3$ is E_y a maximum?

7 A certain region of volume charge density with spherical symmetry is probed experimentally. The following charge-density values are obtained: $0\ \text{C/m}^3$ at the origin, $10\ \text{C/m}^3$ at 1-cm radius, 30 at 2, 60 at 3, 80 at 4, 50 at 5, 20 at 6, and 0 at 7-cm radius. Determine the approximate value of the total charge within the 7-cm radius.

8 When operating with full space charge, the volume charge density in a parallel-plane diode is given by $\rho = -\frac{4}{9}\epsilon_0 V_0 x^{-2/3} d^{-4/3}$, where V_0 is the anode-cathode voltage, the cathode is located at $x = 0$, and the anode is at $x = d$. Find the total charge in a region 1 cm² in cross section extending from cathode to anode if $d = 2$ mm and $V_0 = 200$ V.

9 The electron beam in a certain cathode-ray tube possesses cylindrical symmetry, and the charge density is represented by $\rho = -10^{-13}/(r^2 + 10^{-8})$ for $0 \leq r \leq 3 \times 10^{-4}$ and $\rho = 0$ for $r > 3 \times 10^{-4}$ m. (a) Find the total charge per meter in the beam. (b) If the electron velocity is 5×10^7 m/s, guess at the definition of current and find the beam current.

10 Electrons are in random motion in a fixed region of space. During any 1-microsecond (μs) interval the probability that an electron is found in a subregion of volume 10^{-15} m³ is 27.6 per cent. What volume charge density should be assigned to that subregion?

11 The volume charge density in a certain region is given by $\rho = 10^{-12}\,r^3 e^{-r}$ C/m³, in spherical coordinates. Determine $\mathbf{E}$ at the origin.

12 In order to provide a simple problem to illustrate the mechanics of the integration in Sec. 2.4, Eq. (4), assume ρ is $(x^2 + y^2 + z^2)^{5/2}$ in the region $0 \le x \le 1, 0 \le y \le 1, 0 \le z \le 1$ and is zero elsewhere. Find E_x at the origin.

13 (a) Find $\mathbf{E}$ in the plane $z = 0$ which is produced by a uniform line charge ρ_L extending along the z axis from $z = -L$ to $+L$ in a cylindrical coordinate system. (b) If a finite line charge is approximated by an infinite line charge $(L = \infty)$, by what percentage is E_r in error if $r = 0.5L$? (c) Repeat (b) with $r = 0.1L$.

14 Two semi-infinite uniform line charges ρ_L are located on the z axis. One extends from $z = h$ to infinity, and the other from $z = -h$ to minus infinity. (a) Determine $\mathbf{E}$ at the origin after a consideration of the symmetry present. (b) Find $\mathbf{E}$ in the plane $z = 0$.

15 Two uniform line charges lie on the lines $y = \pm d/2, z = 0$. Determine $\mathbf{E}$ in the plane $y = 0$ (a) if each line charge is ρ_L; (b) if the line charge at $y = -d/2$ is $-\rho_L$ and the other is ρ_L. (c) How does the field of (a) vary with z for very large values of z? (d) How does the field of (b) vary with z for very large values of z?

16 An infinite uniform line charge with $\rho_L = 2 \times 10^{-9}$ C/m lies along the line defined by $\mathbf{r} \times \mathbf{a}_y = 3\mathbf{a}_z$, where $\mathbf{r} = x\mathbf{a}_x + y\mathbf{a}_y + z\mathbf{a}_z$ extends from the origin to a general point on the line. Find $\mathbf{E}$ (a) at (0,5,0); (b) at (1,2,6).

17 A uniform surface charge is in the form of a spherical surface centered at the origin. Use symmetry arguments to determine which components of $\mathbf{E}$ may be present at any point outside or inside the sphere. With which spherical coordinates may they vary? We shall evaluate these fields in the next chapter by a simple procedure.

18 A uniform surface charge is distributed in a strip in the plane $y = 0$, extending from $x = -d/2$ to $x = d/2$, and from $z = -\infty$ to $z = \infty$. Find $\mathbf{E}$ at a general point (x,y,z).

19 Find the $\mathbf{E}$ field on the z axis produced by an annular ring of uniform surface charge density ρ_s in free space. The ring is described by $z = 0, a \le r \le b$, $0 \le \phi \le 2\pi$, in cylindrical coordinates. Take the symmetry of the problem into consideration.

20 From the results of Prob. 19, determine the field of the infinite uniform sheet of charge.

21 Three infinite uniform sheets of charge are located in free space as follows: $\rho_s = -10\epsilon_0$ at $z = -1$, $\rho_s = 20\epsilon_0$ at $z = 0$, and $\rho_s = -10\epsilon_0$ at $z = 1$. Determine $\mathbf{E}$ in all regions.

22 In the region defined by $0 \le x \le 1, 0 \le y \le 1, 0 \le z \le 1$, $\mathbf{E} = 2\mathbf{a}_x - 5\mathbf{a}_y$. Determine how this field might be produced by sheets of charge (a) on the planes $x = -1, y = 4$; (b) on the planes $x = -1$ and $x = y + 1$.

23 An infinite sheet of surface charge $\rho_s = 5\epsilon_0$ occupies the $z = 0$ surface, and an infinite line charge $\rho_L = 10\pi\epsilon_0$ is located at $z = 10, x = -2$. Define the region or regions (a) where $\mathbf{E} = 0$; (b) where $|\mathbf{E}| = 1$.

24 An infinite sheet of surface charge with $\rho_s = 12\epsilon_0$ C/m^2 is located on the plane $x - 2y + 3z = 4$ in free space. Find **E** on the side of the sheet which contains the origin.

25 Using Sec. 2.7, Eq. (1), show that the equation defining the family of streamlines for the field $\mathbf{E} = 2\mathbf{a}_x - 5\mathbf{a}_y$ is $y + 2.5x = C$. Sketch the streamlines for $C = 0, 1, 2$, and 3.

26 Given $\mathbf{E} = (y + 1)\mathbf{a}_x + x\mathbf{a}_y$, show that the streamlines are given by $(y + 1)^2 = x^2 + C$. Sketch the streamlines for $C = 0, \pm1$, and ±2.

27 Determine the streamlines and sketch the field $\mathbf{E} = -2x\mathbf{a}_x + 2y\mathbf{a}_y$.

28 Determine the streamlines and sketch the field for $\mathbf{E} = -e^x (\sin y\ \mathbf{a}_x + \cos y\ \mathbf{a}_y)$ in the region $-\pi/2 < y < \pi/2$.

29 Near the end of Sec. 2.7 it is indicated that a small positively charged particle would accelerate in the direction of the streamline on which it is located. (*a*) Show that this is true. (*b*) Would the particle traverse a single streamline?

30 Refer to F. E. Smith, Fundamental Electrical Measurements, *J. IEE* (London), vol. 81, no. 492, p. 703, December, 1937, and use rationalized mks formulas to find the charge on the larger sphere in coulombs and compare results.

31 Coulomb's torsion balance is described in Alfred Still, "Soul of Amber," Murray Hill Books, Inc., New York, 1944. For the sensitivity stated, determine the force in newtons on the pith balls required to produce a 90° deflection. If their separation then is 2 in., find the charge on each.

FIG. 3.1 The electric flux in the region between a pair of charged concentric spheres. The direction and magnitude of **D** are not functions of the dielectric between the spheres.

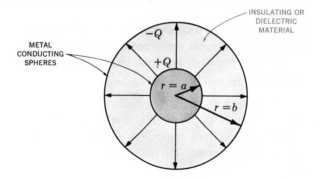

The electric flux density **D** is a vector field and is a member of the "flux density" class of vector fields, as opposed to the "force fields" class, which includes the electric field intensity **E**. The direction of **D** at a point is the direction of the flux lines at that point, and the magnitude is given by the number of flux lines crossing a surface normal to the lines divided by the surface area.

Referring again to Fig. 3.1, the electric flux density is in the radial direction and has a value of

$$\mathbf{D}\Big|_{r=a} = \frac{Q}{4\pi a^2}\,\mathbf{a}_r \qquad \text{(inner sphere)}$$

$$\mathbf{D}\Big|_{r=b} = \frac{Q}{4\pi b^2}\,\mathbf{a}_r \qquad \text{(outer sphere)}$$

and at a radial distance r, where $a \leq r \leq b$,

$$\mathbf{D} = \frac{Q}{4\pi r^2}\,\mathbf{a}_r$$

If we now let the inner sphere become smaller and smaller, while still retaining a charge of Q, it becomes a point charge in the limit, but the electric flux density at a point r m from the point charge is still given by

(1)
$$\boxed{\mathbf{D} = \frac{Q}{4\pi r^2}\,\mathbf{a}_r}$$

for Q lines of flux are symmetrically directed outward from the point and pass through an imaginary spherical surface of area $4\pi r^2$.

This result should be compared with Sec. 2.2, Eq. (5), the radial electric field intensity of a point charge in free space,

$$E = \frac{Q}{4\pi\epsilon_0 r^2} \mathbf{a}_r$$

In free space, therefore,

(2)
$$\mathbf{D} = \epsilon_0 \mathbf{E}$$

Although (2) is applicable only to a vacuum, it is not restricted solely to the field of a point charge. For a general volume charge distribution in free space

(3)
$$\mathbf{E} = \int_{vol} \frac{\rho \, dv}{4\pi\epsilon_0 R^2} \mathbf{a}_R$$

where this relationship was developed from the field of a single point charge. In a similar manner, (1) leads to

(4)
$$\mathbf{D} = \int_{vol} \frac{\rho \, dv}{4\pi R^2} \mathbf{a}_R$$

and (2) is therefore true for any free-space charge configuration; we shall consider (2) as defining **D** in free space.

As a preparation for the study of dielectrics later, it might be well to point out now that, for a point charge embedded in an infinite ideal dielectric medium, Faraday's results show that (1) is still applicable, and thus so is (4). Equation (3) is not applicable, however, and so the relationship between **D** and **E** will be slightly more complicated than (2).

D 3.1 A uniform electric flux density of 2 C/m² is in the direction of the vector $3\mathbf{a}_x - 4\mathbf{a}_y$. After expressing **D** as a vector, determine the magnitude of the electric flux crossing the portion of

(a) The yz plane bounded by $y = 0$, $y = 1$, $z = 0$, $z = 1$
(b) The zx plane bounded by $z = 0$, $z = 1$, $x = 0$, $x = 1$
(c) The xy plane bounded by $x = 0$, $x = 1$, $y = 0$, $y = 1$

Ans. 0; 1.2; 1.6 C

D 3.2 A uniform line charge $\rho_L = 30\pi$ C/m lies along the z axis in free space. Determine the component of **D** in the direction of the line $-\mathbf{a}_x + 2\mathbf{a}_y - 2\mathbf{a}_z$ at the point

(a) (2,0,0)
(b) (0,2,0)
(c) (3,−4,−2)

Ans. −2.2; −2.5; 5 C/m²

The results of Faraday's experiments with the concentric spheres could be summed up as an experimental law by stating that the electric flux passing through any imaginary spherical surface lying between the two conducting spheres is equal to the charge enclosed by this imaginary surface.   This enclosed charge is distributed on the surface of the inner sphere, or it might be concentrated as a point charge at the center of the imaginary sphere.   However, since one coulomb of electric flux is produced by one coulomb of charge, the inner conductor might just as well have been a cube or a brass door key and the total induced charge on the outer sphere would still be the same.   Certainly the flux density would change from its previous symmetrical distribution to some unknown configuration, but $+Q$ coulombs on any inner conductor would produce an induced charge of $-Q$ coulombs on the surrounding sphere.   Going one step farther, we could now replace the two outer hemispheres by an empty (but completely closed) soup can.   Q coulombs on the brass door key would produce $\Psi = Q$ lines of electric flux and would induce $-Q$ coulombs on the tin can.[1]

These generalizations of Faraday's experiment lead to the following statement, which is known as *Gauss's law*:

The electric flux passing through any closed surface is equal to the total charge enclosed by that surface.

The contribution of Gauss, one of the greatest mathematicians the world has ever produced, was actually not in stating the law as we have above, but in providing a mathematical form for this statement, which we shall now obtain.

Let us imagine a distribution of charge, shown as a cloud of point charges in Fig. 3.2, surrounded by a closed surface of any shape. The closed surface may be the surface of some real material, but more generally it is any closed surface we wish to visualize.   If the total charge is Q, then Q coulombs of electric flux will pass through the enclosing surface.   At every point on the surface the electric-flux-density vector $\mathbf{D}$ will have some value $\mathbf{D}_s$, where the subscript s merely reminds us that $\mathbf{D}$ must be evaluated at the surface, and $\mathbf{D}_s$ will in general vary in magnitude and direction from one point on the surface to another.

We must now consider the nature of an incremental element of the surface.   An incremental element of area ΔS is very nearly a portion of a plane surface, and the complete description of this surface element requires not only a statement of its magnitude ΔS, but also

---

[1] If it were a perfect insulator, the soup could even be left in the can without any difference in the results.

FIG. 3.2 The electric flux density $\mathbf{D}_s$ at P due to charge Q. The total flux passing through $\Delta \mathbf{S}$ is $\mathbf{D}_s \cdot \Delta \mathbf{S}$.

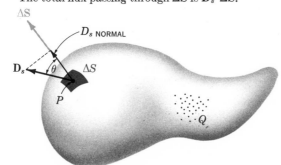

of its orientation in space. In other words, the incremental surface element is a vector quantity. The only unique direction which may be associated with $\Delta \mathbf{S}$ (the vector incremental surface element) is the direction of the normal to that plane which is tangent to the surface at the point in question. There are, of course, two such normals, and the ambiguity is removed by specifying the outward normal whenever the surface is closed and "outward" has a specific meaning.

At any point P consider an incremental element of surface $\Delta \mathbf{S}$ and let $\mathbf{D}_s$ make an angle of θ with $\Delta \mathbf{S}$, as shown in Fig. 3.2. The flux crossing $\Delta \mathbf{S}$ is then the product of the normal component of $\mathbf{D}_s$ and ΔS,

$$\Delta \Psi = \text{flux crossing } \Delta \mathbf{S} = D_{s,\text{norm}} \, \Delta S = D_s \cos \theta \, \Delta S = \mathbf{D}_s \cdot \Delta \mathbf{S}$$

where we are able to apply the definition of the dot product developed in Chap. 1.

The total flux passing through the closed surface is obtained by adding the differential contributions crossing each surface element $\Delta \mathbf{S}$,

$$\Psi = \int d\Psi = \oint_{\substack{\text{closed} \\ \text{surface}}} \mathbf{D}_s \cdot d\mathbf{S}$$

The resultant integral is a *closed surface integral*, and since the surface element dS always involves the differentials of two coordinates, such as $dx \, dy$, $r \, d\phi \, dr$, or $r^2 \sin \theta \, d\theta \, d\phi$, the integral is a double integral. Usually only one integral sign is used for brevity, and we shall always place an s below the integral sign to indicate a surface integral, although this is not actually necessary, because the differential $d\mathbf{S}$ is automatically the signal for a surface integral. One last convention is to place a small circle on the integral sign itself to indicate that the integration is to be performed over a *closed* surface. Such a surface is often called a *Gaussian surface*. We then have the mathematical formulation of Gauss's law,

$$\Psi = \oint_s \mathbf{D}_s \cdot d\mathbf{S} = \text{charge enclosed} = Q$$

The charge enclosed might be several point charges, in which case

$$Q = \Sigma Q_n$$

or a line charge,

$$Q = \int \rho_L \, dL$$

or a surface charge,

$$Q = \int_s \rho_s \, dS$$

or a volume charge distribution,

$$Q = \int_{\text{vol}} \rho \, dv$$

The last form is usually used, and we should agree now that it represents any or all of the other forms. With this understanding Gauss's law may be written in terms of the charge distribution as

(1)
$$\oint_s \mathbf{D}_s \cdot d\mathbf{S} = \int_{\text{vol}} \rho \, dv$$

a mathematical statement meaning simply that the total electric flux through any closed surface is equal to the charge enclosed.

To illustrate the application of Gauss's law, let us check the results of Faraday's experiment by placing a point charge Q at the origin of a spherical coordinate system (Fig. 3.3) and by choosing our closed surface as a sphere of radius a. The electric field intensity of the point charge has been found to be

$$\mathbf{E} = \frac{Q}{4\pi\epsilon_0 r^2} \mathbf{a}_r$$

and since

$$\mathbf{D} = \epsilon_0 \mathbf{E}$$

we have, as before,

$$\mathbf{D} = \frac{Q}{4\pi r^2} \mathbf{a}_r$$

FIG. 3.3 Application of Gauss's law to the field
of a point charge Q on a spherical
closed surface of radius a. **D** is
everywhere normal to the spherical
surface and has constant magnitude
at every point on it.

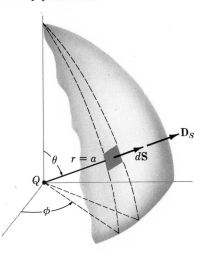

At the surface of the sphere,

$$\mathbf{D}_s = \frac{Q}{4\pi a^2} \mathbf{a}_r$$

The differential element of area on a spherical surface is, in spherical
coordinates from Chap. 1,

$$dS = r^2 \sin \theta \, d\phi \, d\theta = a^2 \sin \theta \, d\phi \, d\theta$$

or

$$d\mathbf{S} = a^2 \sin \theta \, d\phi \, d\theta \, \mathbf{a}_r$$

The integrand is

$$\mathbf{D}_s \cdot d\mathbf{S} = \frac{Q}{4\pi a^2} a^2 \sin \theta \, d\phi \, d\theta \, \mathbf{a}_r \cdot \mathbf{a}_r = \frac{Q}{4\pi} \sin \theta \, d\phi \, d\theta$$

leading to the closed surface integral

$$\int_{\theta=0}^{\theta=\pi} \int_{\phi=0}^{\phi=2\pi} \frac{Q}{4\pi} \sin \theta \, d\phi \, d\theta$$

where the limits on the integrals have been chosen so that the integration is carried over the entire surface of the sphere once.[1]   Inte-

---

[1] Note that if θ and ϕ both cover the range from 0 to 2π, the spherical surface
is covered twice.

grating gives

$$\int_{\theta=0}^{\theta=\pi} \frac{Q}{4\pi} \sin \theta \, 2\pi \, d\theta = \frac{Q}{2} (- \cos \theta) \Big]_0^\pi = Q$$

and we obtain a result showing Q coulombs of electric flux cross the surface, as we should.

The following section contains examples of the application of Gauss's law to problems of a simple symmetrical geometry with the object of finding the electric field intensity.

D 3.3 The plane $z = 0$ contains a nonuniform surface charge density $\rho_s = 50x^2$ C/m². Determine the total electric flux leaving the closed surface defined by

    (a) A cube centered at the origin, 1.8 m on a side, with edges parallel to coordinate axes

    (b) A cylinder of 1.5 m radius, with an axis along the x axis extending from $x = 0$ to $x = 0.9$

    (c) A sphere of 1 m radius, centered at the origin

Ans.   36.4; 39.3; 43.7 C

D 3.4 Find the total charge within a cube 1 m on a side, lying in the first octant with one corner at the origin and with edges parallel to the coordinate axes, if

    (a) $\mathbf{D} = 2(x + 2)^2\mathbf{a}_x$

    (b) $\mathbf{D} = 10 \sin \dfrac{\pi y}{6} \mathbf{a}_y$

    (c) $\mathbf{D} = 12x^2y^2\mathbf{a}_x + 8x^3y\mathbf{a}_y$

Ans.   5; 6; 10 C

3.3 APPLICATION OF GAUSS'S LAW: SOME SYMMETRICAL CHARGE DISTRIBUTIONS

Let us now consider how we may use Gauss's law,

$$\boxed{Q = \oint_s \mathbf{D}_s \cdot d\mathbf{S}}$$

to determine $\mathbf{D}_s$ if the charge distribution is known. This is an example of an integral equation in which the unknown quantity to be determined appears under the integral sign.

The solution is easy if we are able to choose a closed surface which satisfies two conditions:

1. $\mathbf{D}_s$ is everywhere either normal or tangential to the closed surface, so that $\mathbf{D}_s \cdot d\mathbf{S}$ becomes either $D_s \, dS$ or zero, respectively.

2. On that portion of the closed surface for which $\mathbf{D}_s \cdot d\mathbf{S}$ is not zero, $D_s = $ constant.

This allows us to replace the dot product with the product of the scalar magnitudes and then to bring D_s outside of the integral sign.

The remaining integral is then $\int_s dS$ over that portion of the closed surface which $\mathbf{D}_s$ crosses normally, and this is simply the area of this section of that surface.

Only a knowledge of the symmetry of the problem enables us to choose such a closed surface, and this knowledge is obtained easily by remembering that the electric field intensity due to a positive point charge is directed radially outward from the point charge.

Let us first consider a point charge Q at the origin of a spherical coordinate system and decide on a suitable closed surface which will meet the two requirements listed above. The surface in question is obviously a spherical surface, centered at the origin and of any radius r. $\mathbf{D}_s$ is everywhere normal to the surface; D_s has the same value at all points on the surface.

Then we have, in order,

$$Q = \oint_s \mathbf{D}_s \cdot d\mathbf{S} = \oint_{\text{sph}} D_s \, dS$$

$$= D_s \oint_{\text{sph}} dS = D_s \int_{\phi=0}^{\phi=2\pi} \int_{\theta=0}^{\theta=\pi} r^2 \sin\theta \, d\theta \, d\phi$$

$$= 4\pi r^2 D_s$$

and hence

$$D_s = \frac{Q}{4\pi r^2}$$

Since r may have any value and since $\mathbf{D}_s$ is directed radially outward,

$$\boxed{\mathbf{D} = \frac{Q}{4\pi r^2} \mathbf{a}_r \qquad \mathbf{E} = \frac{Q}{4\pi\epsilon_0 r^2} \mathbf{a}_r}$$

which agrees with the results of Chap. 2. The example is a trivial one, and the objection could be raised that we had to know that the field was symmetrical and directed radially outward before we could obtain an answer. This is true, and that leaves the inverse-square-law relationship as the only check obtained from Gauss's law. The example does, however, serve to illustrate a method which we may apply to other problems, including several to which Coulomb's law is almost incapable of supplying an answer.

Are there any other surfaces which would have satisfied our two conditions? The student should satisfy himself that such simple surfaces as a cube or a cylinder do not meet the requirements.

As a second example, let us consider the uniform line charge distribution ρ_L lying along the z axis and extending from $-\infty$ to $+\infty$. We must first obtain a knowledge of the symmetry of the field, and we may consider this knowledge complete when the answers to these two questions are known:

1. With which coordinates does the field vary (or of what variables is D a function)?
2. Which components of **D** are present?

These same questions were asked when the problem of the infinite line charge was considered in Sec. 2.5 from the standpoint of Coulomb's law. We found then that the knowledge obtained from answering them enabled us to make a much simpler integration. The problem could have been (and was) worked without any consideration of symmetry, but it was more difficult.

In using Gauss's law, however, it is not a question of using symmetry to simplify the solution, for the application of Gauss's law depends on symmetry, and if we cannot show that symmetry exists then we cannot use Gauss's law to obtain a solution. The two questions above now become "musts."

From our previous discussion of the uniform line charge, it is evident that only the radial component of **D** is present, or

$$\mathbf{D} = D_r \mathbf{a}_r$$

and this component is a function of r only,

$$D_r = f(r)$$

The choice of a closed surface is now simple, for a cylindrical surface is the only surface to which D_r is everywhere normal and it may be closed by plane surfaces normal to the z axis. A closed right circular cylinder of radius r extending from $z = 0$ to $z = L$ is shown in Fig. 3.4.

We apply Gauss's law,

$$Q = \oint_{\text{cyl}} \mathbf{D}_s \cdot d\mathbf{S} = D_s \int_{\text{sides}} dS + 0 \int_{\text{top}} dS + 0 \int_{\text{bottom}} dS$$

$$= D_s \int_{z=0}^{L} \int_{\phi=0}^{2\pi} r\, d\phi\, dz = D_s 2\pi r L$$

and obtain

$$D_s = D_r = \frac{Q}{2\pi r L}$$

FIG. 3.4 The Gaussian surface for an infinite line charge is a right circular cylinder of length L and radius r. **D** is constant in magnitude and everywhere perpendicular to the cylindrical surface; **D** is parallel to the end faces.

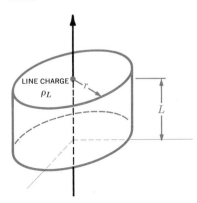

LINE CHARGE ρ_L

In terms of the charge density ρ_L, the total charge enclosed is

$$Q = \rho_L L$$

giving

$$D_r = \frac{\rho_L}{2\pi r}$$

or

$$E_r = \frac{\rho_L}{2\pi\epsilon_0 r}$$

Comparison with Sec. 2.5, Eq. (2), shows that the correct result has been obtained and with much less work. Once the appropriate surface has been chosen, the integration usually amounts only to writing down the area of the surface at which **D** is normal.

The problem of a coaxial capacitor is almost identical with that of the line charge and is an example which is extremely difficult to solve from the standpoint of Coulomb's law. Suppose that we have two coaxial cylindrical conductors, the inner of radius a and the outer of radius b, each infinite in extent (Fig. 3.5). We shall assume a charge distribution of ρ_s on the outer surface of the inner conductor.

FIG. 3.5 The two coaxial cylindrical conductors forming a coaxial capacitor provide an electric flux density within the cylinders given by $D_r = a\rho_s/r$.

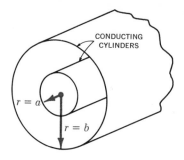

Symmetry considerations show us that only the D_r component is present and that it can be a function only of r. A right circular cylinder of length L and radius r, where $a < r < b$, is necessarily chosen as the Gaussian surface, and we quickly have

$$Q = D_s 2\pi r L$$

The total charge on a length L of the inner conductor is

$$Q = \int_{z=0}^{L} \int_{\phi=0}^{2\pi} \rho_s a \, d\phi \, dz = 2\pi a L \rho_s$$

from which we have

$$D_s = \frac{a\rho_s}{r} \qquad \mathbf{D} = \frac{a\rho_s}{r} \mathbf{a}_r \qquad (a < r < b)$$

This result might be expressed in terms of charge per unit length, because the inner conductor has $2\pi a\rho_s$ coulombs on a meter length, and hence, letting $\rho_L = 2\pi a\rho_s$,

$$\boxed{\mathbf{D} = \frac{\rho_L}{2\pi r} \mathbf{a}_r}$$

and the solution has a form identical with that of the infinite line charge.

Since every line of electric flux starting from the charge on the inner cylinder must terminate on a negative charge on the inner surface of the outer cylinder, the total charge on that surface must be

$$Q_{\text{outer cyl}} = -2\pi a L \rho_{s,\text{inner cyl}}$$

and the surface charge on the outer cylinder is found as

$$2\pi b L \rho_{s,\text{outer cyl}} = -2\pi a L \rho_{s,\text{inner cyl}}$$

or

$$\rho_{s,\text{outer cyl}} = -\frac{a}{b}\rho_{s,\text{inner cyl}}$$

What would happen if we should use a cylinder of radius r, $r > b$, for the Gaussian surface? The total charge enclosed would then be zero, for there are equal and opposite charges on each conducting cylinder. Hence

$$0 = D_s 2\pi r L \qquad (r > b)$$

$$D_s = 0 \qquad\qquad (r > b)$$

An identical result would be obtained for $r < a$. Thus this coaxial capacitor has no external field (we have proved that the outer conductor is a "shield") and there is no field within the center conductor.

D 3.5 Determine the Gaussian surfaces which should be used to determine the electric field about each of the given charge distributions:

(a) An infinite sheet of uniform surface charge density $\rho_s = \rho_{s1}$ at $x = x_1$
(b) Two parallel infinite sheets of uniform surface charge density, ρ_{s1} at $x = x_1$ and ρ_{s2} at $x = x_2$
(c) Three parallel infinite sheets of uniform surface charge density, ρ_{s1} at $x = x_1$, ρ_{s2} at $x = x_2$, and ρ_{s3} at $x = x_3$

Ans. For each part, *several* right cylinders of any cross section, end faces parallel to plane $x = 0$; rectangular parallelepipeds are commonly used.

3.4 APPLICATION OF GAUSS'S LAW: DIFFERENTIAL VOLUME ELEMENT

We are now going to apply the methods of Gauss's law to a slightly different type of problem—one which does not possess any symmetry at all. At first glance it might seem that our case is hopeless, for without symmetry a simple Gaussian surface cannot be chosen such that the normal component of $\mathbf{D}$ is constant or zero everywhere on the surface. Without such a surface, the integral cannot be evaluated. There is only one way to circumvent these difficulties, and that is to choose such a very small closed surface

FIG. 3.6 A differential-sized Gaussian surface about the point P is used to investigate the space rate of change of $\mathbf{D}$ in the neighborhood of P.

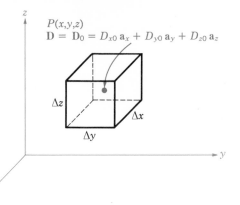

that $\mathbf{D}$ is *almost* constant over the surface, and the small change in $\mathbf{D}$ may be adequately represented by using the first two terms of the Taylor's-series expansion for $\mathbf{D}$. The result will become more nearly correct as the volume enclosed by the Gaussian surface decreases, and we intend eventually to allow this volume to approach zero.

This example also differs from the preceding ones in that we shall not obtain the value of $\mathbf{D}$ as our answer, but instead receive some extremely valuable information about the way $\mathbf{D}$ varies in the region of our small surface. This leads directly to one of Maxwell's four equations, which are basic to all electromagnetic theory.

Let us consider any point P, shown in Fig. 3.6, located by a cartesian coordinate system. The value of $\mathbf{D}$ at the point P may be expressed in cartesian components, $\mathbf{D}_0 = D_{x0}\mathbf{a}_x + D_{y0}\mathbf{a}_y + D_{z0}\mathbf{a}_z$. We choose as our closed surface the small rectangular box, centered at P, having sides of length Δx, Δy, and Δz, and apply Gauss's law,

$$\oint_s \mathbf{D}\cdot d\mathbf{S} = Q$$

In order to evaluate the integral over the closed surface, the integral must be broken up into six integrals, one over each face:

$$\oint_s \mathbf{D}\cdot d\mathbf{S} = \int_{\text{front}} + \int_{\text{back}} + \int_{\text{left}} + \int_{\text{right}} + \int_{\text{top}} + \int_{\text{bottom}}$$

Consider the first of these in detail. Since the surface element is very small, $\mathbf{D}$ is essentially constant (over *this* portion of the entire closed surface) and

$$\int_{\text{front}} \doteq \mathbf{D}_{\text{front}} \cdot \Delta \mathbf{S}_{\text{front}}$$

$$\doteq \mathbf{D}_{\text{front}} \cdot \Delta y \ \Delta z \mathbf{a}_x$$

$$\doteq D_{x,\text{front}} \ \Delta y \ \Delta z$$

where we have only to approximate the value of D_x at this front face. The front face is at a distance of $\Delta x/2$ from P, and hence

$$D_{x,\text{front}} \doteq D_{x0} + \frac{\Delta x}{2} \times \text{rate of change of } D_x \text{ with } x$$

$$\doteq D_{x0} + \frac{\Delta x}{2} \frac{\partial D_x}{\partial x}$$

where D_{x0} is the value of D_x at P, and where a partial derivative must be used to express the rate of change of D_x with x, since D_x in general also varies with y and z. This expression could have been obtained more formally by using the constant term and the term involving the first derivative in the Taylor's-series expansion for D_x in the neighborhood of P.

We have now

$$\int_{\text{front}} \doteq \left(D_{x0} + \frac{\Delta x}{2} \frac{\partial D_x}{\partial x} \right) \Delta y \ \Delta z$$

Consider now the integral over the back surface,

$$\int_{\text{back}} \doteq \mathbf{D}_{\text{back}} \cdot \Delta \mathbf{S}_{\text{back}}$$

$$\doteq \mathbf{D}_{\text{back}} \cdot (-\Delta y \ \Delta z \ \mathbf{a}_x)$$

$$\doteq -D_{x,\text{back}} \ \Delta y \ \Delta z$$

and

$$D_{x,\text{back}} \doteq D_{x0} - \frac{\Delta x}{2} \frac{\partial D_x}{\partial x}$$

giving

$$\int_{\text{back}} \doteq \left(-D_{x0} + \frac{\Delta x}{2} \frac{\partial D_x}{\partial x} \right) \Delta y \ \Delta z$$

If we combine these two integrals,

$$\int_{\text{front}} + \int_{\text{back}} \doteq \frac{\partial D_x}{\partial x} \Delta x \ \Delta y \ \Delta z$$

By exactly the same process we find that

$$\int_{\text{right}} + \int_{\text{left}} \doteq \frac{\partial D_y}{\partial y} \, \Delta x \, \Delta y \, \Delta z$$

and

$$\int_{\text{top}} + \int_{\text{bottom}} \doteq \frac{\partial D_z}{\partial z} \, \Delta x \, \Delta y \, \Delta z$$

and these results may be collected to yield

$$\oint_s \mathbf{D} \cdot d\mathbf{S} \doteq \left(\frac{\partial D_x}{\partial x} + \frac{\partial D_y}{\partial y} + \frac{\partial D_z}{\partial z} \right) \Delta x \, \Delta y \, \Delta z$$

or

(1) $$\int_s \mathbf{D} \cdot d\mathbf{S} = Q \doteq \left(\frac{\partial D_x}{\partial x} + \frac{\partial D_y}{\partial y} + \frac{\partial D_z}{\partial z} \right) \Delta v$$

The expression is an approximation which becomes better as Δv becomes smaller, and in the following section we shall let the volume Δv approach zero. For the moment, we have applied Gauss's law to the closed surface surrounding the volume element Δv and have as a result the approximation (1) stating that

> Charge enclosed in volume $\Delta v \doteq \left(\dfrac{\partial D_x}{\partial x} + \dfrac{\partial D_y}{\partial y} + \dfrac{\partial D_z}{\partial z} \right)$
>
> $\times$ volume Δv

D 3.6 If $\mathbf{D} = 5e^{2x}e^{3y} \, (2\mathbf{a}_x + 3\mathbf{a}_y)$, use the approximate formula above to estimate the total charge contained within a small sphere of 1-mm radius located at

(a) (0,0,0)
(b) (1,−1,1)
(c) (−1,2,3)

Ans.   0.100; 0.272; 14.87 microcoulombs (μC)

3.5   DIVERGENCE

We shall now obtain an exact relationship from Sec. 3.4, Eq. (1), by allowing the volume element Δv to shrink to zero. We write this equation as

$$\frac{\partial D_x}{\partial x} + \frac{\partial D_y}{\partial y} + \frac{\partial D_z}{\partial z} \doteq \frac{\oint_s \mathbf{D} \cdot d\mathbf{S}}{\Delta v} = \frac{Q}{\Delta v}$$

or

$$\frac{\partial D_x}{\partial x} + \frac{\partial D_y}{\partial y} + \frac{\partial D_z}{\partial z} = \lim_{\Delta v \to 0} \frac{\oint_s \mathbf{D} \cdot d\mathbf{S}}{\Delta v} = \lim_{\Delta v \to 0} \frac{Q}{\Delta v}$$

where the approximation has been replaced by an equality. It is evident that the last term is the volume charge density ρ, and hence that

$$(1) \qquad \frac{\partial D_x}{\partial x} + \frac{\partial D_y}{\partial y} + \frac{\partial D_z}{\partial z} = \lim_{\Delta v \to 0} \frac{\oint_s \mathbf{D} \cdot d\mathbf{S}}{\Delta v} = \rho$$

This equation contains too much information to discuss all at once, and we shall write it as two separate equations,

$$(2) \qquad \frac{\partial D_x}{\partial x} + \frac{\partial D_y}{\partial y} + \frac{\partial D_z}{\partial z} = \lim_{\Delta v \to 0} \frac{\oint_s \mathbf{D} \cdot d\mathbf{S}}{\Delta v}$$

and

$$(3) \qquad \frac{\partial D_x}{\partial x} + \frac{\partial D_y}{\partial y} + \frac{\partial D_z}{\partial z} = \rho$$

where we shall save (3) for consideration in the next section.

Equation (2) does not involve charge density, and the methods of the previous section could have been used on any vector $\mathbf{A}$ to find $\oint_s \mathbf{A} \cdot d\mathbf{S}$ for a small closed surface, leading to

$$(4) \qquad \frac{\partial A_x}{\partial x} + \frac{\partial A_y}{\partial y} + \frac{\partial A_z}{\partial z} = \lim_{\Delta v \to 0} \frac{\oint_s \mathbf{A} \cdot d\mathbf{S}}{\Delta v}$$

where $\mathbf{A}$ could represent velocity, temperature gradient, force, or any other vector field.

This operation appeared so many times in physical investigations in the last century that it received a descriptive name, *divergence*. The divergence of $\mathbf{A}$ is defined as

$$(5) \qquad \boxed{\text{Divergence of } \mathbf{A} = \lim_{\Delta v \to 0} \frac{\oint_s \mathbf{A} \cdot d\mathbf{S}}{\Delta v}}$$

and is usually abbreviated div $\mathbf{A}$. The physical interpretation of the divergence of a vector is obtained by describing carefully the operations implied by the right-hand side of (5), where we shall consider **A** as a member of the flux-density family of vectors in order to aid the physical interpretation.

The divergence of the vector flux density **A** *is the outflow of flux from a small closed surface per unit volume as the volume shrinks to zero.*

The physical interpretation of divergence afforded by this statement is often useful in obtaining qualitative information about the divergence of a vector field without resorting to a mathematical investigation. For instance, let us consider the divergence of the velocity of water in a bathtub after the drain has been opened. The net outflow of water through *any* closed surface lying entirely within the water must be zero, for water is essentially incompressible and the water entering and leaving different regions of the closed surface must be equal. Hence the divergence of this velocity is zero.

If, however, we consider the velocity of the air in an inner tube which has just been punctured by a nail, we realize that the air is expanding as the pressure drops, and that consequently there is a net outflow from any closed surface lying within the inner tube. The divergence of this velocity is therefore greater than zero.

A positive divergence for any vector quantity indicates a *source* of that vector quantity at that point. Similarly, a negative divergence indicates a *sink*. Since the divergence of the water velocity above is zero, no source or sink exists.[1] The expanding air, however, produces a positive divergence of the velocity, and each interior point may be considered a source.

Writing (4) with our new term, we have

$$(6) \qquad \text{div } \mathbf{D} = \frac{\partial D_x}{\partial x} + \frac{\partial D_y}{\partial y} + \frac{\partial D_z}{\partial z}$$

This expression is again of a form which does not involve the charge density and which could be written for any vector **A**. It is the result of applying the definition of divergence (5) to a differential volume element in *cartesian coordinates*.

If a differential volume unit $r \, dr \, d\phi \, dz$, in cylindrical coordinates, or $r^2 \sin \theta \, dr \, d\theta \, d\phi$, in spherical coordinates, had been chosen, expressions for divergence involving the components of the vector in the particular coordinate system and involving partial derivatives with respect to the variables of that system would have been

---

[1] Having chosen a differential element of volume within the water, the gradual decrease in water level with time will eventually cause the volume element to lie above the surface of the water. At the instant the surface of the water intersects the volume element, the divergence is positive and the small volume is a source. This complication is avoided above by specifying an internal point.

obtained. These expressions are obtained in Appendix A and are given here for convenience:

(6) $$\text{div } \mathbf{D} = \frac{\partial D_x}{\partial x} + \frac{\partial D_y}{\partial y} + \frac{\partial D_z}{\partial z} \qquad \text{(cartesian)}$$

(7) $$\text{div } \mathbf{D} = \frac{1}{r}\frac{\partial}{\partial r}(rD_r) + \frac{1}{r}\frac{\partial D_\phi}{\partial \phi} + \frac{\partial D_z}{\partial z} \qquad \text{(cylindrical)}$$

(8) $$\text{div } \mathbf{D} = \frac{1}{r^2}\frac{\partial}{\partial r}(r^2 D_r) + \frac{1}{r\sin\theta}\frac{\partial}{\partial\theta}(\sin\theta\, D_\theta) + \frac{1}{r\sin\theta}\frac{\partial D_\phi}{\partial\phi}$$
$$\text{(spherical)}$$

It should be noted that the divergence is an operation which is performed on a vector, but that the result is a scalar. We should recall that, in a somewhat similar way, the dot, or scalar, product was a multiplication of two vectors which yielded a scalar product.

For some reason it is a common mistake on meeting divergence for the first time to impart a vector quality to the operation by scattering unit vectors around in the partial derivatives. Divergence merely tells us *how much* flux is leaving a small volume on a per-unit-volume basis and does not describe the "direction" of this flux at all.

D 3.7   Evaluate the divergence of the given vector field at the origin:

(a) $\mathbf{A} = 2e^{3x}\sin 5y\, \mathbf{a}_x - 2e^{3x}\cos 5y\, \mathbf{a}_y + 3ze^{4z}\mathbf{a}_z$
(b) $\mathbf{r} = r\mathbf{a}_r$ (cylindrical coordinates)
(c) $\mathbf{r} = r\mathbf{a}_r$ (spherical coordinates)

Ans.   2; 3; 3

3.6   MAXWELL'S FIRST EQUATION (ELECTROSTATICS)

We now wish to consolidate the gains of the last two sections and to provide an interpretation of the divergence operation as it relates to electric flux density. The expressions developed there may be written as

(1) $$\text{div } \mathbf{D} = \lim_{\Delta v \to 0} \frac{\oint_s \mathbf{D}\cdot d\mathbf{S}}{\Delta v}$$

(2) $$\text{div } \mathbf{D} = \frac{\partial D_x}{\partial x} + \frac{\partial D_y}{\partial y} + \frac{\partial D_z}{\partial z}$$

and

(3)   div **D** $= \rho$

where the first equation is the definition of divergence, the second is the result of applying the definition to a differential volume element in cartesian coordinates, giving us an equation by which the divergence of a vector expressed in cartesian coordinates may be evaluated, and the third is merely (3) of the last section, written using the new term div **D**. Equation (3) is almost an obvious result if we have achieved any familiarity at all with the concept of divergence as defined by (1), for given Gauss's law,

$$\oint_s \mathbf{D} \cdot d\mathbf{S} = Q$$

per unit volume

$$\frac{\oint_s \mathbf{D} \cdot d\mathbf{S}}{\Delta v} = \frac{Q}{\Delta v}$$

as the volume shrinks to zero,

$$\lim_{\Delta v \to 0} \frac{\oint_s \mathbf{D} \cdot d\mathbf{S}}{\Delta v} = \lim_{\Delta v \to 0} \frac{Q}{\Delta v}$$

we should see div **D** on the left and volume charge density on the right,

$$\boxed{\text{div } \mathbf{D} = \rho}$$

This is the first of Maxwell's four equations as they apply to electrostatics and steady magnetic fields, and it states that the electric flux per unit volume leaving a vanishingly small volume unit is exactly equal to the volume charge density there. This equation (3) is aptly called the *point form of Gauss's law*. Gauss's law relates the flux leaving any closed surface to the charge enclosed, and Maxwell's first equation makes an identical statement on a per-unit-volume basis for a vanishingly small volume, or at a point. Remembering that the divergence may be expressed as the sum of three partial derivatives, Maxwell's first equation is also described as the differential-equation form of Gauss's law, and conversely, Gauss's law is recognized as the integral form of Maxwell's first equation.

As a specific illustration, consider the divergence of **D** qualitatively in the region about a line charge (but not on the line charge). In any small closed region, just as many lines of electric flux enter the surface as leave it, since there is no charge within the region on which a flux line may terminate, and the divergence of **D** must be zero. At every point in space surrounding this isolated line charge, div **D** = 0. (If a point on the line charge itself is selected, we find div **D** is infinite, because the volume charge density is infinite; that is, the line charge provides a finite amount of charge but has zero volume.) The simple mathematical proof that the divergence is zero is a part of the following drill problem.

D 3.8 Find the volume charge density ρ which gives rise to the three expressions for the electric flux density given below in cylindrical coordinates:

(a) $\mathbf{D} = 2\mathbf{a}_r$ C/m^2

(b) $\mathbf{D} = \dfrac{2}{r}\,\mathbf{a}_r$ C/m^2

(c) $\mathbf{D} = \dfrac{2}{r^2}\,\mathbf{a}_r$ C/m^2

Ans.   0 (except at $r = 0$); $-\dfrac{2}{r^3}$; $\dfrac{2}{r}$ C/m^3

3.7 THE VECTOR OPERATOR ∇ AND THE DIVERGENCE THEOREM

If we remind ourselves again that divergence is an operation on a vector yielding a scalar result, just as the dot product of two vectors gives a scalar result, it seems possible that we can find something which may be dotted formally with **D** to yield the scalar

$$\frac{\partial D_x}{\partial x} + \frac{\partial D_y}{\partial y} + \frac{\partial D_z}{\partial z}$$

Obviously, this cannot be accomplished by using a dot *product*; the process must be a dot *operation*.

Let us define the *del operator* ∇ as a *vector operator*,

(1)
$$\nabla = \frac{\partial}{\partial x}\,\mathbf{a}_x + \frac{\partial}{\partial y}\,\mathbf{a}_y + \frac{\partial}{\partial z}\,\mathbf{a}_z$$

Similar *scalar operators* appear in several methods of solving differential equations, where we often let D replace d/dx, D^2 replace d^2/dx^2, and so forth.[1] We agree on defining ∇ (pronounced "del") so that it shall be treated in every way as an ordinary vector with the one important exception that partial derivatives result instead of products of scalars.

---

[1] This scalar operator D, which will not appear again, is not to be confused with the electric flux density.

Consider $\nabla \cdot \mathbf{D}$, signifying

$$\nabla \cdot \mathbf{D} = \left(\frac{\partial}{\partial x} \mathbf{a}_x + \frac{\partial}{\partial y} \mathbf{a}_y + \frac{\partial}{\partial z} \mathbf{a}_z \right) \cdot (D_x \mathbf{a}_x + D_y \mathbf{a}_y + D_z \mathbf{a}_z)$$

We first consider the dot products of the unit vectors, discarding the six zero terms and having left

$$\nabla \cdot \mathbf{D} = \frac{\partial}{\partial x} (D_x) + \frac{\partial}{\partial y} (D_y) + \frac{\partial}{\partial z} (D_z)$$

where the parentheses are now removed by operating or differentiating:

$$\nabla \cdot \mathbf{D} = \frac{\partial D_x}{\partial x} + \frac{\partial D_y}{\partial y} + \frac{\partial D_z}{\partial z}$$

This is recognized as the divergence of $\mathbf{D}$, so that we have

$$\boxed{\operatorname{div} \mathbf{D} = \nabla \cdot \mathbf{D} = \frac{\partial D_x}{\partial x} + \frac{\partial D_y}{\partial y} + \frac{\partial D_z}{\partial z}}$$

The use of $\nabla \cdot \mathbf{D}$ is much more prevalent than that of div $\mathbf{D}$, although both usages have their advantages. Writing $\nabla \cdot \mathbf{D}$ allows us to obtain simply and quickly the correct partial derivatives, but only in cartesian coordinates, as we shall see below. On the other hand, div $\mathbf{D}$ is an excellent reminder of the physical interpretation of divergence. We shall use the operator notation $\nabla \cdot \mathbf{D}$ from now on to indicate the divergence operation.

The vector operator ∇ not only is used with divergence, but will appear in several other very important operations later. One of these is ∇u, where u is any scalar, and leads to

(2) $$\nabla u = \left(\frac{\partial}{\partial x} \mathbf{a}_x + \frac{\partial}{\partial y} \mathbf{a}_y + \frac{\partial}{\partial z} \mathbf{a}_z \right) u = \frac{\partial u}{\partial x} \mathbf{a}_x + \frac{\partial u}{\partial y} \mathbf{a}_y + \frac{\partial u}{\partial z} \mathbf{a}_z$$

The operator ∇ does not have a specific form in other coordinate systems. If we are considering $\mathbf{D}$ in cylindrical coordinates, then $\nabla \cdot \mathbf{D}$ still indicates the divergence of $\mathbf{D}$, or

$$\nabla \cdot \mathbf{D} = \frac{1}{r} \frac{\partial}{\partial r} (r D_r) + \frac{1}{r} \frac{\partial D_\phi}{\partial \phi} + \frac{\partial D_z}{\partial z}$$

where this expression has been taken from Sec. 3.5. We have no form for ∇ itself to help us obtain this sum of partial derivatives. This means that ∇u, as yet unnamed but easily written above in cartesian coordinates, cannot be expressed by us at this time in cylindrical coordinates. Such an expression will be obtained when ∇u is defined in Chap. 4.

We shall close our discussion of divergence by presenting a theorem which will be needed several times in later chapters, the *divergence theorem*. We have actually obtained it already and now have little more to do than point it out and name it, for starting from Gauss's law,

$$\oint_s \mathbf{D} \cdot d\mathbf{S} = Q$$

and letting

$$Q = \int_{vol} \rho \, dv$$

and then replacing ρ by its equal,

$$\mathbf{\nabla} \cdot \mathbf{D} = \rho$$

we have

$$\oint_s \mathbf{D} \cdot d\mathbf{S} = Q = \int_{vol} \rho \, dv = \int_{vol} \mathbf{\nabla} \cdot \mathbf{D} \, dv$$

The first and last expressions constitute the divergence theorem,

(3)
$$\oint_s \mathbf{D} \cdot d\mathbf{S} = \int_{vol} \mathbf{\nabla} \cdot \mathbf{D} \, dv$$

which may be stated as follows:

The integral of the normal component of any vector field over a closed surface is equal to the integral of the divergence of this vector field throughout the volume enclosed by the closed surface.

It should be noted that the divergence theorem is true for any vector field, although we have obtained it specifically for the electric flux density **D**, and we shall have occasion to apply it to several different fields. Its benefits derive from the fact that it relates a triple integration *throughout some volume* to a double integration *over the surface* of that volume. For example, it is much easier to look for leaks in a bottle full of some agitated liquid by an inspection of the surface than by calculating the velocity at every internal point.

The divergence theorem becomes obvious physically if we consider a volume v, shown in cross section in Fig. 3.7, which is surrounded by a closed surface S. Division of the volume into a number of small compartments of differential size and consideration of one cell shows that the flux diverging from such a cell *enters*, or *converges* on, the adjacent cells unless the cell contains a portion of the outer surface. Summing up, the divergence of the flux density

FIG. 3.7 The divergence theorem states that the total flux crossing the closed surface is equal to the integral of the divergence of the flux density throughout the enclosed volume.

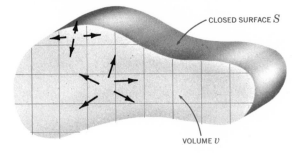

CLOSED SURFACE S

VOLUME v

throughout a volume leads, then, to the same result as determining the net flux crossing the enclosing surface.

As a simple check on the validity of the theorem, consider a field $\mathbf{D} = x\mathbf{a}_x$ and the surface of a unit cube centered at the origin with its edges parallel to the axes. Evaluating the surface integral first, we see that $\mathbf{D}$ is parallel to four of the six faces, and the remaining two give

$$\oint_s \mathbf{D} \cdot d\mathbf{S} = \int_{-1/2}^{1/2} \int_{-1/2}^{1/2} (-\tfrac{1}{2}\mathbf{a}_x) \cdot (-dy\,dz\,\mathbf{a}_x)$$

$$+ \int_{-1/2}^{1/2} \int_{-1/2}^{1/2} (\tfrac{1}{2}\mathbf{a}_x) \cdot (dy\,dz\,\mathbf{a}_x)$$

$$= 1$$

Since $\nabla \cdot \mathbf{D} = \dfrac{\partial}{\partial x}(x) = 1$, the volume integral becomes

$$\int_{\text{vol}} \nabla \cdot \mathbf{D}\,dv = \int_{-1/2}^{1/2} \int_{-1/2}^{1/2} \int_{-1/2}^{1/2} 1\,dx\,dy\,dz = 1$$

and the check is accomplished. Remembering Gauss's law, we see that we have also determined that a total charge of 1 C lies within this unit cube.

SUGGESTED REFERENCES

1 Apostol, T. M.: (see Suggested References for Chap. 1). The physical interpretation of divergence is presented on pp. 260–262 of vol. II.

2 Skilling, H. H.: "Fundamentals of Electric Waves," 2d ed., John Wiley & Sons, Inc., New York, 1948. The operations of vector calculus are well illustrated. Divergence is discussed on pp. 22 and 38. Chapter 1 is interesting reading.

PROBLEMS

1   Let us assume the following sequence of operations for Faraday's concentric sphere experiment: (1) start with uncharged components; (2) charge inner sphere with 2 nanocoulombs (nC); (3) clamp hemispheres on; (4) discharge outer sphere; (5) remove hemispheres and touch each to a Leyden jar which we shall assume accepts 99 per cent of the charge; (6) discharge hemispheres completely; (7) clamp hemispheres on again; (8) repeat (4); (9) repeat (5); (10) repeat (6); (11) repeat (7); (12) repeat (4), ... (a) What charge is in the Leyden jar at the end of step (5)? (b) What charge would have been in it if step (4) had been omitted? (c) What charge is in the Leyden jar at the end of step (25)? (d) What charge would have been in the Leyden jar at the end of step (25) if steps (6), (10), (14), ... , had been omitted?

2   Along the z axis there is a uniform line charge with $\rho_L = 4\pi$ C/m, and in the $x = 1$ plane there is a surface charge with $\rho_s = 20$ C/m². Find the electric flux density at $(0.5,0,0)$.

3   For the charge configuration of Prob. 2, find the total flux leaving a spherical surface of 2-m radius centered at the origin.

4   Use Gauss's law to show that a uniform field in cylindrical coordinates, $\mathbf{D} = k\mathbf{a}_r$, requires every cylindrical shell of 1-m thickness to contain $2\pi k$ C of charge per meter of length. Does this indicate a continuous volume charge distribution? If so, how does the charge density vary with r?

5   (a) If $\mathbf{D} = r\mathbf{a}_r/(r^2 + 1)$, find the total charge contained within a sphere of radius a centered at the origin. (b) Find the average charge density within the sphere for $a = 1, 0.5, 0.1$, and 0.01 m. (c) Take the limit as a approaches zero, and find the exact volume charge density at the origin.

6   Gaussian surfaces may often be constructed very near to or very distant from a charge configuration in order to obtain approximate values of the field strength. Given a line charge of 10^{-9} C/m in the form of a ring of 0.5-m radius centered at the origin and lying in the xy plane, describe a suitable Gaussian surface and determine an approximate value of $\mathbf{E}$ (a) at $(0.51,0,0)$; (b) at $(10,10,10)$.

7   A point charge Q is located at the origin, a uniform surface charge ρ_{sa} is located at the spherical surface $r = a$, and a second uniform surface charge ρ_{sb} is located at $r = b$. Determine $\mathbf{D}$ in all regions.

8   A cylindrical shell of uniform charge density ρ_0 lies in the region $b \geq r \geq a$. (a) Determine $\mathbf{D}$ in all regions. (b) What uniform line charge should be placed at $r = 0$ to reduce the external field $(r \geq b)$ to zero?

9   A point charge of 1 C is located at the origin. Without using any involved integrations, determine the electric flux cutting each of these surfaces: (a) the plane $x = 1$; (b) the portion of the plane $y = 1$ bounded by $x = -1$ and $x = 1$; (c) the portion of the plane $z = 1$ bounded by $x = -1, x = 1$, $y = -1$, and $y = 1$.

10 The sun radiates a total power of about 2×10^{26} watts (W). If we imagine the sun's surface to be marked off in latitude and longitude and assume uniform radiation, (a) what power is radiated by the region lying between latitude 50°N and 60°N and longitude 12°W and 27°W? (b) What is the power density on a spherical surface 93,000,000 miles from the sun (in watts per square meter)?

11 A light source inside a translucent sphere of 20-cm diameter causes a light flux density at the spherical surface of $1,000$ $(\cos \frac{1}{2}\theta)^2$ $\mathbf{a}_r$ lumens/m². (a) In what direction is the flux density a maximum? (b) Determine the angle $\theta = \theta_0$ at which the flux density is one-half its maximum value. (c) Determine the angle $\theta = \theta_1$ such that one-half the total light flux is emitted within the cone defined by $\theta \le \theta_1$.

12 What requirements should be placed on the radii of the two conductors of a cylindrical capacitor if a ratio of 2 is desired for (a) the magnitudes of the surface charge densities; (b) the electric flux densities at the conductor surfaces; (c) the electric field intensities at the conductor surfaces; (d) the magnitudes of the total charges on each conductor?

13 A spherical capacitor is formed by the region between two spherical conducting shells of radii a and b, $b > a$. Assume a surface charge density of ρ_{sa} on the outer surface of the inner sphere and find (a) Q_a; (b) $\mathbf{D}$; (c) ρ_{sb}; (d) Q_b.

14 In spherical coordinates, a volume charge density $\rho = 10e^{-2r}$ is present. Determine $\mathbf{D}$.

15 A long, straight filament of tungsten has a negligible radius and is emitting electrons uniformly at the rate of 6.24×10^{18} electrons/s per meter length. Assume that steady-state operation is achieved and assume further that the electrons maintain a constant radial velocity of 10^7 m/s. Within any incremental volume element in space, then, the electron population is constant with time (if the volume element is assumed much larger than the electron). (a) Find ρ. (b) Find $\mathbf{E}$. (c) Show that the (simplifying) assumption of a constant velocity is incorrect by considering the force on the electrons.

16 Construct an incremental volume element in spherical coordinates of sides Δr, r $\Delta\theta$, and $r \sin \theta$ $\Delta\phi$ centered at a general point (r_0, θ_0, ϕ_0) at which $\mathbf{D}_0 = D_{r0}\mathbf{a}_r + D_{\theta0}\mathbf{a}_\theta + D_{\phi0}\mathbf{a}_\phi$. Compute the flux passing through each face, and show that the charge enclosed is

$$\left[\frac{1}{r^2}\frac{\partial}{\partial r}(r^2 D_r) + \frac{1}{r \sin \theta}\frac{\partial}{\partial \theta}(D_\theta \sin \theta) + \frac{1}{r \sin \theta}\frac{\partial D_\phi}{\partial \phi}\right] r^2 \sin \theta \; \Delta r \; \Delta\theta \; \Delta\phi$$

17 It is known that the charge density at (0.2, 0.3, 0.1) is zero. (a) If $D_x = 3.50$ at (0.15, 0.3, 0.1) and 3.82 at (0.25, 0.3, 0.1), $D_y = 6.63$ at (0.2, 0.25, 0.1) and 4.89 at (0.2, 0.35, 0.1), and $D_z = 1.04$ at (0.2, 0.3, 0.05), determine an approximate value for D_z at (0.2, 0.3, 0.15). (b) The values above were calculated from $\mathbf{D} = \mathbf{a}_r/r^2$. Calculate the exact value of D_z at (0.2, 0.3, 0.15) and compare with the approximate value determined in part (a).

18 If $\mathbf{D} = D_0 \sin (\pi x/a)$ $\mathbf{a}_x$, find (a) $\mathbf{D}$ at (a,0,0); (b) ρ at (a,0,0); (c) $\mathbf{D}$ at (a/2,0,0); (d) ρ at (a/2,0,0).

19 Suppose $\mathbf{D} = D_r\mathbf{a}_r$ in cylindrical coordinates. Describe the dependency of ρ on r, ϕ, and z if (a) $D_r = f(\phi,z)$; (b) $D_r = (1/r)f(\phi,z)$; (c) $D_r = f(r)$.

20 Show that $\mathbf{\nabla \cdot D}$ is zero for the field of a point charge and of a uniform sheet of charge everywhere except at the charge.

21 Evaluate $\mathbf{\nabla \times A}$ in cartesian coordinates.

22 By expansion in cartesian coordinates show that $\mathbf{\nabla} \cdot u\mathbf{A} = u\mathbf{\nabla \cdot A} + \mathbf{A} \cdot \mathbf{\nabla}u$.

23 If $\mathbf{\nabla \cdot A} = x + 3y$, determine which of the following are correct $\mathbf{A}$ fields: (a) $\frac{1}{2}x^2\mathbf{a}_x + \frac{3}{2}y^2\mathbf{a}_y$; (b) $xy(3\mathbf{a}_x + \mathbf{a}_y)$; (c) $(xz + 3yz + x^2 \sin x)\mathbf{a}_z$; (d) $\ln x\,\mathbf{a}_x + e^y\mathbf{a}_y + (zx + 3zy - ze^y - z/x)\mathbf{a}_z$.

24 State whether the divergence of the following vector fields is positive, negative, or zero: (a) the mass rate of flow (in kilograms per square meter per second) below the surface of the water in a basin when the water is circulating clockwise, as viewed from above; (b) the light flux density (in lumens per square meter) at a point within the bulb of a mercury-vapor lamp; (c) the thermal energy flow (in joules per square meter per second) at a point within the coffee in a cup of hot coffee just placed on the table; (d) the thermal energy flow at a point within the milk in a cold glass of milk just placed on the table.

25 If we have a perfect gas of density ρ kg/m³ and assign a velocity $\mathbf{U}$ m/s to each differential element, then the mass rate of flow is $\rho\mathbf{U}$ kg/s-m². Physical reasoning then leads to the *continuity equation* $\mathbf{\nabla} \cdot \rho\mathbf{U} = -\partial\rho/\partial t$. (a) Explain in words the physical interpretation of this equation. (b) Show

that $\oint_s \rho\mathbf{U} \cdot d\mathbf{S} = -dM/dt$, where M is the total mass of the gas within the

constant closed surface, and explain the physical significance of the equation.

26 Evaluate both sides of the divergence theorem for the spherical shell defined by $1 \leq r \leq 2$ if $\mathbf{A} = (\mathbf{a}_r/r^3)\cos^2\phi$.

27 In Michael Faraday's letter to R. Phillips, Esq., F.R.S., as published in "Great Books of the Western World," vol. 45, Encyclopaedia Britannica, Inc., Chicago, 1952, p. 850, use Gauss's law to show that the second sentence of the last paragraph ("Suppose a thin uncharged metallic globe... of the globe itself.") is true. This letter is the basis of what we have described as the concentric-spheres experiment.

28 On p. 61 of H. H. Skilling, "Fundamentals of Electric Waves," John Wiley & Sons, Inc., New York, 1948, the writer describes an experiment performed by Cavendish, and later by Maxwell, which substantiates Coulomb's law. Prove that it does so.

4 ENERGY AND POTENTIAL

In the previous two chapters we have become acquainted with Coulomb's law and its use in finding the electric field about several simple distributions of charge, and also Gauss's law and its application in determining the field about some symmetrical charge arrangements. The use of Gauss's law was invariably easier for these highly symmetrical distributions, for the problem of integration always disappeared when the proper closed surface was chosen.

However, if we had attempted to find a slightly more complicated field, such as that of two unlike point charges separated by a small distance, we would have found it impossible to choose a suitable Gaussian surface and obtain an answer. Coulomb's law, however, is more powerful and enables us to solve problems for which Gauss's law is not applicable. The application of Coulomb's law is laborious, detailed, and often quite complex, the reason for this being precisely the fact that the electric field intensity, a vector field, must be found directly from the charge distribution. Three different integrations are needed in general, one for each component, and the resolution of the vector into components usually adds to the complexity of the integrals.

Certainly it would be desirable if we could find some as yet undefined scalar function with a single integration and then determine the electric field from this scalar by some simple straightforward procedure, such as differentiation.

This scalar function does exist and is known as the potential, or potential field. We shall find that it has a very real physical interpretation and is more familiar to most of us than is the electric field which it will be used to find.

We should expect, then, to be equipped soon with a third method of finding electric fields—a single scalar integration, although not always as simple as we might wish, followed by a pleasant differentiation.

The remaining difficult portion of the task, the integration, we intend to remove in Chap. 7.

4.1 ENERGY EXPENDED IN MOVING A POINT CHARGE IN AN ELECTRIC FIELD

The electric field intensity was defined as the force on a unit test charge at that point at which we wish to find the value of this vector field. If we attempt to move the test charge against the electric field, we have to exert an equal and opposite force to that exerted by the field, and this requires us to expend energy, or do work. If we wish to move the charge in the direction of the field, our energy expenditure turns out to be negative; we do not do the work, the field does.

Suppose we wish to move a charge Q a distance $d\mathbf{L}$ in an electric field $\mathbf{E}$. The force on Q due to the electric field is

$$\mathbf{F}_E = Q\mathbf{E}$$

where the subscript reminds us that this force is due to the field, and the component of this force in the direction $d\mathbf{L}$ which we must overcome is

$$F_{LE} = \mathbf{F}_E \cdot \mathbf{a}_L = Q\mathbf{E} \cdot \mathbf{a}_L$$

where $\mathbf{a}_L = $ a unit vector in the direction of $d\mathbf{L}$.

The force which we must apply is equal and opposite to the force due to the field,

$$F_{\text{appl}} = -Q\mathbf{E} \cdot \mathbf{a}_L$$

and our expenditure of energy is the product of the force and distance,

Differential work done by
external source moving $Q = -Q\mathbf{E} \cdot \mathbf{a}_L\, dL = -Q\mathbf{E} \cdot d\mathbf{L}$

or

(1)
$$dW = -Q\mathbf{E} \cdot d\mathbf{L} \qquad \text{J}$$

where we have replaced $\mathbf{a}_L\, dL$ by the simpler expression $d\mathbf{L}$.

This differential amount of work required may be zero under several conditions determined easily from (1). There are the trivial conditions for which $\mathbf{E}$, Q, or $d\mathbf{L}$ are zero and a much more important case in which $\mathbf{E}$ and $d\mathbf{L}$ are perpendicular. Here the charge is moved always in a direction at right angles to the electric field. We can draw on a good analogy between the electric field and the gravitational field, where again energy must be expended to move against the field. Sliding a mass around with constant velocity on a frictionless uneven surface is an effortless process if the mass is moved along a constant elevation contour; positive or negative work must be done in moving it to a higher or lower elevation, respectively.

Returning to the charge in the electric field, the work required to move the charge a finite distance must be determined by integrating,

(2)
$$W = -Q \int_{init}^{final} \mathbf{E} \cdot d\mathbf{L}$$

where the path must be specified before the integral can be evaluated.

This definite integral is basic to field theory, and we shall devote the following section to its interpretation and evaluation.

D 4.1 To illustrate the application of (1), let the field be $\mathbf{E} = (2y + 1)\mathbf{a}_x + 2x\mathbf{a}_y - 3\mathbf{a}_z$ and find the work done in moving a charge of 5 μC along an incremental 1-mm-long path beginning at $(1,2,-1)$ and extending toward

 (a) $(2,2,-1)$
 (b) $(11,6,-7)$
 (c) $(3,-3,-1)$

Ans. $0; -25; -30.8$ nanojoules (nJ)

D 4.2 Repeat Prob. D 4.1 for the same field, the same charge, the same path length, and the same direction, but start at the point $(2,3,0)$. That is, the paths now extend toward

 (a) $(3,3,0)$
 (b) $(12,7,-6)$
 (c) $(4,-2,0)$

Ans. $5.57; -35; -42.2$ nJ

4.2 **THE LINE INTEGRAL**

The integral expression for the work done in moving a point charge Q from one position to another [Sec. 4.1, Eq. (2)] is an example of a line integral, which in vector-analysis notation always takes the form of the integral along some prescribed path of the dot product of a vector field and a differential vector path length $d\mathbf{L}$. Without using vector analysis we should have to write

$$W = -Q \int_{init}^{final} E_L \, dL$$

where E_L = component of $\mathbf{E}$ along $d\mathbf{L}$.

A line integral is like many other integrals which appear in advanced analysis, including the surface integral appearing in Gauss's law, in that it is essentially descriptive. We like to look at it much more than we like to work it out. It tells us to choose a path, break it up into a large number of very small segments, multiply the component of the field along each segment by the length of the segment, and then add the results for all the segments. This is a summation, of course, and the integral is obtained exactly only when the number of segments becomes infinite.

FIG. 4.1 A graphical interpretation of a line integral in a uniform field. The line integral of E between points B and A is independent of the path selected, even in a nonuniform electric field; this result is not in general true for time-varying fields.

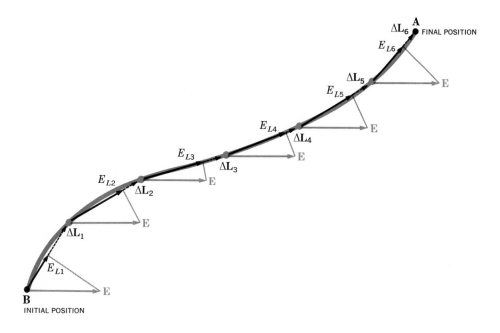

This procedure is indicated in Fig. 4.1, where a path has been chosen from an initial position B to a final position[1] A and a *uniform electric field* selected for simplicity. The path is divided into six segments, ΔL_1, ΔL_2, ... , ΔL_6, and the components of $\mathbf{E}$ along each segment denoted by E_{L1}, E_{L2}, ... , E_{L6}. The work involved in moving a charge Q from B to A is then approximately

$$W = -Q(E_{L1}\,\Delta L_1 + E_{L2}\,\Delta L_2 + \cdots + E_{L6}\,\Delta L_6)$$

or, using vector notation,

$$W = -Q(\mathbf{E}_1 \cdot \Delta \mathbf{L}_1 + \mathbf{E}_2 \cdot \Delta \mathbf{L}_2 + \cdots + \mathbf{E}_6 \cdot \Delta \mathbf{L}_6)$$

and since we have assumed a uniform field,

$$\mathbf{E}_1 = \mathbf{E}_2 = \cdots = \mathbf{E}_6$$

$$W = -Q\mathbf{E} \cdot (\Delta \mathbf{L}_1 + \Delta \mathbf{L}_2 + \cdots + \Delta \mathbf{L}_6)$$

What is this sum of vector segments in the parentheses above? Vectors add by the parallelogram law, and the sum is just the vector

---

[1] The final position is given the designation A to correspond with the convention for potential difference, as discussed in the following section.

directed from the initial point B to the final point A, $\mathbf{L}_{BA}$. Therefore

(1) $\qquad W = -Q\mathbf{E}\cdot\mathbf{L}_{BA}$

Remembering the summation interpretation of the line integral, this result for the uniform field can be obtained rapidly now from the integral expression

(2) $\qquad W = -Q\displaystyle\int_B^A \mathbf{E}\cdot d\mathbf{L}$

as applied to a uniform field

$$W = -Q\mathbf{E}\cdot\int_B^A d\mathbf{L}$$

where the last integral becomes $\mathbf{L}_{BA}$ and

$$W = -Q\mathbf{E}\cdot\mathbf{L}_{BA}$$

For this special case of a uniform electric field intensity, we should note that the work involved in moving the charge depends only on Q, $\mathbf{E}$, and $\mathbf{L}_{BA}$, a vector drawn from the initial to the final point of the path chosen. It does not depend on the particular path we have selected along which to carry the charge. We may proceed from B to A on a straight line or via the Old Chisholm Trail; the answer is the same. We shall show in Sec. 4.5 that an identical statement may be made for any nonuniform (static) $\mathbf{E}$ field.

In order to illustrate the mechanics of setting up the line integral (2) let us select the nonuniform field

$$\mathbf{E} = y\mathbf{a}_x + x\mathbf{a}_y + 2\mathbf{a}_z$$

and determine the work expended in carrying 2 C from B $(1,0,1)$ to A $(0.8,0.6,1)$ along the shorter arc of the circle

$$x^2 + y^2 = 1 \qquad z = 1$$

Working in cartesian coordinates, the differential path $d\mathbf{L}$ is $dx\,\mathbf{a}_x + dy\,\mathbf{a}_y + dz\,\mathbf{a}_z$, and the integral becomes

$$W = -Q\int_B^A \mathbf{E}\cdot d\mathbf{L}$$

$$= -2\int_B^A (y\mathbf{a}_x + x\mathbf{a}_y + 2\mathbf{a}_z)\cdot(dx\,\mathbf{a}_x + dy\,\mathbf{a}_y + dz\,\mathbf{a}_z)$$

$$= -2\int_1^{0.8} y\,dx - 2\int_0^{0.6} x\,dy - 4\int_1^1 dz$$

where the limits on the integrals have been chosen to agree with the initial and final values of the appropriate variable of integration. Using the equation of the circular path (and selecting the sign of the radical which is appropriate for the quadrant involved), we have

$$W = -2\int_{1}^{0.8} \sqrt{1 - x^2}\, dx - 2\int_{0}^{0.6} \sqrt{1 - y^2}\, dy - 0$$

$$= -\left[x\sqrt{1 - x^2} + \sin^{-1} x\right]_{1}^{0.8} - \left[y\sqrt{1 - y^2} + \sin^{-1} y\right]_{0}^{0.6}$$

$$= -(0.48 + 0.927 - 0 - 1.571) - (0.48 + 0.644 - 0 - 0)$$

$$= -0.96 \text{ J}$$

If we now select the straight-line path from B to A, then we must determine the equations of the straight line. Any two of the following three equations for planes passing through the line are sufficient to define the line:

$$y - y_B = \frac{y_A - y_B}{x_A - x_B}(x - x_B)$$

$$z - z_B = \frac{z_A - z_B}{y_A - y_B}(y - y_B)$$

$$x - x_B = \frac{x_A - x_B}{z_A - z_B}(z - z_B)$$

From the first equation above we have

$$y = -3(x - 1)$$

and from the second we obtain

$$z = 1$$

Thus

$$W = -2\int_{1}^{0.8} y\, dx - 2\int_{0}^{0.6} x\, dy - 4\int_{1}^{1} dz$$

$$= 6\int_{1}^{0.8} (x - 1)\, dx - 2\int_{0}^{0.6} \left(1 - \frac{y}{3}\right) dy$$

$$= -0.96 \text{ J}$$

This is the same answer we found using the circular path between the same two points, and it again demonstrates the statement (unproved) that the work done is independent of the path taken in any electrostatic field.

It should be noted that the equations of the straight line show that $dy = -3dx$ and $dx = -\frac{1}{3}dy$. These substitutions may be

FIG. 4.2 (a) A circular path and (b) a radial path along which a charge of Q is carried in the field of an infinite line charge. No work is expended in the former case.

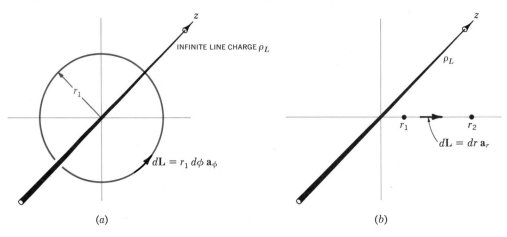

(a)   (b)

made in the first two integrals above, along with a change in limits, and the answer may be obtained by evaluating the new integrals. This method is often simpler if the integrand is a function of only one variable.

Note that the expression for $d\mathbf{L}$ in cartesian coordinates is always $dx\,\mathbf{a}_x + dy\,\mathbf{a}_y + dz\,\mathbf{a}_z$; in cylindrical or spherical coordinates, the differential elements of length are seen from the first chapter to be $d\mathbf{L} = dr\,\mathbf{a}_r + r\,d\phi\,\mathbf{a}_\phi + dz\,\mathbf{a}_z$ and $d\mathbf{L} = dr\,\mathbf{a}_r + r\,d\theta\,\mathbf{a}_\theta + r\sin\theta\,d\phi\,\mathbf{a}_\phi$, respectively.

As a final example illustrating the evaluation of the line integral, let us investigate several paths which we might take near an infinite line charge. The field has been obtained several times and is entirely in the radial direction,

$$\mathbf{E} = E_r\mathbf{a}_r = \frac{\rho_L}{2\pi\epsilon_0 r}\,\mathbf{a}_r$$

Let us first find the work done in carrying the positive charge Q about a circular path of radius r_1, centered at the line charge, as illustrated in Fig. 4.2a. Without lifting a pencil, we see that the work must be nil, for the path is always perpendicular to the electric field intensity, or the force on the charge is always exerted at right angles to the direction in which we are moving it. For practice, however, let us set up the integral and obtain the answer.

The differential element $d\mathbf{L}$ is chosen in cylindrical coordinates, and the circular path selected demands that dr and dz be zero, so

Energy and Potential 86

$d\mathbf{L} = r_1\, d\phi\, \mathbf{a}_\phi$.   The work is then

$$W = -Q \int_{\text{init}}^{\text{final}} \frac{\rho_L}{2\pi\epsilon_0 r_1} \mathbf{a}_r \cdot r_1\, d\phi\, \mathbf{a}_\phi$$

$$= -Q \int_0^{2\pi} \frac{\rho_L}{2\pi\epsilon_0}\, d\phi\, \mathbf{a}_r \cdot \mathbf{a}_\phi = 0$$

Let us now carry the charge from r_1 to r_2 along a radial path (Fig. 4.2b).   Here $d\mathbf{L} = dr\, \mathbf{a}_r$ and

$$W = -Q \int_{\text{init}}^{\text{final}} \frac{\rho_L}{2\pi\epsilon_0 r} \mathbf{a}_r \cdot dr\, \mathbf{a}_r = -Q \int_{r_1}^{r_2} \frac{\rho_L}{2\pi\epsilon_0} \frac{dr}{r}$$

or

$$W = -\frac{Q\rho_L}{2\pi\epsilon_0} \ln \frac{r_2}{r_1}$$

Since r_2 is larger than r_1, $\ln (r_2/r_1)$ is positive, and we see that the work done is negative, indicating that the external source moving the charge receives energy.

One of the pitfalls in evaluating line integrals is a tendency to use too many minus signs when a charge is moved in the direction of a *decreasing* coordinate value.   This is taken care of completely by the limits on the integral, and no misguided attempt should be made to change the sign of $d\mathbf{L}$.   Suppose we carry Q from r_2 to r_1 (Fig. 4.2b).   We still have $d\mathbf{L} = dr\, \mathbf{a}_r$ and show the different direction by recognizing $r = r_2$ as the initial point and $r = r_1$ as the final point,

$$W = -Q \int_{r_2}^{r_1} \frac{\rho_L}{2\pi\epsilon_0} \frac{dr}{r} = \frac{Q\rho_L}{2\pi\epsilon_0} \ln \frac{r_2}{r_1}$$

This is the negative of the previous answer and is obviously correct.

D 4.3   Find the work done in moving a charge of 1 C from infinity to $(a,0,0)$ along the x axis in the field

(a) $\mathbf{E} = y\mathbf{a}_x + x\mathbf{a}_y + 2\mathbf{a}_z$

(b) $\mathbf{E} = \dfrac{1}{x^2 + y^2 + z^2} (x\mathbf{a}_x + y\mathbf{a}_y)$

(c) $\mathbf{E} = \dfrac{1}{(x^2 + y^2 + z^2)^{3/2}} (x\mathbf{a}_x + y\mathbf{a}_y + z\mathbf{a}_z)$

Ans. $0;\ \dfrac{1}{a};$ infinite J

D 4.4 Find the work involved in moving a charge of 1 C

(a) From $(6,8,-10)$ to $(3,4,-5)$ along a single straight line in the field
$\mathbf{E} = -x\mathbf{a}_x + y\mathbf{a}_y - 3\mathbf{a}_z$

(b) From $(r = 1, \theta = 30°, \phi = 0°)$ to $(r = 0.5, \theta = 60°, \phi = 90°)$ by proceeding in the directions $\mathbf{a}_\phi$, $\mathbf{a}_\theta$, and $-\mathbf{a}_r$ (in that sequence) in the field $\mathbf{E} = (1/r^2)\mathbf{a}_r - [1/(r \sin \theta)]\mathbf{a}_\theta - [1/(r \sin \theta)]\mathbf{a}_\phi$

(c) From $(r = 1, \phi = 0°, z = 0)$ to $(r = 1, \phi = 90°, z = 5)$ along the helical path $z = 10\phi/\pi, r = 1$, in the field $\mathbf{E} = (1/r)\mathbf{a}_r - (1/r)\mathbf{a}_\phi + 2\mathbf{a}_z$

Ans. 3.34; -8.43; 25.5 J

4.3 DEFINITION OF POTENTIAL DIFFERENCE AND POTENTIAL

We are now ready to define a new concept from the expression for the work done by an external source in moving a charge Q from one point to another in an electric field $\mathbf{E}$,

$$W = -Q \int_{\text{init}}^{\text{final}} \mathbf{E} \cdot d\mathbf{L}$$

In much the same way as we defined the electric field intensity as the force on a *unit* test charge, we now define *potential difference* as the work done (by an external source) in moving a *unit* positive charge from one point to another in an electric field,

$$\text{Potential difference} = -\int_{\text{init}}^{\text{final}} \mathbf{E} \cdot d\mathbf{L}$$

We shall have to agree on the direction of movement, as implied by our language, and we do this by stating that V_{AB} signifies the potential difference between points A and B and is the work done in moving the unit charge from B (last named) to A (first named). Thus, in determining V_{AB}, B is the initial point and A is the final point. The reason for this somewhat peculiar definition will become clearer shortly, when it is seen that the initial point B is often taken at infinity, whereas the final point A represents the fixed position of the charge; point A is thus inherently more significant.

Potential difference is measured in joules per coulomb, for which the *volt* is defined as a more common unit, represented by V and abbreviated as V. Hence the potential difference between points A and B is

(1)
$$V_{AB} = -\int_B^A \mathbf{E} \cdot d\mathbf{L} \quad \text{V}$$

and V_{AB} is positive if work is done in carrying the positive charge from B to A.

From the line-charge example of the last section we found that the work done in taking the charge from r_2 to r_1 was

$$W = \frac{Q\rho_L}{2\pi\epsilon_0} \ln \frac{r_2}{r_1}$$

and the potential difference between points at r_1 and r_2 is

(2) $\quad V_{12} = \frac{W}{Q} = \frac{\rho_L}{2\pi\epsilon_0} \ln \frac{r_2}{r_1}$

We can try out this definition by finding the potential difference between points A and B at radial distances r_A and r_B from a point charge Q. Choosing a spherical coordinate system centered at Q,

$$\mathbf{E} = E_r \mathbf{a}_r = \frac{Q}{4\pi\epsilon_0 r^2} \mathbf{a}_r$$

and

$$d\mathbf{L} = dr\, \mathbf{a}_r$$

we have

(3) $\quad V_{AB} = -\int_B^A \mathbf{E} \cdot d\mathbf{L} = -\int_{r_B}^{r_A} \frac{Q}{4\pi\epsilon_0 r^2}\, dr = \frac{Q}{4\pi\epsilon_0} \left(\frac{1}{r_A} - \frac{1}{r_B} \right)$

If $r_B > r_A$, the potential difference V_{AB} is positive, indicating that energy is expended by the external source in bringing the positive charge from r_B to r_A. This agrees with the physical picture showing the two like charges repelling each other.

It is often convenient to speak of the *potential*, or *absolute potential*, of a point, rather than the potential difference between two points, but this means only that we agree to measure every potential difference with respect to a specified reference point which we consider to have zero potential. Common agreement must be reached on the zero reference before a statement of the potential has any significance. A person having one hand on the deflection plates of a cathode-ray tube which are "at a potential of 50 V" and his other hand on the cathode terminal would probably be too shaken up to understand that the cathode is not the zero reference, but that all potentials in that circuit are customarily measured with respect to the metallic shield about the tube.

Perhaps the most universal zero reference point in experimental or physical potential measurements is "ground," by which we mean the potential of the surface region of the earth itself. Theoretically, we usually represent this surface by an infinite plane at zero potential, although some large-scale problems, such as those involving propagation across the Atlantic Ocean, require a spherical surface at zero potential.

Another widely used reference "point" is infinity. This usually appears in theoretical problems approximating a physical situation in which the earth is relatively far removed from the region in which we are interested, such as the static field near the wing tip of an airplane which has acquired a charge in flying through a thunderhead, or the field inside an atom. Working with the *gravitational* potential field on earth, the zero reference is normally taken at sea level; for an interplanetary mission, however, the zero reference is more conveniently selected at infinity.

A cylindrical surface of some definite radius may occasionally be used where cylindrical symmetry is present and infinity proves inconvenient. And, of course, there are numerous special problems, such as those for which a two-sheeted hyperboloid or an oblate spheroid must be selected as the zero-potential reference, but these need not concern us immediately.

If the potential at point A is V_A and that at B is V_B, then

$$V_{AB} = V_A - V_B$$

where we necessarily agree that V_A and V_B shall have the same zero reference point.

D 4.5 If the potential difference between points A (1,0,0) and B (2,0,0) is 10 V, determine c for point C $(c,0,0)$ such that $V_{BC} = 6$ V

(a) In the field of a point charge located at the origin
(b) In the field of an infinite line charge on the z axis
(c) In a uniform field

Ans. 2.60; 3.03; 5.00 m

4.4 THE POTENTIAL FIELD OF A POINT CHARGE

In the previous section we found an expression [Eq. (3)] for the potential difference between two points located at $r = r_A$ and $r = r_B$ in the field of a point charge Q placed at the origin,

(1) $$V_{AB} = \frac{Q}{4\pi\epsilon_0}\left(\frac{1}{r_A} - \frac{1}{r_B}\right) = V_A - V_B$$

It was assumed there that the two points lay on the same radial line or had the same θ and ϕ coordinate values, allowing us to set up a simple path on this radial line along which to carry our positive charge. We now should ask whether different θ and ϕ coordinate values for the initial and final position will affect our answer and whether we could choose more complicated paths between the two points without changing the results. Let us answer both ques-

FIG. 4.3 A general path between general points B and A in the
field of a point charge Q. The potential difference
V_{AB} is independent of the path selected.

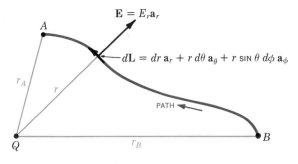

tions at once by choosing two general points A and B (Fig. 4.3) at
radial distances of r_A and r_B and any values for the other coordinates.

The differential path length $d\mathbf{L}$ has r, θ, and ϕ components, and
the electric field has only a radial component. Taking the dot
product then leaves us only

$$V_{AB} = - \int_{r_B}^{r_A} E_r \, dr = - \int_{r_B}^{r_A} \frac{Q}{4\pi\epsilon_0 r^2} \, dr = \frac{Q}{4\pi\epsilon_0} \left(\frac{1}{r_A} - \frac{1}{r_B} \right)$$

We obtain the same answer and see, therefore, that the potential
difference between two points in the field of a point charge depends
only on the distance of each point from the charge and does not
depend on the particular path used to carry our unit charge from
one point to the other.

How might we conveniently define a zero reference for potential?
The simplest possibility is to let $V = 0$ at infinity. If we let the
point at $r = r_B$ recede to infinity the potential at r_A becomes

$$V_A = \frac{Q}{4\pi\epsilon_0 r_A}$$

or, since there is no reason to identify this point with the A subscript,

(2) $$\boxed{V = \frac{Q}{4\pi\epsilon_0 r}}$$

This expression defines the potential at any point r m from a
point charge Q, the potential at infinite radius being taken as
the zero reference. Returning to a physical interpretation, we may
say that $Q/4\pi\epsilon_0 r$ J of work must be done in carrying a 1-C charge
from infinity to any point r m from the charge Q.

A convenient method to express the potential without selecting a specific zero reference entails identifying r_A as r once again and letting $Q/4\pi\epsilon_0 r_B$ be a constant. Then

$$(3) \qquad V = \frac{Q}{4\pi\epsilon_0 r} + C_1$$

and C_1 may be selected so that $V = 0$ at any desired value of r. We could also select the zero reference indirectly by electing to let V be V_0 at $r = r_0$.

It should be noted that the *potential difference* between two points is not a function of C_1.

Equations (2) or (3) represent the potential field of a point charge. The potential is a scalar field and does not involve any unit vectors.

Let us now define an *equipotential surface* as a surface composed of all those points having the same value of potential. No work is involved in moving a unit charge around on an equipotential surface, for, by definition, there is no potential difference between any two points on this surface.

The equipotential surfaces in the potential field of a point charge are spheres centered at the point charge.

An inspection of the form of the potential field of a point charge shows that it is an inverse-distance field, whereas the electric field intensity was found to be an inverse-square-law relationship. A similar result occurs for the gravitational force field of a point mass (inverse-square law) and the gravitational potential field (inverse distance). The gravitational force exerted on an object one million miles from the earth is four times that exerted on the same object two million miles away. The kinetic energy given to a freely falling object starting from the end of the universe with zero velocity, however, is only twice as much at one million miles as it is at two million miles.

D 4.6 If $Q = 10^{-9}$ C, select C_1 in (3) so that

(a) $V = 0$ at ∞
(b) $V = 0$ at $r = 3$ m
(c) $V = 10$ at $r = 3$ m

Ans. $-3; 0; 7$ V

D 4.7 Point charges of $+Q$ and $-Q$ are located at $(0,0,1)$ and $(0,0,-1)$, respectively. The potential field of each individual charge has a zero reference at infinity. Find the ratio of the total potential at $(0,0,100)$ to the total potential at

(a) $(0,0,200)$
(b) $(0,0,400)$
(c) $(0,0,800)$

Ans. $64.0; 4.00; 16.00$

The potential at a point has been defined as the work done in bringing a unit positive charge from the zero reference to the point, and
we have suspected that this work, and hence the potential, is independent of the path taken.   If it were not potential would not
be a very useful concept.

Let us now prove our assertion.   We do so by beginning with the
potential field of the single point charge for which we showed the
independence with regard to the path in the last section, noting that
the field is linear with respect to charge so that superposition is
applicable, and it then follows that the potential of a system of
charges has a value at any point which is independent of the path
taken in carrying the test charge to that point.

Thus the potential field of a single point charge, which we shall
identify as Q_1, involves only the distance from Q_1 to the field point
at which we are establishing the value of the potential.   Let us
designate this distance as R_1, where the capital letter should remind
us that no special coordinate system is necessary, and we have

$$V = \frac{Q_1}{4\pi\epsilon_0 R_1}$$

The potential due to two charges, Q_1 and Q_2, is a function only
of R_1 and R_2, the distances from Q_1 and Q_2 to the field point, respectively,

$$V = \frac{Q_1}{4\pi\epsilon_0 R_1} + \frac{Q_2}{4\pi\epsilon_0 R_2}$$

Continuing to add charges, we find that the potential due to n point
charges is

(1) $$V = \frac{Q_1}{4\pi\epsilon_0 R_1} + \frac{Q_2}{4\pi\epsilon_0 R_2} + \cdots + \frac{Q_n}{4\pi\epsilon_0 R_n}$$

$$= \sum_{m=1}^{n} \frac{Q_m}{4\pi\epsilon_0 R_m}$$

and if each point charge is now represented as a small element of
a continuous volume charge distribution $\rho \, \Delta v$, then

$$V = \frac{\rho_1 \, \Delta v_1}{4\pi\epsilon_0 R_1} + \frac{\rho_2 \, \Delta v_2}{4\pi\epsilon_0 R_2} + \cdots + \frac{\rho_n \, \Delta v_n}{4\pi\epsilon_0 R_n}$$

As we allow the number of elements to become infinite, we obtain
the integral expression

(2) $$\boxed{V = \int_{\text{vol}} \frac{\rho \, dv}{4\pi\epsilon_0 R}}$$

We have come quite a distance from the potential field of the single point charge, and it might be helpful to examine (2) and refresh ourselves as to the meaning of each term. The potential V is determined with respect to a zero-reference potential at infinity and is an exact measure of the work done in bringing a unit charge from infinity to the point, say A, at which we are finding the potential. The volume charge density ρ and differential volume element dv combine to represent a differential amount of charge $\rho\,dv$ located at some point in general different from A. The distance R is that distance from the element of charge $\rho\,dv$ to the point at which the potential is to be determined, A. The integral is a multiple (volume) integral.

If the charge distribution takes the form of a line charge or a surface charge, the integration is along the line or over the surface:

$$(3) \quad V = \int \frac{\rho_L\,dL}{4\pi\epsilon_0 R}$$

$$(4) \quad V = \int_s \frac{\rho_s\,dS}{4\pi\epsilon_0 R}$$

These integral expressions for potential in terms of the charge distribution should be compared with similar expressions for the electric field intensity, such as Sec. 2.4, Eq. (4):

$$\mathbf{E} = \int_{\text{vol}} \frac{\rho\,dv}{4\pi\epsilon_0 R^2}\,\mathbf{a}_R$$

The potential again is inverse distance, and the electric field intensity, inverse-square law. The latter, of course, is also a vector field.

To summarize, then:

1. The potential due to a single point charge is the work done in carrying a unit positive charge from infinity to the point at which we desire the potential, and the work is independent of the path chosen between those two points.
2. The potential field in the presence of a number of point charges is the sum of the individual potential fields arising from each charge.
3. The potential due to a number of point charges or any continuous charge distribution may therefore be found by carrying a unit charge from infinity to the point in question along any path we choose.

Energy and Potential   94

In other words, the expression for potential (zero reference at infinity),

$$V_A = -\int_\infty^A \mathbf{E} \cdot d\mathbf{L}$$

or potential difference,

$$V_{AB} = V_A - V_B = -\int_B^A \mathbf{E} \cdot d\mathbf{L}$$

is not dependent on the path chosen for the line integral, regardless of the source of the $\mathbf{E}$ field.

This result is often stated concisely by recognizing that no work is done in carrying the unit charge around any *closed path*, or

(5)
$$\oint \mathbf{E} \cdot d\mathbf{L} = 0$$

A small circle is placed on the integral sign to indicate the closed nature of the path. This symbol also appeared in the formulation of Gauss's law, where a closed *surface* integral was used.

Equation (5) is true for static fields, but we shall see much later that Faraday demonstrated it was incomplete when time-varying magnetic fields were present. One of Maxwell's greatest contributions to electromagnetic theory was in showing that a time-varying electric field produced a magnetic field, and therefore we should expect to find later that (5) is then not correct when either $\mathbf{E}$ or $\mathbf{H}$ varies with time.

Restricting our attention to the static case where $\mathbf{E}$ does not change with time, consider the d-c circuit shown in Fig. 4.4. Two points, A and B, are marked, and (5) states that no work is involved in carrying a unit charge from A through R_2 and R_3 to B and back to A through R_1, or that the sum of the potential differences around any closed path is zero.

Equation (5) is therefore just a more general form of Kirchhoff's circuital law for voltages, more general in that we can apply it to any region where an electric field exists and we are not restricted to a conventional circuit composed of wires, resistances, and batteries. Although (5) is not true for time-varying fields, Kirchhoff's voltage law is often applicable to circuits in which currents and voltages vary with time; this is discussed in Chap. 13.

Any field that satisfies an equation of the form of (5), i.e., where the closed line integral of the field is zero, is said to be a *conservative field*. The name arises from the fact that no work is done (or that energy is *conserved*) around a closed path. The gravitational field is also conservative, for any energy expended in moving (raising)

FIG. 4.4   A simple d-c-circuit problem which must be solved by applying $\oint \mathbf{E} \cdot d\mathbf{L} = 0$ in the form of Kirchhoff's voltage law.

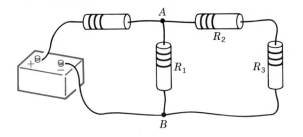

an object against the field is recovered exactly when the object is returned (lowered) to its original location. A nonconservative gravitational field would solve our energy problems forever.

D 4.8   Use Eq. (3) or (4) to find the potential at $(0,0,5)$ caused by a total charge of 10^{-8} C distributed uniformly along

(a) A ring of radius 5 m, lying in the $z = 0$ plane and centered at the origin

(b) A disk of radius 5 m, lying in the $z = 0$ plane and centered at the origin

(c) A square loop, 10 m on a side, lying in the $z=0$ plane and centered at the origin

Ans.   11.85; 12.73; 14.91 V

4.6   POTENTIAL GRADIENT

We now have two methods of determining potential, one directly from the electric field intensity by means of a line integral, and another from the basic charge distribution itself by a volume integral. Neither method is very helpful in determining the fields in most practical problems, however, for, as we shall see later, neither the electric field intensity nor the charge distribution is very often known. Preliminary information is much more apt to consist of a description of two equipotential surfaces, such as the statement that we have two parallel conductors of circular cross section at potentials of 100 and -100 V. Perhaps we wish to find the capacitance between the conductors, or the charge and current distribution on the conductors from which losses may be calculated.

These quantities may be easily obtained from the potential field, and our immediate goal will be a simple method of finding the electric field intensity from the potential.

FIG. 4.5 A vector incremental element of length $\Delta \mathbf{L}$ is shown making an angle of θ with an $\mathbf{E}$ field, indicated by its streamlines. The sources of the field are not shown.

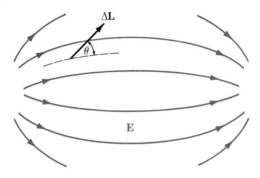

We already have the general line-integral relationship between these quantities,

(1)
$$V = -\int \mathbf{E} \cdot d\mathbf{L}$$

but this is much easier to use in the reverse direction: given $\mathbf{E}$, find V.

However, (1) may be applied to a very short element of length $\Delta \mathbf{L}$ along which $\mathbf{E}$ is essentially constant, leading to an incremental potential difference ΔV,

(2) $\Delta V \doteq -\mathbf{E} \cdot \Delta \mathbf{L}$

Let us see first if we can determine any new information about the relation of V to $\mathbf{E}$ from this equation. Consider a general region of space, as shown in Fig. 4.5, in which $\mathbf{E}$ and V both change as we move from point to point. Equation (2) tells us to choose an incremental vector element of length $\Delta \mathbf{L} = \Delta L\, \mathbf{a}_L$ and multiply it by the component of $\mathbf{E}$ in the direction of $\mathbf{a}_L$ (one interpretation of the dot product) to obtain the small potential difference between the final and initial points of $\Delta \mathbf{L}$.

If we designate the angle between $\Delta \mathbf{L}$ and $\mathbf{E}$ as θ, then

$$\Delta V \doteq -E\,\Delta L \cos \theta$$

which becomes an exact expression in terms of the derivative dV/dL,

$$\frac{dV}{dL} = -E \cos \theta$$

FIG. 4.6 A potential field is shown by its equipotential surfaces. At any point the **E** field is normal to the equipotential surface passing through that point and is directed toward the more negative surfaces.

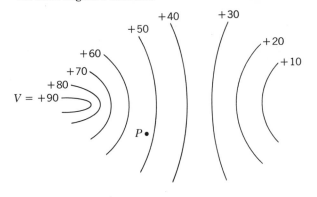

In which direction should Δ**L** be placed to obtain a maximum value of ΔV? Remember that **E** is a definite value at the point at which we are working and is independent of the direction of Δ**L**. The magnitude ΔL is also constant, and our variable is $\mathbf{a}_L$, the unit vector showing the direction of Δ**L**. It is obvious that the maximum positive increment of potential, $\Delta V_{\max}$, will occur when $\cos\theta$ is -1, or Δ**L** points in the direction *opposite* to **E**. For this condition,

$$\left.\frac{dV}{dL}\right|_{\max} = E$$

This little exercise shows us two characteristics of the relationship between **E** and V at any point:

1. The magnitude of the electric field intensity is given by the maximum value of the rate of change of potential with distance.
2. This maximum value is obtained when the direction of the distance increment is opposite to **E** or, in other words, the direction of **E** is opposite to the direction in which the potential is increasing the most rapidly.

Let us now illustrate these relationships in terms of potential. Figure 4.6 is intended to show the information we have been given about some potential field. It does this by showing the equipotential surfaces (shown as lines in the two-dimensional sketch). We desire information about the electric field intensity at point P. Starting at P, we lay off a small incremental distance Δ**L** in various directions, hunting for that direction in which the potential is changing (increasing) the most rapidly. From the sketch, this direction appears to be to the left and slightly upward. From our second characteristic above, the electric field intensity is therefore oppositely directed, or to the right and slightly downward at P. Its magnitude is given by dividing the small increase in potential by the small element of length.

It seems likely that the direction in which the potential is increasing the most rapidly is perpendicular to the equipotentials (in the direction of *increasing* potential), and this is correct, for if $\Delta \mathbf{L}$ is directed along an equipotential, $\Delta V = 0$ by our definition of an equipotential surface. But then

$$\Delta V = -\mathbf{E} \cdot \Delta \mathbf{L} = 0$$

and since neither $\mathbf{E}$ nor $\Delta \mathbf{L}$ is zero, $\mathbf{E}$ must be perpendicular to this $\Delta \mathbf{L}$ or perpendicular to the equipotentials.

Since the potential field information is more likely to be determined first, let us describe the direction of $\Delta \mathbf{L}$ which leads to a maximum increase in potential mathematically in terms of the potential field rather than the electric field intensity. We do this by letting $\mathbf{a}_N$ be a unit vector normal to the equipotential surface and directed toward the higher potentials. The electric field intensity is then expressed in terms of the potential,

$$(3) \quad \mathbf{E} = -\left. \frac{dV}{dL} \right|_{\text{max}} \mathbf{a}_N$$

which shows that the magnitude of $\mathbf{E}$ is given by the maximum space rate of change of V and the direction of $\mathbf{E}$ is *normal* to the equipotential surface (in the direction of *decreasing* potential).

Since $dV/dL\,|_{\text{max}}$ occurs when $\Delta \mathbf{L}$ is in the direction of $\mathbf{a}_N$, we may remind ourselves of this fact by letting

$$\left. \frac{dV}{dL} \right|_{\text{max}} = \frac{dV}{dN}$$

and

$$(4) \quad \mathbf{E} = -\frac{dV}{dN} \mathbf{a}_N$$

Equation (3) or (4) serves to provide a physical interpretation of the process of finding the electric field intensity from the potential. Both are descriptive of a general procedure, and we do not intend to use them directly to obtain quantitative information. This procedure leading from V to $\mathbf{E}$ is not unique to this pair of quantities, however, but has appeared as the relationship between a scalar and a vector field in hydraulics, thermodynamics, magnetics, and indeed in almost every field to which vector analysis has been applied.

The operation on V by which $-\mathbf{E}$ is obtained is known as the *gradient*, and the gradient of a scalar field T is defined as

(5)
$$\text{Gradient of } T = \text{grad } T = \frac{dT}{dN}\mathbf{a}_N$$

where $\mathbf{a}_N$ is a unit vector directed normally to the equipotential surfaces and that normal is chosen which points in the direction of increasing values of T.

Using this new term, we now may write the relationship between V and $\mathbf{E}$ as

(6)
$$\mathbf{E} = -\text{grad } V$$

In order to obtain an expression which is convenient for the evaluation of the gradient, let us return to the electric field and (2). If $\Delta\mathbf{L}$ is taken in the x direction, $\Delta\mathbf{L} = \Delta x\,\mathbf{a}_x$, and

$$\Delta V \doteq -(E_x\mathbf{a}_x + E_y\mathbf{a}_y + E_z\mathbf{a}_z)\cdot\Delta x\,\mathbf{a}_x = -E_x\,\Delta x$$

or

$$E_x \doteq -\frac{\Delta V}{\Delta x}$$

This expression is exact only as Δx approaches zero. Since no change is being made in y or z, the quotient of the increments becomes a partial derivative in the limit,

$$\lim_{\Delta x \to 0}\frac{\Delta V}{\Delta x}\bigg|_{y,z\text{ const}} = \frac{\partial V}{\partial x}$$

and

$$E_x = -\frac{\partial V}{\partial x}$$

In a similar manner we obtain

$$E_y = -\frac{\partial V}{\partial y}$$

$$E_z = -\frac{\partial V}{\partial z}$$

These results may be combined vectorially to yield

(7)
$$\mathbf{E} = -\left(\frac{\partial V}{\partial x}\mathbf{a}_x + \frac{\partial V}{\partial y}\mathbf{a}_y + \frac{\partial V}{\partial z}\mathbf{a}_z\right)$$

and comparison of (6) and (7) provides us with an expression which may be used to evaluate the gradient in cartesian coordinates,

$$(8) \qquad \boxed{\text{grad } V = \frac{\partial V}{\partial x}\, \mathbf{a}_x + \frac{\partial V}{\partial y}\, \mathbf{a}_y + \frac{\partial V}{\partial z}\, \mathbf{a}_z}$$

The gradient of a scalar is a vector, and experience has shown that the unit vectors which are often incorrectly added to the divergence expression appear to be those which were incorrectly removed from the gradient. Once the physical interpretation of the gradient, expressed by (5), is grasped as showing the maximum space rate of change of a scalar quantity and *the direction in which this maximum occurs*, the vector nature of the gradient should be self-evident.

The vector operator

$$\nabla = \frac{\partial}{\partial x}\, \mathbf{a}_x + \frac{\partial}{\partial y}\, \mathbf{a}_y + \frac{\partial}{\partial z}\, \mathbf{a}_z$$

may be used formally as an operator on a scalar T, ∇T, producing

$$\nabla T = \frac{\partial T}{\partial x}\, \mathbf{a}_x + \frac{\partial T}{\partial y}\, \mathbf{a}_y + \frac{\partial T}{\partial z}\, \mathbf{a}_z$$

from which we see that

$$\boxed{\nabla T = \text{grad } T}$$

This allows us to use a very compact expression to relate $\mathbf{E}$ and V,

$$(9) \qquad \boxed{\mathbf{E} = -\nabla V}$$

The gradient may be expressed in terms of partial derivatives in other coordinate systems through application of its definition (5). These expressions are derived in Appendix A and repeated below for convenience when dealing with problems having cylindrical or spherical symmetry:

$$(10) \qquad \boxed{\nabla V = \frac{\partial V}{\partial x}\, \mathbf{a}_x + \frac{\partial V}{\partial y}\, \mathbf{a}_y + \frac{\partial V}{\partial z}\, \mathbf{a}_z \qquad \text{(cartesian)}}$$

$$(11) \qquad \boxed{\nabla V = \frac{\partial V}{\partial r}\, \mathbf{a}_r + \frac{1}{r}\frac{\partial V}{\partial \phi}\, \mathbf{a}_\phi + \frac{\partial V}{\partial z}\, \mathbf{a}_z \qquad \text{(cylindrical)}}$$

$$(12) \qquad \boxed{\nabla V = \frac{\partial V}{\partial r}\, \mathbf{a}_r + \frac{1}{r}\frac{\partial V}{\partial \theta}\, \mathbf{a}_\theta + \frac{1}{r \sin \theta}\frac{\partial V}{\partial \phi}\, \mathbf{a}_\phi \qquad \text{(spherical)}}$$

FIG. 4.7 See Prob. D4.9.

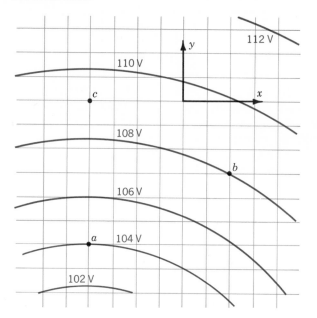

Note that the denominator of each term has the form of one of the components of $d\mathbf{L}$ in that coordinate system, except that partial differentials replace ordinary differentials; for example, $r \sin \theta \, d\phi$ becomes $r \sin \theta \, \partial\phi$.

As a simple example of the use of the gradient in finding the electric field intensity from the potential, let us start with the potential field of a point charge in spherical coordinates [Sec. 4.4, Eq. (2)],

$$V = \frac{Q}{4\pi\epsilon_0 r}$$

The gradient in spherical coordinates is given by (12), and we see that since V is a function only of r, the only component of $\mathbf{E}$ will be the radial component. Taking the partial derivative as indicated by (12), we obtain

$$\mathbf{E} = -\nabla V = \frac{Q}{4\pi\epsilon_0 r^2} \mathbf{a}_r$$

D 4.9 A portion of a two-dimensional $(E_z = 0)$ potential field is shown in Fig. 4.7. The grid lines are 1 mm apart in the actual field. Determine $\mathbf{E}$ in cartesian components at

(a) a
(b) b
(c) c

Ans. $-670\mathbf{a}_y; -1{,}110\mathbf{a}_y; -330\mathbf{a}_x - 670\mathbf{a}_y$ V/m

D 4.10 The potential fields given below are associated with volume charge distributions. By using the gradient operation to find **E** and then taking the divergence, determine ρ at the origin for each field:

(a) $V = 2(x + 1)^2(y - 1)^2 z^2$
(b) $V = 3r^2(2 \cos^2 \phi - \sin^2 \phi)$, in cylindrical coordinates
(c) $V = r^2 \cos^2 \theta$

Ans. $-2\epsilon_0; -4\epsilon_0; -6\epsilon_0$ C/m³

4.7 THE DIPOLE

The dipole fields which we shall develop in this section are quite important in that they form the basis for the behavior of dielectric materials in electric fields, as discussed in part of the following chapter. Moreover, this development will serve to illustrate the importance of the potential concept presented in this chapter.

An *electric dipole*, or simply a *dipole*, is the name given to two point charges of equal magnitude and opposite sign, separated by a distance which is small compared to the distance to the point P at which we want to know the electric and potential fields. The dipole iš shown in Fig. 4.8. The distant point P is described by

FIG. 4.8 The geomecry of the problem of an electric dipole. The dipole moment $\mathbf{p} = Q\mathbf{d}$ is in the $\mathbf{a}_z$ direction.

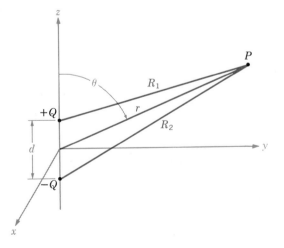

the spherical coordinates r, θ, and $\phi = 90°$, in view of the azimuthal symmetry. The positive and negative point charges are separated d m and located at $(0,0,\frac{1}{2}d)$ and $(0,0,-\frac{1}{2}d)$, respectively.

So much for the geometry. What should we do next? Should we find the total electric field intensity by adding the known fields of each point charge? Would it be easier to find the total potential field first? In either case, having found one, we shall find the other from it before calling the problem solved.

If we choose to find **E** first, we shall have two components to keep track of in spherical coordinates (symmetry shows E_ϕ is zero), and then the only way to find V from **E** is by use of the line integral. This last step includes establishing a suitable zero reference for potential, since the line integral gives us only the potential difference between the two points at the ends of the integral path.

On the other hand, the determination of V first, which is a single quantity, not a vector, and has a slightly simpler expression in the case of one point charge, followed by the gradient operation to find **E**, seems like a much easier problem.

Choosing this simpler method, we let the distances from Q and $-Q$ to P be R_1 and R_2, respectively, and write the total potential as

$$V = \frac{Q}{4\pi\epsilon_0}\left(\frac{1}{R_1} - \frac{1}{R_2}\right) = \frac{Q}{4\pi\epsilon_0}\frac{R_2 - R_1}{R_1R_2}$$

For a distant point, $R_1 \doteq R_2$, and the R_1R_2 product in the denominator may be replaced by r^2. The approximation may not be made in the numerator, however, without obtaining the trivial answer that the potential field approaches zero as we go very far away from the dipole. Coming back a little closer to the dipole, we see from Fig. 4.8 that $R_2 - R_1$ may be approximated very easily if R_1 and R_2 are assumed to be parallel,

$$R_2 - R_1 \doteq d\cos\theta$$

The final result is then

$$(1) \qquad V = \frac{Qd\cos\theta}{4\pi\epsilon_0 r^2}$$

Using the gradient relationship in spherical coordinates,

$$\mathbf{E} = -\nabla V = -\left(\frac{\partial V}{\partial r}\mathbf{a}_r + \frac{1}{r}\frac{\partial V}{\partial\theta}\mathbf{a}_\theta + \frac{1}{r\sin\theta}\frac{\partial V}{\partial\phi}\mathbf{a}_\phi\right)$$

we obtain

$$(2) \qquad \mathbf{E} = -\left(-\frac{Qd \cos \theta}{2\pi\epsilon_0 r^3} \mathbf{a}_r - \frac{Qd \sin \theta}{4\pi\epsilon_0 r^3} \mathbf{a}_\theta \right)$$

or

$$\mathbf{E} = \frac{Qd}{4\pi\epsilon_0 r^3} (2 \cos \theta \, \mathbf{a}_r + \sin \theta \, \mathbf{a}_\theta)$$

These are the desired distant fields of the dipole, obtained with a very small amount of work. Any student who has several hours to spend may try to work the problem in the reverse direction—the author considers the process too long and detailed to include even for effect.

The potential field of the dipole, Eq. (1), may be simplified by making use of the dipole moment. Let us first identify the vector length directed from $-Q$ to $+Q$ as $\mathbf{d}$ and then define the *dipole moment* as $Q\mathbf{d}$ and assign it the symbol $\mathbf{p}$. Thus

$$(3) \qquad \mathbf{p} = Q\mathbf{d}$$

and since $\mathbf{d} \cdot \mathbf{a}_r = \cos \theta$, we then have

$$(4) \qquad V = \frac{\mathbf{p} \cdot \mathbf{a}_r}{4\pi\epsilon_0 r^2}$$

This result may be generalized as

$$(5) \qquad V = \frac{\mathbf{p} \cdot \mathbf{a}_R}{4\pi\epsilon_0 R^2}$$

where $\mathbf{R} = R\mathbf{a}_R$ is the vector directed from the dipole center to the field point P. Equation (5) is independent of any coordinate system.

The dipole moment $\mathbf{p}$ will appear again when we discuss dielectric materials. Since it is equal to the product of the charge and the separation, neither the dipole moment nor the potential will change as Q increases and $\mathbf{d}$ decreases, provided the product remains constant. The limiting case of a *point dipole* is achieved when we let $\mathbf{d}$ approach zero and Q approach infinity such that the product $\mathbf{p}$ is finite.

Turning our attention to the resultant fields, it is interesting to note that the potential field now decreases as the inverse *square* of the distance, and the electric field intensity decreases as the inverse *cube* of the distance from the dipole. Each field falls off faster than the corresponding field for the point charge, but this is no more than we should expect, for the opposite charges appear to be closer together at greater distances and to act more like a single point charge of zero coulombs.

Symmetrical arrangements of larger numbers of point charges produce fields decreasing as the inverse of higher and higher powers of r. These charge distributions are called *multipoles*, and they are used in infinite series to approximate more unwieldy charge configurations.

D 4.11 Find the potential at $(r = 10, \theta = 60°, \phi = 0°)$ produced by a dipole

    (a) $Q = 10^{-7}$ C at $(10^{-3}/2,0,0)$ and -10^{-7} C at $(-10^{-3}/2,0,0)$
    (b) $\mathbf{p} = 10^{-10} \, (\mathbf{a}_x + \mathbf{a}_z)$ at the origin
    (c) $\mathbf{p} = 10^{-10} \, \mathbf{a}_z$ at $(2,0,2)$

Ans.   4.50; 6.93; 12.29 mV

4.8 ENERGY DENSITY IN THE ELECTROSTATIC FIELD

We have introduced the potential concept by considering the work done, or energy expended, in moving a point charge around in an electric field, and now we must tie up the loose ends of that discussion by tracing the energy flow one step further.

Bringing a positive charge from infinity into the field of another positive charge requires work, the work being done by the external source moving the charge. Let us imagine that the external source carries the charge up to a point near the fixed charge and then holds it there. Energy must be conserved, and the energy expended in bringing this charge into position now represents potential energy, for if the external source released its hold on the charge it would accelerate away from the fixed charge, acquiring kinetic energy of its own and the capability of doing work.

In order to find the potential energy present in a system of charges, we must find the work done by an external source in positioning the charges.

We may start by visualizing an empty universe. Bringing a charge Q_1 from infinity to any position requires no work, for there is no field present.[1] The positioning of Q_2 at a point in the field of Q_1 requires an amount of work given by the product of the charge Q_2 and the potential at that point due to Q_1. If we represent this potential as $V_{2,1}$, where the first subscript indicates the location and the second subscript the source, that is, $V_{2,1}$ is the potential at the location of Q_2 due to Q_1, then

Work to position $Q_2 = Q_2 V_{2,1}$

---

[1] However, somebody in the workshop at infinity had to do an infinite amount of work to create the point charge in the first place! How much energy is required to bring two half-charges into coincidence to make a unit charge?

Similarly, we may express the work required to position each additional charge in the field of all those already present:

Work to position $Q_3 = Q_3 V_{3,1} + Q_3 V_{3,2}$

Work to position $Q_4 = Q_4 V_{4,1} + Q_4 V_{4,2} + Q_4 V_{4,3}$

and so forth. The total work is obtained by adding each contribution:

(1) Total positioning work = potential energy of field = W_E

$$= Q_2 V_{2,1} + Q_3 V_{3,1} + Q_3 V_{3,2} + Q_4 V_{4,1} + Q_4 V_{4,2} + Q_4 V_{4,3} + \cdots$$

Noting the form of a representative term in the above equation,

$$Q_3 V_{3,1} = Q_3 \frac{Q_1}{4\pi\epsilon_0 R_{13}} = Q_1 \frac{Q_3}{4\pi\epsilon_0 R_{31}}$$

we see that it might equally well have been written as $Q_1 V_{1,3}$. If each term of the total energy expression is replaced by its equal, we have

(2) $W_E = Q_1 V_{1,2} + Q_1 V_{1,3} + Q_2 V_{2,3} + Q_1 V_{1,4} + Q_2 V_{2,4} + Q_3 V_{3,4} + \cdots$

Adding the two energy expressions (1) and (2) gives us a chance to simplify the result a little:

$$
\begin{aligned}
2W_E = \quad & Q_1(V_{1,2} + V_{1,3} + V_{1,4} + \cdots) \\
+ & Q_2(V_{2,1} + V_{2,3} + V_{2,4} + \cdots) \\
+ & Q_3(V_{3,1} + V_{3,2} + V_{3,4} + \cdots) \\
+ & \cdots
\end{aligned}
$$

because each sum of potentials in parentheses is the combined potential due to all the charges, except for the charge at the point where this combined potential is being found. In other words,

$$V_{1,2} + V_{1,3} + V_{1,4} + \cdots = V_1$$

the potential at the location of Q_1 due to the presence of Q_2, Q_3, ... We therefore have

(3) $W_E = \frac{1}{2}(Q_1 V_1 + Q_2 V_2 + Q_3 V_3 + \cdots) = \frac{1}{2} \sum\limits_{m=1}^{m=N} Q_m V_m$

In order to obtain an expression for the energy stored in a region of continuous charge distribution each charge is replaced by $\rho \, dv$ and the summation becomes an integral,

(4) $$\boxed{\; W_E = \frac{1}{2} \int_{\text{vol}} \rho V \, dv \;}$$

Energy Density in the Electrostatic Field   107

Equations (3) and (4) allow us to find the total potential energy present in a system of point charges or distributed volume charge density. Similar expressions may be easily written in terms of line or surface charge density. Usually we prefer to use (4) and let it represent all the various types of charge which may have to be considered. Before we undertake any interpretation of this result we should consider a few lines of more difficult vector analysis and obtain an expression equivalent to (4) but written in terms of the electric field intensity.

Using Maxwell's first equation, replace ρ by its equal $\mathbf{\nabla}\cdot\mathbf{D}$ and make use of a vector identity which is true for any scalar function V and any vector function $\mathbf{D}$,

(5) $\qquad \mathbf{\nabla}\cdot(V\mathbf{D}) \equiv V(\mathbf{\nabla}\cdot\mathbf{D}) + \mathbf{D}\cdot(\mathbf{\nabla}V)$

the proof of which is naturally left as a problem (at the end of the previous chapter). We then have, successively,

$$W_E = \tfrac{1}{2}\int_{\text{vol}} \rho V \, dv = \tfrac{1}{2}\int_{\text{vol}} (\mathbf{\nabla}\cdot\mathbf{D}) V \, dv$$

$$= \tfrac{1}{2}\int_{\text{vol}} [\mathbf{\nabla}\cdot(V\mathbf{D}) - \mathbf{D}\cdot(\mathbf{\nabla}V)] \, dv$$

Using the divergence theorem from the last chapter, the first volume integral of the last equation is changed into a closed surface integral, where the closed surface surrounds the volume considered. This volume, first appearing in (4), must contain *every* charge, and there can then be no charges outside of the volume. We may therefore consider the volume as *infinite* in extent if we wish. We have

$$W_E = \tfrac{1}{2}\oint_{s} (V\mathbf{D})\cdot d\mathbf{S} - \tfrac{1}{2}\int_{\text{vol}} \mathbf{D}\cdot(\mathbf{\nabla}V) \, dv$$

The surface integral is equal to zero, for over this closed surface surrounding the universe we see that V is approaching zero at least as rapidly as $1/r$ (the charges look like a point charge from there), $\mathbf{D}$ is approaching zero at least as rapidly as $1/r^2$, while the differential element of surface, looking more and more like a portion of a sphere, is increasing only as r^2. Since the integrand is zero, the integral is zero. Substituting $\mathbf{E} = -\mathbf{\nabla}V$ in the remaining volume integral, we have our answer,

(6) $\qquad \boxed{W_E = \tfrac{1}{2}\int_{\text{vol}} \mathbf{D}\cdot\mathbf{E} \, dv = \tfrac{1}{2}\int_{\text{vol}} \epsilon_0 E^2 \, dv}$

Let us use (6) to calculate the energy stored in a section of a coaxial capacitor L m long. From the previous chapter we have

$$\mathbf{E} = \frac{a\rho_s}{\epsilon_0 r}\mathbf{a}_r$$

and

$$W_E = \frac{1}{2}\int_0^L\int_a^b\int_0^{2\pi}\epsilon_0\frac{a^2\rho_s^2}{\epsilon_0^2 r^2}\,r\,d\phi\,dr\,dz = \frac{\pi L a^2\rho_s^2}{\epsilon_0}\ln\frac{b}{a}$$

This expression takes on a more familiar form if we recognize the total charge on the inner conductor as $Q = 2\pi a L\rho_s$ and also recognize the potential difference between the conductors as

$$V_{ab} = -\int_b^a\frac{a\rho_s}{\epsilon_0 r}\,dr = \frac{a\rho_s}{\epsilon_0}\ln\frac{b}{a}$$

which may be substituted above to show that

$$\boxed{W_E = \frac{1}{2}QV_{ab}}$$

which should be familiar as the energy stored in a capacitor.

The question of where the energy is stored in an electric field has not yet been answered. Potential energy can never be pinned down precisely in terms of physical location. One lifts a pencil, and the pencil acquires potential energy. Is the energy stored in the molecules of the pencil, in the gravitational field between the pencil and the earth, or in some obscure place? Is the energy in a capacitor stored in the charges themselves, in the field, or where? No one can offer any proof for his own private opinion, and the matter of deciding may be left to the philosophers.

Electromagnetic field theory makes it easy to believe that the energy of an electric field or a charge distribution is stored in the field itself, for if we take (6), an exact and rigorously correct expression,

$$W_E = \frac{1}{2}\int_{vol}\mathbf{D}\cdot\mathbf{E}\,dv$$

and write it on a differential basis,

$$dW_E = \frac{1}{2}\mathbf{D}\cdot\mathbf{E}\,dv$$

or

$$\boxed{\frac{dW_E}{dv} = \frac{1}{2}\mathbf{D}\cdot\mathbf{E}}$$

we obtain a quantity $\frac{1}{2}\mathbf{D}\cdot\mathbf{E}$, which has the dimensions of an energy density, or joules per cubic meter. We know that if we integrate this energy density over the entire field-containing volume, the result is truly the total energy present, but we have no justification for saying that the energy stored in each differential volume element dv is $\frac{1}{2}\mathbf{D}\cdot\mathbf{E}\,dv$. The picture is a convenient one, however, and we shall use it until proved wrong.

SUGGESTED REFERENCES

1 Attwood, S. S.: "Electric and Magnetic Fields," 3d ed., John Wiley & Sons, Inc., New York, 1949. There are a large number of well-drawn field maps of various charge distributions, including the dipole field. Vector analysis is not used.

2 Benumoff, R.: "Concepts in Electricity and Magnetism," Holt, Rinehart and Winston, Inc., New York, 1961. Electromagnetics is treated without introducing gradient, divergence, and curl. Potential is discussed in chap. 3; a number of the problems have answers given.

3 Kraus, J. D.: "Electromagnetics," McGraw-Hill Book Company, New York, 1953. There are numerous illustrative examples which are clearly explained. An extensive bibliography is included.

4 Skilling, H. H.: (see Suggested References for Chap. 3). Gradient is described on pp. 19–21.

PROBLEMS

1 An incremental energy of 10^{-10} J is expended in moving a 10^{-9} C test charge a distance $\Delta\mathbf{L}$ from the origin in the field $\mathbf{E} = e^{2x-y+3z}(-8\mathbf{a}_x + 4\mathbf{a}_y - 12\mathbf{a}_z)$. Show that the final location of the test charge must be on the plane $x - 0.5y + 1.5z = 0.0125$.

2 Prescribe the direction, by an appropriate unit vector, in which a positive test charge should be moved from $(1,3,-1)$ in the field $\mathbf{E} = -x\mathbf{a}_x + y\mathbf{a}_y + 3\mathbf{a}_z$ to experience (a) a maximum opposing force; (b) a maximum aiding force.

3 A charge of $+1$ C is moved from $x = 6$ to $x = 10$ along the x axis in the the field $\mathbf{E} = (2y^2 - 0.3x^2)\mathbf{a}_x - 4xy\mathbf{a}_y$. (a) Divide the path into four equal segments, determine $\mathbf{E}$ at the midpoint of each segment, assume a uniform field of this value along the segment, and approximate the total work by adding the contributions from the four segments without integrating. (b) If only a single segment were used, what would the approximate value of the work be? (c) Determine the exact value of work by integrating.

4 It is found that the energy expended in carrying a charge of $+4$ C from the origin to $(x,0,0)$ along the x axis is directly proportional to the square of the path length. If $E_x = 7$ V/m at $(1,0,0)$, determine E_x on the x axis as a function of x.

5 If $\mathbf{H} = (I/2\pi r)\mathbf{a}_\phi$, where I is the constant value of the current in an infinitely long straight filamentary conductor and $\mathbf{H}$ is the magnetic field which it produces, evaluate $\int\mathbf{H}\cdot d\mathbf{L}$ on a circular path in the $\mathbf{a}_\phi$ direction from $\phi = 0$ to $\phi = 2\pi$ at a radius r.

6 Determine the work done in carrying a -2-C charge from $(2,1,-1)$ to $(8,2,-1)$ in the field $\mathbf{E} = y\mathbf{a}_x + x\mathbf{a}_y$ along (a) the parabola $x = 2y^2$; (b) the hyperbola $x = 8/(7 - 3y)$; (c) a straight line $x = 6y - 4$.

7 The force field $\mathbf{F} = y\mathbf{a}_x - x\mathbf{a}_y$ is nonconservative, and the work done in opposing the field, $-\displaystyle\int_B^A \mathbf{F}\cdot d\mathbf{L}$, depends on the path followed from B to A.

Let B be $(0,1,0)$ and let A be $(0,-1,0)$. Determine the work done in following these paths consisting of straight line segments: (a) $(0,1,0)$ to $(1,1,0)$ to $(1,-1,0)$ to $(0,-1,0)$; (b) $(0,1,0)$ to $(0,-1,0)$; (c) $(0,1,0)$ to $(-1,1,0)$ to $(-1,-1,0)$ to $(0,-1,0)$.

8 Given the electric field $\mathbf{E} = (y + 1)\mathbf{a}_x + (x - 1)\mathbf{a}_y + 2\mathbf{a}_z$, find the potential difference between points (a) $(2,-2,-1)$ and $(0,0,0)$; (b) $(3,2,-1)$ and $(-2,-3,4)$.

9 An infinite uniform line charge lies on the z axis, and a point charge Q is located at $(1,0,0)$ in free space. Given the points A $(4,0,0)$, B $(5,0,0)$, and C $(8,0,0)$, if $V_{AB} = V_{BC} = 1$ V, find (a) ρ_L for the line charge; (b) Q.

10 In spherical coordinates, $\mathbf{E} = 2r/(r^2 + a^2)^2\,\mathbf{a}_r$. Find the potential at any point, using the reference (a) $V = 0$ at ∞; (b) $V = 0$ at $r = 0$; (c) $V = 100$ at $r = a$.

11 Positive point charges Q_i are located at $(x_i,0,0)$, where $Q_i = 4\pi\epsilon_0/2^i$ C, $x_i = 2^i$ m, and $i = 0,1,2,\ldots$. Select a zero reference at infinity and find V at the origin. The fact that $1 + a + a^2 + a^3 + \cdots = 1/(1 - a)$ is helpful.

12 If $\rho = \rho_0 a/r$, in spherical coordinates, (a) use Gauss's law to find D_r and E_r; (b) find V from E_r if $V = 0$ at $r = 0$.

13 Find the potential at the origin produced by a line charge $\rho_L = kx/(x^2 + a^2)$ extending along the x axis from $x = a$ to $+\infty$, where $a > 0$. Assume a zero reference at infinity.

14 Set up the integral which will yield the potential at P (x,y,z) caused by the charge distribution of Prob. 13.

15 Given $\mathbf{F} = xy\mathbf{a}_x + x^2\mathbf{a}_y$, (a) evaluate $\oint\mathbf{F}\cdot d\mathbf{L}$ around the straight-line-segment path from $(1,1,0)$ to $(-1,1,0)$ to $(-1,-1,0)$ to $(1,-1,0)$ to $(1,1,0)$. (b) Is $\mathbf{F}$ a conservative field? (c) Evaluate $\oint\mathbf{F}\cdot d\mathbf{L}$ around the path from $(0,0,0)$ to $(1,0,0)$ to $(1,1,0)$ to $(0,1,0)$ to $(0,0,0)$. (d) Is $\mathbf{F}$ a conservative field?

16 Use the concept of the closed line integral to decide which of the following fields are conservative: (a) the mass rate of flow (in kilograms per square meter per second) of an incompressible fluid; (b) the current density (in amperes per square meter) in a d-c circuit; (c) a uniform field.

17 (a) What is the incremental potential difference between points A and B in the field $\mathbf{E} = 2e^{2x-3y+4z}(-2\mathbf{a}_x + 3\mathbf{a}_y - 4\mathbf{a}_z)$, given B at $(0,0°,0)$ and A at $(10^{-3},\phi,10^{-4})$, in cylindrical coordinates?   (b) What value of ϕ provides the maximum value of ΔV?

18 Refer to the data of Chap. 2, Prob. 1, and assume an earth isolated in space.   (a) Express the gravitational force field on a point mass m in spherical geocentric coordinates.   (b) What is g at the surface of the earth (assuming an average radius of 6,371 kilometers)?   (c) Determine the gravitational potential field if the zero reference is at infinity.   (d) How much energy must be supplied to a 1-kg mass to lift it from the earth's surface to an infinite "height"?   (e) If this energy is supplied as kinetic energy at the surface of the earth, determine the escape velocity.

19 A long solid metallic cylinder of radius a is heated externally in such a manner that steady-state temperature distribution is $T = 400 + 100(r/a)^2 \cos 2\phi$ °K.   Determine the direction in which the space rate of change of T is a positive maximum at (a) $\phi = 0°$, $r = 0.5a$; (b) $\phi = 45°$, $r = 0.5a$; (c) $\phi = 67.5°$, $r = 0.5a$.   (d) Show that the magnitude of the spatial rate of change of T within the cylinder is a maximum at the surface of the cylinder.

20 Show that $\rho = -\epsilon_0 \nabla \cdot \nabla V$.

21 (a) Show that $\nabla \cdot \nabla V = \partial^2 V/\partial x^2 + \partial^2 V/\partial y^2 + \partial^2 V/\partial z^2$.   (b) Determine $\nabla \cdot \nabla V$ in cylindrical coordinates.   (c) Repeat for spherical coordinates.

22 Let us assume that we have a very thin, square, imperfectly conducting plate 2 m on a side, located in the plane $z = 0$ with one corner at the origin such that it lies entirely in the first quadrant.   The potential at any point in the plate is given as $V = -e^{-x} \sin y$.   (a) An electron enters the plate at $x = 0$, $y = \pi/3$ with no initial velocity; in what direction is its initial movement?   (b) Because of collisions with the particles in the plate, the electron achieves a relatively low velocity and little acceleration (the work which the field does on it is largely converted into heat).   The electron therefore moves approximately along a streamline.   Where does it leave the plate and in what direction is it moving at that time?

23 For each of the potential fields given below find V, ρ, $\mathbf{D}$, and $\mathbf{E}$ at $x = y = z = d$: (a) $V = V_0(x + y)(x + z)/d^2$; (b) $V = (V_0/d)r \cos \phi \, e^{-z/d}$; (c) $V = V_0 d^2 (\sin \theta)(\cos \phi)/r^2$.

24 (a) Show that the intersections of the equipotential surfaces of the dipole with a plane $\phi = \phi_1$ are given by $r^2 = k_A \cos \theta$.   (b) Show that the stream-lines for the electric field of the dipole in any plane $\phi = \phi_1$ are given by $r = k_B \sin^2 \theta$.

25 Find the potential field for a dipole consisting of $+Q$ at $(\frac{1}{2}d,0,0)$ and $-Q$ at $(-\frac{1}{2}d,0,0)$ at a distant point (r,θ,ϕ), in spherical coordinates.

26 A more general definition of the dipole moment for a system of N point charges is $\mathbf{p} = \sum_{i=1}^{N} \mathbf{R}_i Q_i$, where $\mathbf{R}_i$ is the vector from the point P at which $\mathbf{p}$ is to be determined to Q_i.   Use this definition to find the dipole moment at

P (x,y,z) of (a) $+Q$ at $(0,0,\frac{1}{2}d)$ and $-Q$ at $(0,0,-\frac{1}{2}d)$; (b) $+Q$ at $(d,0,0)$ and $(0,0,d)$ and $-2Q$ at $(0,0,0)$; (c) $+Q$ at $(\frac{1}{2}d,0,\frac{1}{2}d)$ and $(-\frac{1}{2}d,0,-\frac{1}{2}d)$ and $-Q$ at $(-\frac{1}{2}d,0,\frac{1}{2}d)$ and $(\frac{1}{2}d,0,-\frac{1}{2}d)$; (d) $+2Q$ at $(0,0,\frac{1}{2}d)$ and $-Q$ at $(0,0,-\frac{1}{2}d)$.

27 Find the energy stored in the region $r > a$ for a point charge Q at the origin.

28 Using the field of the dipole discussed in Sec. 4.7, (a) find the energy stored in the region $r > a$. (b) Why can we not let a approach zero as a limit?

29 Derive eq. (2) in the paper by V. K. Zworykin and J. A. Rajchman, The Electrostatic Electron Multiplier, *Proc. IRE*, vol. 27, no. 9, pp. 558–566, September, 1939.

30 Refer to H. K. Farr and W. R. Wilson, Some Engineering Applications of the Electrolytic Field Analyzer, *Trans. AIEE*, part II, vol. 70, pp. 1301–1308, and list the fields which are analogous to the electrostatic potential field.

5 CONDUCTORS, DIELECTRICS, AND CAPACITANCE

In this chapter we intend to look at the application of the laws and methods of the previous chapters to some of the materials with which an engineer must work. After defining current and current density and developing the fundamental continuity equation, we shall consider the conductor and present Ohm's law in both its microscopic and macroscopic forms. With these results we may calculate resistance values for a few of the simpler geometrical forms that resistors may assume. Conditions which must be met at conductor boundaries will also be obtained.

After a brief consideration of a general semiconductor, we shall investigate the polarization of dielectric materials and introduce relative permittivity, or the dielectric constant, an important engineering parameter. Having both conductors and dielectrics, we may then put them together to form capacitors. Most of the work of the previous chapters will be required to determine the capacitance of the several capacitors which we shall construct.

The fundamental electromagnetic principles on which resistors and capacitors depend are really the subject of this chapter; the inductor will not be introduced until Chap. 9.

5.1 CURRENT AND CURRENT DENSITY

Electric charges in motion constitute a *current*. The unit of current is the ampere (A), defined as a rate of movement of charge passing a given reference point (or crossing a given reference plane) of one coulomb per second. Current is thus defined as the motion of positive charges, although conduction in metals takes place through the motion of electrons, as we shall see shortly.

In field theory we are usually interested in events occurring at a point rather than within some large region, and we shall find the concept of *current density*, measured in amperes per square meter (A/m²), more useful. Current density is a vector[1] represented by **J**.

---

[1] Current is not a vector, for it is easy to visualize a problem in which a total current I in an irregularly shaped conductor (such as a sphere) may have a different direction at each point of a given cross section. Current in an exceedingly fine wire, or a *filamentary current*, may be defined as a vector, but we usually prefer to be consistent and give the direction to the filament, or path, and not to the current.

FIG. 5.1 An increment of charge, $\Delta Q = \rho \, \Delta S \, \Delta L$, which moves a distance Δx in a time Δt produces a component of current density in the limit of $J_x = \rho U_x$.

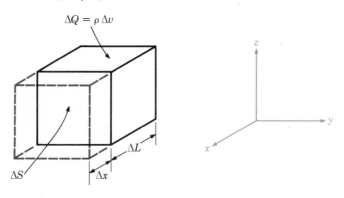

The increment of current ΔI crossing an incremental surface ΔS normal to the current density is

$$\Delta I = J_n \, \Delta S$$

and in the case where the current density is not perpendicular to the surface,

$$\Delta I = \mathbf{J} \cdot \Delta \mathbf{S}$$

Total current is obtained by integrating,

(1) $$I = \int_s \mathbf{J} \cdot d\mathbf{S}$$

Current density may be related to the velocity of volume charge density at a point. Consider the element of charge $\Delta Q = \rho \, \Delta v = \rho \, \Delta S \, \Delta L$, shown in Fig. 5.1. To simplify the explanation, let us assume that the charge element is oriented with its edges parallel to the coordinate axes and that it possesses only an x component of velocity. In the time interval Δt, the front face (of area ΔS) has moved a distance Δx to the dotted position. The charge which has passed through the reference area ΔS, marking the original location of the front face, is $\rho \, \Delta v \, (\Delta x / \Delta L) = \rho \, \Delta S \, \Delta x$, and the resultant current is therefore

$$\Delta I = \rho \, \Delta S \, \frac{\Delta x}{\Delta t}$$

As we take the limit with respect to time, we have

$$\Delta I = \rho \, \Delta S \, U_x$$

where U_x represents the x component of the velocity **U**. In terms of current density, we find

$$J_x = \rho U_x$$

and in general

(2) $$\boxed{\mathbf{J} = \rho \mathbf{U}}$$

$$J = \frac{D\mathbf{I}}{DS}$$

This last result shows very clearly that charge in motion constitutes a current. It also shows that the current density is related linearly to charge density as well as to velocity. The mass rate of flow of cars per square foot per second in the Holland tunnel could be increased either by going to higher speeds or by raising the density of cars per cubic foot, if drivers were only capable of doing so.

D 5.1 Find the total current crossing the plane $z = 0$ in the $\mathbf{a}_z$ direction if

(a) $\mathbf{J} = 0.1\mathbf{a}_z/(r^2 + 10^{-6})$ for $10^{-3} \geq r \geq 0$ and $\mathbf{J} = 0$ for $r > 10^{-3}$, in cylindrical coordinates
(b) $\mathbf{J} = -0.1e^{-r}\mathbf{a}_\theta$, in spherical coordinates
(c) An electron beam has a charge density of $-10^{-9}e^{-r}$ C/m³, in cylindrical coordinates, with a velocity of $-2 \times 10^7 \mathbf{a}_z$ m/s

Ans. 0.1256; 0.218; 0.628 A

5.2 CONTINUITY OF CURRENT

Although we are supposed to be studying static fields at this time, the introduction of the concept of current is logically followed by a discussion of the conservation of charge and the continuity equation. The principle of conservation of charge states simply that charges can be neither created nor destroyed, although equal amounts of positive and negative charge may be *simultaneously* created, obtained by separation, destroyed or lost by recombination.

The continuity equation follows from this principle when we consider any region bounded by a closed surface. The current through the closed surface is

$$I = \oint_s \mathbf{J} \cdot d\mathbf{S}$$

and this *outward* flow of positive charge must be balanced by a decrease of positive charge (or perhaps an increase of negative charge) within the closed surface. If the charge inside the closed surface is denoted by Q_i, then the rate of decrease is $-dQ_i/dt$ and the principle of conservation of charge requires

(1) $$I = \oint_s \mathbf{J} \cdot d\mathbf{S} = -\frac{dQ_i}{dt}$$

It might be well to answer here an often-asked question, "Isn't there a sign error? I thought $I = dQ/dt$." The presence or absence of the negative sign depends on what current and charge we consider. In circuit theory we usually associate the current flow *into* one terminal of a capacitor with the time rate of increase of charge on that plate. The current of (1) is an *outward-flowing* current. Our definition of current itself as the movement of charge involves counting elements of charge flowing from, say, left to right past some reference point. The increment of charge ΔQ represents an increase in the amount of charge to the right of the reference point, and again the current *into* that right-hand region is given by $+dQ/dt$.

Equation (1) is the integral form of the continuity equation, and the differential, or point, form is obtained by changing the surface integral to a volume integral by the divergence theorem,

$$\oint_s \mathbf{J} \cdot d\mathbf{S} = \int_{vol} (\mathbf{\nabla} \cdot \mathbf{J}) \, dv$$

and representing the enclosed charge Q_i by the volume integral of the charge density,

$$\int_{vol} (\mathbf{\nabla} \cdot \mathbf{J}) \, dv = -\frac{d}{dt} \int_{vol} \rho \, dv$$

If we agree to keep the surface constant, the derivative becomes a partial derivative and may appear within the integral,

$$\int_{vol} (\mathbf{\nabla} \cdot \mathbf{J}) \, dv = \int_{vol} -\frac{\partial \rho}{\partial t} \, dv$$

Since the expression is true for any volume, however small, it is true for an incremental volume,

$$(\mathbf{\nabla} \cdot \mathbf{J}) \, \Delta v = -\frac{\partial \rho}{\partial t} \, \Delta v$$

from which we have our point form of the continuity equation,

(2)
$$\boxed{\mathbf{\nabla} \cdot \mathbf{J} = -\frac{\partial \rho}{\partial t}}$$

Remembering the physical interpretation of divergence, this equation indicates that the current, or charge per second, diverging from a small volume per unit volume is equal to the time rate of decrease of charge per unit volume at every point.

Our first use of this principle will be in Sec. 5.7 when we look briefly at the flow of charge from the interior to the surface of conductors and dielectrics.

D 5.2 If a and b are positive constants, state whether ρ at the origin is increasing, decreasing, or is constant with time, given

(a) $\mathbf{J} = are^{-br}\mathbf{a}_z$, in cylindrical coordinates
(b) $\mathbf{J} = are^{-br}\mathbf{a}_r$, in cylindrical coordinates
(c) $\mathbf{J} = are^{-br}\mathbf{a}_r$, in spherical coordinates

Ans. Constant; decreasing; decreasing

5.3 METALLIC CONDUCTORS

Physicists today describe the behavior of the electrons surrounding the positive atomic nucleus in terms of the total energy of the electron with respect to a zero reference level for an electron at an infinite distance from the nucleus. The total energy is the sum of the kinetic and potential energies, and since energy must be given to an electron to pull it away from the nucleus, the energy of every electron in the atom is a negative quantity. Even though the picture has some limitations, it is convenient to associate these energy values with orbits surrounding the nucleus, the more negative energies corresponding to orbits of smaller radius. According to the quantum theory, only certain discrete energy levels or energy states are permissible in a given atom, and an electron must therefore absorb or emit discrete amounts of energy, or quanta, in passing from one level to another. A normal atom at absolute zero temperature has an electron occupying every one of the lower energy shells, starting outward from the nucleus and continuing until the supply of electrons is exhausted.

In a crystalline solid, such as a metal or a diamond, atoms are packed closely together, many more electrons are present, and many more permissible energy levels are available because of the interaction forces between adjacent atoms. We find that the energies which may be possessed by electrons are grouped into broad ranges, or "bands," each band consisting of very numerous, closely spaced, discrete levels. At a temperature of absolute zero, the normal solid also has every level occupied, starting with the lowest and proceeding in order until all the electrons are located. If the electron with the greatest energy lies *within* a permissible band, i.e., not at the upper limit of the band, additional kinetic energy may be given to the electron and its neighbors by an external electric field, resulting in an electron flow. The solid is called a metallic conductor.

If, however, the electron with the greatest energy occupies the top level in a band, it cannot accept additional energy in small amounts, and the material is an insulator. If a very large amount of energy can be transferred to the electron, however, it may be sufficiently excited to jump the gap into the next band, where conduction can again occur easily. Here the insulator breaks down.

Conductors, Dielectrics, and Capacitance   118

An intermediate condition occurs when only a small "forbidden region" separates the two bands. Small amounts of thermal energy may raise the energy of the electrons at the top of the filled band and provide the basis for conduction. These materials are insulators which display many of the properties of conductors and are called *semiconductors*.

Let us first consider the conductor. Here the valence electrons, or *conduction*, or *free*, electrons, move under the influence of an electric field. With a field $\mathbf{E}$, an electron having a charge $Q = -e$ will experience a force

$$\mathbf{F} = -e\mathbf{E}$$

In free space the electron would accelerate and continually increase its velocity (and energy); in the crystalline material the progress of the electron is impeded by continual collisions with the thermally excited crystalline lattice structure, and a constant average velocity is soon attained. This velocity $\mathbf{U}_d$ is termed the *drift velocity*, and it is linearly related to the electric field intensity by the *mobility* of the electron in the given material. We designate mobility by the symbol μ (mu), and

(1)
$$\mathbf{U}_d = -\mu_e\mathbf{E}$$

where μ_e is the mobility of an electron and is positive by definition. Equation (1) shows that mobility is measured in the units of square meters per volt-second; typical values are 0.0014 for aluminum, 0.0032 for copper, and 0.0052 for silver.

For these good conductors a drift velocity of a few inches per second is sufficient to produce a noticeable temperature rise and can cause the wire to melt if the heat cannot be quickly removed by thermal conduction or radiation.

Substituting (1) into Eq. (2) of Sec. 5.1,

(2)
$$\mathbf{J} = -\rho_e\mu_e\mathbf{E}$$

where ρ_e is the free-electron charge density; the total charge density ρ is zero, since equal positive and negative charge is present in the neutral material.

The relationship between $\mathbf{J}$ and $\mathbf{E}$ for a metallic conductor, however, is also specified by the conductivity σ (sigma),

(3)
$$\mathbf{J} = \sigma\mathbf{E}$$ ⟵ pt. form

where σ is measured in mhos per meter ($\mho/m$). A mho is one ampere per volt, and it (and the ohm) honor Georg Simon Ohm, a German physicist who first described the current-voltage relation-

FIG. 5.2 Uniform current density **J** and electric field intensity **E** in a cylindrical region of length L and cross-sectional area S. Here $V = IR$, where $R = L/\sigma S$.

ship implied by (3). We call this equation the *point form of Ohm's law*; we shall look at the more common form of Ohm's law shortly.

First, however, it is informative to note the conductivity of several metallic conductors; typical values (in mhos per meter) are 3.72×10^7 for aluminum, 5.80×10^7 for copper, and 6.17×10^7 for silver. On seeing data such as these, it is only natural to assume that we are being presented with *constant* values; this is essentially true. The conductivity of a metallic conductor does not vary appreciably with **J** or **E**; thus the conductivity relationship is *linear*. Furthermore, **J** and **E** have the same orientation in space, and therefore σ is a scalar and not a tensor; the metallic material is said to be *isotropic*, or to have the same properties in any direction.

The conductivity is a function of temperature, however. The resistivity, which is the reciprocal of the conductivity, varies almost linearly with temperature in the region of room temperature, and for aluminum, copper, and silver it increases about 0.4 per cent for a 1°K rise in temperature. For several metals the resistivity drops abruptly to zero at a temperature of a few degrees Kelvin; this property is termed *superconductivity*. Copper and silver are not superconductors, although aluminum is.

If we now combine (2) and (3), the conductivity may be expressed in terms of the charge density and the electron mobility,

(4)
$$\sigma = -\rho_e \mu_e$$

From the definition of mobility (1), it is now satisfying to note that a higher temperature infers a greater crystalline lattice vibration, more impeded electron progress for a given electric field strength, lower drift velocity, lower mobility, lower conductivity from (4), and higher resistivity as stated.

The application of Ohm's law in point form as we have it to a macroscopic (visible to the naked eye) region leads to a more familiar form. Initially, let us assume that **J** and **E** are *uniform*, as they are in the cylindrical region shown in Fig. 5.2. Since they are uniform,

$$(5) \quad I = \int_s \mathbf{J} \cdot d\mathbf{S} = JS$$

and

$$V_{ab} = -\int_b^a \mathbf{E} \cdot d\mathbf{L} = -\mathbf{E} \cdot \int_b^a d\mathbf{L} = -\mathbf{E} \cdot \mathbf{L}_{ba}$$

$$= \mathbf{E} \cdot \mathbf{L}_{ab}$$

or

$$(6) \quad V = EL$$

Thus

$$J = \frac{I}{S} = \sigma \frac{V}{L} \qquad J = \sigma E$$

or

$$(7) \quad V = \frac{L}{\sigma S} I$$

The ratio of the potential difference between the two ends of the cylinder to the current entering the more positive end, however, is recognized from elementary circuit analysis as the *resistance* of the cylinder, and therefore

$$(8) \quad \boxed{V = IR}$$

where

$$(9) \quad \boxed{R = \frac{L}{\sigma S}}$$

Equation (8) is, of course, known as *Ohm's law*, and (9) enables us to compute the resistance R, measured in ohms (abbreviated as Ω), of conducting objects which possess uniform fields. If the fields are not uniform, the resistance may still be defined as the ratio of V to I, where V is the potential difference between two specified equipotential surfaces in the material and I is the total current crossing the more positive surface into the material. We cannot solve these nonuniform problems at this time, but we should be able to solve several of them after perusing Chaps. 6 and 7.

As an example of the determination of the resistance of a cylinder, consider a #16 copper wire, which has a diameter of 0.0508 in., or

1.291 × 10^{-3} m. The area of the cross section is thus 1.309 × 10^{-6} m², and the resistance of a wire 1 mile (1,609 m) long is

$$R = \frac{1,609}{(5.80 \times 10^7)(1.309 \times 10^{-6})} = 21.2 \ \Omega$$

This wire can safely carry about 10 A, corresponding to a current density of 7.64 × 10^6 A/m², or 7.64 A/mm². With this current the potential difference between the two ends of the wire is 212 V, the electric field intensity is 0.132 V/m, the drift velocity is 0.000422 m/s, or a little more than 8 miles per year, and the free-electron charge density is −1.81 × 10^{10} C/m³, or about one electron in a cube two Ångstrom units on a side.

D 5.3 Find the scalar current density in a copper object within which

(a) There exists a uniform electric field intensity of 0.1 V/m
(b) The free-electron drift velocity is 0.1 mm/s
(c) A uniformly distributed total current of 400 A flows radially through an annular cross section of inner radius 0.25 in. and outer radius 0.3 in.

Ans.   1.81 × 10^6; 5.8 × 10^6; 7.18 × 10^6 A/m²

D 5.4 By what factor

(a) Is the resistance of 100 ft of #18 copper wire greater than that of 100 ft of #12 copper wire?
(b) Does the resistance of a given copper conductor increase as the temperature increases from 0 to 90°F?
(c) Is the resistance of 1 lb of copper wire 100 ft long greater than that of 1 lb of aluminum wire of equal length if the cross sections are both circular?

Ans.   1.20; 2.11; 4.02

5.4   CONDUCTOR PROPERTIES

Once again we must temporarily depart from our assumed static conditions and let time vary for a fraction of a microsecond to see what happens when the charge distribution is suddenly unbalanced within a conducting material. Let us suppose, for the sake of the argument, that there suddenly appear a number of electrons in the interior of a conductor. The electric fields set up by these electrons are not counteracted by any positive charges, and the electrons therefore begin to accelerate away from each other. This continues until the electrons reach the surface of the conductor, or until a number of electrons equal to the number injected have reached the surface.

Here the outward progress of the electrons is stopped, for the material surrounding the conductor is an insulator not possessing a convenient conduction band. No charge may remain within the conductor. If it did, the resulting electric field would force the charges to the surface. The time during which the charge flows is extremely short, but we shall wait until we have discussed dielectric materials before we obtain any numerical results.

Hence the final result within a conductor is zero charge density, and a surface charge density resides on the exterior surface. This is one of the two characteristics of a good conductor.

The other characteristic, stated for static conditions in which no current may flow, follows directly from Ohm's law: the electric field intensity within a homogeneous conductor is zero. Physically, we see that if an electric field were present, the conduction electrons would move and produce a current, thus leading to a nonstatic condition.

Summarizing for electrostatics, no charge and no electric field may exist within a conducting material. Charge may, however, appear on the surface as a surface charge density, and our next investigation concerns the fields *external* to the conductor.

We wish to relate these external fields to the charge on the surface of the conductor. The problem is a simple one, and we may first talk our way to the solution with little mathematics.

If the external electric field intensity is decomposed into two components, one tangential and one normal to the conductor surface, the tangential component is seen to be zero. If it were not zero, a tangential force would be applied to the elements of the surface charge, resulting in their motion and nonstatic conditions. Since static conditions are assumed, the tangential electric field intensity and electric flux density are zero.

Gauss's law answers our questions concerning the normal component. The electric flux leaving a small increment of surface must be equal to the charge residing on that incremental surface. The flux cannot leave the charge in the tangential direction, for this component is zero, and it cannot penetrate into the conductor, for the total field there is zero. It must then leave the surface normally. Quantitatively, we may say that the electric flux density in coulombs per square meter leaving the surface normally is equal to the surface charge density in coulombs per square meter, or $D_n = \rho_s$.

If we use some of our previously derived results in making a more careful analysis (and incidentally introducing a general method which we must use later), we should set up a conductor-free-space boundary (Fig. 5.3) showing tangential and normal components of **D** and **E** on the free-space side of the boundary. Both fields are

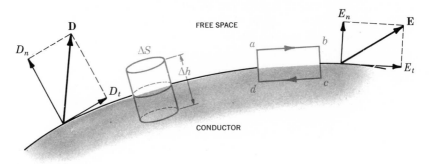

zero in the conductor. The tangential field may be determined by applying Sec. 4.5, Eq. (5),

$$\oint \mathbf{E} \cdot d\mathbf{L} = 0$$

around the small closed path *abcda*. The integral must be broken up into four parts,

$$\int_a^b + \int_b^c + \int_c^d + \int_d^a = 0$$

and if the length from *a* to *b* or *c* to *d* is Δw and from *b* to *c* or *d* to *a* is Δh, then

$$E_t \, \Delta w - E_{n,\text{at } b}\tfrac{1}{2} \, \Delta h + E_{n,\text{at } a}\tfrac{1}{2} \, \Delta h = 0$$

As we allow Δh to approach zero, keeping Δw small but finite, it makes no difference whether or not the normal fields are equal at *a* and *b*, for Δh causes these terms to become negligibly small. Hence

$$E_t \, \Delta w = 0$$

and therefore

$$E_t = 0$$

The condition on the normal field is found most readily by considering D_n rather than E_n and choosing a small cylinder as the Gaussian surface. Let the height be Δh and the area of the circular top and bottom faces be ΔS. Again we shall let Δh approach zero. Using Gauss's law,

$$\oint_s \mathbf{D} \cdot d\mathbf{S} = Q$$

we integrate over the three distinct surfaces,

$$\int_{top} + \int_{bottom} + \int_{sides} = Q$$

and find that the last two are zero. Then

$$D_n \, \Delta S = Q = \rho_s \, \Delta S$$

or

$$D_n = \rho_s$$

These are the desired *boundary conditions* for the conductor-free-space boundary in electrostatics,

(1) $$\boxed{D_t = E_t = 0}$$

(2) $$\boxed{D_n = \epsilon_0 E_n = \rho_s}$$

The electric flux leaves the conductor in a direction normal to the surface, and the value of the electric flux density is numerically equal to the surface charge density.

An immediate and important consequence of a zero tangential electric field intensity is the fact that a conductor surface is an equipotential surface. The evaluation of the potential difference between any two points on the surface by the line integral leads to a zero result, because the path may be chosen on the surface itself where $\mathbf{E} \cdot d\mathbf{L} = 0$.

To summarize the principles which apply to conductors in electrostatic fields, we may state that

1. The static electric field intensity inside a conductor is zero.
2. The static electric field intensity at the surface of a conductor is everywhere directed normal to that surface.
3. The conductor surface is an equipotential surface.

D 5.5 Determine the surface charge density on a conductor in free space

(a) If the conductor is a 5-cm-diameter sphere and the potential of the sphere is -5 V with zero reference at infinity

(b) At point $(1, -1, 0)$ on the conductor surface in the potential field, $V = 100xy$ if the potential just off the surface is more positive than it is on the surface

(c) $\mathbf{E} = 20\mathbf{a}_x - 40\mathbf{a}_y + 50\mathbf{a}_z$ V/m at the conductor surface and $\rho_s < 0$

Ans. $-0.594 \times 10^{-9}; -1.25 \times 10^{-9}; -1.77 \times 10^{-9}$ C/m^2

5.5 SEMICONDUCTORS

If we now turn our attention to an intrinsic semiconductor material, two types of current carriers are present, electrons and *holes*. The electrons are those from the top of the filled valence band which have received sufficient energy (usually thermal) to cross the relatively small forbidden band into the conduction band. The forbidden-band energy gap in typical semiconductors is of the order of one electron volt. The vacancies left by these electrons represent unfilled energy states in the valence band which may also move from atom to atom in the crystal. The vacancy is called a *hole*, and many semiconductor properties may be described by treating the hole as if it had a positive charge of e, a mobility μ_h, and an effective mass comparable to but less than that of the electron. Both carriers move in an electric field, and they move in opposite directions; hence each contributes a component of the total current which is in the same direction as that provided by the other. The conductivity is therefore a function of both hole and electron concentrations and mobility,

$$ (1) \qquad \sigma = -\rho_e \mu_e + \rho_h \mu_h $$

For pure, or *intrinsic*, germanium the electron and hole mobilities are 0.36 and 0.17, respectively, while for the other important semiconductor, silicon, the mobilities are, respectively, 0.12 and 0.025. These values are given in square meters per volt-second and range from 10 to 100 times as large as those for aluminum, copper, silver, and other metallic conductors. The mobilities listed above are given for a temperature of 300°K.

The electron and hole concentrations depend strongly on temperature; at 300°K the electron and hole volume charge densities are both 4.0 C/m³ in magnitude in intrinsic germanium and 0.011 C/m³ in intrinsic silicon. These values lead to conductivities of 2.1 ℧/m in germanium and 0.0016 ℧/m in silicon. As temperature increases, the mobilities decrease, but the charge densities increase very rapidly. As a result, the conductivity of germanium increases by a factor of 10 as the temperature increases from 300 to about 360°K and decreases by a factor of 10 as the temperature drops from 300 to about 255°K. Note that the conductivity of the intrinsic semiconductor increases with temperature, while that of a metallic conductor decreases with temperature; this is one of the characteristic differences between metallic conductors and intrinsic semiconductors.

Intrinsic semiconductors also satisfy the point form of Ohm's law; that is, the conductivity is reasonably constant with current density and with the direction of the current density. $J = \sigma E$

The range of value of the conductivity is extreme as we go from the best insulating materials to semiconductors and the finest conductors. In mhos per meter, σ ranges from 10^{-17} for fused quartz, 10^{-7} for poor plastic insulators, and roughly unity for semiconductors to almost 10^8 for metallic conductors at room temperature. These values cover the remarkably large range of some twenty-five orders of magnitude.

5.6 THE NATURE OF DIELECTRIC MATERIALS

Although we have mentioned insulators and dielectric materials, we do not as yet have any quantitative relationships in which they are involved. We shall soon see, however, that a dielectric in an electric field can be viewed as a free-space arrangement of microscopic electric dipoles, or bound charges which have been forced apart slightly by an electric field; these charges can be treated as any other sources of the electrostatic field. If we did not wish to, therefore, we would not need to introduce the dielectric constant as a new parameter or to deal with permittivities different than that of free space; however, the alternative would be to consider *every charge within a piece of dielectric material.* This is too great a price to pay for using all our previous equations in an unmodified form, and we shall therefore spend some time theorizing about dielectrics in a qualitative way, introducing polarization $\mathbf{P}$ and relative permittivity ϵ_R, and developing some quantitative relationships involving these new quantities.

The characteristic which all dielectric materials have in common, whether they are solid, liquid, or gas, and whether or not they are crystalline in nature, is their ability to store electrical energy. This storage takes place by a shift in the relative positions of the internal positive and negative charges against the normal molecular and atomic forces.

This displacement against a restraining force is analogous to lifting a weight or stretching a spring and represents potential energy. The source of the energy is the external field, the motion of the shifting charges resulting perhaps in a transient current through a battery producing the field.

The actual mechanism of the charge displacement differs in the various dielectric materials. Some molecules, termed *polar* molecules, have a permanent displacement existing between the centers of "gravity" of the positive and negative charges, and each pair of charges acts as a dipole. Normally the dipoles are oriented in a random way throughout the interior of the material, and the action of the external field is to align these molecules to some extent in the same direction. A sufficiently strong field may even produce an additional displacement between the positive and negative charges.

A *nonpolar* molecule does not have this dipole arrangement until after a field is applied. The negative and positive charges shift in opposite directions against their mutual attraction and produce a dipole which is aligned with the electric field.

Either type of dipole may be described by its dipole moment $\mathbf{p}$, as developed in Sec. 4.7, Eq. (3),

(1) $\quad \mathbf{p} = Q\mathbf{d}$

where Q is the positive one of the two bound charges comprising the dipole and $\mathbf{d}$ is the vector from the negative to the positive charge. If there are n identical dipoles per unit volume in the dielectric, then we may define the *polarization* $\mathbf{P}$ as

(2) $\quad \boxed{\mathbf{P} = nQ\mathbf{d}}$

and identify it as the *dipole moment per unit volume*; the units of $\mathbf{P}$ are in coulombs per square meter. We shall treat $\mathbf{P}$ as a typical continuous vector field, even though it is obvious that it is essentially undefined at points within an atom or molecule. Instead, we should think of its value at any point as an average value taken over a sample volume v large enough to contain many molecules (nv in number), but yet sufficiently small to be considered incremental in concept. Thus $\mathbf{P}$ may be interpreted as an average over the sample volume v,

$$\mathbf{P} = \frac{1}{v}\,(Q_1\mathbf{d}_1 + Q_2\mathbf{d}_2 + \cdots + Q_{nv}\mathbf{d}_{nv})$$

or

(3) $\quad \mathbf{P} = \dfrac{1}{v}\sum_{i=1}^{nv} Q_i\mathbf{d}_i = \dfrac{1}{v}\sum_{i=1}^{nv} \mathbf{p}_i$

Our immediate goal is to show that the bound-volume charge density acts like the free-volume charge density in producing an external field; we shall obtain a result which is similar to $\nabla \cdot \mathbf{D} = \rho$.

To be specific, let us assume that we have a dielectric containing nonpolar molecules. No molecule has a dipole moment and $\mathbf{P} = 0$ throughout the material. Somewhere in the interior of the dielectric we select an incremental surface element $\Delta\mathbf{S}$, as shown in Fig. 5.4, and inspect the movement of bound charge across $\Delta\mathbf{S}$ as an electric field is applied. The electric field produces a moment $\mathbf{p} = Q\mathbf{d}$ in each molecule such that $\mathbf{p}$ and $\mathbf{d}$ make an angle θ with $\Delta\mathbf{S}$. Every molecule that was initially centered in the volume element $\frac{1}{2}d \cos\theta\, \Delta S$ below the surface thus contributes the move-

FIG. 5.4 An incremental surface element $\Delta\mathbf{S}$ in the interior of a dielectric containing nonpolar molecules of dipole moment $\mathbf{p}$. In order to produce a nonzero value of $\mathbf{P}$, there is a net transfer of bound charge across $\Delta\mathbf{S}$.

ment of a charge $+Q$ across $\Delta\mathbf{S}$ in an upward direction. In a similar manner, every molecule in the volume $\frac{1}{2}d \cos\theta\ \Delta S$ above the surface provides a passage of $-Q$ across $\Delta\mathbf{S}$ in a downward direction. Since there are n molecules/m³, the *net* total charge which crosses the elemental surface in an *upward* direction is $nQd \cos\theta\ \Delta S$, or

$$\Delta Q_b = nQ\mathbf{d}\cdot\Delta\mathbf{S}$$

where the subscript on Q_b reminds us that we are dealing with a bound charge and not a free charge. In terms of the polarization, we have

$$\Delta Q_b = \mathbf{P}\cdot\Delta\mathbf{S} \qquad P = nQd$$

If we interpret $\Delta\mathbf{S}$ as an element of a closed surface, it is directed outward, and the net increase in the bound charge *within* the closed surface is obtained through the integral

(4) $$Q_b = -\int_s \mathbf{P}\cdot d\mathbf{S}$$

We may consider this charge to be distributed with a density ρ_b, or

$$Q_b = \int_{vol} \rho_b\ dv$$

and thus

$$\int_{vol} \rho_b\ dv = -\oint_s \mathbf{P}\cdot d\mathbf{S}$$

Applying the divergence theorem to the right side of this equation,

$$\int_{\text{vol}} \rho_b \, dv = - \int_{\text{vol}} (\nabla \cdot \mathbf{P}) \, dv$$

it follows that

(5) $$\boxed{\nabla \cdot \mathbf{P} = -\rho_b}$$

A similar development leads to the same result for a polar dielectric.

Since ρ_b is a volume charge density, a comparison of this result with the point form of Gauss's law shows that there must be a close relationship of the polarization $\mathbf{P}$ to electric flux density $\mathbf{D}$. This is indeed the case, and we shall develop this concept in the paragraphs below.

Let us write the point form of Gauss's law, or Maxwell's first equation, in terms of the electric field intensity $\mathbf{E}$,

(6) $$\nabla \cdot \epsilon_0 \mathbf{E} = \rho$$

There is no question that this equation is completely correct even with materials present; the volume charge density merely represents the totality of charge, and these charges may then be considered to reside in free space. The reason we have avoided using $\mathbf{D}$, the electric flux density, in this equation is that we intend to change our previous definition of $\mathbf{D}$ (which was $\mathbf{D} = \epsilon_0 \mathbf{E}$) to take the dielectric materials into account.

We now recognize that the volume charge density is composed of free charges and bound charges, the former arising from conduction electrons and the latter from the polarization of the dielectric material:

$$\nabla \cdot \epsilon_0 \mathbf{E} = \rho_f + \rho_b$$

Using (5), we have

(7) $$\nabla \cdot \epsilon_0 \mathbf{E} = \rho_f - \nabla \cdot \mathbf{P}$$

Finally, we may define $\mathbf{D}$ in more general terms than we did before,

(8) $$\boxed{\mathbf{D} = \epsilon_0 \mathbf{E} + \mathbf{P}}$$

There is thus an added term to $\mathbf{D}$ which appears when polarizable material is present. Using (8) in (7), we now have an alternate form of Maxwell's first equation,

(9) $$\boxed{\nabla \cdot \mathbf{D} = \rho_f}$$

This should be compared with (6),

(6)
$$\nabla \cdot \epsilon_0 \mathbf{E} = \rho$$

Both are correct, but the effect of the dielectric material is taken into account in different ways. In (9), $\mathbf{D}$ includes a term involving $\mathbf{P}$; in (6), ρ is the total charge density, including the bound charges.

In order to make any real use of these new concepts it is necessary to know the relationship between the electric field intensity $\mathbf{E}$ and the polarization $\mathbf{P}$ which results. This relationship will, of course, be a function of the type of material, and we shall essentially limit our discussion to those isotropic materials for which $\mathbf{E}$ and $\mathbf{P}$ are linearly related. In an isotropic material the vectors $\mathbf{E}$ and $\mathbf{P}$ are always parallel, regardless of the orientation of the field. Although most engineering dielectrics are linear for moderate-to-large field strengths and are also isotropic, single crystals may be anisotropic. The periodic nature of crystalline materials causes dipole moments to be formed most easily along the crystal axes, and not necessarily in the direction of the applied field.

In *ferroelectric* materials the relationship between $\mathbf{P}$ and $\mathbf{E}$ is not only nonlinear, but also shows hysteresis effects; that is, the polarization produced by a given electric field intensity depends on the past history of the sample. Important examples of this type of dielectric are barium titanate and Rochelle salt.

The linear relationship between $\mathbf{P}$ and $\mathbf{E}$ is

$$\mathbf{P} = \chi_e \epsilon_0 \mathbf{E}$$

where χ_e (chi) is the *electric susceptibility* of the material. In terms of the parameters used in engineering applications, the constant of proportionality is not written quite as simply,

(10) $\mathbf{P} = (\epsilon_R - 1)\epsilon_0 \mathbf{E}$

but we may use (8) to write

$\mathbf{D} = \epsilon_0 \mathbf{E} + (\epsilon_R - 1)\epsilon_0 \mathbf{E}$

or

(11) $\mathbf{D} = \epsilon_0 \epsilon_R \mathbf{E} = \epsilon \mathbf{E}$

where

(12)
$$\epsilon = \epsilon_R \epsilon_0$$

and ϵ is the *permittivity* and ϵ_R is the *relative permittivity*, or *dielectric constant*, of the material. The dielectric constants are given for some representative materials in Appendix C.

Anisotropic dielectric materials cannot be described in terms of a simple susceptibility or permittivity parameter. Instead, we find that each component of $\mathbf{D}$ may be a function of every component of $\mathbf{E}$, and the simple relationship (11) is replaced by the three equations

$$D_x = \epsilon_{xx}E_x + \epsilon_{xy}E_y + \epsilon_{xz}E_z$$

$$D_y = \epsilon_{yx}E_x + \epsilon_{yy}E_y + \epsilon_{yz}E_z$$

$$D_z = \epsilon_{zx}E_x + \epsilon_{zy}E_y + \epsilon_{zz}E_z$$

The nine ϵ_{ij} are collectively called a *tensor*. $\mathbf{D}$ and $\mathbf{E}$ (and $\mathbf{P}$) are no longer parallel, and although $\mathbf{D} = \epsilon_0\mathbf{E} + \mathbf{P}$ remains a valid equation for anisotropic materials, we may continue to use $\mathbf{D} = \epsilon\mathbf{E}$ only by interpreting ϵ as a tensor. We shall concentrate our attention on linear isotropic materials and reserve the general case for a more advanced text.

In summary, then, we now have a relationship between $\mathbf{D}$ and $\mathbf{E}$ which depends on the dielectric material present,

(11)
$$\mathbf{D} = \epsilon\mathbf{E}$$

where

(12)
$$\epsilon = \epsilon_R\epsilon_0$$

This electric flux density is still related to the free charge by either the point or integral form of Gauss's law:

(9)
$$\nabla \cdot \mathbf{D} = \rho_f$$

(13)
$$\oint_s \mathbf{D} \cdot d\mathbf{S} = Q_f$$

The use of the relative permittivity, as indicated by (11) above, makes consideration of the polarization, dipole moments, and bound charge unnecessary. However, when anisotropic or non-linear materials must be considered, the relative permittivity, in the simple scalar form that we have discussed, is no longer applicable.

Let us now illustrate these new concepts by discussing an example in which there is a slab of Teflon in the region $0 \le x \le a$, and free space where $x < 0$ and $x > a$. Outside the Teflon there is a uniform field $\mathbf{E}_{\text{out}} = E_0\mathbf{a}_x$ V/m. The dielectric constant of Teflon is 2.1, and thus the electric susceptibility is 1.1.

Outside the slab we have immediately that $\mathbf{D}_{out} = \epsilon_0 E_0 \mathbf{a}_x$. Also, since there is no dielectric material there, $\mathbf{P}_{out} = 0$. Now, any of the last four or five equations will enable us to relate the several fields inside the material to each other. Thus

$$\mathbf{D}_{in} = 2.1\epsilon_0 \mathbf{E}_{in} \qquad (0 \le x \le a)$$

$$\mathbf{P}_{in} = 1.1\epsilon_0 \mathbf{E}_{in} \qquad (0 \le x \le a)$$

As soon as we establish a value for any of these three fields within the dielectric, the other two can be found immediately. The difficulty lies in crossing over the boundary from the known fields external to the dielectric to the unknown ones within it. To do this we need a boundary condition, and this is the subject of the next exciting section.

In the remainder of this text we shall describe polarizable materials in terms of $\mathbf{D}$ and ϵ rather than $\mathbf{P}$ and χ_e. To simplify the nomenclature we shall drop the subscript on ρ_f and Q_f in (9) and (13) above, and thus ρ and Q will henceforth signify free charges only. We therefore have tacitly assumed that we shall limit our discussion to isotropic materials.

D 5.6 Find the dielectric constant of a material which

(a) Contains 10^{21} molecules/m^3, each of which has a moment of 2×10^{-27} C-m parallel to an electric field of 10^5 V/m
(b) Has an electric susceptibility of 3.26
(c) Has an electric flux density numerically equal to 4.26 times the polarization

Ans.   1.307; 3.26; 4.26

D 5.7 Find the polarization $\mathbf{P}$ in a material in which $\mathbf{E} = 3 \times 10^4 \mathbf{a}_x$ V/m and

(a) $\epsilon_R = 5$
(b) $\mathbf{D} = 10^{-6} \mathbf{a}_x$ C/m^2
(c) It is known that the material is polyethylene

Ans. $0.335 \times 10^{-6} \mathbf{a}_x$; $0.734 \times 10^{-6} \mathbf{a}_x$; $1.06 \times 10^{-6} \mathbf{a}_x$ C/m^2

5.7 BOUNDARY CONDITIONS FOR PERFECT DIELECTRIC MATERIALS

How do we attack a problem in which there are two different dielectrics, or a dielectric and a conductor? This is another example of a *boundary condition*, such as our discovery that at the surface of a conductor the tangential fields are zero and the normal electric flux density is equal to the surface charge density on the conductor. Now we take the first step in solving a two-dielectric problem, or a dielectric-conductor problem, by determining the behavior of the fields at the dielectric interface.

FIG. 5.5 The boundary between perfect dielectrics of permittivity ϵ_1 and ϵ_2. The continuity of D_n is shown by the Gaussian surface, and the continuity of $E_{\tan}$ by the line integral about the closed path.

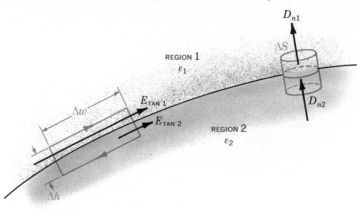

Let us first consider the interface between two dielectrics having permittivities ϵ_1 and ϵ_2 and occupying regions 1 and 2, as shown in Fig. 5.5. We first examine the tangential components by using

$$\oint \mathbf{E}\cdot d\mathbf{L} = 0$$

around the small closed path indicated, obtaining

$$E_{\tan 1}\,\Delta w - E_{\tan 2}\,\Delta w = 0$$

The small contribution to the line integral by the normal component of $\mathbf{E}$ along the lengths Δh becomes negligible as Δh decreases and the closed path crowds the surface. Immediately, then,

(1) $$\boxed{E_{\tan 1} = E_{\tan 2}}$$

and we might feel that Kirchhoff's voltage law is still applicable to this case. Certainly we have shown that the potential difference between two points on the boundary separated a distance Δw is the same immediately above or below the boundary.

If the tangential electric field intensity is continuous across the boundary, then tangential $\mathbf{D}$ is discontinuous, for

$$\frac{D_{\tan 1}}{\epsilon_1} = E_{\tan 1} = E_{\tan 2} = \frac{D_{\tan 2}}{\epsilon_2}$$

or

(2) $$\frac{D_{\tan 1}}{D_{\tan 2}} = \frac{\epsilon_1}{\epsilon_2}$$

FIG. 5.6 The refraction of **D** at a dielectric interface. For the case shown, $\epsilon_1 > \epsilon_2$; $\mathbf{E}_1$ and $\mathbf{E}_2$ are directed along $\mathbf{D}_1$ and $\mathbf{D}_2$; with $D_1 > D_2$ and $E_1 < E_2$.

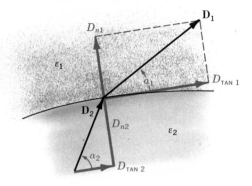

The boundary conditions on the normal components are found by applying Gauss's law to the small "pillbox" shown in Fig. 5.5. The sides are again very short, and the flux leaving the top and bottom surfaces is

$$D_{n1}\,\Delta S - D_{n2}\,\Delta S = \Delta Q = \rho_s\,\Delta S$$

from which

$$\boxed{D_{n1} - D_{n2} = \rho_s}$$

What is this surface charge density? It cannot be a *bound* surface charge density, because we are taking the polarization of the dielectric into effect by using a dielectric constant different from unity; that is, instead of considering bound charges in free space, we are using an increased permittivity. Also, it is extremely unlikely that any *free* charge is on the interface, for no free charge is available in the perfect dielectrics we are considering. This charge must then have been placed there deliberately, thus unbalancing the total charge in and on this dielectric body. Except for this special case, then, we may assume ρ_s is zero on the interface and

(3) $$\boxed{D_{n1} = D_{n2}}$$

or the normal component of **D** is continuous. It follows that

(4) $$\epsilon_1 E_{n1} = \epsilon_2 E_{n2}$$

and normal **E** is discontinuous.

These conditions may be combined to show the change in the

vectors $\mathbf{D}$ and $\mathbf{E}$ at the surface. Let $\mathbf{D_1}$ (and $\mathbf{E_1}$) make an angle α_1 with the surface (Fig. 5.6). Since the normal components of $\mathbf{D}$ are continuous,

(5) $\quad D_1 \sin \alpha_1 = D_2 \sin \alpha_2$

The ratio of the tangential components is given by (2) as

$$\frac{D_1 \cos \alpha_1}{D_2 \cos \alpha_2} = \frac{\epsilon_1}{\epsilon_2}$$

or

(6) $\quad \dfrac{\epsilon_2}{\epsilon_1} D_1 \cos \alpha_1 = D_2 \cos \alpha_2$

and division of these two equalities gives

(7) $\quad \tan \alpha_2 = \dfrac{\epsilon_1}{\epsilon_2} \tan \alpha_1$

In Fig. 5.6 we have assumed that $\epsilon_1 > \epsilon_2$, and therefore $\alpha_2 > \alpha_1$.

The direction of $\mathbf{E}$ on each side of the boundary is identical with the direction of $\mathbf{D}$, because $\mathbf{D} = \epsilon \mathbf{E}$.

The magnitude of $\mathbf{D}$ in region 2 may be found from (5) and (6),

(8) $\quad D_2 = D_1 \sqrt{\sin^2 \alpha_1 + \left(\dfrac{\epsilon_2}{\epsilon_1}\right)^2 \cos^2 \alpha_1}$

and the magnitude of $\mathbf{E_2}$ is then

(9) $\quad E_2 = E_1 \sqrt{\cos^2 \alpha_1 + \left(\dfrac{\epsilon_1}{\epsilon_2}\right)^2 \sin^2 \alpha_1}$

An inspection of these equations shows that D is larger in the region of larger permittivity (unless $\alpha_1 = \alpha_2 = 90°$, where the magnitude is unchanged) and that E is larger in the region of smaller permittivity (unless $\alpha_1 = \alpha_2 = 0°$, where its magnitude is unchanged). These boundary conditions, (1) to (4), or the magnitude and direction relations derived from them, (7) to (9), allow us quickly to find the field on one side of a boundary *if we know the field on the other side*. In the example we began at the end of the previous section this was the case, and we are now able to determine that the fields within the dielectric are

$\mathbf{D}_{in} = \epsilon_0 E_0 \mathbf{a}_x \qquad (0 \le x \le a)$

$\mathbf{E}_{in} = 0.476 E_0 \mathbf{a}_x \qquad (0 \le x \le a)$

$\mathbf{P}_{in} = 0.524 \epsilon_0 E_0 \mathbf{a}_x \qquad (0 \le x \le a)$

A practical problem most often does not provide us with a direct knowledge of the field on either side of the boundary. The boundary conditions must be used to help us determine the fields on both sides of the boundary from the other information which is given. A simple problem of this type will be considered in Sec. 5.9.

The boundary conditions existing at the interface between a conductor and a dielectric are much simpler than those above. First, we know that **D** and **E** are both zero inside the conductor. Second, the tangential **E** and **D** field component must both be zero to satisfy

$$\oint \mathbf{E} \cdot d\mathbf{L} = 0$$

and

$$\mathbf{D} = \epsilon \mathbf{E}$$

Finally, the application of Gauss's law,

$$\oint_s \mathbf{D} \cdot d\mathbf{S} = Q_f$$

shows once more that both **D** and **E** are normal to the conductor surface and that $D_n = \rho_s$ and $E_n = \rho_s/\epsilon$. We see, then, that the boundary conditions we developed previously for the conductor–free-space boundary are valid for the conductor-dielectric boundary if we replace ϵ_0 by ϵ. Thus

(10)
$$\boxed{D_t = E_t = 0}$$

(11)
$$\boxed{D_n = \epsilon E_n = \rho_s}$$

It is interesting to spend a moment discovering how any charge that is introduced *internally* within a conducting material arrives at the surface as a surface charge. We should understand that this is not a common occurrence, but it does give us some additional insight into the characteristics of a conductor.

Given Ohm's law,

$$\mathbf{J} = \sigma \mathbf{E}$$

and the continuity equation,

$$\nabla \cdot \mathbf{J} = -\frac{\partial \rho}{\partial t}$$

in which **J** and ρ both involve only free charges, we have

$$\nabla \cdot \sigma \mathbf{E} = -\frac{\partial \rho}{\partial t}$$

or

$$\nabla \cdot \frac{\sigma}{\epsilon} \mathbf{D} = -\frac{\partial \rho}{\partial t}$$

If we assume that the medium is homogeneous,

$$\nabla \cdot \mathbf{D} = -\frac{\epsilon}{\sigma} \frac{\partial \rho}{\partial t}$$

Now we may use Maxwell's first equation to obtain

$$\rho = -\frac{\epsilon}{\sigma} \frac{\partial \rho}{\partial t}$$

The solution of this equation may be obtained by rearranging and integrating,

$$\rho = \rho_0 e^{-(\sigma/\epsilon)t}$$

where ρ_0 = charge density at $t = 0$. This shows an exponential decay of charge density at every point with a time constant of ϵ/σ. This time constant, often called the *relaxation time*, may be approximated for copper by using the free-space value of ϵ, giving

$$\frac{\epsilon_0}{\sigma} = 8.854 \times \frac{10^{-12}}{5.8 \times 10^7} = 1.5 \times 10^{-19} \text{ s}$$

In less than $\frac{1}{6}$ $\mu\mu$s any charge we place in the interior of a piece of copper has dropped to about 37 per cent of its initial value. This rapid decay is characteristic of good conductors and shows that, except for an extremely short transient period, we may safely consider the charge density is always zero within a good conductor.

With the physical materials with which we must work, no dielectric material is without some few free electrons; all have conductivities different from zero, and representative values are given in Appendix C. Charge introduced internally in any of them, however, will eventually reach the surface.

With the knowledge we now have of conducting materials, dielectric materials, and the necessary boundary conditions, we are ready to define and discuss capacitance.

D 5.8 The region $x > 0$ contains a dielectric material for which $\epsilon_{R1} = 5$, and in the region $x < 0$, $\epsilon_{R2} = 3$. If $\mathbf{E}_2 = 20\mathbf{a}_x + 30\mathbf{a}_y - 40\mathbf{a}_z$ V/m, find

(a) $\mathbf{D}_2$
(b) $\mathbf{D}_1$
(c) $\mathbf{P}_1$

Ans. $\epsilon_0(60\mathbf{a}_x + 90\mathbf{a}_y - 120\mathbf{a}_z)$; $\epsilon_0(60\mathbf{a}_x + 150\mathbf{a}_y - 200\mathbf{a}_z)$; $\epsilon_0(48\mathbf{a}_x + 120\mathbf{a}_y - 160\mathbf{a}_z)$ C/m²

D 5.9 Find the angle by which the direction of **E** changes as it crosses the boundary between dielectrics 2 and 1 if $\epsilon_{R2} = 1$, $\alpha_2 = 45°$, and

    (*a*) $\epsilon_{R1} = 2$
    (*b*) $\epsilon_{R1} = 5$
    (*c*) $\epsilon_{R1} = 100$

Ans. $18.4; 33.7; 44.4°$

D 5.10 Using data in Appendix C, calculate the relaxation time for

    (*a*) Bakelite
    (*b*) Porcelain
    (*c*) Distilled water

Ans. $3.54 \times 10^{-6}; 4.34 \times 10^{-2}; 2.66 \times 10^{2}$ s

5.8 CAPACITANCE

Now let us consider two conductors embedded in a homogeneous dielectric (Fig. 5.7). Conductor M_2 carries a total positive charge Q, and M_1 carries an equal negative charge. There are no other charges present, and the *total* charge of the system is zero.

We now know that the charge is carried on the surface as a surface charge density and also that the electric field is normal to the conductor surface. Each conductor is, moreover, an equipotential surface, and since M_2 carries the positive charge, the electric flux

FIG. 5.7 Two oppositely charged conductors M_1 and M_2 surrounded by a uniform dielectric. The ratio of the magnitude of the charge on either conductor to the magnitude of the potential difference between them is the capacitance C.

FIG. 5.8 The problem of the parallel-plate capacitor. The capacitance per square meter of surface area is ϵ/d.

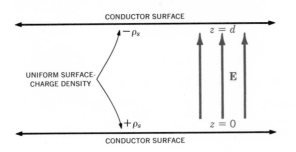

is directed from M_2 to M_1, and M_2 is at the more positive potential. In other words, work must be done to carry a positive charge from M_1 to M_2.

Let us designate the potential difference between M_2 and M_1 as V_0. We now may define the *capacitance* of this two-conductor system as the ratio of the magnitudes of the total charge on either conductor to the potential difference between conductors,

$$(1) \qquad \boxed{C = \frac{Q}{V_0}}$$

The capacitance is independent of the potential and total charge, for their ratio is constant. If the charge density is increased by a factor of N, Gauss's law indicates that the electric flux density or electric field intensity also increases by N, as does the potential difference. The capacitance is a function only of the physical dimensions of the system of conductors and of the permittivity of the homogeneous dielectric.

Capacitance is measured in *farads* (F), where a farad is defined as one coulomb per volt. Common values of capacitance are apt to be very small fractions of a farad, and consequently more practical units are the microfarad (μF) and picofarad (pF).

We can apply the definition of capacitance to a simple two-conductor system in which the conductors are identical, infinite, parallel planes of separation d (Fig. 5.8). Choosing the lower conducting plane at $z = 0$ and the upper one at $z = d$, a uniform sheet of surface charge $\pm\rho_s$ on each conductor leads to the uniform field [Sec. 2.6, Eq. (3)]

$$\mathbf{E} = \frac{\rho_s}{\epsilon}\mathbf{a}_z$$

where the permittivity of the homogeneous dielectric is ϵ, and

$$\mathbf{D} = \rho_s \mathbf{a}_z$$

The charge on the lower plane must then be positive, since $\mathbf{D}$ is directed upward, and the normal value of $\mathbf{D}$,

$$D_n = D_z = \rho_s$$

is equal to the surface charge density there. On the upper plane,

$$D_n = -D_z$$

and the surface charge there is the negative of that on the lower plane.

The potential difference between lower and upper planes is

$$V_0 = -\int_{\text{upper}}^{\text{lower}} \mathbf{E} \cdot d\mathbf{L} = -\int_d^0 \frac{\rho_s}{\epsilon} \, dz = \frac{\rho_s}{\epsilon} d$$

Since the total charge on either plane is infinite, the capacitance is infinite. A more practical answer is obtained by considering planes, each of area S, whose linear dimensions are much greater than their separation d. The electric field and charge distribution are then almost uniform at all points not adjacent to the edges, and this latter region contributes only a small percentage of the total capacitance, allowing us to write the familiar result

$$Q = \rho_s S$$

$$V_0 = \frac{\rho_s}{\epsilon} d$$

(2)
$$\boxed{C = \frac{Q}{V_0} = \frac{\epsilon S}{d}}$$

More rigorously, we might consider (2) as the capacitance of a portion of the infinite-plane arrangement having a surface area S. Methods of calculating the effect of the unknown and nonuniform distribution near the edges must wait until we are able to solve more complicated potential problems.

As an example, consider a capacitor having a mica dielectric, $\epsilon_R = 6$, a plate area of 10 in.², and a separation of 0.01 in. The capacitance is 1,350 pF. The large plate area is obtained in capacitors of small physical dimensions by stacking smaller plates in 50- or 100-decker sandwiches, or by rolling up foil plates separated by a flexible dielectric.

If more than two conductors are involved, *partial capacitances* between each pair of conductors must be defined. This is interestingly discussed in Maxwell's works.[1]

[1] See the bibliography at the end of the chapter.

Finally, the total energy stored in the capacitor is

$$
(3) \qquad W_E = \frac{1}{2} \int_{\text{vol}} \epsilon E^2 \, dv = \frac{1}{2} \int_0^S \int_0^d \frac{\epsilon \rho_s^2}{\epsilon^2} \, dz \, dS
$$

$$
= \frac{1}{2} \frac{\rho_s^2}{\epsilon} Sd = \frac{1}{2} \frac{\epsilon S}{d} \frac{\rho_s^2 d^2}{\epsilon^2} = \tfrac{1}{2} C V_0^2 = \tfrac{1}{2} Q V_0 = \frac{1}{2} \frac{Q^2}{C}
$$

which are all familiar expressions. Equation (3) also indicates that the energy stored in a capacitor with a fixed potential difference across it increases as the dielectric constant of the medium increases.

D 5.11 Find the capacitance of a parallel-plate capacitor if

(a) $\epsilon_R = 1{,}000$, $S = 30$ cm², and $d = 0.2$ mm
(b) $V_0 = 100$ V and $W_E = 0.001$ J
(c) Every linear dimension of the capacitor in (a) is doubled

Ans. 0.133; 0.2; 0.266 μF

5.9 SEVERAL CAPACITANCE EXAMPLES

As our first example we choose a spherical capacitor, formed by two concentric conducting spherical shells of radius a and b, $b > a$, and use the expression for the electric field obtained previously by Gauss's law,

$$
E_r = \frac{Q}{4\pi\epsilon r^2}
$$

where the region between the spheres is a dielectric with permittivity ϵ. The expression for potential difference was found from this by the line integral

$$
V_{ab} = \frac{Q}{4\pi\epsilon} \left(\frac{1}{a} - \frac{1}{b} \right)
$$

Here Q represents the total charge on the inner sphere, and the capacitance becomes

$$
(1) \qquad C = \frac{Q}{V_{ab}} = \frac{4\pi\epsilon}{1/a - 1/b}
$$

If we allow the outer sphere to become infinitely large, we obtain the capacitance of an isolated spherical conductor,

$$
(2) \qquad C = 4\pi\epsilon a
$$

For a diameter of 1 cm, or a sphere about the size of a marble,

$$C = 0.556 \text{ pF}$$

in free space.

Coating this sphere with a different dielectric layer, for which $\epsilon = \epsilon_1$, extending from $r = a$ to $r = r_1$,

$$D_r = \frac{Q}{4\pi r^2}$$

$$E_r = \frac{Q}{4\pi \epsilon_1 r^2} \qquad (a < r < r_1)$$

$$= \frac{Q}{4\pi \epsilon_0 r^2} \qquad (r_1 < r)$$

and the potential difference is

$$V_a - V_\infty = -\int_{r_1}^{a} \frac{Q\,dr}{4\pi\epsilon_1 r^2} - \int_{\infty}^{r_1} \frac{Q\,dr}{4\pi\epsilon_0 r^2}$$

$$= \frac{Q}{4\pi}\left[\left(\frac{1}{a} - \frac{1}{r_1}\right)\frac{1}{\epsilon_1} + \frac{1}{r_1}\frac{1}{\epsilon_0}\right]$$

Therefore

$$C = \frac{4\pi}{(1/a - 1/r_1)/\epsilon_1 + (1/r_1)/\epsilon_0}$$

The capacitance of a coaxial cable or coaxial capacitor of inner radius a, outer radius b, and length L is easily determined from the potential difference given in Sec. 4.3, Eq. (2),

$$\boxed{C = \frac{2\pi\epsilon L}{\ln(b/a)}}$$

A more difficult but very useful example might be obtained by investigating the potential field of two infinite line charges. Following the configuration shown in Fig. 5.9 for a positive line charge in the xz plane at $x = a$ and a negative line charge at $x = -a$, we start from the potential of a single line charge with zero reference at r_0,

$$V = \frac{\rho_L}{2\pi\epsilon}\ln\frac{r_0}{r}$$

and write the expression for the combined potential field in terms

FIG. 5.9 Two parallel infinite line charges carrying opposite charge. The positive line is at $x = a$, $y = 0$, and the negative line is at $x = -a$, $y = 0$. A general point in the xy plane is radially distant R_1 and R_2 from the positive and negative lines, respectively. The equipotential surfaces are circular cylinders.

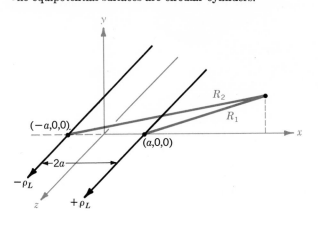

of the radial distance from the positive and negative line, R_1 and R_2, respectively,

$$V = \frac{\rho_L}{2\pi\epsilon}\left(\ln\frac{R_{10}}{R_1} - \ln\frac{R_{20}}{R_2}\right) = \frac{\rho_L}{2\pi\epsilon}\ln\frac{R_{10}R_2}{R_{20}R_1}$$

We choose $R_{10} = R_{20}$, thus placing the zero reference at equal distances from each line. This surface is the $x = 0$ plane. Expressing R_1 and R_2 in terms of x and y,

$$V = \frac{\rho_L}{2\pi\epsilon}\ln\sqrt{\frac{(x+a)^2+y^2}{(x-a)^2+y^2}} = \frac{\rho_L}{4\pi\epsilon}\ln\frac{(x+a)^2+y^2}{(x-a)^2+y^2}$$

In order to recognize the equipotential surfaces and adequately understand the problem we are going to solve, some algebraic manipulations are necessary. Choosing an equipotential surface $V = V_1$, let

$$K_1 = e^{4\pi\epsilon V_1/\rho_L}$$

and then

$$K_1 = \frac{(x+a)^2+y^2}{(x-a)^2+y^2}$$

After multiplying and collecting like powers, we obtain

$$x^2 - 2ax\frac{K_1 + 1}{K_1 - 1} + y^2 + a^2 = 0$$

We may complete the square,

$$\left(x - a\frac{K_1 + 1}{K_1 - 1}\right)^2 + y^2 = \left(\frac{2a\sqrt{K_1}}{K_1 - 1}\right)^2$$

showing that the $V = V_1$ equipotential surface is independent of z (or is a cylinder) and intersects the xy plane in a circle of radius b,

$$b = \frac{2a\sqrt{K_1}}{K_1 - 1}$$

which is centered at $x = h, y = 0$, where

$$h = a\frac{K_1 + 1}{K_1 - 1}$$

We can now specify a physical problem by asking for the capacitance between a conducting cylinder of radius b and a plane at a distance h from the cylinder. The conductors may serve as our equipotential surfaces, and we fit our conditions by choosing the circle of radius b and center at $x = h, y = 0$, as given in the two equations above, and solving for a, the location of the equivalent line charge, and K_1, a simplifying parameter which is a function of the potential V_1:

$$a = \sqrt{h^2 - b^2}$$

$$\sqrt{K_1} = e^{2\pi\epsilon V_1/\rho_L} = \frac{h + \sqrt{h^2 - b^2}}{b}$$

Since the plane is at zero potential and the circular cylinder is at potential V_1, the potential difference is V_1, or

$$V_1 = \frac{\rho_L}{2\pi\epsilon} \ln \frac{h + \sqrt{h^2 - b^2}}{b}$$

The magnitude of the charge on the cylinder, on the plane, or on the equivalent line charge is ρ_L by Gauss's law, and the capacitance of a length L is therefore

(3)
$$\boxed{C = \frac{\rho_L L}{V_1} = \frac{2\pi\epsilon L}{\ln\left[(h + \sqrt{h^2 - b^2})/b\right]} = \frac{2\pi\epsilon L}{\cosh^{-1}(h/b)}}$$

Figure 5.10 shows a cylinder of 5 m radius at a potential of 100 V separated 13 m from a plane at zero potential. Numerical values are obtained for the total charge per unit length on the cylinder,

FIG. 5.10 A numerical example of the capacitance, linear charge density, position of an equivalent line charge, and characteristics of the mid-equipotential surface for a cylindrical conductor of 5-m radius at a potential of 100 V parallel to and 13 m from a conducting plane at zero potential.

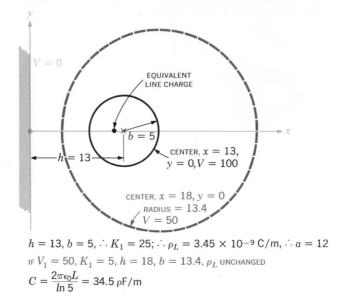

$h = 13, b = 5, \therefore K_1 = 25; \therefore \rho_L = 3.45 \times 10^{-9}\ \text{C/m}, \therefore a = 12$

IF $V_1 = 50, K_1 = 5, h = 18, b = 13.4, \rho_L$ UNCHANGED

$$C = \frac{2\pi\epsilon_0 L}{\ln 5} = 34.5\ \text{pF/m}$$

the capacitance between cylinder and plane, the position of the 50-V equipotential surface, and the position of the filamentary line charge which could produce identical equipotential surfaces.

For a conductor of small radius located far from the plane we find

(4)
$$C \doteq \frac{2\pi\epsilon L}{\ln (2h/b)}$$

The capacitance between two circular conductors separated $2h$ is one-half the capacitance given by (3) or (4). These latter answers are of interest because they allow us to compute the capacitance of a section of two-wire transmission line.

D 5.12 Find the capacitance of

(a) A spherical satellite 5 ft in diameter in free space
(b) A 1-m length of coaxial cable filled with polyethylene, with the radius of the inner conductor 0.5 mm and the inner radius of outer conductor 3 mm
(c) A 1-m length of an infinitely long horizontal conductor of 1-mm radius suspended 10 m over a conducting plane and parallel to it in air

Ans. 5.61; 70.1; 84.7 pF

Suppose we are given a parallel-plate capacitor of area S and spacing d, with the usual assumption that d is small compared to the linear dimensions of the plates. The capacitance is $\epsilon_1 S/d$, using a dielectric of permittivity ϵ_1. Now let us replace a part of this dielectric by another of permittivity ϵ_2, placing the boundary between the two dielectrics parallel to the plates (Fig. 5.11).

Some of us may immediately suspect that this combination is effectively two capacitors in series, yielding a total capacitance of

$$C = \frac{1}{(1/C_1) + (1/C_2)}$$

where $C_1 = \epsilon_1 S/d_1$ and $C_2 = \epsilon_2 S/d_2$. This is the correct result, but we can obtain it using less intuition and a more basic approach.

Since our capacitance definition, $C = Q/V$, involves a charge and a voltage, we may assume either and then find the other in terms of it. The capacitance is not a function of either, but only of the dielectrics and the geometry. Suppose we assume a potential difference V_0 between the plates. The electric field intensities in the two regions, E_2 and E_1, are both uniform, and $V_0 = E_1 d_1 + E_2 d_2$. At the dielectric interface E is normal and $D_{n1} = D_{n2}$, or $\epsilon_1 E_1 = \epsilon_2 E_2$. Using our V_0 relation,

$$E_1 = \frac{V_0}{d_1 + (\epsilon_1/\epsilon_2)d_2}$$

and the surface charge density therefore has the magnitude

$$\rho_{s1} = D_1 = \epsilon_1 E_1 = \frac{V_0}{d_1/\epsilon_1 + d_2/\epsilon_2}$$

Since $D_1 = D_2$, the magnitude of the surface charge is the same on each plate. The capacitance is then

$$C = \frac{Q}{V_0} = \frac{\rho_s S}{V_0} = \frac{1}{d_1/\epsilon_1 S + d_2/\epsilon_2 S} = \frac{1}{1/C_1 + 1/C_2}$$

We might have assumed the charge Q on one plate, leading to a surface charge Q/S and a value of D that is also Q/S. This is true in both regions, as $D_{n1} = D_{n2}$ and D is normal. Then $E_1 = D/\epsilon_1 = Q/\epsilon_1 S$, $E_2 = D/\epsilon_2 = Q/\epsilon_2 S$, and the potential difference across each region is $V_1 = E_1 d_1 = Qd_1/\epsilon_1 S$, $V_2 = E_2 d_2 = Qd_2/\epsilon_2 S$. The capacitance is

$$C = \frac{Q}{V} = \frac{Q}{V_1 + V_2} = \frac{1}{d_1/\epsilon_1 S + d_2/\epsilon_2 S}$$

FIG. 5.11 A parallel-plate capacitor containing two dielectrics with the dielectric interface parallel to the conducting plates; $C = 1/[(d_1/\epsilon_1 S) + (d_2/\epsilon_2 S)]$.

How would the method of solution or the answer change if there were a third conducting plane along the interface? We would now expect to find surface charge on each side of this conductor, and the magnitudes of these charges should be equal. In other words, we do not think of the electric lines as passing directly from one outer plate to the other but as terminating on one side of this interior plane and then continuing on the other side. The capacitance is unchanged, provided, of course, that the added conductor is of negligible thickness. The addition of a thick conducting plate will increase the capacitance if the separation of the outer plates is kept constant, and this is an example of a more general theorem which states that the replacement of any portion of the dielectric by a conducting body will cause an increase in the capacitance.

If the dielectric boundary were placed *normal* to the two conducting plates and the dielectrics occupied areas of S_1 and S_2, then an assumed potential difference V_0 would produce field strengths $E_1 = E_2 = V_0/d$. These are tangential fields at the interface, and they must be equal. Then we may find in succession D_1, D_2, ρ_{s1}, ρ_{s2}, and Q, obtaining a capacitance

$$C = \frac{\epsilon_1 S_1 + \epsilon_2 S_2}{d} = C_1 + C_2$$

as we should expect.

At this time we can do very little with a capacitor in which two dielectrics are used in such a way that the interface is not everywhere normal or parallel to the fields. Certainly we know the boundary conditions at each conductor and at the dielectric interface; however, we do not know the fields to which to apply the boundary conditions. Such a problem must be put aside until our knowledge of field theory has increased and we are willing and able to use more advanced mathematical techniques.

D 5.13 Find the capacitance of the capacitor shown in Fig. 5.11 if $S = 36\pi$ cm^2, $d = 5$ mm, $\epsilon_{R1} = 10$, and $\epsilon_{R2} = 3$, and d_1 and d_2 are selected such that

(a) $V_1 = V_2$

(b) The energy stored in each dielectric is half the total energy

(c) $\dfrac{d_2}{d_1} = \dfrac{\epsilon_1}{\epsilon_2}$

Ans.   71.6; 130; 130 pF

SUGGESTED REFERENCES

1 Adler, R. B., A. C. Smith, and R. L. Longini: "Introduction to Semiconductor Physics," John Wiley & Sons, Inc., New York, 1964. Semiconductor theory is treated at an undergraduate level.

2 Dekker, A. J.: "Electrical Engineering Materials," Prentice-Hall, Inc., Englewood Cliffs, N.J., 1959. This admirable little book covers dielectrics, conductors, semiconductors, and magnetic materials.

3 Fano, R. M., L. J. Chu, and R. B. Adler: "Electromagnetic Fields, Energy, and Forces," John Wiley & Sons, Inc., New York, 1960. Polarization in dielectrics is discussed in the first part of chap. 5. This junior-level text presupposes a full-term physics course in electricity and magnetism, and it is therefore slightly more advanced in level. The introduction beginning on p. 1 should be read.

4 Maxwell, J. C.: "A Treatise on Electricity and Magnetism," 3d ed., Oxford University Press, New York, 1904, or an inexpensive paperback edition, Dover Publications, Inc., New York, 1954.

5 Matsch, L. W.: "Capacitors, Magnetic Circuits, and Transformers," Prentice-Hall, Inc., Englewood Cliffs, N.J., 1964. Many of the practical aspects of capacitors are discussed in chap. 2.

PROBLEMS

1 Assume that a uniform electron beam of circular cross section with radius of 0.2 mm is generated by a cathode at $x = 0$ and collected by an anode at $x = 20$ cm. The velocity of the electrons varies with x, $U_x = 10^8 x^{1/2}$. If the current density at the anode is 10^4 A/m^2, find the volume charge density and current density as functions of x.

2 Given $\mathbf{J} = -10^4(y\mathbf{a}_x + x\mathbf{a}_y)$, determine the current crossing the $y = 0$ plane in the $-\mathbf{a}_y$ direction between $z = 0$ and 1 and $x = 0$ and 2.

3 In spherical coordinates, a current density $\mathbf{J} = (k_1/r)\mathbf{a}_\phi - [k_2/(r \sin \theta)]\mathbf{a}_\theta$ exists in a conducting medium. Determine the total current in the $\mathbf{a}_z$ direction which crosses a circular disk of radius R_1, located at $z = h$ and centered on the z axis.

4 Given $\mathbf{J} = a^2\mathbf{a}_r/r^2$, in spherical coordinates, (a) find $\nabla \cdot \mathbf{J}$ at $r = a$; (b) find dQ_i/dt within the spherical surface $r = a$. (c) Is $\nabla \cdot \mathbf{J} = 0$ everywhere within the spherical surface $r = a$?

5 (a) Show that the continuity equation for a compressible fluid of density ρ kg/m^3 and velocity $\mathbf{U}$ is $\nabla \cdot \rho \mathbf{U} = -\partial\rho/\partial t$. (b) Obtain the integral form of this equation and express it in words.

6 If volume charge density is given as $\rho = (\cos \omega t)/r^2$, in spherical coordinates, find $\mathbf{J}$. It is reasonable to assume that $\mathbf{J}$ is not a function of θ or ϕ.

7 A 1- by-10-cm copper bus bar of rectangular cross section carries 500 A. It has a length of 150 cm. (a) Find the current density. (b) Determine the total resistance. (c) Find the potential difference between the end faces. (d) What power is lost in heating the bar, and will it cause an appreciable temperature rise? (e) Determine the drift velocity of the electrons.

8 A solid wire with conductivity σ_1 and radius a has a jacket made of a material of conductivity σ_2 with an inner radius a and an outer radius b. Show that the ratio of the current densities in the two materials is independent of a and b.

9 A truncated cone has a height of 16 cm and radii of the two circular faces of 0.1 and 2 mm. If the material from which this solid cone is constructed has a conductivity of 2×10^6 ℧/m, use some very good approximations to determine the resistance between the two circular faces.

10 A large brass washer has a 2-cm inside diameter and a 4-cm outside diameter and is 0.6 cm thick; $\sigma = 1.5 \times 10^7$ ℧/m. The washer is cut in half along a diameter, and good electrical connections are made to the two rectangular faces of one part. The resultant current density is $\mathbf{J} = 10^4 \mathbf{a}_\phi/r$, where the z axis is the axis of the washer. (a) What total current is flowing? (b) What is the maximum E at any point within the half washer? (c) What is the potential difference between the two faces? (d) What is the total resistance between the two faces?

11 A conical conducting surface is described in spherical coordinates by $\theta = 0.1\pi$. The region $0.1\pi < \theta < \pi/2$ is free space in which the potential $V = -100 \ln (\tan \frac{1}{2}\theta)$. Find (a) the surface charge density on the cone; (b) the total charge between $r = 0$ and $r = 1$ m.

12 At a certain point on a conductor surface, $\mathbf{E} = 0.2\mathbf{a}_x - 0.7\mathbf{a}_z$ V/m. (a) What two unit vectors might describe the outward normal to the surface there? (b) What value of surface charge density would be associated with each choice of normal?

13 Given the potential field $V = 6\phi + 20 \ln r$ V, in cylindrical coordinates, it is known that the point $(r = 1, \phi = \pi, z = 100)$ lies on a conductor surface. (a) Determine the equation of the conductor surface. (b) Find the magnitude of the surface charge density at any point on the surface.

14 The conductivity of intrinsic germanium is given as a function of temperature by $\sigma = 4.35 \times 10^6 e^{-4,350/T}$ ℧/m. (a) Evaluate σ at $T = 300$ and $360°$K. (b) What are the electron and hole densities at $300°$K? (c) Repeat for silicon if $\sigma = 3.45 \times 10^6 e^{-6,450/T}$.

15 A small bar of intrinsic germanium has a square cross section 1 mm on a side and is 1.5 cm long. A voltage of 0.25 V is applied between the ends. At $T = 300°$K determine (a) E; (b) σ; (c) J; (d) I; (e) U_d for electrons.

16 A field of 10,000 V/m is applied in helium gas. The electron cloud in each atom shifts 0.75×10^{-18} m with respect to the nucleus. Find (a) p; (b) P, if the density is such that $n = 2.5 \times 10^{25}$ atoms/m³; (c) ϵ_R.

17 Two equal but opposite point charges of $10^{-5}/3$ C are held x m apart by a spring, where $F_{\text{spring}} = 12(0.5 - x)$ N. Without any force of attraction, the spring would be fully extended to 0.5 m. (a) Determine the charge separation. (b) What is the dipole moment?

18 Find the dielectric constant for a material in which the electric flux density is four times the polarization.

19 The boundary between a semi-infinite slab of dielectric and free space is the $z = 0$ plane. A smoothed expression for $\mathbf{P}$ near $z = 0$ shows that $\mathbf{P} = 0$ for $z < 0$, $\mathbf{P}$ is in the $\mathbf{a}_z$ direction for $z > 0$, P increases linearly from 0 to 10^{-6} C/m² as z changes from 0 to 10^{-10} m, and $\mathbf{P} = 10^{-6}\mathbf{a}_z$ for $z > 10^{-10}$. (a) Estimate ρ_b in all regions. (b) Estimate ρ_{sb} on the dielectric surface.

20 A sphere of radius a is made of a homogeneous dielectric with dielectric constant ϵ_R. The sphere is centered at the origin in free space. The potential field within the sphere is

$$V_{\text{in}} = -\frac{3rE_0 \cos \theta}{\epsilon_R + 2}$$

Outside, we have

$$V_{\text{out}} = -rE_0 \cos \theta + \frac{a^3 E_0}{r^2} \frac{\epsilon_R - 1}{\epsilon_R + 2} \cos \theta$$

(a) Show that $\mathbf{E}_{\text{in}}$ is uniform. (b) Show that for $r \gg a$, $\mathbf{E}_{\text{out}} \doteq E_0\mathbf{a}_z$. (c) Show that the fields satisfy all dielectric boundary conditions at $r = a$.

21 Show that the boundary conditions on $\mathbf{P}$ at a dielectric interface are

$$\frac{P_{t2}}{P_{t1}} = \frac{\epsilon_{R2} - 1}{\epsilon_{R1} - 1} \quad \text{and} \quad \frac{P_{n2}}{P_{n1}} = \frac{\epsilon_{R1}(\epsilon_{R2} - 1)}{\epsilon_{R2}(\epsilon_{R1} - 1)}$$

22 Show that the *bound* surface charge density ρ_{sb} on the boundary between dielectrics 1 and 2 is related to the discontinuity in the polarization at the boundary by the expression $P_{n2} - P_{n1} = \rho_{sb}$, where P_{n2} and P_{n1} are directed toward region 1.

23 Show that the capacitance per unit length of a cylinder of radius a is zero.

24 An air capacitor with plate separation $d = 1$ mm and plate area $S = 36\pi$ cm² is connected to a 100-V battery. The battery is left connected and the separation of the plates is increased by a factor of 5. Determine by what factor each of the following quantities changes: (a) V_0; (b) C; (c) E; (d) D; (e) Q; (f) ρ_s; (g) W_E.

25 Repeat Prob. 24 assuming the battery disconnected before the separation of the plates is increased.

26 A coaxial cable has dimensions of $a = 1$ mm and $b = 2.718$ mm. The inner conductor is supported by dielectric spacers ($\epsilon_R = 5$) in the form of washers with a hole radius of 1 mm, an outer radius of 2.718 mm, and a thickness of 3 mm. The spacers are located every 2 cm down the cable. (a) By what factor do the spacers increase the capacitance per meter length? (b) If 100 V is maintained across the cable, find **E** at all points.

27 Two concentric conducting spheres of radius a and b, $b > a$, are separated by an insulating material having a conductivity σ. Show that the resistance R between the spheres is $\epsilon/\sigma C$, where C is the capacitance between the spheres when a lossless dielectric of permittivity ϵ is substituted for the lossy material.

28 A two-wire transmission line is to be constructed to provide a capacitance of 20 pF/m. The center-to-center conductor spacing is fixed at 1 cm. (a) What size of wire should be used in free space? (b) What would the wire size be if the wires were embedded in a dielectric with $\epsilon_R = 2$?

29 A parallel-plate capacitor with plate area S, separation d, and air dielectric has a charge Q_0. Find the energy required to separate the plates Δx, and from this determine the force of attraction between the capacitor plates.

30 A parallel-plate capacitor with square plates a on a side, separation x, and dielectric $\epsilon = \epsilon_R \epsilon_0$ has a charge Q_0. If the dielectric is now withdrawn a distance x in a direction parallel to an edge, where $x < a$, find the force on the dielectric and state whether it tends to pull the dielectric back into the capacitor or to expel it. If $a = 0.1$ m, $d = 2$ mm, $\epsilon_R = 5,000$, $x = 0.8a$, and $Q_0 = 10^{-6}$ C, find F.

31 A coaxial capacitor of inner radius a, outer radius b, and length L contains one dielectric layer for which $\epsilon_R = 2$ in the region $a < r < r_1$ and another dielectric for which $\epsilon_R = 4$ in the region $r_1 < r < b$. (a) Find C. (b) If $V = 0$ at $r = b$ and $V = V_0$ at $r = a$, find E_r, D_r, and P_r at $r = r_1^+$ and $r = r_1^-$.

32 A 5-cm-radius copper sphere has a capacitance C_1. A uniform dielectric layer of thickness d is placed on the sphere. If $\epsilon_R = 3$, determine d such that the new capacitance is $2C_1$.

33 In J. Bardeen and W. H. Brattain, Principles of Transistor Action, *Bell System Tech. J.*, vol. 28, no. 2, p. 260, April, 1949, formulas are given [eqs. (3.2) and (3.3)] for hole and electron mobilities in germanium. Calculate the mobilities at 300°K and compare these values with the more recent ones given in Sec. 5.5 of this text.

34 Two capacitor plates of area 240π cm² are separated 10 mm. The space between them is filled with several sheets of different dielectric, each of the same thickness, with the dielectric interfaces parallel to the plates. Find the capacitance if (a) there are two dielectrics, $\epsilon_{R1} = 3.5$ and $\epsilon_{R2} = 8.5$; (b) there are 10 dielectrics, $\epsilon_{R1} = 1.5$, $\epsilon_{R2} = 2.5$, ... , $\epsilon_{R10} = 10.5$; (c) there is one inhomogeneous dielectric, with ϵ_R varying linearly from 1 to 11.

35 In T. S. McLeod and C. M. Deavin, Development of a Capacitance Altimeter, *Proc. IEE*, vol. 110, no. 9, p. 1505, September, 1963, the first equation is presented as a "first approximation." Describe the assumption and then derive the equation. Note the system of units used.

36 In L. J. Giacoletto, Energy Storage and Conversion, *IEEE Spectrum*, vol. 2, no. 2, p. 95, February, 1965, derive eq. (4) and use it to determine the density of Mylar. The relative dielectric constant of this material is approximately 3.

6 EXPERIMENTAL MAPPING METHODS

We have seen in the last few chapters that the potential is the gateway to any information we desire about the electrostatic field at a point. The path is straight, and travel on it is easy in whichever direction we wish to go. The electric field intensity may be found from the potential by the gradient operation, which is a differentiation, and the electric field intensity may then be used to find the electric flux density by multiplying by the permittivity. The divergence of the flux density, again a differentiation, gives the volume charge density, and the surface charge density on any conductors in the field is quickly found by evaluating the flux density at the surface. Our boundary conditions show that it must be normal to such a surface.

Integration is still required if we need more information than the value of a field or charge density *at a point*. Finding the total charge on a conductor, the total energy stored in an electrostatic field, or a capacitance or resistance value are examples of such problems, each requiring an integration. These integrations cannot generally be avoided, no matter how extensive our knowledge of field theory becomes, and indeed, we should find that the greater this knowledge becomes, the more integrals we should wish to evaluate. Potential can do one important thing for us, and that is to furnish us quickly and easily with the quantity we must integrate.

Our goal, then, is to find the potential first. This cannot be done in terms of a charge configuration in a practical problem, because no one is kind enough to tell us exactly how the charges are distributed. Instead, we are usually given several conducting objects or conducting boundaries and the potential difference between them. Unless we happen to recognize the boundary surfaces as belonging to a simple problem we have already disposed of, we can do little now and must wait until Laplace's equation is discussed in the following chapter.

Although we thus postpone the mathematical solution to this important type of practical problem, we may acquaint ourselves with several experimental methods of finding the potential field. These methods may involve special equipment such as an electrolytic trough, a fluid-flow device, resistance paper and the associated bridge equipment, or rubber sheets. They may involve only pencil, paper, and a good supply of erasers. The *exact* potential can never be determined, but sufficient accuracy for engineering purposes can usually be attained. One other method, called the *iteration* method, does allow us to achieve any desired accuracy for the potential, but the number of calculations required increases very rapidly as the desired accuracy increases.

We should note carefully for the experimental methods to be described below that the procedures are most often based on an analogy with the electrostatic field, rather than directly on measurements on this field itself.

Finally, we cannot introduce this subject of experimental methods of finding potential fields without emphasizing the fact that many practical problems possess such a complicated geometry that no exact method of finding that field is possible or feasible and experimental techniques are the only ones which can be used.

6.1 CURVILINEAR SQUARES

Our first method is a graphical one, requiring only pencil and paper. Besides being economical, it is also capable of yielding good accuracy if used skillfully and patiently. Fair accuracy (5 to 10 per cent on a capacitance determination) may be obtained by a beginner who does no more than follow the few rules and hints of the art.

The method to be described is applicable only to fields in which no variation exists in the direction normal to the plane of the sketch. The procedure is based on several facts we have already demonstrated:

1. A conductor boundary is an equipotential surface.
2. The electric field intensity and electric flux density are both perpendicular to the equipotential surfaces.
3. $\mathbf{E}$ and $\mathbf{D}$ are therefore perpendicular to the conductor boundaries and possess zero tangential values.
4. The lines of electric flux or streamlines begin and terminate on charge and hence, in a charge-free, homogeneous dielectric, begin and terminate only on the conductor boundaries.

Let us consider the implications of these statements by drawing the streamlines on a sketch which already shows the equipotential surfaces. In Fig. 6.1a two conductor boundaries are shown, and equipotentials have been drawn with a constant potential difference between lines. We should remember that these lines are only the cross sections of the equipotential surfaces, which are cylinders (although not circular), since no variation in the direction normal to the surface of the paper is permitted. We arbitrarily choose to begin a streamline or flux line at A on the surface of the more positive conductor. It leaves the surface normally and must cross at right angles the undrawn but very real equipotential surfaces between the conductor and the first surface shown. The line is continued to the other conductor, obeying the single rule that the

FIG. 6.1 (a) Sketch of the equipotential surfaces between two conductors. The increment of potential between each two adjacent equipotentials is the same. (b) One flux line has been drawn from A to A', and a second from B to B'.

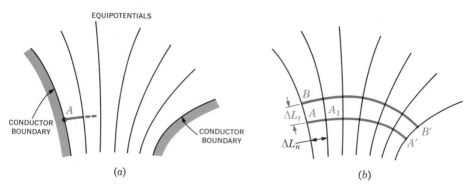

(a)   (b)

intersection with each equipotential must be square. Turning the paper from side to side as the line progresses enables us to maintain perpendicularity more accurately. The line has been completed in Fig. 6.1b.

In a similar manner, we may start at B and sketch another streamline ending at B'. Before continuing, let us interpret the meaning of this pair of streamlines. The streamline, by definition, is everywhere tangent to the electric field intensity or to the electric flux density. Since it is tangent to the electric flux density, the flux density is tangent to the streamline and no electric flux may cross any streamline. In other words, if there is a charge of 5 μC on the surface between A and B (and extending 1 m into the paper), then 5 μC of flux begins in this region and all must terminate between A' and B'. Such a pair of lines is sometimes called a *flux tube*, because it physically seems to carry flux from one point to another without losing any.

We now wish to construct a third streamline, and both the mathematical and visual interpretations we may make from the sketch will be greatly simplified if we draw this line starting from some point C chosen so that the same amount of flux is carried in the tube BC as is contained in AB. How do we choose the position of C?

The electric field intensity at the midpoint of the line joining A to B may be found approximately by assuming a value for the flux in the tube AB, say $\Delta\Psi$, which allows us to express the electric flux density by $\Delta\Psi/\Delta L_t$, where the depth of the tube is 1 m and ΔL_t is the length of line joining A to B. The magnitude of E is then

$$E = \frac{1}{\epsilon}\frac{\Delta\Psi}{\Delta L_t}$$

However, we may also find the magnitude of the electric field intensity by dividing the potential difference between points A and A_1, lying on two adjacent equipotential surfaces, by the distance from A to A_1. If this distance is designated ΔL_n and an increment of potential between equipotentials of ΔV is assumed, then

$$E = \frac{\Delta V}{\Delta L_n}$$

This value applies most accurately to the point at the middle of the line segment from A to A_1, while the previous value was most accurate at the midpoint of the line segment from A to B. If, however, the equipotentials are close together (ΔV small) and the two streamlines are close together ($\Delta \Psi$ small), the two values found for the electric field intensity must be approximately equal,

(1) $$\frac{1}{\epsilon} \frac{\Delta \Psi}{\Delta L_t} = \frac{\Delta V}{\Delta L_n}$$

Throughout our sketch we have assumed a homogeneous medium (ϵ constant), a constant increment of potential between equipotentials (ΔV constant), and a constant amount of flux per tube ($\Delta \Psi$ constant). To satisfy all these conditions, (1) shows that

(2) $$\boxed{\frac{\Delta L_t}{\Delta L_n} = \text{constant} = \frac{1}{\epsilon} \frac{\Delta \Psi}{\Delta V}}$$

A similar argument might be made at any point in our sketch, and we are therefore led to the conclusion that a constant ratio must be maintained between the distance between streamlines as measured along an equipotential, and the distance between equipotentials as measured along a streamline. It is this *ratio* which must have the same value at every point, not the individual lengths. Each length must decrease in regions of greater field strength, because ΔV is constant.

The simplest ratio we can use is unity, and the streamline from B to B' in Fig. 6.1b was started at a point for which $\Delta L_t = \Delta L_n$. Since the ratio of these distances is kept at unity, the streamlines and equipotentials divide the field-containing region into curvilinear squares, a term implying a planar geometric figure which differs from a true square in having slightly curved and slightly unequal sides but approaches a square as its dimensions decrease. Those incremental surface elements in our three coordinate systems which are planar should be recognized as curvilinear squares.

We may now rapidly sketch in the remainder of the streamlines by keeping each small box as square as possible. The complete sketch is shown in Fig. 6.2.

FIG. 6.2 The remainder of the streamlines have been added to Fig. 6.1*b* by beginning each new line normally to the conductor and maintaining curvilinear squares throughout the sketch.

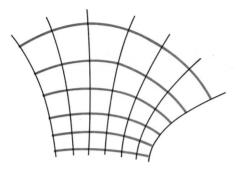

The only difference between this example and the production of a field map using the method of curvilinear squares is that the intermediate potential surfaces are not given. The streamlines and equipotentials must both be drawn on an original sketch which shows only the conductor boundaries. Only one solution is possible, as we shall prove later by the uniqueness theorem for Laplace's equation, and the rules we have outlined above are sufficient. One streamline is begun, an equipotential line is roughed in, another streamline is added, forming a curvilinear square, and the map is gradually extended throughout the desired region. Since none of us can ever expect to be perfect at this, we shall soon find that we can no longer make squares and also maintain right-angle corners. An error is accumulating in the drawing, and our present troubles should indicate the nature of the correction to make on some of the earlier work. It is usually best to start again on a fresh drawing, with the old one available as a guide.

The construction of a useful field map is an art; the science merely furnishes the rules. Proficiency in any art requires practice. A good problem for beginners is the coaxial cable or coaxial capacitor, since all the equipotentials are circles, and the next sketch attempted should be two parallel circular conductors, where the equipotentials are again circles, but with a varying center. Each of these is given as a problem at the end of the chapter, and the accuracy of the sketch may be checked by a capacitance calculation as outlined below.

Figure 6.3 shows a completed map for a cable containing a square inner conductor surrounded by a circular conductor. The capacitance is found from $C = Q/V_0$ by replacing Q by $N_Q \Delta Q = N_Q \Delta \Psi$, where N_Q is the number of flux tubes joining the two conductors, and letting $V_0 = N_V \Delta V$, where N_V is the number of potential in-

FIG. 6.3 An example of a curvilinear-square field map. The side of the square is two-thirds the radius of the circle. $N_Q = 32$ and $N_V = 4.6$, and therefore $C = \epsilon_0 N_Q / N_V = 61.5\ \text{pF/m}$.

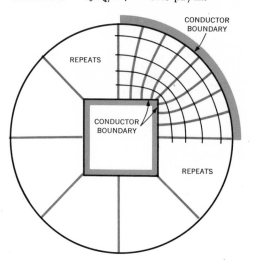

crements between conductors,

$$C = \frac{N_Q \Delta Q}{N_V \Delta V}$$

and then using (2),

(3)
$$C = \frac{N_Q}{N_V} \epsilon \frac{\Delta L_t}{\Delta L_n} = \epsilon \frac{N_Q}{N_V}$$

since $\Delta L_t / \Delta L_n = 1$. The determination of the capacitance from a flux plot merely consists of counting squares in two directions, between conductors and around either conductor. From Fig. 6.3 we obtain

$$C = \epsilon_0 \frac{32}{4.6} = 61.5\ \text{pF/m}$$

Ramo, Whinnery, and Van Duzer have an excellent discussion with examples of the construction of field maps by curvilinear squares. They offer the following suggestions:[1]

1 Plan on making a number of rough sketches, taking only a minute or so apiece, before starting any plot to be made with care. The use of

[1] By permission from S. Ramo, J. R. Whinnery, and T. Van Duzer, "Fields and Waves in Communication Electronics," John Wiley & Sons, Inc., New York, 1965, pp. 160–161.

FIG. 6.4   Two cylindrical conductors.

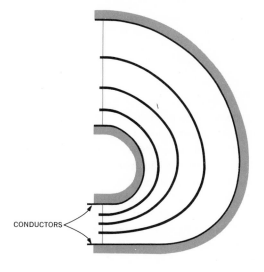

CONDUCTORS

transparent paper over the basic boundary will speed up this preliminary sketching.

2   Divide the known potential difference between electrodes into an equal number of divisions, say four or eight to begin with.

3   Begin the sketch of equipotentials in the region where the field is known best, as for example in some region where it approaches a uniform field.   Extend the equipotentials according to your best guess throughout the plot.   Note that they should tend to hug acute angles of the conducting boundary, and be spread out in the vicinity of obtuse angles of the boundary.

4   Draw in the orthogonal set of field lines.   As these are started, they should form curvilinear squares, but, as they are extended, the condition of orthogonality should be kept paramount, even though this will result in some rectangles with ratios other than unity.

5   Look at the regions with poor side ratios, and try to see what was wrong with the first guess of equipotentials.   Correct them and repeat the procedure until reasonable curvilinear squares exist throughout the plot.

6   In regions of low field intensity, there will be large figures, often of five or six sides.   To judge the correctness of the plot in this region, these large units should be subdivided.   The subdivisions should be started back a way, and, each time a flux tube is divided in half, the potential divisions in this region must be divided by the same factor.

D 6.1   Figure 6.4 shows two (noncircular) cylindrical conductors, one inside the other in air.   The potential of the inner conductor is 100 V and that of the outer one is 0.   The 25-V, 50-V, and 75-V equipotentials are sketched.   The maximum diameter of the inner conductor is 5 cm.

   (a)   Complete the curvilinear-square sketch and determine the capacitance per meter length.

(b) What would the capacitance be if the outer conductor lay along the 25-V equipotential surface?

(c) What would the capacitance be if the left half of the interior were polyethylene instead of air?

Ans. 54; 72; 88 pF/m

6.2 PHYSICAL MODELS

The analogy between the electric field and the gravitational field has been mentioned several times previously and may be used to permit the construction of physical models which are capable of yielding solutions to electrostatic problems of complicated geometry. The basis of the analogy is simply this: in the electrostatic field the potential difference between two points is the difference in potential energy of unit positive charges at these points, and in a uniform gravitational field the difference in potential energy of point masses at two points is proportional to their difference in height. In other words,

$$\Delta W_E = Q\,\Delta V \qquad \text{(electrostatic)}$$

$$\Delta W_G = Mg\,\Delta h \qquad \text{(gravitational)}$$

where M is the point mass and g is the acceleration due to gravity, essentially constant at the surface of the earth. For the same energy difference, then,

$$\Delta V = \frac{Mg}{Q}\,\Delta h = k\,\Delta h$$

where k is the constant of proportionality. This shows the direct analogy between difference in potential and difference in elevation.

This analogy allows us to construct a physical model of a known potential field by fabricating a surface, perhaps from wood, whose elevation h above any point (x,y) located in the zero-elevation zero-potential plane is proportional to the potential at that point. Note that fields in which the potential varies in three dimensions,

$$V = V(x,y,z)$$

cannot be handled because we have no method of showing the elevation of a "three-dimensional" point.

The field of an infinite line charge,

$$V = \frac{\rho_L}{2\pi\epsilon}\ln\frac{r_B}{r}$$

is shown on such a model in Fig. 6.5, which provides an accurate picture of the variation of potential with radius between r_A and r_B. The potential and elevation at r_B are conveniently set equal to zero.

FIG. 6.5 A model of the potential field of an infinite line charge. The difference in potential is proportional to the difference in elevation. Contour lines indicate equal potential increments.

Such a model may be constructed for any two-dimensional potential field and enables us to visualize the field a little better. Besides furnishing us with this three-dimensional picture, the model is capable of providing information on the paths taken by charged particles in the field. From the definition of the gradient, it is apparent that the gradient of the elevation h at any point is a vector whose magnitude is the maximum slope of the surface at that point and whose direction is "upward," or toward increasing elevation. The "point" in question is specified by its x and y coordinate values and lies in the xy plane; the slope is measured on the model surface. Since the potential is proportional to the elevation, the gradient of the potential is proportional to the gradient of the elevation, or the electric field intensity is proportional to the negative gradient of the elevation at any point.

A positively charged particle in this field experiences a force,

$$\mathbf{F}_E = Q\mathbf{E}$$

whereas a small point mass M, such as a steel marble, placed on the surface of the physical model, experiences an accelerating force due to gravity,

$$\mathbf{F}_G = Mg \sin \theta \, \mathbf{a}_F$$

where g equals the acceleration due to gravity, and θ equals the angle of inclination, measured with respect to a horizontal surface. The sine of this angle may be expressed in other terms by noting that $\sin\theta \doteq \tan\theta$ for small angles (less than about 18° for less than 5 per cent error), and $\tan\theta$ is given by the magnitude of the gradient of the elevation. For small slopes, then,

$$F_G = Mg|\nabla h|$$

$$\mathbf{F}_G = -Mg\ \nabla h$$

and in view of the elevation-potential analogy,

$$\frac{\mathbf{F}_E}{\mathbf{F}_G} = \frac{-Q\ \nabla V}{-Mg\ \nabla h} = \frac{-Q(Mg/Q)\ \nabla h}{-Mg\ \nabla h} = 1$$

or

$$\mathbf{F}_E = \mathbf{F}_G$$

As long as the model has only gentle slopes, the gravitational and electrical forces are analogous. This allows us to obtain the trajectories of charged particles by releasing frictionless marbles at various points on the surface of the model.

The construction of the models themselves is enormously simplified, both physically and theoretically, by the use of rubber sheets. The sheet is placed under moderate tension and approximates closely the *elastic membrane* of applied mechanics. It can be shown[1] that the vertical displacement h of the membrane satisfies the second-order partial differential equation

$$\frac{\partial^2 h}{\partial x^2} + \frac{\partial^2 h}{\partial y^2} = 0$$

if the surface slope is small. We shall see in the next chapter that every potential field in a charge-free region also satisfies this equation, Laplace's equation in two dimensions,

$$\frac{\partial^2 V}{\partial x^2} + \frac{\partial^2 V}{\partial y^2} = 0$$

We shall also prove a uniqueness theorem which assures us that if a potential solution in some specified region satisfies the above equation and also gives the correct potential on the boundaries of this region, then this solution is the only solution. Hence we need only force the elevation of the sheet to corresponding prescribed potential values on the boundaries, and the elevation at all other points is proportional to the potential.

For instance, the infinite-line-charge field may be displayed by recognizing the circular symmetry and fastening the rubber sheet

[1] See, for instance, Spangenberg, pp. 75–76, in the bibliography at the end of the chapter.

FIG. 6.6 A rubber-sheet model of the electrostatic field of a cylindrical triode with six grid rods and no space charge. (*From W. E. Rogers, "Introduction to Electric Fields," McGraw-Hill Book Company, New York, 1954. By permission of the publishers.*)

at zero elevation around a circle by the use of a large clamping ring of radius r_B. Since the potential is constant at r_A, we raise that portion of the sheet to a greater elevation by pushing a cylinder of radius r_A up against the rubber sheet. The analogy breaks down for large-surface slopes, and only a slight displacement at r_A is possible. The surface then represents the potential field, and marbles may be used to determine particle trajectories, in this case obviously radial lines as viewed from above.

Figure 6.6 shows the surface corresponding to the potential field inside a cylindrical triode vacuum tube (operating without space charge) possessing six grid rods rather than a mesh grid. The theoretical solution of this problem can only be approximated. The map is illuminated by a projector, with a ruled grating to show the equipotential contours.

D 6.2 In the region $0 \le x \le 10^3, 0 \le y \le 10^3$, where x and y are measured along the horizontal, the height of the land above sea level is given by $h = 500 + 100 \ln \left[(x - 10^3)^2 + (y - 2 \times 10^3)^2 \right]$. Determine the angle that the surface of the ground makes with the horizontal at

    (*a*) (0,0)
    (*b*) (0,10³)
    (*c*) (10³,10³)

Ans. 5.11; 8.05; 11.3°

6.3 CURRENT ANALOGIES

Several experimental methods depend upon an analogy between current density in conducting media and electric flux density in dielectric media. The analogy is easily demonstrated, for in a conducting medium Ohm's law and the gradient relationship are, for direct currents only,

$$\mathbf{J} = \sigma\mathbf{E}_\sigma$$

$$\mathbf{E}_\sigma = -\nabla V_\sigma$$

whereas in a homogeneous dielectric

$$\mathbf{D} = \epsilon\mathbf{E}_\epsilon$$

$$\mathbf{E}_\epsilon = -\nabla V_\epsilon$$

The subscripts serve to identify the analogous problems. It is evident that the potentials V_σ and V_ϵ, the electric field intensities $\mathbf{E}_\sigma$ and $\mathbf{E}_\epsilon$, the conductivity and permittivity σ and ϵ, and the current density and electric flux density $\mathbf{J}$ and $\mathbf{D}$ are analogous in pairs. Referring to a curvilinear-square map, we should interpret flux tubes as current tubes, each tube now carrying an incremental current which cannot leave the tube.

Finally, we must look at the boundaries. What is analogous to a conducting boundary which terminates electric flux normally and is an equipotential surface? The analogy furnishes the answer, and we see that the surface must terminate current density normally and again be an equipotential surface. This is the surface of a *perfect* conductor, although in practice it is necessary only to use one whose conductivity is many times that of the conducting medium.

Therefore, if we wished to find the field within a coaxial capacitor, which, as we have seen several times before, is a portion of the field of an infinite line charge, we might take two copper cylinders and fill the region between them with, for convenience, an electrolytic solution. Applying a potential difference between the cylinders, we may use a probe to establish the potential at any intermediate point, or to find all those points having the same potential. This is the essence of the electrolytic trough or tank. The greatest advantage of this method lies in the fact that it is not limited to two-dimensional problems. Practical suggestions for the construction and use of the tank are given in many places.[1]

The determination of capacitance from electrolytic-trough measurements is particularly easy. The total current leaving the more positive conductor is

$$I = \oint_s \mathbf{J} \cdot d\mathbf{S} = \sigma \oint_s \mathbf{E} \cdot d\mathbf{S}$$

[1] Weber is good. See the bibliography at the end of the chapter.

where the closed surface integral is taken over the entire conductor surface. The potential difference is given by the negative line integral from the less to the more positive plate,

$$V_0 = - \int \mathbf{E} \cdot d\mathbf{L}$$

and the total resistance is therefore

$$R = \frac{V_0}{I} = \frac{- \int \mathbf{E} \cdot d\mathbf{L}}{\sigma \oint_s \mathbf{E} \cdot d\mathbf{S}}$$

The capacitance is given by the ratio of the total charge to the potential difference,

$$C = \frac{Q}{V_0} = \frac{\epsilon \oint_s \mathbf{E} \cdot d\mathbf{S}}{- \int \mathbf{E} \cdot d\mathbf{L}}$$

and therefore

(1)
$$RC = \frac{\epsilon}{\sigma}$$

Knowing the conductivity of the electrolyte and the permittivity of the dielectric, we may determine the capacitance by a simple resistance measurement.

A simpler technique is available for two-dimensional problems. Conducting paper is available upon which silver paint may be used to draw the conducting boundaries. In the case of the coaxial capacitor, we should draw two circles of radius r_A and r_B, $r_B > r_A$, extending the paint a small distance outward from r_B and inward from r_A to provide sufficient area to make a good contact with wires to an external potential source. A probe is again used to establish potential values between the circles (cylinders).

D 6.3 (a) A square conductor inside a square tube is 1 m in length. The space between the conductors is filled with distilled water ($\sigma = 2 \times 10^{-4}$ ℧/m), a voltage of 12 V is applied, and a current of 2 mA is measured between conductors. If the distilled water is now removed and a good liquid dielectric with $\epsilon_R = 3$ is placed in the tube, what is the capacitance between conductors?

(b) The cross section of an air-filled cable of peculiar shape is drawn in silver paint on conducting paper. The paper has a resistance of 5,000 Ω per square; that is, the resistance between opposite edges of a square sheet of the paper of any size is 5,000 Ω. The measured resistance between the two silver conductors is 560 Ω. Find C for a 1-m length of the cable.

(*c*) Two conducting spheres are lowered into a tank of distilled water by insulated wires. A resistance of 900 Ω is measured between them. What is their capacitance in air?

Ans.   22.1; 49.2; 79.0 pF

6.4   FLUID-FLOW MAPS

An analogy also exists between electrostatics and hydraulics and is particularly useful in obtaining photographs of the streamlines or flux lines. The proof of the analogy will not be given here,[1] but the assumptions require an incompressible fluid flowing in a thin sheet. This is satisfied by the flow of water between parallel planes, closely spaced; one of the planes should be glass. Conductor boundaries represent sources and sinks, or regions at which the flow of the water originates and terminates. The flow lines are made visible by placing small crystals of potassium permanganate on the lower plane before the flow begins. As the crystals dissolve, the flow lines or streamlines become visible.

This process is described completely by Moore in a number of publications[2] which include many excellent photographs. Figure 6.7 shows several photographs taken by these techniques.

[1] See Weber, pp. 76–78.
[2] See the bibliography at the end of the chapter.

FIG. 6.7   Fluid-flow maps photographed by Moore.   (*a*) The field of four equal line charges.   (*b*) The field of a triode having six grid rods. The streamlines from the plate which terminate on the grid rods all lie within the regions having the white background; those which terminate on the cathode pass through the large region with a gray background.   (*Courtesy of A. D. Moore.*)

(*a*)   (*b*)

In potential problems where the potential is completely specified on the boundaries of a given region, particularly problems in which the potential does not vary in one direction, i.e., two-dimensional potential distributions, there exists a pencil-and-paper repetitive method which is capable of yielding any desired accuracy.   Digital computers should be used when the value of the potential is required with high accuracy; otherwise the time required is prohibitive except in the simplest problems.   The iterative method, to be described below, is well suited for calculation by any digital computer.

Let us assume a two-dimensional problem in which the potential does not vary with the z coordinate and divide the interior of a cross section of the region where the potential is desired into squares of length h on a side.   A portion of this region is shown in Fig. 6.8. The unknown values of the potential at five adjacent points are indicated as V_0, V_1, V_2, V_3, and V_4.   If the region is charge-free and contains a homogeneous dielectric, then $\nabla \cdot \mathbf{D} = 0$ and $\nabla \cdot \mathbf{E} = 0$, from which we have, in two dimensions,

$$\frac{\partial E_x}{\partial x} + \frac{\partial E_y}{\partial y} = 0$$

But the gradient operation gives $E_x = -\partial V / \partial x$ and $E_y = -\partial V / \partial y$, from which we obtain[1]

$$\frac{\partial^2 V}{\partial x^2} + \frac{\partial^2 V}{\partial y^2} = 0$$

Approximate values for these partial derivatives may be obtained in terms of the assumed potentials, for

$$\left. \frac{\partial V}{\partial x} \right|_a \doteq \frac{V_1 - V_0}{h}$$

and

$$\left. \frac{\partial V}{\partial x} \right|_c \doteq \frac{V_0 - V_3}{h}$$

from which

$$\left. \frac{\partial^2 V}{\partial x^2} \right|_0 \doteq \frac{\left. \dfrac{\partial V}{\partial x} \right|_a - \left. \dfrac{\partial V}{\partial x} \right|_c}{h} \doteq \frac{V_1 - V_0 - V_0 + V_3}{h^2}$$

and similarly,

$$\left. \frac{\partial^2 V}{\partial y^2} \right|_0 \doteq \frac{V_2 - V_0 - V_0 + V_4}{h^2}$$

---

[1] This is Laplace's equation in two dimensions.   The three-dimensional form will be derived in the following chapter.

FIG. 6.8 A portion of a region containing a two-dimensional potential field, divided into squares of side h. The potential V_0 is approximately equal to the average of the potentials at the four neighboring points.

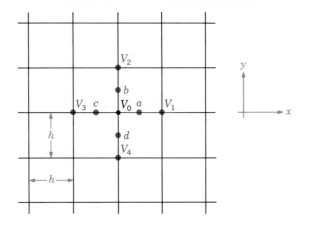

Combining, we have

$$\frac{\partial^2 V}{\partial x^2} + \frac{\partial^2 V}{\partial y^2} \doteq \frac{V_1 + V_2 + V_3 + V_4 - 4V_0}{h^2} = 0$$

or

(1)
$$\boxed{V_0 \doteq \tfrac{1}{4}(V_1 + V_2 + V_3 + V_4)}$$

The expression becomes exact as h approaches zero, and we shall write it without the approximation sign. It is intuitively correct, telling us that the potential is the average of the potential at the four neighboring points. The iterative method merely uses (1) to determine the potential at the corner of every square subdivision in turn, and then the process is repeated over the entire region as many times as is necessary until the values no longer change. The method is best shown in detail by an example.

For simplicity, consider a square region with conducting boundaries (Fig. 6.9). The potential of the top is 100 V and that of the sides and bottom is zero. The problem is two-dimensional, and the sketch is a cross section of the physical configuration. The region is divided first into 16 squares, and some estimate of the potential must now be made at every corner before applying the iterative method. These values could be obtained from a rough curvilinear-square map, but it is easier here to apply (1) to the large squares. At the center of the figure the potential estimate is then $\tfrac{1}{4}(100 + 0 + 0 + 0) = 25.0$.

FIG. 6.9 Cross section of a square trough with sides and bottom at zero potential and top at 100 V. The cross section has been divided into 16 squares, with the potential estimated at every corner. More accurate values may be determined by using the iteration method.

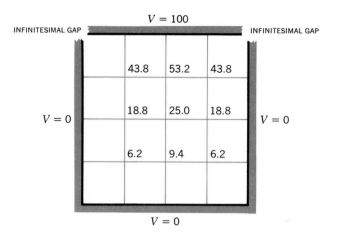

The potential may now be estimated at the centers of the four double-sized squares by taking the average of the potentials at the four corners, or applying (1) along a diagonal set of axes. Use of this "diagonal average" is made only in preparing initial estimates. For the two upper double squares, we select a potential of 50 V for the gap (the average of 0 and 100), and then $V = \frac{1}{4}(50 + 100 + 25 + 0) = 43.8$ (to the nearest tenth of a volt[1]), and for the lower ones,

$$V = \frac{1}{4}(0 + 25 + 0 + 0) = 6.2$$

The potential at the remaining four points may now be obtained by applying (1) directly. The complete set of estimated values is shown in Fig. 6.9.

The initial traverse is now made to obtain a corrected set of potentials, beginning in the upper left corner (with the 43.8 value, not with the boundary where the potentials are known and fixed), working across the row to the right, and then dropping down to the second row and proceeding from left to right again. Thus the 43.8 value changes to $\frac{1}{4}(100 + 53.2 + 18.8 + 0) = 43.0$. The best or newest potentials are always used when applying (1), so both points marked 43.8 are changed to 43.0, because of the evident

[1] When rounding off a decimal ending exactly with a 5, the preceding digit should be made *even;* e.g., 42.75 becomes 42.8 and 6.25 becomes 6.2. This generally ensures a random process leading to better accuracy than would be obtained by always increasing the previous digit by 1.

FIG. 6.10 The results of each of the four necessary traverses of the problem of Fig. 6.9 are shown in order in the columns. The final values, unchanged in the last traverse, are at the bottom of each column.

$$V = 100$$

	43.0 42.6 42.8 42.8	52.8 52.5 52.6 52.6	43.0 42.6 42.8 42.8	
$V = 0$	18.6 18.6 18.7 18.7	24.8 24.8 25.0 25.0	18.6 18.6 18.7 18.7	$V = 0$
	7.0 7.1 7.1 7.1	9.7 9.8 9.8 9.8	7.0 7.1 7.1 7.1	

$$V = 0$$

symmetry, and the 53.2 value becomes $\frac{1}{4}(100 + 43.0 + 25.0 + 43.0) = 52.8$.

Because of the symmetry, little would be gained by continuing across the top line. Each point of this line has now been improved once. Dropping down to the next line, the 18.8 value becomes

$$\frac{1}{4}(43.0 + 25.0 + 6.2 + 0) = 18.6$$

and the traverse is completed in this manner. The values at the end of this traverse are shown as the top numbers in each column of Fig. 6.10. Additional traverses must now be made until the value at each corner shows no change. The values for the successive traverses are usually entered below each other in column form, as shown in Fig. 6.10, and the final value is shown at the bottom of each column. Only four traverses are required in this example.

Since there is a large difference in potential from square to square, we should not expect our answers to be accurate to the tenth of a volt shown (and perhaps not to the nearest volt). Increased accuracy comes from dividing each square into four smaller squares, and not from finding the potential to a larger number of significant figures at each corner.

FIG. 6.11   The problem of Figs. 6.9 and 6.10 divided into smaller squares.   Values obtained on the nine successive traverses are listed in order in the columns.

$V = 100$

GAP

LINE OF SYMMETRY

$V = 0$ (left)

			LINE OF SYMMETRY	
48.2	66.2	73.8	75.0	73.8
	66.2	73.0	74.6	73.0
	66.0	72.8	74.7	72.8
	66.0	72.9	74.8	72.9
	66.0	73.0	74.8	73.0
	66.0		74.9	
	66.0			
	66.0			
	66.1			
48.2	66.1	73.0	74.9	73.0
26.6	42.8	51.0	52.6	51.0
26.6	42.9	50.8	53.2	50.8
26.8	43.0	50.9	53.4	50.9
26.9	43.0	51.0	53.4	51.0
	43.0	51.1	53.5	51.1
	43.0	51.1	53.6	51.1
	43.0	51.2		51.2
	43.1			
26.9	43.1	51.2	53.6	51.2
15.4	27.9	34.8	36.8	34.8
16.2	28.2	34.8	37.0	34.8
16.4		34.9	37.0	34.9
		34.9	37.0	34.9
		34.9	37.1	34.9
		35.0	37.2	35.0
16.4	28.2	35.0	37.2	35.0
10.1	18.7	23.4	25.0	23.4
10.4	18.4			
10.3				
10.3	18.4	23.4	25.0	23.4
6.4	11.8	15.2	16.3	15.2
6.5		15.2	16.3	15.2
		15.1	16.2	15.1
6.5	11.8	15.1	16.2	15.1
3.8	7.1	9.1	9.8	9.1
	7.0	9.0	9.7	9.0
3.8	7.0	9.0	9.7	9.0
1.8	3.3	4.2	4.6	4.2
	3.2		4.5	
1.8	3.2	4.2	4.5	4.2

$V = 0$

In Fig. 6.11, which shows only one of the symmetrical halves plus an additional column, this subdivision is accomplished, and the potential at the newly created corners is estimated by applying (1) directly where possible and diagonally when necessary. The set of estimated values appears at the top of each column, and the values produced by the successive traverses appear in order below. Here nine sets of values are required, and it might be noted that no values change on the last traverse (a necessary condition for the *last* traverse) and only one value changes on each of the preceding three traverses. No value in the bottom four rows changes after the second traverse; this results in a great saving in time, for if none of the four potentials in (1) changes, the answer is of course unchanged.

For this problem, it is possible to compare our final values with the exact potentials, obtained by evaluating some infinite series, as discussed at the end of the following chapter. At the point for which the original estimate was 53.2, the final value for the coarse grid was 52.6, the final value for the finer grid was 53.6, and the final value for a 16 × 16 grid (solved by digital computer, as suggested in Prob. 15 at the end of the chapter) is 53.93 V to two decimals, the exact potential obtained by a Fourier expansion is 54.05 V to two decimals. Two other points are also compared in tabular form, as shown in Table 6.1.

TABLE 6.1

Original estimate	53.2	25.0	9.4
4 × 4 grid	52.6	25.0	9.8
8 × 8 grid	53.6	25.0	9.7
16 × 16 grid	53.93	25.00	9.56
Exact	54.05	25.00	9.54

A refinement of the iteration method is known as the *relaxation method*. In general it requires less work but more care in carrying out the arithmetical steps.[1]

D 6.4 In Fig. 6.12 a square grid is shown in an irregular potential trough. Using the iteration method to find the potential to the nearest volt, determine the final value at

(a) Point a
(b) Point b
(c) Point c

Ans. 2; 41; 56 V

[1] A detailed description appears in Scarborough, and the basic procedure and one example are in Hayt. See the bibliography at the end of the chapter.

FIG. 6.12   See Prob. D6.4.

SUGGESTED REFERENCES

1   Hayt, W. H., Jr.: "Engineering Electromagnetics," McGraw-Hill Book Company, New York, 1958, pp. 150–152.

2   Moore, A. D.: Fields from Fluid Flow Mappers, *J. Appl. Phys.*, vol. 20, pp. 790–804, August, 1949; Soap Film and Sandbed Mapper Techniques, *J. Appl. Mech.* (bound with *Trans. ASME*), vol. 17, pp. 291–298, September, 1950; Four Electromagnetic Propositions, with Fluid Mapper Verifications, *Elec. Eng.*, vol. 69, pp. 607–610, July, 1950; The Further Development of Fluid Mappers, *Trans. AIEE*, vol. 69, part II, pp. 1615–1624, 1950; Mapping Techniques Applied to Fluid Mapper Patterns, *Trans. AIEE*, vol. 71, 1952.

3   Ramo, S., J. R. Whinnery, and T. Van Duzer: "Fields and Waves in Communication Electronics," John Wiley & Sons, Inc., New York, 1965. This book is essentially the third edition of the senior authors' popular texts of 1944 and 1953.   Although it is directed primarily toward beginning graduate students, it may be profitably read by anyone who is familiar with basic electromagnetic concepts.   Curvilinear maps are discussed on pp. 159–163.

4   Salvadori, M. G., and M. L. Baron: "Numerical Methods in Engineering," 2d ed., Prentice-Hall, Inc., Englewood Cliffs, N.J., 1961.   Iteration and relaxation methods are discussed in chap. 1.

5   Scarborough, J. B.: "Numerical Mathematical Analysis," 3d ed., The Johns Hopkins Press, Baltimore, 1955.   Describes iteration and relaxation methods and gives several complete examples. Inherent errors are discussed.

6   Soroka, W. W.: "Analog Methods in Computation and Simulation," McGraw-Hill Book Company, New York, 1954.

7   Spangenberg, K. R.: "Vacuum Tubes," McGraw-Hill Book Company, New York, 1948.   Experimental mapping methods are discussed on pp. 75–82.

8 Weber, E.: "Electromagnetic Fields," vol. I, John Wiley & Sons, Inc., New York, 1950. Experimental mapping methods are discussed in chap. 5.

PROBLEMS

1 Construct a curvilinear-square map for a coaxial capacitor of inner radius 3 cm and outer radius 10 cm. These dimensions are suitable for the drawing. As a check on the accuracy, compute the capacitance per meter both from your sketch and from the exact formula.

2 Construct a curvilinear-square map of the potential field about two parallel circular cylinders, each of 2-cm radius, separated a center-to-center distance of 20 cm. These dimensions are suitable for the actual sketch if symmetry is considered. As a check, compute the capacitance per meter both from your sketch and from the exact formula.

3 Construct a curvilinear-square map of the potential field between two parallel circular cylinders, one of 3-cm radius inside one of 10-cm radius. The two axes are displaced by 5 cm. These dimensions are suitable for the drawing. As a check on the accuracy, compute the capacitance per meter from the sketch and from the exact expression $C = 2\pi\epsilon/\cosh^{-1}\left[(a^2 + b^2 - D^2)/2ab\right]$ pF/m, where a and b are the conductor radii and D is the distance between axes.

4 A rectangular trough, similar to that shown in Fig. 6.9, has a width of 10 cm and a height of 8 cm. The potential of the top is 100 V and the sides and bottom are at zero potential. Construct a curvilinear-square plot of this potential field, noting the unfamiliar behavior of the field at the top corners. (For example, what is the potential in the center of the infinitesimal gap?) After the map is completed, estimate the potential at a point 2 cm from the top and 4 cm from the left side and compare with the exact value of 60.1 V.

5 Given an electrode having the shape of the hyperbolic cylinder $y^2 = x^2 + 9$, $y > 0$, at a potential of 100 V, and a second electrode in the form of a V-shaped cylindrical trough $y = |x|$ at zero potential, make a curvilinear-square map of the region between the two electrodes. Specifically, estimate the potential at $(0,2)$ and $(2,3)$.

6 An electrolytic tank is filled with tap water, and the resistance between the grid and cathode of a special mock-up of a new vacuum tube is measured as 1,250 Ω. The model is 50 times actual size. With a voltage of 12 V applied between grid and cathode, the maximum field strength measured in the water is 6 V/cm at the grid wires. The conductivity of the electrolyte is measured by filling a standard holder with it, measuring the resistance as 500 Ω, and knowing that the holder has a capacitance in air of 200 pF. (*a*) What is the grid-to-cathode capacitance of the model? (*b*) What will it be for the actual tube? (*c*) What will the maximum electric field intensity be at the grid in the actual vacuum tube with a grid-to-cathode voltage of 5 V?

7 (*a*) The region between the plates in a parallel-plate capacitor is half air and half barium titanate with $\epsilon_R = 5,000$. The interface is normal to the plates. What percentage of the electric flux is confined to the high-dielectric-constant material? (*b*) In view of the answer to (*a*), it is obviously possible to make some simplifying assumptions in problems dealing with high-dielectric-constant materials. For example, take a 1-cm-diameter barium titanate rod which is 5 cm long and place electrodes on the two circular ends. The flux may be assumed to be all in the dielectric, and hence the device may be treated as a parallel-plate capacitor. Find the capacitance. (c) Now take a hollow barium titanate cylinder with radii of 1 and 2 cm and length of 3 cm, cut it in half along a diameter, and deposit silver electrodes on the two rectangular faces of one half. One method by which the capacitance may be determined, among several possible methods, is by using the current analogy and Sec. 6.3, Eq. (1). Do so. (As a little help, the form of $\mathbf{J}$ is given in Chap. 5, Prob. 10.) (d) As a variation of this technique, assume that the semiannulus is cut from a sheet of the resistance paper described in Prob. D6.3b and that contact is made by silver paint at the two straight edges. What resistance would be measured?

8 Subdivide the interior of the rectangular trough of Prob. 4 into a 2-cm grid and use the iteration method to determine the potential at these 12 points. The curvilinear-square map may be used to provide initial estimates.

9 The parallel-plane model of a triode has a cathode at the $y = 0$ plane, an anode at $y = 10$, and filamentary grid wires parallel to the anode and cathode at $(0,4)$, $(\pm 4,4)$, $(\pm 8,4)$, ... (a) Using one section of this periodic structure and a 2×2 grid, determine the potential values, given $V_{\text{cath}} = 0$, $V_{\text{anode}} = 100$, and $V_{\text{grid}} = -10$ V. (b) Repeat for a 1×1 grid and sketch the -5-, 0-, and 10-V equipotentials.

10 A strip transmission line consists of two 1-cm-wide parallel strips in air, with their flat sides separated by 1 cm. (a) If the (very poor) assumption is made that the cross section represents a parallel-plane capacitor whose plate dimensions are much greater than their separation, calculate the capacitance per meter. (b) If the potentials of the strips are selected as $+100$ and -100 V, make a curvilinear-square map. Note that the 0-V equipotential surface is a plane, and also note that one flux line leaves the center of each side of each strip and is forever straight. Therefore only one-quarter of the region need be mapped. (c) From the sketch calculate the capacitance per unit length.

11 In drawing a good curvilinear-square plot from the calculated results of the iteration method, some guide for the construction of flux lines is helpful. The numerical data may be used to indicate the direction of the flux lines. Refer to Fig. 6.8 and show that the slope of the flux line passing through the central point may be approximated by $dy/dx = (V_4 - V_2)/(V_3 - V_1)$. Moreover, show that the slope of the equipotential passing through that point is $(V_1 - V_3)/(V_4 - V_2)$.

12 Grid points near the sides of irregularly shaped conductors often present the problem of a nonuniform grid. (a) Refer to Fig. 6.13a and show that

$$V_0 = \frac{V_1}{(1 + h_1/h_3)(1 + h_1h_3/h_2h_4)} + \frac{V_2}{(1 + h_2/h_4)(1 + h_2h_4/h_3h_1)}$$

$$+ \frac{V_3}{(1 + h_3/h_1)(1 + h_3h_1/h_4h_2)} + \frac{V_4}{(1 + h_4/h_2)(1 + h_4h_2/h_1h_3)}$$

(b) Determine V_0 in Fig. 6.13b.

FIG. 6.13 See Prob. 12.

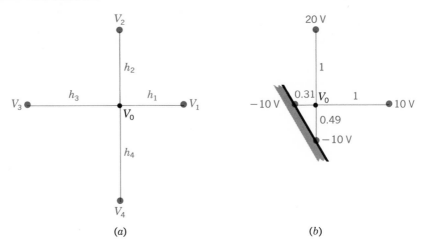

(a)   (b)

13 (a) Use the iteration method to determine the potential at each of the 10 marked points in Fig. 6.14a. Work to the nearest volt. (b) The square corner is rounded with a 90° circular arc with a radius of two units, as shown in Fig. 6.14b. Recompute the 10 potential values, using the equation given in Prob. 12a where necessary.

14 In Fig. 6.15 a region bounded by the planes $x = 0$, $x = 2$, $y = 0$, and $y = 1$ has the potential specified at intervals on the boundary, except for that portion of the plane $y = 0$ from $x = 0$ to $x = 1$. However, $y = 0$ is a plane of symmetry, and the potentials below it are the same as those above. Use an iterative procedure to obtain the potential values at the marked points,

FIG. 6.14 See Prob. 13.

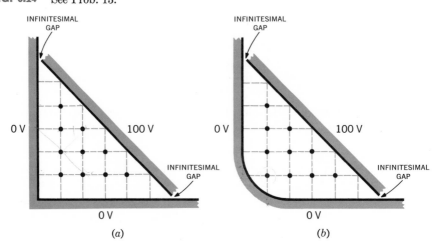

(a)   (b)

FIG. 6.15   See Prob. 14.

	89	78	68	58	50	42	38	33

CONDUCTING
PLANE
$V = 100$ V

× × × × × × ×   26

b c
× × × × × × ×   18

× × × × × × ×   9

y

a
x × × ×

$x = 1$

$y = 0$ CONDUCTING PLANE
$V = 0$

× × ×

working to the nearest volt. After you have completed the iteration, check your results at points a, b, and c by solving these equations for the potentials at those points: $a = 2c + 2$, $3c = b + 20$, and $2a + c = 2b + 14$.

15   The example presented in Sec. 6.5 to illustrate the iteration method used a 16-square mesh first, and then a 64-square mesh. Repeat for a 256-square mesh, finding the potentials to the nearest $1/100$ V. (It is suggested that a digital computer be used.) Compare these results with the exact values tabulated at the end of that section.

16   In the Scarborough text (see the bibliography above) eq. (9), on p. 324, gives a close approximation to the true value of the potential at a grid point when the iteration method has been applied twice, the second time for a grid spacing half that of the initial solution. Apply this equation to the three tabulated points for our example in Sec. 6.5 and compare the new approximate values with the exact values.

17   With reference to the article by C. Weber, Calculations of Potential Fields and Electron Trajectories Using an Electronic Computer, *Phillips Tech. Rev.*, vol. 24, nos. 4/5, p. 130, April, 1963, derive eq. (9) from Laplace's equation in cylindrical coordinates. Note the fairly obvious error in this equation.

7 POISSON'S AND LAPLACE'S EQUATIONS

A study of the previous chapter shows that several of the analogies used to obtain experimental field maps involved demonstrating that the analogous quantity satisfies Laplace's equation. This is true for small deflections of an elastic membrane and the flow of a fluid in a thin layer, and we might have proved the current analogy by showing that the d-c density in a conducting medium also satisfies Laplace's equation. It appears that this is a fundamental equation in more than one field of science, and it also is apparent that without our knowledge we have spent this last chapter in obtaining solutions for it by experimental, graphical, and numerical methods. This is quite true. Now we are ready to obtain this equation formally and discuss several methods by which it may be solved rigorously.

It may seem that this material properly belongs before that of the previous chapter; as long as we are solving one equation by so many methods, would it not be fitting to see the equation first? The disadvantage of this more logical order lies in the fact that solving Laplace's equation is an exercise in mathematics, and unless we have the physical problem well in mind, we may easily miss completely the physical significance of what we are doing. A rough curvilinear map can tell us much about a field and then may be used later to check our mathematical solutions for gross errors or to indicate certain peculiar regions in the field which require special treatment.

With this explanation let us finally obtain the equations of Laplace and Poisson.

7.1 POISSON'S AND LAPLACE'S EQUATIONS

Obtaining Poisson's equation is exceedingly simple, for from the point form of Gauss's law,

$$(1) \quad \nabla \cdot \mathbf{D} = \rho$$

the definition of $\mathbf{D}$,

$$(2) \quad \mathbf{D} = \epsilon \mathbf{E}$$

and the gradient relationship,

$$(3) \quad \mathbf{E} = -\nabla V$$

by substitution we have

$$\nabla \cdot \mathbf{D} = \nabla \cdot (\epsilon \mathbf{E}) = -\nabla \cdot (\epsilon \nabla V) = \rho$$

or

(4) $\quad \nabla \cdot \nabla V = -\dfrac{\rho}{\epsilon}$

for ϵ constant.

Equation (4) is *Poisson's equation,* but the "double ∇" operation must be interpreted and expanded, at least in cartesian coordinates, before the equation can be useful. In cartesian coordinates,

$$\nabla \cdot \mathbf{A} = \frac{\partial A_x}{\partial x} + \frac{\partial A_y}{\partial y} + \frac{\partial A_z}{\partial z}$$

$$\nabla V = \frac{\partial V}{\partial x}\, \mathbf{a}_x + \frac{\partial V}{\partial y}\, \mathbf{a}_y + \frac{\partial V}{\partial z}\, \mathbf{a}_z$$

and therefore

(5) $\quad \nabla \cdot \nabla V = \dfrac{\partial}{\partial x}\left(\dfrac{\partial V}{\partial x}\right) + \dfrac{\partial}{\partial y}\left(\dfrac{\partial V}{\partial y}\right) + \dfrac{\partial}{\partial z}\left(\dfrac{\partial V}{\partial z}\right)$

$$= \frac{\partial^2 V}{\partial x^2} + \frac{\partial^2 V}{\partial y^2} + \frac{\partial^2 V}{\partial z^2}$$

Usually the operation $\nabla \cdot \nabla$ is abbreviated ∇^2 (and pronounced "del squared"), a good reminder of the second-order partial derivatives appearing in (5), and we have

(6) $\quad \boxed{\nabla^2 V = \dfrac{\partial^2 V}{\partial x^2} + \dfrac{\partial^2 V}{\partial y^2} + \dfrac{\partial^2 V}{\partial z^2} = -\dfrac{\rho}{\epsilon}}$

in cartesian coordinates.

If $\rho = 0$, indicating zero *volume* charge density but allowing point charges, line charge, and surface charge density to exist on the boundaries as sources of the field, then

(7) $\quad \boxed{\nabla^2 V = 0}$

which is *Laplace's equation.* The ∇^2 operation is called the *Laplacian of V.*

In cartesian coordinates Laplace's equation is

(8) $\quad \boxed{\nabla^2 V = \dfrac{\partial^2 V}{\partial x^2} + \dfrac{\partial^2 V}{\partial y^2} + \dfrac{\partial^2 V}{\partial z^2} = 0}$

and the form of $\nabla^2 V$ in cylindrical and spherical coordinates may be obtained by using the expressions for the divergence and gradient already obtained in those coordinate systems. For reference, the Laplacian in cylindrical coordinates is

$$(9) \qquad \boxed{\nabla^2 V = \frac{1}{r}\frac{\partial}{\partial r}\left(r\frac{\partial V}{\partial r}\right) + \frac{1}{r^2}\left(\frac{\partial^2 V}{\partial \phi^2}\right) + \frac{\partial^2 V}{\partial z^2} \qquad \text{(cylindrical)}}$$

and in spherical coordinates is

$$(10) \qquad \boxed{\begin{aligned} \nabla^2 V = {} & \frac{1}{r^2}\frac{\partial}{\partial r}\left(r^2\frac{\partial V}{\partial r}\right) + \frac{1}{r^2\sin\theta}\frac{\partial}{\partial\theta}\left(\sin\theta\frac{\partial V}{\partial\theta}\right) \\ & + \frac{1}{r^2\sin^2\theta}\frac{\partial^2 V}{\partial\phi^2} \qquad \text{(spherical)} \end{aligned}}$$

These equations may be expanded by taking the indicated partial derivatives, but it is usually more helpful to have them in the forms given above. Furthermore, it is much easier to expand them later if necessary than it is to put the broken pieces back together again.

Laplace's equation is all-embracing, for, applying as it does wherever volume charge density is zero, it states that every conceivable configuration of electrodes or conductors produces a field for which $\nabla^2 V = 0$. All these fields are different, with different potential values and different spatial rates of change, yet for each of them $\nabla^2 V = 0$. Since *every* field (if $\rho = 0$) satisfies Laplace's equation, how can we expect to reverse the procedure and use Laplace's equation to find one specific field in which we happen to have an interest? Obviously, more information is required, and we shall find that we must solve Laplace's equation subject to certain *boundary conditions*.

Every physical problem must contain at least one conducting boundary and usually contains two or more. The potentials on these boundaries are assigned values, perhaps V_0, V_1, ... , or perhaps numerical values. These definite equipotential surfaces will provide the boundary conditions for the type of problem to be solved in this chapter.

Before using Laplace's equation or Poisson's equation in several examples, we must first pause to show that if our answer satisfies Laplace's equation and also satisfies the boundary conditions, then it is the only possible answer. It would be very distressing to work a problem by solving Laplace's equation with two different approved methods and then to obtain two different answers. We shall show that the two answers must be identical.

D 7.1 In each of the following potential functions find the most general expression for the constant b that will force V to satisfy Laplace's equation for all x, y, and z:

   (a) $V = (a^2 + k^2)e^{bx}$
   (b) $V = ke^{bx} \sin ay + 2ke^{bx} \cos ay$
   (c) $V = Ae^{ax}e^{ky} \sin bz$

Ans. $\pm a;\, 0;\, \pm \sqrt{a^2 + k^2}$

D 7.2 Given the following potential functions in spherical coordinates, find the volume charge density associated with each:

   (a) $V = A \sin \theta \sin \phi / r^2$
   (b) $V = Ar$
   (c) $V = A\phi$

Ans. $0;\, 0;\, -2A\epsilon/r$ C/m^3

7.2 UNIQUENESS THEOREM

Let us assume that we have two solutions of Laplace's equation, V_1 and V_2, both general functions of the coordinates used. Therefore

$$\nabla^2 V_1 = 0$$

and

$$\nabla^2 V_2 = 0$$

from which

$$\nabla^2 (V_1 - V_2) = 0$$

Each solution must also satisfy the boundary conditions, and if we represent the given potential values on the boundaries by V_b, then the value of V_1 on the boundary V_{1b} and the value of V_2 on the boundary V_{2b} must both be identical to V_b,

$$V_{1b} = V_{2b} = V_b$$

or

$$V_{1b} - V_{2b} = 0$$

In Sec. 4.8, Eq. (5), we made use of a vector identity,

$$\nabla \cdot (V\mathbf{D}) \equiv V(\nabla \cdot \mathbf{D}) + \mathbf{D} \cdot (\nabla V)$$

which holds for any scalar V and any vector $\mathbf{D}$. For the present application we shall select $V_1 - V_2$ as the scalar and $\nabla(V_1 - V_2)$ as the vector, giving

$$\nabla \cdot [(V_1 - V_2) \nabla(V_1 - V_2)]$$
$$\equiv (V_1 - V_2)[\nabla \cdot \nabla(V_1 - V_2)] + \nabla(V_1 - V_2) \cdot \nabla(V_1 - V_2)$$

which we shall integrate throughout the volume *enclosed* by the boundary surfaces specified:

(1)
$$\int_{vol} \boldsymbol{\nabla} \cdot [(V_1 - V_2)\boldsymbol{\nabla}(V_1 - V_2)]\, dv$$

$$\equiv \int_{vol} (V_1 - V_2)[\boldsymbol{\nabla} \cdot \boldsymbol{\nabla}(V_1 - V_2)]\, dv + \int_{vol} [\boldsymbol{\nabla}(V_1 - V_2)]^2\, dv$$

The divergence theorem allows us to replace the volume integral on the left side of the equation by the closed surface integral over the surface surrounding the volume. This surface consists of the boundaries already specified on which $V_{1b} = V_{2b}$, and therefore

$$\int_{vol} \boldsymbol{\nabla} \cdot [(V_1 - V_2)\boldsymbol{\nabla}(V_1 - V_2)]\, dv$$

$$= \oint_s [(V_{1b} - V_{2b})\boldsymbol{\nabla}(V_{1b} - V_{2b})] \cdot d\mathbf{S} = 0$$

One of the factors of the first integral on the right side of (1) is $\boldsymbol{\nabla} \cdot \boldsymbol{\nabla}(V_1 - V_2)$, or $\boldsymbol{\nabla}^2(V_1 - V_2)$, which is zero by hypothesis, and therefore that integral is zero. Hence the remaining volume integral must be zero:

$$\int_{vol} [\boldsymbol{\nabla}(V_1 - V_2)]^2\, dv = 0$$

There are in general two reasons why an integral may be zero: either the integrand (the quantity under the integral sign) is everywhere zero, or the integrand is positive in some regions, negative in others, and the contributions cancel algebraically. In this case the first reason must hold because $[\boldsymbol{\nabla}(V_1 - V_2)]^2$ cannot be negative. Therefore

$$[\boldsymbol{\nabla}(V_1 - V_2)]^2 = 0$$

and

$$\boldsymbol{\nabla}(V_1 - V_2) = 0$$

Finally, if the gradient of $V_1 - V_2$ is everywhere zero, then $V_1 - V_2$ cannot change with any coordinates and

$$V_1 - V_2 = \text{constant}$$

If we can show that this constant is zero, we shall have accomplished our proof. The constant is easily evaluated by considering a point on the boundary. Here $V_1 - V_2 = V_{1b} - V_{2b} = 0$, and we see that the constant is indeed zero, and therefore

$$V_1 = V_2$$

giving two identical solutions.

The uniqueness theorem also applies to Poisson's equation, for if $\nabla^2 V_1 = -\rho/\epsilon$ and $\nabla^2 V_2 = -\rho/\epsilon$, then $\nabla^2(V_1 - V_2) = 0$ as before. Boundary conditions still require that $V_{1b} - V_{2b} = 0$, and the proof is identical from this point.

This constitutes the proof of the uniqueness theorem. Viewed as the answer to a question, "How do two solutions of Laplace's or Poisson's equation compare if they both satisfy the same boundary conditions?" the uniqueness theorem should please us by its assurance that the answers are identical. Once we can find any method of solving Laplace's or Poisson's equation subject to given boundary conditions, we have solved our problem once and for all. No other method can ever give a different answer.

D 7.3 If V_1 and V_2 are each solutions to Laplace's equation and each satisfies the boundary conditions of the particular problem,

(a) Does $V_1 + V_2$ satisfy Laplace's equation?
(b) Does $V_1 + V_2$ satisfy the boundary conditions?
(c) Is $V_1 = V_2$?

Ans. No; yes; yes

7.3 EXAMPLES OF THE SOLUTION OF LAPLACE'S EQUATION

Several methods have been developed for solving the second-order partial differential equation known as Laplace's equation. The first and simplest method is that of direct integration, and we shall use this technique to work several examples in various coordinate systems in this section. In Sec. 7.5 one other method will be used on a more difficult problem. Additional methods, requiring a more advanced mathematical knowledge, are described in the references given at the end of the chapter.

The method of direct integration is applicable only to problems which are "one-dimensional," or in which the potential field is a function of only one of the three coordinates. Since we are working with only three coordinate systems, it might seem, then, that there are nine problems to be solved, but a little reflection will show that a field which varies only with x is fundamentally the same as a field which varies only with y. Rotating the physical problem a quarter turn is no change. Actually, there are only five problems to be solved, one in cartesian coordinates, two in cylindrical, and two in spherical. We shall solve them all.

Example 1   Let us assume that V is a function only of x and worry later about which physical problem we are solving when we have a need for boundary conditions. Laplace's equation reduces to

$$\frac{\partial^2 V}{\partial x^2} = 0$$

and the partial derivative may be replaced by an ordinary derivative, since y and z are not involved,

$$\frac{d^2 V}{dx^2} = 0$$

We integrate twice, obtaining

$$\frac{dV}{dx} = A$$

and

(1) $V = Ax + B$

where A and B are constants of integration. Equation (1) contains two such constants, as we should expect for a second-order differential equation. These constants can be determined only from the boundary conditions.

What boundary conditions should we supply? They are our choice, since no physical problem has yet been specified, with the exception of the original hypothesis that the potential varied only with x. We should now attempt to visualize such a field. Most of us probably already have the answer, but it may be obtained by exact methods.

Since the field varies only with x and is not a function of y and z, if x is a constant, then V is a constant, or in other words, the equipotential surfaces are described by setting x constant. These surfaces are parallel planes normal to the x axis. The field is thus that of a parallel-plate capacitor, and as soon as we specify the potential on any two planes we may evaluate our constants of integration.

To be very general, let $V = V_1$ at $x = x_1$ and $V = V_2$ at $x = x_2$. These values are then substituted into (1), giving

$$V_1 = Ax_1 + B \qquad V_2 = Ax_2 + B$$

$$A = \frac{V_1 - V_2}{x_1 - x_2} \qquad B = \frac{V_2 x_1 - V_1 x_2}{x_1 - x_2}$$

and

(2) $$V = \frac{V_1(x - x_2) - V_2(x - x_1)}{x_1 - x_2}$$

A simpler answer would have been obtained by choosing simpler boundary conditions. If we had fixed $V = 0$ at $x = 0$ and $V = V_0$ at $x = d$, then

$$A = \frac{V_0}{d} \qquad B = 0$$

and

(3)
$$\boxed{V = \frac{V_0 x}{d}}$$

Suppose our primary aim is to find the capacitance of a parallel-plate capacitor. We have solved Laplace's equation, obtaining (1) with the two constants A and B. Should they be evaluated or left alone? Presumably we are not interested in the potential field itself, but only in the capacitance, and we may continue successfully with A and B or we may simplify the algebra by a little foresight. Capacitance is given by the ratio of charge to potential difference, so we may choose now the potential *difference* as V_0, which is equivalent to one boundary condition, and then choose whatever second boundary condition seems to help the form of the equation the most. This is the essence of the second set of boundary conditions which produced (3). The potential difference was fixed as V_0 by choosing the potential of one plate zero and the other V_0; the location of these plates was made as simple as possible by letting $V = 0$ at $x = 0$.

Using (3), then, we still need the total charge on either plate before the capacitance can be found. We should remember that when we first solved this capacitor problem in Chap. 5 the sheet of charge provided our starting point. We did not have to work very hard to find the charge, for all the fields were expressed in terms of it. The work then was spent in finding potential difference. Now the problem is reversed (and simplified).

The necessary steps are these after the choice of boundary conditions has been made:

1. Given V, use $\mathbf{E} = -\nabla V$ to find $\mathbf{E}$.
2. Use $\mathbf{D} = \epsilon \mathbf{E}$ to find $\mathbf{D}$.
3. Evaluate $\mathbf{D}$ at either capacitor plate, $\mathbf{D} = \mathbf{D}_s = D_n \mathbf{a}_n$.
4. Recognize that $\rho_s = D_n$.
5. Find Q by a surface integration over the capacitor plate,

$$Q = \int_s \rho_s \, dS$$

Here we have

$$V = V_0 \frac{x}{d}$$

$$\mathbf{E} = -\frac{V_0}{d} \mathbf{a}_x$$

$$\mathbf{D} = -\epsilon \frac{V_0}{d} \mathbf{a}_x$$

$$\mathbf{D}_s = \mathbf{D} \Big|_{x=0} = -\epsilon \frac{V_0}{d} \mathbf{a}_x$$

$$\mathbf{a}_n = \mathbf{a}_x$$

$$D_n = -\epsilon \frac{V_0}{d} = \rho_s$$

$$Q = \int_s \frac{-\epsilon V_0}{d} dS = -\epsilon \frac{V_0 S}{d}$$

and the capacitance is

$$\boxed{C = \frac{|Q|}{V_0} = \frac{\epsilon S}{d}}$$

We shall use this procedure several times in the examples to follow.

Example 2   Since no new problems are solved by choosing fields which vary only with y or with z in cartesian coordinates, we pass on to cylindrical coordinates for our next example. Variations with respect to z are again nothing new, and we finally assume variation with respect to r only. Laplace's equation becomes

$$\frac{1}{r} \frac{\partial}{\partial r} \left(r \frac{\partial V}{\partial r} \right) = 0$$

or

$$\frac{1}{r} \frac{d}{dr} \left(r \frac{dV}{dr} \right) = 0$$

We may multiply by r and then integrate,

$$r \frac{dV}{dr} = A$$

rearrange, and integrate again,

(4) $V = A \ln r + B$

The equipotential surfaces are given by $r = $ constant and are cylinders, and the problem is that of the coaxial capacitor or coaxial transmission line. We choose a potential difference of V_0 by letting $V = V_0$ at $r = a$, $V = 0$ at $r = b$, $b > a$, and obtain

$$V = V_0 \frac{\ln (b/r)}{\ln (b/a)}$$

from which

$$E = \frac{V_0}{r} \frac{1}{\ln (b/a)} \mathbf{a}_r$$

$$D_{n(r=a)} = \frac{\epsilon V_0}{a \ln (b/a)}$$

$$Q = \frac{\epsilon V_0 2\pi a L}{a \ln (b/a)}$$

$$C = \frac{2\pi\epsilon L}{\ln (b/a)}$$

Example 3   Now let us assume that V is a function only of ϕ in cylindrical coordinates. We might look at the physical problem first for a change and see that equipotential surfaces are given by $\phi = $ constant. These are radial planes. Boundary conditions might be $V = 0$ at $\phi = 0$ and $V = V_0$ at $\phi = \alpha$, leading to the physical problem detailed in Fig. 7.1.

Laplace's equation is now

$$\frac{1}{r^2} \frac{\partial^2 V}{\partial \phi^2} = 0$$

or

$$\frac{d^2 V}{d\phi^2} = 0$$

from which we have

$$V = A\phi + B$$

FIG. 7.1 Two infinite radial planes with an interior angle α. An infinitesimal insulating gap exists at $r = 0$. The potential field may be found by applying Laplace's equation in cylindrical coordinates.

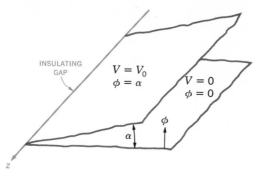

The boundary conditions determine A and B, and

(5)
$$V = V_0 \frac{\phi}{\alpha}$$

Taking the gradient of (5) produces the electric field intensity,

$$\mathbf{E} = -\frac{V_0 \mathbf{a}_\phi}{\alpha r}$$

and it is interesting to note that E is a function of r and not of ϕ. This does not contradict our original assumptions, which were restrictions only on the potential field. Note, however, that the vector field $\mathbf{E}$ is a function of ϕ.

A problem involving the capacitance of these two radial planes is included at the end of the chapter.

Example 4 We now turn to spherical coordinates, dispose immediately of variations with respect to ϕ only as having just been solved, and treat first $V = V(r)$.

The details are left for a problem later, but the final potential field is given by

(6)
$$V = V_0 \frac{1/r - 1/b}{1/a - 1/b}$$

where the boundary conditions are evidently $V = 0$ at $r = b$ and $V = V_0$ at $r = a$, $b > a$. The problem is that of concentric spheres.

The capacitance has been found previously (by a somewhat different method) and is

$$C = \frac{4\pi\epsilon}{1/a - 1/b}$$

Example 5   In spherical coordinates we now restrict the potential function to $V = V(\theta)$, obtaining

$$\frac{1}{r^2 \sin \theta} \frac{d}{d\theta} \left(\sin \theta \frac{dV}{d\theta} \right) = 0$$

from which

$$\sin \theta \frac{dV}{d\theta} = A$$

The second integral is then

$$V = \int \frac{A \, d\theta}{\sin \theta} + B$$

which is not as obvious as the previous ones.   From integral tables (or a good memory) we have

$$V = A \ln (\tan \theta/2) + B$$

The equipotential surfaces are cones, and if $V = 0$ at $\theta = \pi/2$ and $V = V_0$ at $\theta = \alpha$, $\alpha < \pi/2$, then

(7)
$$V = V_0 \frac{\ln (\tan \theta/2)}{\ln (\tan \alpha/2)}$$

In order to find the capacitance between a conducting cone with its vertex separated from a conducting plane by an infinitesimal insulating gap and its axis normal to the plane, let us first find the field strength:

$$\mathbf{E} = -\nabla V = -\frac{1}{r} \frac{\partial V}{\partial \theta} \mathbf{a}_\theta = -\frac{V_0}{r \sin \theta \ln (\tan \alpha/2)} \mathbf{a}_\theta$$

The surface charge density on the cone is then

$$\rho_s = \frac{-\epsilon V_0}{r \sin \alpha \ln (\tan \alpha/2)}$$

producing a total charge Q,

$$Q = \frac{-\epsilon V_0}{\sin \alpha \ln (\tan \alpha/2)} \int_0^\infty \int_0^{2\pi} \frac{r \sin \alpha \, d\phi \, dr}{r}$$

This leads to an infinite value of charge and capacitance, and it becomes necessary to consider a cone of finite size. Our answer will now be only an approximation, because the theoretical equipotential surface is $\theta = \alpha$, a conical surface extending from $r = 0$ to $r = \infty$, whereas our physical conical surface extends only from $r = 0$, to, say, $r = r_1$. The approximate capacitance is

$$C \doteq \frac{2\pi\epsilon r_1}{\ln(\cot\alpha/2)}$$

If we desire a more accurate answer we may make an estimate of the capacitance of the base of the cone, a circular plate of radius r_1, to the zero potential plane and add this amount to our answer above. Fringing, or nonuniform, fields in this region have been neglected and introduce an additional source of error.

D 7.4 Find the potential difference between these two conductors in air if the electric field intensity has the specified value:

(a) Radial planes at $\phi = \pi/6$ and $\pi/4$, extending from $r = 0.002$ to 0.5 m and from $z = 0$ to 1 m, $E_\phi = 250$ V/m at $r = 0.2$ m, $\phi = \pi/5$
(b) Concentric cylinders at $r = 0.002$ and 0.015 m, extending from $z = 0$ to 1 m, $E_r = 250$ V/m at $r = 0.01$ m
(c) Coaxial cones at $\theta = \pi/6$ and $\pi/4$, extending from $r = 0$ to 0.5 m, $E_\theta = 250$ V/m at $r = 0.2$ m, $\theta = \pi/5$

Ans. 5.04; 12.8; 13.09 V

D 7.5 Find the total energy stored in the electric field of each of the conductor configurations described in Prob. D7.4. Neglect fringing.

Ans. 3.49×10^{-10}; 52.3×10^{-10}; 160×10^{-10} J

7.4 EXAMPLE OF THE SOLUTION OF POISSON'S EQUATION

In order to select a reasonably simple problem which might illustrate the application of Poisson's equation we shall have to assume that the volume charge density is specified. This is not usually the case, however; in fact, it is often the quantity about which we are seeking further information. The type of problem which we might encounter later would begin with a knowledge only of the boundary values of the potential, the electric field intensity, and the current density. From these we would have to apply Poisson's equation, the continuity equation, and some relationship expressing the forces on the charged particles, such as the Lorentz force equation or the diffusion equation, and solve the whole system of equations simultaneously. Such an ordeal is beyond the scope of this text, and we shall therefore assume a reasonably large amount of information.

As an example, let us select a *pn* junction between two halves of a semiconductor bar extending in the x direction. We shall assume that the region for $x < 0$ is doped p type and that the region for $x > 0$ is n type. The degree of doping is identical on each side of the junction. To review qualitatively some of the facts about the semiconductor junction, we note that initially there is an excess of holes to the left of the junction and an excess of electrons to the right. Each diffuses across the junction until an electric field is built up in such a direction that the diffusion current drops to zero. Thus, in order to prevent more holes from moving to the right, the electric field in the neighborhood of the junction must be directed to the left; E_x is negative there. This field must be produced by a net positive charge to the right of the junction and a net negative charge to the left. Note that the layer of positive charge consists of two parts, the holes which have crossed the junction and the positive donor ions from which the electrons have departed. The negative layer of charge is constituted in the opposite manner by electrons and negative acceptor ions. The net volume charge density is *not* zero near the junction.

The type of charge distribution which results is shown in Fig. 7.2a, and the negative field which it produces is shown in Fig. 7.2b. After looking at these two figures, the previous paragraph might be read again profitably.

A charge distribution of this form may be approximated by many different expressions. One of these is

(1) $$\rho = 2\rho_0 \operatorname{sech} \frac{x}{a} \tanh \frac{x}{a}$$

which has a maximum charge density $\rho_{max} = \rho_0$ that occurs at $x = 0.881a$. The maximum charge density ρ_0 may be related to other familiar semiconductor parameters by noting that the electrons and holes have essentially all been removed from the donor and acceptor ions in this region (the *depletion* layer), and thus

$$\rho_0 = eN_a = eN_d$$

where N_a and N_d are the acceptor and donor concentrations, respectively, in meters^{-3}, and e is the electronic charge.

Let us now solve Poisson's equation,

$$\nabla^2 V = -\frac{\rho}{\epsilon}$$

subject to the charge distribution assumed above,

$$\frac{d^2 V}{dx^2} = -\frac{2\rho_0}{\epsilon} \operatorname{sech} \frac{x}{a} \tanh \frac{x}{a}$$

Example of the Solution of Poisson's Equation   191

FIG. 7.2 (a) The charge density, (b) the electric field intensity, and (c) the potential are plotted for a *pn* junction as functions of distance from the center of the junction. The *p*-type material is on the left, and the *n*-type is on the right.

(a)

(b)

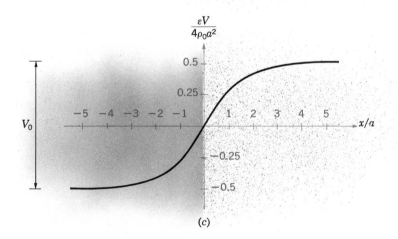

(c)

in this one-dimensional problem in which variations with y and z are not present. We integrate once,

$$\frac{dV}{dx} = \frac{2\rho_0 a}{\epsilon} \operatorname{sech} \frac{x}{a} + C_1$$

and obtain the electric field intensity,

$$E_x = -\frac{2\rho_0 a}{\epsilon} \operatorname{sech} \frac{x}{a} - C_1$$

We might pause to evaluate the constant of integration C_1 by noting that no net charge density and no fields can exist *far* from the junction. Thus, as $x \to \pm\infty$, E_x must approach zero. Therefore $C_1 = 0$, and

$$(2) \quad E_x = -\frac{2\rho_0 a}{\epsilon} \operatorname{sech} \frac{x}{a}$$

Integrating again,

$$V = \frac{4\rho_0 a^2}{\epsilon} \tan^{-1} e^{x/a} + C_2$$

Let us arbitrarily select our zero reference of potential at the center of the junction, $x = 0$,

$$0 = \frac{4\rho_0 a^2}{\epsilon} \frac{\pi}{4} + C_2$$

and finally,

$$(3) \quad V = \frac{4\rho_0 a^2}{\epsilon} \left(\tan^{-1} e^{x/a} - \frac{\pi}{4} \right)$$

Fig. 7.2 shows the charge distribution, electric field intensity, and the potential, as given by (1), (2), and (3), respectively.

The potential is constant once we are a distance of about $4a$ or $5a$ from the junction. The total potential difference V_0 across the junction is obtained from (3),

$$(4) \quad V_0 = \frac{2\pi\rho_0 a^2}{\epsilon}$$

This expression suggests the possibility of determining the total charge on one side of the junction and then using (4) to find a junction capacitance. The total positive charge is

$$Q = S \int_0^\infty 2\rho_0 \operatorname{sech} \frac{x}{a} \tanh \frac{x}{a} \, dx = 2\rho_0 a S$$

Example of the Solution of Poisson's Equation   193

where S is the area of the junction cross section. If we make use of (4) to eliminate the distance parameter a, the charge becomes

$$(5) \quad Q = S \sqrt{\frac{2\rho_0 \epsilon V_0}{\pi}}$$

Since the total charge is a function of the potential difference, we have to be careful in defining a capacitance. Thinking in "circuit" terms for a moment,

$$I = \frac{dQ}{dt} = C\frac{dV_0}{dt}$$

and thus

$$C = \frac{dQ}{dV_0}$$

By differentiating (5) we therefore have the capacitance,

$$(6) \quad C = \sqrt{\frac{\rho_0 \epsilon}{2\pi V_0}}\, S = \frac{\epsilon S}{2\pi a}$$

The first form of (6) shows that the capacitance varies inversely as the square root of the voltage; the higher the voltage, the greater the separation of the charge layers, and the smaller the capacitance. The second form is interesting in that it indicates that we may think of the junction as a parallel-plate capacitor with a "plate" separation of $2\pi a$. In view of the dimensions of the region in which the charge is concentrated, this is a logical result.

Poisson's equation enters into any problem involving volume charge density. Besides semiconductor diode and transistor models, vacuum tubes, magnetohydrodynamic energy conversion, and ion propulsion require its use in constructing satisfactory theories.

D 7.6 Assume that a germanium-junction diode has a circular cross section at the junction with a radius of 0.1 mm, donor and acceptor concentrations of 10^{21} atoms/m^3, a potential difference of 4 V across the junction, and a relative dielectric constant of 16.

(a) Find the junction capacitance.
(b) Increase V_0 to 8 V and find the capacitance.
(c) With $V_0 = 4$ V, increase the doping to 2×10^{21} atoms/m^3 (more heavily doped) and find C.

Ans.   0.666; 0.943; 1.33 pF

D 7.7   If V is known to be a function of x only, find V, given

(a) $\rho = a\rho_0$

(b) $\rho = \dfrac{\rho_0 x}{a}$

(c) $\rho = \dfrac{\rho_0 a}{x}$

Ans. $-\dfrac{\rho_0 x^3}{6a\epsilon} + Ax + B;\ -\dfrac{a\rho_0 x^2}{2\epsilon} + Ax + B;\ -\dfrac{a\rho_0 x}{\epsilon}\ln x + Ax + B$ V

7.5   PRODUCT SOLUTION OF LAPLACE'S EQUATION

In this section we are confronted with the class of potential fields which vary with more than one of the three coordinates, and in particular, the three cartesian coordinates. Although our examples are taken in this simplest coordinate system, the general method is applicable to the other coordinate systems. We shall avoid these applications because the potential fields are given in terms of more advanced mathematical functions, such as Bessel functions and spherical and cylindrical harmonics, and our interest now does not lie with new mathematical functions but with the techniques and methods of solving electrostatic field problems.

We may provide ourselves with a general class of problems by specifying merely that the potential is a function of x and y alone, so that

(1) $\dfrac{\partial^2 V}{\partial x^2} + \dfrac{\partial^2 V}{\partial y^2} = 0$

We now assume that the potential is expressible as the *product* of a function of x alone and a function of y alone. It might seem that this prohibits too many solutions, such as $V = x + y$, or any *sum* of a function of x and a function of y, but we should realize that Laplace's equation is linear and the sum of any two solutions is also a solution. We could treat $V = x + y$ as the sum of $V_1 = x$ and $V_2 = y$, where each of these latter potentials is now a (trivial) product solution.

Representing the function of x by X and the function of y by Y, we have

(2) $V = XY$

which is substituted into (1),

$$Y\frac{\partial^2 X}{\partial x^2} + X\frac{\partial^2 Y}{\partial y^2} = 0$$

Since X does not involve y and Y does not involve x, ordinary derivatives may be used,

(3) $\quad Y\dfrac{d^2X}{dx^2} + X\dfrac{d^2Y}{dy^2} = 0$

Equation (3) may be solved by separating the variables through division by XY, giving

$$\frac{1}{X}\frac{d^2X}{dx^2} + \frac{1}{Y}\frac{d^2Y}{dy^2} = 0$$

or

$$\frac{1}{X}\frac{d^2X}{dx^2} = -\frac{1}{Y}\frac{d^2Y}{dy^2}$$

Now we need one of the cleverest arguments of mathematics: since $(1/X)d^2X/dx^2$ involves no y and $-(1/Y)d^2Y/dy^2$ involves no x, and since the two quantities are equal, then $(1/X)d^2X/dx^2$ cannot be a function of x either, and similarly, $-(1/Y)d^2Y/dy^2$ cannot be a function of y! In other words, we have shown that each of these terms must be a constant. For convenience, let us call this constant α^2

(4) $\quad \dfrac{1}{X}\dfrac{d^2X}{dx^2} = \alpha^2$

(5) $\quad -\dfrac{1}{Y}\dfrac{d^2Y}{dy^2} = \alpha^2$

The constant α^2 is called the *separation constant*, because its use results in separating one equation into two simpler equations.

Equation (4) may be written as

(6) $\quad \dfrac{d^2X}{dx^2} = \alpha^2 X$

and must now be solved. There are several methods by which a solution may be obtained. The first method is experience, or recognition, which becomes more powerful with practice. We are just beginning and can barely recognize Laplace's equation itself. The second method might be that of direct integration, when applicable, of course. Applying it here, we should write

$$d\left(\frac{dX}{dx}\right) = \alpha^2 X\, dx$$

$$\frac{dX}{dx} = \alpha^2 \int X\, dx$$

and then pass on to the next method, for X is some unknown function of x, and the method of integration is not applicable here. The third method we might describe as intuition, common sense, or inspection. It involves taking a good look at the equation, perhaps putting the operation into words. This method will work on (6) for some of us if we ask ourselves, "What function has a second derivative which has the same form as the function itself, except for multiplication by a constant?" The answer is the exponential function, of course, and we could go on from here to construct the solution. Instead, let us work with those of us whose intuition is suffering from exposure and apply a very powerful but long method, the infinite-power-series substitution.

We assume hopefully that X may be represented by

$$X = \sum_{n=0}^{\infty} a_n x^n$$

and substitute into (6), giving

$$\frac{d^2X}{dx^2} = \sum_0^{\infty} n(n-1) a_n x^{n-2} = \alpha^2 \sum_0^{\infty} a_n x^n$$

If these two different infinite series are to be equal for all x, they must be identical, and the coefficients of like powers of x equated term by term. Thus

$$2 \times 1 \times a_2 = \alpha^2 a_0$$

$$3 \times 2 \times a_3 = \alpha^2 a_1$$

and in general we have the recurrence relationship

$$(n+2)(n+1) a_{n+2} = \alpha^2 a_n$$

The even coefficients may be expressed in terms of a_0 as

$$a_2 = \frac{\alpha^2}{1 \times 2} a_0$$

$$a_4 = \frac{\alpha^2}{3 \times 4} a_2 = \frac{\alpha^4}{4!} a_0$$

$$a_6 = \frac{\alpha^6}{6!} a_0$$

and in general, for n even, as

$$a_n = \frac{\alpha^n}{n!} a_0 \qquad (n \text{ even})$$

For odd values of n, we have

$$a_3 = \frac{\alpha^2}{2 \times 3} a_1 = \frac{\alpha^3}{3!} \frac{a_1}{\alpha}$$

$$a_5 = \frac{\alpha^5}{5!} \frac{a_1}{\alpha}$$

and in general, for n odd,

$$a_n = \frac{\alpha^n}{n!} \frac{a_1}{\alpha} \qquad (n \text{ odd})$$

Substituting back into the original power series for X, we obtain

$$X = a_0 \sum_{0,\text{even}}^{\infty} \frac{\alpha^n}{n!} x^n + \frac{a_1}{\alpha} \sum_{1,\text{odd}}^{\infty} \frac{\alpha^n}{n!} x^n$$

or

$$X = a_0 \sum_{0,\text{even}}^{\infty} \frac{(\alpha x)^n}{n!} + \frac{a_1}{\alpha} \sum_{1,\text{odd}}^{\infty} \frac{(\alpha x)^n}{n!}$$

The sum of these two infinite series is the solution of the differential equation in x, although the form of the solution may be improved immeasurably by recognizing the first series as the hyperbolic cosine,

$$\cosh \alpha x = \sum_{0,\text{even}}^{\infty} \frac{(\alpha x)^n}{n!} = 1 + \frac{(\alpha x)^2}{2!} + \frac{(\alpha x)^4}{4!} + \cdots$$

and the second series as the hyperbolic sine,

$$\sinh \alpha x = \sum_{1,\text{odd}}^{\infty} \frac{(\alpha x)^n}{n!} = \alpha x + \frac{(\alpha x)^3}{3!} + \frac{(\alpha x)^5}{5!} + \cdots$$

The solution may therefore be written as

$$X = a_0 \cosh \alpha x + \frac{a_1}{\alpha} \sinh \alpha x$$

or

$$X = A \cosh \alpha x + B \sinh \alpha x$$

where the slightly simpler terms A and B have replaced a_0 and a_1/α and are the two constants which must be evaluated in terms of the boundary conditions. The separation constant is not an arbitrary constant as far as the solution of (6) is concerned, for it appears in that equation.

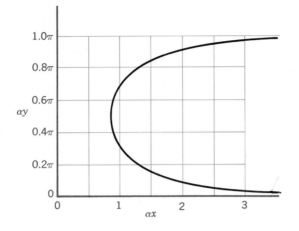

An alternate form of the solution is obtained by expressing the hyperbolic functions in terms of exponentials, collecting terms, and selecting new arbitrary constants, A' and B',

$$X = A'e^{\alpha x} + B'e^{-\alpha x}$$

The solution of (5) proceeds along similar lines, leading to two power series representing the sine and cosine, and we have

$$Y = C \cos \alpha y + D \sin \alpha y$$

from which the potential is

(7) $$V = XY = (A \cosh \alpha x + B \sinh \alpha x)(C \cos \alpha y + D \sin \alpha y)$$

Before describing a physical problem and forcing the constants appearing in (7) to fit the boundary conditions prescribed, let us consider the physical nature of the potential field given by a simple choice of these constants. Letting $A = 0$, $C = 0$, $BD = V_1$, we have

(8) $$V = V_1 \sinh \alpha x \sin \alpha y$$

The $\sinh \alpha x$ factor is zero at $x = 0$ and increases smoothly with x, soon becoming nearly exponential in form, since

$$\sinh \alpha x = \tfrac{1}{2}(e^{\alpha x} - e^{-\alpha x})$$

The $\sin \alpha y$ term causes the potential to be zero at $y = 0$, $y = \pi/\alpha$, $y = 2\pi/\alpha$, and so forth. We therefore may place zero-potential conducting planes at $x = 0$, $y = 0$, and $y = \pi/\alpha$. Finally, we can

FIG. 7.4 Cross section of the $V = 0$ and $V = V_1$ equipotential surfaces for the potential field $V = V_1 \sinh \alpha x \sin \alpha y$.

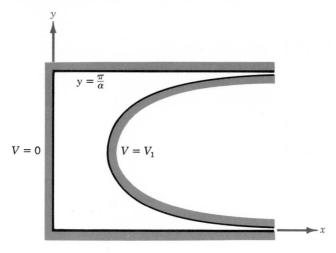

describe the V_1 equipotential surface by setting $V = V_1$ in (8), obtaining

$$\sinh \alpha x \sin \alpha y = 1$$

or

$$\alpha y = \sin^{-1} \frac{1}{\sinh \alpha x}$$

This is not a familiar equation, but a slide rule or a set of tables can furnish enough numerical values to allow us to plot αy as a function of αx. Such a curve is shown in Fig. 7.3. Note that the curve is double-valued and symmetrical about the line $\alpha y = \pi/2$. The information of Fig. 7.3 is transferred directly to the $V = 0$ and $V = V_1$ equipotential conducting surfaces in Fig. 7.4. The surfaces are shown in cross section, since the potential is not a function of z.

It is very unlikely that we shall ever be asked to find the potential field of these peculiarly shaped electrodes, but we should bear in mind the possibility of combining a number of the fields having the form given by (7) or (8) and thus satisfying the boundary conditions of a more practical problem. One example of such a combination will be our final example.

The problem to be solved is that shown in Fig. 7.5. The boundary conditions shown are $V = 0$ at $x = 0$, $y = 0$, and $y = b$, and $V = V_0$ at $x = d$ for all y between 0 and b. It is immediately apparent that the potential field given by (8) and outlined in Fig. 7.4 satisfies

FIG. 7.5 Potential problem requiring an infinite summation of fields of the form $V = V_1 \sinh \alpha x \sin \alpha y$. A similar configuration was analyzed by the iteration method in Chap. 6.

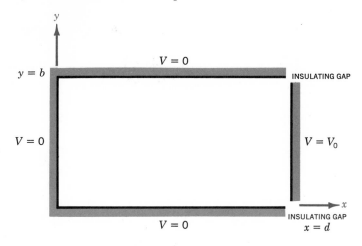

two of the four boundary conditions. A third condition, $V = 0$ at $y = b$, may be satisfied by the choice of α, for the substitution of these values into (8) leads to the equation

$$0 = V_1 \sinh \alpha x \sin \alpha b$$

which may be satisfied by setting

$$\alpha b = m\pi \qquad (m = 1, 2, 3, \ldots)$$

or

$$\alpha = \frac{m\pi}{b}$$

The potential function

$$V = V_1 \sinh \frac{m\pi x}{b} \sin \frac{m\pi y}{b}$$

thus produces the correct potential at $x = 0$, $y = 0$, and $y = b$, regardless of the choice of m or the value of V_1. It is impossible to choose m or V_1 in such a way that $V = V_0$ at $x = d$ for each and every value of y between 0 and b. We must combine an infinite number of these fields, each with a different value of m and a corresponding value of V_1,

$$(9) \qquad V = \sum_{m=0}^{\infty} V_{1m} \sinh \frac{m\pi x}{b} \sin \frac{m\pi y}{b}$$

The subscript on V_{1m} indicates that this amplitude factor will have a different value for each different value of m. Applying the last boundary condition now,

$$V_0 = \sum_{m=0}^{\infty} V_{1m} \sinh \frac{m\pi d}{b} \sin \frac{m\pi y}{b} \qquad (0 < y < b, \, m = 1, 2, \ldots)$$

Since $V_{1m} \sinh (m\pi d/b)$ is only a function of m, we may simplify the expression by replacing this factor by c_m,

$$V_0 = \sum_{m=0}^{\infty} c_m \sin \frac{m\pi y}{b} \qquad (0 < y < b, \, m = 1, 2, \ldots)$$

This is a Fourier sine series, and the c_m coefficients may be determined by the standard Fourier-series methods[1] if we can interpret V_0 as a periodic function of y. Since our physical problem is bounded by conducting planes at $y = 0$ and $y = b$, and our interest in the potential does not extend outside of this region, we may *define* the potential at $x = d$ for y *outside* of the range 0 to b in any manner we choose. Probably the simplest periodic expression is obtained by selecting the interval $0 < y < b$ as the half period and choosing $V = -V_0$ in the adjacent half period, or

$$V = V_0 \qquad (0 < y < b)$$

$$V = -V_0 \qquad (b < y < 2b)$$

The c_m coefficients are then

$$c_m = \frac{1}{b}\left[\int_0^b V_0 \sin \frac{m\pi y}{b} \, dy + \int_b^{2b} (-V_0) \sin \frac{m\pi y}{b} \, dy \right]$$

leading to

$$c_m = \frac{4V_0}{m\pi} \qquad (m \text{ odd})$$

$$= 0 \qquad (m \text{ even})$$

However, $c_m = V_{1m} \sinh (m\pi d/b)$, and therefore

$$V_{1m} = \frac{4V_0}{m\pi \sinh (m\pi d/b)} \qquad (m \text{ odd only})$$

which may be substituted into (9) to give the desired potential function,

$$(10) \quad V = \frac{4V_0}{\pi} \sum_{1,\text{odd}}^{\infty} \frac{1}{m} \frac{\sinh (m\pi x/b)}{\sinh (m\pi d/b)} \sin \frac{m\pi y}{b}$$

[1] Fourier series are discussed in almost every electrical engineering text on circuit theory. The author is partial to the Hayt and Kemmerly reference given in the bibliography at the end of the chapter.

FIG. 7.6 The field map corresponding to

$$V = \frac{4V_0}{\pi} \sum_{1,\text{odd}}^{\infty} \frac{1}{m} \frac{\sinh (m\pi x/b)}{\sinh (m\pi d/b)} \sin \frac{m\pi y}{b}$$

with $b = d$ and $V_0 = 100$ V.

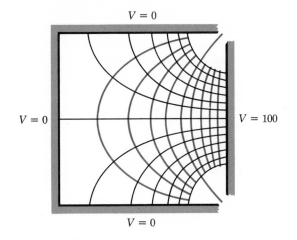

$V = 0$

$V = 0$ $V = 100$

$V = 0$

The map of this field may be obtained by evaluating (10) at a number of points and drawing equipotentials by interpolation between these points. If we let $b = d$ and $V_0 = 100$, the problem is identical with that used as the example in the discussion of the iteration method. Checking one of the grid points in that problem, we let $x = d/4 = b/4$, $y = b/2 = d/2$, and $V_0 = 100$ and obtain

$$V = \frac{400}{\pi} \sum_{1,\text{odd}}^{\infty} \frac{1}{m} \frac{\sinh m\pi/4}{\sinh m\pi} \sin m\pi/2$$

$$= \frac{400}{\pi} \left(\frac{\sinh \pi/4}{\sinh \pi} - \frac{1}{3} \frac{\sinh 3\pi/4}{\sinh 3\pi} + \frac{1}{5} \frac{\sinh 5\pi/4}{\sinh 5\pi} - \cdots \right)$$

$$= \frac{400}{\pi} \left(\frac{0.8687}{11.549} - \frac{5.228}{3 \times 6,195.8} + \cdots \right)$$

$$= \frac{400}{\pi} (0.07522 - 0.00028 + \cdots)$$

$$= 9.541 \text{ V}$$

The equipotentials are drawn for increments of 10 V in Fig. 7.6 and flux lines have been added graphically to produce a curvilinear map.

The material covered in this discussion of the product solution has been more difficult than much of the preceding work, and it has, moreover, presented three new ideas. The first new technique was the assumption that the potential might be expressed as the product of a function of x and a function of y, and the resultant separation of Laplace's equation into two simpler ordinary differential equations. The second new approach was employed when an infinite-power-series solution was assumed as the solution for one of the ordinary differential equations. Finally, we considered an example which required the combination of an infinite number of simpler product solutions, each having a different amplitude and a different variation in one of the coordinate directions. All these techniques are very powerful. They are useful in all coordinate systems, and they can be used in problems in which the potential varies with all three coordinates.

We have merely introduced the subject here, and more information can be obtained from the references listed at the end of the chapter, several of which devote hundreds of pages to the solution of Laplace's equation.

D 7.8 Given the following recurrence relationships as they apply to an infinite power series, evaluate $\sum\limits_{n=0}^{\infty} a_n x^n$ for $x = \frac{1}{2}$ if $a_0 = 1$:

(a) $a_{n+1} = a_n$

(b) $a_{n+1} = \dfrac{a_n}{n+1}$

(c) $a_{2n+2} = -\dfrac{a_{2n}}{4(n+1)^2}$, $a_{2n+1} = 0$

Ans.   0.9385; 1.6487; 2.0000

D 7.9 With reference to the final example of this section (the square trough), the potential at $x = b/4$, $y = b/2$ was found to be 9.54 V. At $x = b/2$, $y = b/4$ it is 18.20 V. Use superposition to determine the potential at $x = b/4$, $y = b/2$ if

(a) $V = 0$ at $x = 0$, $V = 0$ at $y = 0$, $V = 0$ at $x = b$, $V = 40$ at $y = b$
(b) $V = 0$ at $x = 0$, $V = 0$ at $y = 0$, $V = 50$ at $x = b$, $V = 40$ at $y = b$
(c) $V = 0$ at $x = 0$, $V = -30$ at $y = 0$, $V = 50$ at $x = b$, $V = 40$ at $y = b$

Ans.   6.59; 7.28; 12.05 V

SUGGESTED REFERENCES

1   Dekker, A. J.: (see Suggested References for Chap. 5).

2   Hayt, W. H., Jr., and J. E. Kemmerly: "Engineering Circuit Analysis," McGraw-Hill Book Company, New York, 1962.

3 Ramo, S., J. R. Whinnery, and T. Van Duzer: (see Suggested References for Chap. 6). A more complete and advanced discussion of methods of solving Laplace's equation is given in chap. 3.

4 Smythe, W. R.: "Static and Dynamic Electricity," 2d ed., McGraw-Hill Book Company, New York, 1950. An advanced treatment of potential theory is given in chap. 4.

5 Weber, E.: (see Suggested References for Chap. 6). There are a tremendous number of potential solutions given with the original references.

PROBLEMS

1 Show that in a charge-free inhomogeneous region $\nabla^2 V = -(1/\epsilon)\, \nabla\epsilon \cdot \nabla V$.

2 Given that $\nabla^2 V = 0$, work in cartesian coordinates and find (a) $\nabla^2(kV)$, where $k =$ constant; (b) $\nabla^2(V^2)$; (c) $\nabla^2(1/V)$.

3 Show that in a homogeneous medium of conductivity σ the potential field V_σ satisfies Laplace's equation if any volume charge density present does not vary with time.

4 If $R = [(x - x_1)^2 + (y - y_1)^2 + (z - z_1)^2]^{\frac{1}{2}}$, find (a) ∇R; (b) $\nabla^2 R$.

5 (a) Show that the potential function, in cylindrical coordinates, $V = V_0 zr$ $(\cos\phi + \sin\phi)/a^2$, satisfies Laplace's equation; (b) determine the direction of $\mathbf{E}$ at $(r = a, \phi = 0°, z = a)$.

6 Show that the potential field of a spherical capacitor satisfies Laplace's equation.

7 Given the spherically symmetrical potential field $V = V_0 e^{-r/a}$, find (a) ρ at $r = a$; (b) the total charge in this universe.

8 In a certain region the potential is a function of x only. Experimentally determined values in volts and centimeters are $V = 9$ at $x = 3$, $V = 10$ at $x = 4$, $V = 12$ at $x = 5$, $V = 14$ at $x = 6$, $V = 15$ at $x = 7$. If $\epsilon = \epsilon_0$, estimate ρ at $x = 4$ and $x = 5$.

9 Show that $V_1 = 2x$ and $V_2 = \ln\left[e^{2x}\sqrt{(1 + x)/(1 - x)}\right] - \tanh^{-1} x$ both satisfy Laplace's equation and the boundary conditions $V = 0$ at $x = 0$ and $V = 1$ at $x = \frac{1}{2}$. Does this violate the uniqueness theorem?

10 The functions $V_1 = 6r^2\cos 2\phi$ and $V_2 = 6r^2\cos 2\phi + \ln(r/a)$ both seem to satisfy Laplace's equation in cylindrical coordinates and the boundary condition $V = 6a^2\cos 2\phi$ at $r = a$; yet they are obviously not identical. Explain.

11 A potential function is to be found which meets the boundary conditions $V = 0$ at $x = 0$ and $V = 1$ at $x = 1$. An undergraduate student proposes the solution $V_1 = x$; a graduate student who knows more complex mathematical techniques obtains the function $V_2 = x + e^{\pi y}\sin \pi x$. Check both solutions and discuss the appropriateness of the uniqueness theorem to this case.

12 If $x = a\sinh\eta\sin\psi\cos\phi$, $y = a\sinh\eta\sin\psi\sin\phi$, and $z = a\cosh\eta\cos\psi$, then the surfaces $\eta =$ constant are prolate spheroids (football-shaped), the surfaces $\psi =$ constant are hyperboloids of two sheets (somewhat like cones with rounded vertices), and ϕ is the same angle we have used previously. In prolate spheroidal coordinates, Laplace's equation is

$$\nabla^2 V = \frac{1}{a^2(\sinh^2 \eta + \sin^2 \psi)} \left(\frac{\partial^2 V}{\partial \eta^2} + \coth \eta \, \frac{\partial V}{\partial \eta} + \frac{\partial^2 V}{\partial \psi^2} + \cot \psi \, \frac{\partial V}{\partial \psi} \right)$$

$$+ \frac{1}{a^2 \sinh^2 \eta \, \sin^2 \psi} \frac{\partial^2 V}{\partial \phi^2} = 0$$

(a) Assume V varies only with η and find the general form of V. (b) Find V if V is a function of ψ alone. (c) Find V if $V = f(\phi)$.

13 Given the potential function $V = A \ln r + B$, in cylindrical coordinates, find V at $r = 1$ and $r = 5$ if $E_r = 20$ at $r = 2$ and $V = 10$ at $r = 3$.

14 Show that the potential field in a parallel-plate capacitor with $V = 0$ at $x = 0$, $V = 100$ at $x = 1$ and an inhomogeneous dielectric $\epsilon = \epsilon_0(1 + x^2)$ is $V = (400/\pi) \tan^{-1} x$.

15 The region between two spheres whose radii differ by 10 cm is filled with a homogeneous material of dielectric constant 3. If the inner sphere is 60 V positive with respect to the outer sphere and the capacitance between them is 3000 pF, find the maximum electric field intensity at any point between them.

16 Two square conducting plates are parallel, 1 m on a side, and 1 mm apart in air. Find the capacitance C. One plane is now rotated slightly about an axis, parallel to an edge and passing through the center of the plate, until the separation is 0.5 mm at one side and 1.5 mm at the other. By considering the plates as parts of radial planes (see Fig. 7.1), find the new capacitance C' and the percentage of increase.

17 (a) The hemisphere $0 < r < 1$ mm, $0 < \theta < \pi/2$ is filled with a homogeneous conducting material for which $\sigma = 10$, and it rests on a perfectly conducting plane. The material in the conical region $0 < r < 1$ mm, $0 < \theta < \pi/6$ is now removed, and a perfectly conducting wire with a conical point that just fits the hole is inserted in it. What resistance is measured between the two perfect conductors? (b) What is the effect on the resistance of "sharpening" the point of the wire and at the same time reducing the angle of the conical hole to provide a perfect fit in the hemisphere? Let the angle of the point be halved and find R.

18 In regions in which the temperature does not change with time and in which there are no sources of heat that are distributed throughout a volume, $\nabla^2 T = 0$, where T is the temperature. Given a cylindrical pipe of inner radius 1.5 cm and outer radius 3 cm, carrying ice water in an ambient atmosphere which we shall assume is constant at 20°C, plot the temperature in degrees centigrade as a function of radius.

19 In regions in which the temperature does not change with time, $\nabla^2 T = -kp$, where T is the temperature, k is a positive constant, and p is the heat power generated per unit volume. (a) Assume that ohmic heating by a uniformly distributed current causes p to be uniform ($p = p_0$) within a copper wire of circular cross section with radius a, and find the temperature distribution at all points within the wire. (b) If the wire carries a uniform d-c-current density J and has a conductivity σ, find p_0.

20 The region between two concentric conducting cylinders with radii of 2 and 5 cm contains a uniform volume charge distribution of -10^{-8} C/m³. If E_r and V are both zero at the inner cylinder, find V at the outer cylinder.

21 If the form of the volume charge density assumed for the junction diode is $\rho = 1.5\sqrt{3}\rho_0 \operatorname{sech}^2 (x/a) \tanh (x/a)$, use the methods of Sec. 7.4 to find (a) the graph of ρ as a function of x, including the maximum value and its location; (b) E_x, including a comparison of the maximum value of E_x with that maximum value resulting from the volume charge density assumed previously; (c) the junction capacitance, including a comparison with the values obtained from the previous analysis.

22 In the assumed product solution for Laplace's equation, $V = XY$, show that X and Y do not in general satisfy Laplace's equation.

23 Assume $V = XYZ$ as a solution for Laplace's equation in three dimensions. Separate Laplace's equation into three ordinary differential equations and state the necessary relationship between the several separation constants.

24 Suppose that we try to solve Laplace's equation in cartesian coordinates by assuming a "sum" solution instead of a product solution. Thus, in two dimensions, $V = X + Y$. Determine the most general forms possible for X and Y.

25 Given $V = 100 \sin (\pi x/2) e^{-\pi y/2}$, (a) show that $V = XY$, where X and Y have the general forms developed in Sec. 7.5; (b) describe the $V = 0$ surface; (c) plot the 100-V equipotential surface in the region $0 < x < 2$.

26 For the rectangular trough shown in Fig. 7.5, replace the constant potential at $x = d$ with the triangular distribution $V = V_0 - (2V_0/b) |y - (b/2)|$, $0 < y < b$. The other potentials and dimensions are unchanged. (a) If $V < 0$ for $0 > y > -b$, show that

$$V = \sum_{m=1,\text{odd}}^{\infty} \frac{8V_0}{m^2\pi^2} (-1)^{(m-1)/2} \frac{\sinh (m\pi x/b)}{\sinh (m\pi d/b)} \sin \frac{m\pi y}{b}$$

(b) If $V_0 = 100$ V, $b = d$, and $x = y = b/2$, find V.

27 The junction-capacitance theory presented in Dekker (see the bibliography above), pp. 189–192, leads to a capacitance expression which, for equal donor and acceptor concentrations, is slightly different from Sec. 7.4, Eq. (6). (a) What form of charge distribution is assumed? (b) By what percentage is that capacitance value greater than ours?

28 Refer to the initial discussion of Laplace's equation in P. M. Morse and H. Feshbach, "Methods of Theoretical Physics," McGraw-Hill Book Company, New York, 1953, and describe how the authors use the concept of "bulginess" and "lumpiness" to clarify the Laplacian.

8 THE STEADY MAGNETIC FIELD

At this point the concept of a field should be a familiar one. Since we first accepted the experimental law of forces existing between two point charges and defined the electric field intensity as the force per unit charge on a test charge in the presence of a second charge, we have met numerous fields. These fields possess no real physical basis, for physical measurements must always be in terms of the forces on the charges in the detection equipment. Those charges which are the source cause measurable forces to be exerted on other charges which we may think of as detector charges. The fact that we attribute a field to the source charges and then determine the effect of this field on the detector charges amounts merely to a division of the basic problem into two parts for our own convenience.

We shall begin our study of the magnetic field with a definition of the magnetic field itself and show how it arises from a current distribution. The effect of this field on other currents, or the second half of the physical problem, will be discussed in the following chapter. As we did with the electric field, we shall confine our initial discussion to free-space conditions, and the effect of material media will be saved for discussion in the following chapter.

The relation of the steady magnetic field to its source is more complicated than is the relation of the electrostatic field to its source. We shall find it necessary to accept several laws temporarily on faith alone, relegating their proof to the (rather difficult) final section in this chapter. This section may well be omitted when meeting magnetic fields for the first time. It is included to make acceptance of the laws a little easier; the proof of the laws does exist and is available for the disbelievers or the more advanced student.

8.1 BIOT-SAVART LAW

The source of the steady magnetic field may be a permanent magnet, an electric field changing linearly with time, or a direct current. We shall largely ignore the permanent magnet and save the time-varying electric field for a later discussion. Our present relationships will concern the magnetic field produced by a differential d-c element.

We may think of this differential current element as a vanishingly small section of a current-carrying filamentary conductor, where a

FIG. 8.1 The law of Biot-Savart expresses the magnetic field intensity $d\mathbf{H}_2$ produced by a differential current element $I_1\, d\mathbf{L}_1$. The direction of $d\mathbf{H}_2$ is into the page.

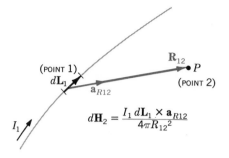

$$dH_2 = \frac{I_1\, d\mathbf{L}_1 \times \mathbf{a}_{R12}}{4\pi R_{12}^2}$$

filamentary conductor is the limiting case of a cylindrical conductor of circular cross section as the radius approaches zero. We assume a current I flowing in a differential vector length of the filament $d\mathbf{L}$. The experimental law of Biot-Savart[1] then states that at any point P the magnitude of the magnetic field intensity produced by the differential element is proportional to the product of the current, the magnitude of the differential length, and the sine of the angle lying between the filament and a line connecting the filament to the point P where the field is desired. The magnitude of the magnetic field intensity is inversely proportional to the square of the distance from the differential element to the point P. The direction of the magnetic field intensity is normal to the plane containing the differential filament and the line drawn from the filament to the point P. Of the two possible normals, that one is to be chosen which is in the direction of progress of a right-handed screw turned from $d\mathbf{L}$ through the smaller angle to the line from the filament to P. Using rationalized mks units, the constant of proportionality is $1/4\pi$.

The *Biot-Savart law*, described above in some 150 words, may be written concisely using vector notation as

$$(1) \qquad d\mathbf{H} = \frac{I\, d\mathbf{L} \times \mathbf{a}_R}{4\pi R^2}$$

The units of the *magnetic field intensity* $\mathbf{H}$ are evidently amperes per meter, abbreviated A/m. The geometry is illustrated in Fig. 8.1. Subscripts may be used to indicate the point to which each of the quantities in (1) refers. If we locate the current element at point

[1] Biot and Savart were colleagues of Ampère, and all three were professors of physics at the Collège de France at one time or another. The Biot-Savart law was proposed in 1820.

1 and describe the point P at which the field is to be determined as point 2, then

$$(2) \qquad \boxed{d\mathbf{H}_2 = \frac{I_1\, d\mathbf{L}_1 \times \mathbf{a}_{R12}}{4\pi R_{12}{}^2}}$$

The law of Biot-Savart is sometimes called *Ampère's law for the current element*, but we shall retain the former name because of possible confusion with Ampère's circuital law, to be met later.

It is impossible to check experimentally the law of Biot-Savart as expressed by (1) or (2) because the differential current element cannot be isolated. We have restricted our attention to direct currents only, for which the charge density is not a function of time. The continuity equation in Sec. 5.2, Eq. (2),

$$\nabla \cdot \mathbf{J} = -\frac{\partial \rho}{\partial t}$$

therefore shows that

$$\nabla \cdot \mathbf{J} = 0$$

or upon applying the divergence theorem,

$$\oint_s \mathbf{J} \cdot d\mathbf{S} = 0$$

The total current crossing any closed surface is zero, and this condition may be satisfied only by assuming a current flow around a closed path. It is this current flowing in a closed circuit which must be our experimental source, not the differential element.

It follows that only the integral form of the Biot-Savart law can be verified experimentally,

$$(3) \qquad \boxed{\mathbf{H} = \oint \frac{I\, d\mathbf{L} \times \mathbf{a}_R}{4\pi R^2}}$$

Equation (1) or (2), of course, leads directly to the integral form (3), but other differential expressions also yield the same integral formulation. Any term may be added to (1) whose integral around a closed path is zero; $d\mathbf{L}$ itself is such a term, for example, as we found in Sec. 4.5, Eq. (5). Although we might feel somewhat foolish doing so, we could multiply $d\mathbf{L}$ by a unit-changing constant k and then add the term $k\, d\mathbf{L}$ to (1) without changing (3) in the slightest. This qualification on (1) or (2) is mentioned to show that if we later ask some foolish questions, not subject to any experimental check, concerning the force exerted by one *differential* current element on another, we should expect foolish answers.

The Biot-Savart law may also be expressed in terms of distributed sources, such as current density $\mathbf{J}$, and *surface current density* $\mathbf{K}$, which we shall define shortly. Surface current flows in a sheet of vanishingly small thickness, and the current density $\mathbf{J}$, measured in amperes per square meter, is therefore infinite. Surface current density, however, is measured in amperes per meter width and designated by $\mathbf{K}$. If the surface current density is uniform, the total current I in any width b is

$$I = Kb$$

where we have assumed that the width b is measured perpendicularly to the direction in which the current is flowing. For a nonuniform surface current density, integration is necessary:

(4)
$$I = \int K \, dn$$

where dn is a differential element of the path *across* which the current is flowing. Thus the differential current element $I \, d\mathbf{L}$, where $d\mathbf{L}$ is in the direction of the current, may be expressed in terms of surface current density $\mathbf{K}$ or current density $\mathbf{J}$,

(5) $$I \, d\mathbf{L} = \mathbf{K} \, dS = \mathbf{J} \, dv$$

and alternate forms of the Biot-Savart law obtained,

(6)
$$\mathbf{H} = \int_S \frac{\mathbf{K} \times \mathbf{a}_R \, dS}{4\pi R^2}$$

and

(7)
$$\mathbf{H} = \int_{\text{vol}} \frac{\mathbf{J} \times \mathbf{a}_R \, dv}{4\pi R^2}$$

We may illustrate the application of the Biot-Savart law by considering an infinitely long straight filament. We shall apply (2) first and then integrate. This, of course, is the same as using the integral form (3) in the first place.[1]

Referring to Fig. 8.2, we should recognize the symmetry of this field. No variation with z or with ϕ can exist. Point 2, at which

[1] The closed path for the current may be considered to include a return filament parallel to the first filament and infinitely far removed. An outer coaxial conductor of infinite radius is another theoretical possibility. Practically, the problem is an impossible one, but we should realize that our answer will be quite accurate near a very long straight wire having a distant return path for the current.

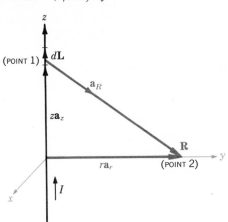

we shall determine the field, is therefore chosen in the $z = 0$ plane, and the unit vector $\mathbf{a}_{R12}$ is found from

$$\mathbf{R}_{12} = r\mathbf{a}_r - z\mathbf{a}_z$$

by

$$\mathbf{a}_{R12} = \frac{r\mathbf{a}_r - z\mathbf{a}_z}{\sqrt{r^2 + z^2}}$$

The direction of $d\mathbf{L}$ is in the direction in which I flows, or

$$d\mathbf{L} = dz\, \mathbf{a}_z$$

and (2) becomes

$$d\mathbf{H}_2 = \frac{I\, dz\mathbf{a}_z \times (r\mathbf{a}_r - z\mathbf{a}_z)}{4\pi (r^2 + z^2)^{3/2}}$$

The integral becomes

$$\mathbf{H}_2 = \int_{-\infty}^{\infty} \frac{I\, dz\mathbf{a}_z \times (r\mathbf{a}_r - z\mathbf{a}_z)}{4\pi (r^2 + z^2)^{3/2}}$$

$$= \frac{I}{4\pi} \int_{-\infty}^{\infty} \frac{r\, dz\mathbf{a}_\phi}{(r^2 + z^2)^{3/2}}$$

At this point the unit vector $\mathbf{a}_\phi$ under the integral sign should be investigated, for it is not always a constant, as are the unit vectors of the cartesian coordinate system. A vector is constant when its magnitude and direction are both constant. The unit

FIG. 8.3 The streamlines of the magnetic field intensity about an infinitely long straight filament carrying a direct current I. The direction of I is into the page.

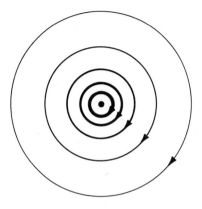

vector certainly has constant magnitude, but its direction may change. Here $\mathbf{a}_\phi$ changes with the coordinate ϕ but not with r or z. Fortunately, the integration is with respect to z, and $\mathbf{a}_\phi$ is a constant in this case and may be removed from under the integral sign,

$$\mathbf{H}_2 = \frac{Ir\mathbf{a}_\phi}{4\pi} \int_{-\infty}^{\infty} \frac{dz}{(r^2 + z^2)^{3/2}}$$

$$= \frac{Ir\mathbf{a}_\phi}{4\pi} \left. \frac{z}{r^2\sqrt{r^2 + z^2}} \right|_{-\infty}^{\infty}$$

and

(8) $$\boxed{\mathbf{H}_2 = \frac{I}{2\pi r} \mathbf{a}_\phi}$$

The magnitude of the field is not a function of ϕ or z and varies inversely as the distance from the filament. The direction of the magnetic field intensity vector is circumferential. The streamlines are therefore circles about the filament, and the field may be mapped in cross section as in Fig. 8.3.

The separation of the streamlines is proportional to the radius or inversely proportional to the magnitude of $\mathbf{H}$. To be specific, the streamlines have been drawn with curvilinear squares in mind. As yet we have no name for the family of lines which are perpendicular to these circular streamlines, but the spacing of the streamlines has been adjusted so that the addition of this second set of lines will produce an array of curvilinear squares.

A comparison of Fig. 8.3 with the map of the *electric* field about an infinite line *charge* shows that the streamlines of the magnetic field correspond exactly to the equipotentials of the electric field, and the unnamed (and undrawn) perpendicular family of lines in the magnetic field corresponds to the streamlines of the electric field. This correspondence is not an accident, but there are several other concepts which must be mastered before the analogy between electric and magnetic fields can be explored more thoroughly.

Using the Biot-Savart law to find **H** is in many respects similar to the use of Coulomb's law to find **E**. Each requires the determination of a moderately complicated integrand containing vector quantities, followed by an integration. When we were concerned with Coulomb's law we solved a number of examples, including the field of the point charge, line charge, and sheet of charge. The law of Biot-Savart can be used to solve analogous problems in magnetic fields, and some of these problems now appear as exercises at the end of the chapter rather than as examples here.

D 8.1 Find the incremental magnetic field intensity in cartesian coordinates produced at the origin by a current element $I\ \Delta\mathbf{L} = 4\pi \times 10^{-4}\mathbf{a}_\theta$ at

$(a)\ \left(r = 2\sqrt{2}, \theta = \dfrac{\pi}{2}, \phi = \dfrac{\pi}{4}\right)$

$(b)\ \left(r = 3, \phi = \dfrac{\pi}{2}, z = 4\right)$

$(c)\ (x = 0.8,\ y = 0.6,\ z = \sqrt{3})$

Ans. $-4\mathbf{a}_z;\ -8.85\,(\mathbf{a}_x - \mathbf{a}_y);\ -15\mathbf{a}_x + 20\mathbf{a}_y \qquad \mu\text{A/m}$

D 8.2 A current of 2π A is flowing in the $\mathbf{a}_z$ direction in a filament extending along the z axis. Find **H** at $(1,0,0)$ if the filament goes between

$(a)\ -\infty$ and $+\infty$
$(b)\ -10$ and $+10$
$(c)\ -1$ and $+1$

Ans. $0.707\mathbf{a}_\phi;\ 0.995\mathbf{a}_\phi;\ \mathbf{a}_\phi \qquad$ A/m

8.2 AMPÈRE'S CIRCUITAL LAW

After solving a number of simple electrostatic problems with Coulomb's law, we found that the same problems could be solved much more easily by using Gauss's law, if a high degree of symmetry was present. Again, an analogous procedure exists in magnetic fields. Here, the law that helps us solve problems more easily is known as *Ampère's circuital law*, sometimes called Ampère's work law. This law may be derived from the Biot-Savart law, and the derivation

FIG. 8.4 A conductor has a total current I. The line integral of **H** about the closed paths a and b is equal to I, and the integral around path c is less than I, since the entire current is not enclosed by the path.

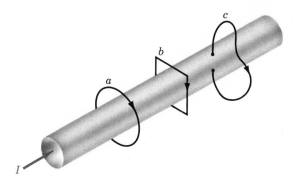

is accomplished in Sec. 8.7. For the present we might agree to accept Ampère's circuital law temporarily as another law capable of experimental proof. Its use will also require careful consideration of the symmetry of the problem to determine which variables and components are present.

Ampère's circuital law states that the line integral of **H** about any *closed* path is exactly equal to the current enclosed by that path,

(1)
$$\oint \mathbf{H} \cdot d\mathbf{L} = I$$

We define positive current as flowing in the direction of advance of a right-handed screw turned in the direction in which the closed path is traversed.

Referring to Fig. 8.4, which shows a circular wire carrying a direct current I, the line integral of **H** about the closed paths lettered a and b results in an answer of I; the integral about the closed path c which passes through the conductor gives an answer less than I and is exactly that portion of the total current which is enclosed by the path c. Although paths a and b give the same answer, the integrands are, of course, different. The line integral directs us to multiply the component of **H** in the direction of the path by a small increment of path length at one point of the path, move along the path to the next incremental length and repeat the process, continuing until the path is completely traversed. Since **H** will in general vary from point to point and since paths a and b are not alike, the contributions to the integral made by, say, each millimeter of path length are quite different. Only the final answers are the same.

We should also consider exactly what is meant by the expression "current enclosed by the path." Suppose we solder a circuit together after passing the conductor once through a rubber band, which we shall use to represent the closed path. Some strange and formidable paths can be constructed by twisting and knotting the rubber band, but if neither the rubber band nor the conducting circuit is broken, the current enclosed by the path is that carried by the conductor. Now let us replace the rubber band by a circular ring of spring steel across which is stretched a rubber sheet. The steel loop forms the closed path, and the current-carrying conductor must pierce the rubber sheet if the current is to be enclosed by the path. Again, we may twist the steel loop, and we may also deform the rubber sheet by pushing our fist into it or folding it in any way we wish. A single current-carrying conductor still pierces the sheet once, and this is the true measure of the current enclosed by the path. If we should thread the conductor once through the sheet from front to back and once from back to front, the total current enclosed by the path is the algebraic sum, which is zero.

In more general language, given a closed path, we recognize this path as the perimeter of an infinite number of surfaces (not closed surfaces). Any current-carrying conductor enclosed by the path must pass through every one of these surfaces once. Certainly some of the surfaces may be chosen in such a way that the conductor pierces them twice in one direction and once in the other direction, but the algebraic total current is still the same.

We shall find that the closed path is usually of an extremely simple nature and can be drawn on a plane. The simplest surface is, then, that portion of the plane enclosed by the path. We need merely find the total current passing through this plane.

The application of Gauss's law involves finding the total charge enclosed by a closed surface; the application of Ampère's circuital law involves finding the total current enclosed by a closed path.

Let us again find the magnetic field intensity produced by an infinitely long filament carrying a current I. The filament lies on the z axis, and the current flows in the direction given by $\mathbf{a}_z$. Symmetry inspection comes first, showing that there is no variation with z or ϕ. Next we consider the components of $\mathbf{H}$ which are present by using the Biot-Savart law. Without specifically using the cross product, we may say that the direction of $d\mathbf{H}$ is perpendicular to the plane containing $d\mathbf{L}$ and $\mathbf{R}$ and therefore is in the direction of $\mathbf{a}_\phi$. Hence the only component of $\mathbf{H}$ is H_ϕ, and it is a function only of r.

We therefore choose a path to any section of which $\mathbf{H}$ is either perpendicular or tangential and along which H is constant. The first requirement (perpendicularity or tangency) allows us to replace the dot product of Ampère's circuital law with the product of

FIG. 8.5 Cross section of a coaxial cable carrying a uniformly distributed current I in the inner conductor and $-I$ in the outer conductor. The magnetic field at any point is most easily determined by applying Ampère's circuital law about a circular path.

the scalar magnitudes, except along that portion of the path where **H** is normal to the path and the dot product is zero; the second requirement (constancy) then permits us to remove the magnetic field intensity from the integral sign. The integration required is usually trivial and consists of finding the length of that portion of the path to which **H** is parallel.

In our example the path must be a circle of radius r, and Ampère's circuital law becomes

$$\oint \mathbf{H} \cdot d\mathbf{L} = \int_0^{2\pi} H_\phi r \, d\phi = H_\phi r \int_0^{2\pi} d\phi = H_\phi 2\pi r = I$$

or

$$H_\phi = \frac{I}{2\pi r}$$

as before.

As a second example of the application of Ampère's circuital law, consider a coaxial transmission line carrying a uniformly distributed total current I in the center conductor and $-I$ in the outer conductor. The line is shown in Fig. 8.5. Symmetry shows that H is not a function of ϕ or z. In order to determine the components present we may use the results of the previous example by considering the solid conductors as being composed of a large number of filaments. No filament has a z component of **H**. Furthermore, the H_r component at $\phi = 0°$ produced by one filament located at $r = r_1$, $\phi = \phi_1$, is canceled by the H_r component produced by a symmetrically located filament at $r = r_1$, $\phi = -\phi_1$. Again we find only an H_ϕ component which varies with r.

A circular path of radius r, where r is larger than the radius of the inner conductor but less than the inner radius of the outer conductor, then leads immediately to

$$H_\phi = \frac{I}{2\pi r} \qquad (b > r > a)$$

If we choose r smaller than the radius of the inner conductor, the current enclosed is

$$I_{\text{encl}} = I\frac{r^2}{a^2}$$

and

$$H_\phi = \frac{Ir}{2\pi a^2} \qquad (a > r)$$

If the radius r is larger than the outer radius of the outer conductor, no current is enclosed and

$$H_\phi = 0 \qquad (r > c)$$

Finally, if the path lies within the outer conductor, we have

$$H_\phi = \frac{I}{2\pi r}\frac{c^2 - r^2}{c^2 - b^2} \qquad (c > r > b)$$

The magnetic-field-strength variation with radius is shown in Fig. 8.6 for a coaxial cable in which $b = 3a$, $c = 4a$. It should be noted that the magnetic field intensity $\mathbf{H}$ is continuous at all the

FIG. 8.6 The magnetic field intensity as a function of radius in a coaxial transmission line with an inner radius of the outer conductor and an outer radius of the outer conductor three and four times the radius of the inner conductor, respectively.

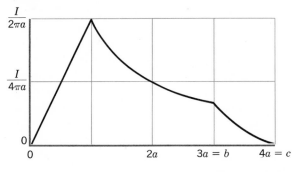

FIG. 8.7 A uniform sheet of surface current $\mathbf{K} = \mathbf{K}_y\,\mathbf{a}_y$ in the $z = 0$ plane. $\mathbf{H}$ may be found by applying Ampère's circuital law about the paths 1-1'-2'-2-1 and 3-3'-2'-2-3.

conductor boundaries. In other words, a slight increase in the radius of the closed path does not result in the enclosure of a tremendously different current. The value of H_ϕ shows no sudden jumps.

The external field is zero. This, we see, results from equal positive and negative currents enclosed by the path. Each produces an external field of magnitude $I/2\pi r$, but complete cancellation occurs. This is another example of "shielding;" such a coaxial cable carrying large currents would not produce any noticeable effect in an adjacent circuit.

As a final example, let us consider a sheet of current flowing in the positive y direction and located in the $z = 0$ plane. We may think of the return current as equally divided between two distant sheets on either side of the sheet we are considering. The sheet of current of uniform surface current density $\mathbf{K} = K_y\mathbf{a}_y$ is shown in Fig. 8.7. $\mathbf{H}$ cannot vary with x or y. If the sheet is subdivided into a number of filaments, it is evident that no filament can produce an H_z component. Moreover, the Biot-Savart law shows that the contributions to H_y produced by a symmetrically located pair of filaments cancel. Thus, H_y is zero also; only an H_x component is present. We therefore choose the path 1-1'-2'-2-1 composed of straight line segments and have

$$H_{x1}L + H_{x2}(-L) = K_yL$$

or

$$H_{x1} - H_{x2} = K_y$$

If the path 3-3'-2'-2-3 is now chosen, the same current is enclosed and

$$H_{x3} - H_{x2} = K_y$$

and therefore

$$H_{z3} = H_{z1}$$

It follows that H_x is the same for all positive z. Similarly, H_x is the same for all negative z. Because of the symmetry, then, the magnetic field intensity on one side of the current sheet is the negative of that on the other. Above the sheet

$$H_x = \tfrac{1}{2}K_y \qquad (z > 0)$$

while below it

$$H_x = -\tfrac{1}{2}K_y \qquad (z < 0)$$

Letting $\mathbf{a}_n$ be a unit vector normal to the current sheet, the result may be written in a form correct for all z as

(2)
$$\boxed{\mathbf{H} = \tfrac{1}{2}\mathbf{K} \times \mathbf{a}_n}$$

If a second sheet of current flowing in the opposite direction, $\mathbf{K} = -K_y\mathbf{a}_y$, is placed at $z = h$, (2) shows that the field in the region between the current sheets is

(3)
$$\boxed{\mathbf{H} = \mathbf{K} \times \mathbf{a}_n \qquad (0 < z < h)}$$

and is zero elsewhere,

(4)
$$\boxed{\mathbf{H} = 0 \qquad (z < 0, \quad z > h)}$$

The most difficult part of the application of Ampère's circuital law is the determination of the components of the field which are present. The surest method is the logical application of the Biot-Savart law and a knowledge of the magnetic fields of simple form. Problem 15 at the end of this chapter outlines the steps involved in applying Ampère's circuital law to an infinitely long solenoid of radius a and uniform current density $K_a\mathbf{a}_\phi$; for reference, the result is:

(5a) $\quad \mathbf{H} = K_a\mathbf{a}_z \qquad r < a$

(5b) $\quad \mathbf{H} = 0 \qquad r > a$

D 8.3 A toroid whose axis is the z axis cuts the $z = 0$ plane with its inner radius of 10 cm and outer radius of 14 cm. The cross section of the toroid is a circle of 2-cm radius. The toroid is wound with 60 turns of a filamentary conductor carrying a current of 2 A. At $z = 0$, $r = 10$ cm the current is directed mostly in the $\mathbf{a}_z$ direction, but with a small component in the $\mathbf{a}_y$ direction. Determine the value of $\oint \mathbf{H}\cdot d\mathbf{L}$, including sign, for the path of

(a) A straight line from the origin to $(0.12,0,0)$, quadrant of 12-cm radius circle to $(0,0.12,0)$, straight line to origin

(b) Straight line segments from $(1,1,0)$ to $(1,-1,0)$ to $(-1,-1,0)$ to $(-1,1,0)$ to $(1,1,0)$

(c) Straight line segments from $(0,0.05,0.05)$ to $(0,0.05,-0.05)$ to $(0,0.15,-0.05)$ to $(0,0.15,0.05)$ to $(0,0.05,0.05)$.

Ans. $-2; 0; 30$ A

D 8.4   A coaxial cable is constructed of copper and has radii of a, b, and c mm (see Fig. 8.5). Each of the two conductors has a resistance of 0.5Ω per 100 m. If the ratio of H_ϕ at $r = b$ to H_ϕ at $r = a$ is 0.3, find

(a) a
(b) b
(c) c

Ans. $1.048; 3.49; 3.65$ mm

8.3   CURL

We completed our study of Gauss's law by applying this law to a differential volume element and were led to the concept of divergence. We shall now apply Ampère's circuital law to a differential closed path and meet the third and last of the special derivatives of vector analysis, the curl. Our immediate objective is to obtain the point form of Ampère's circuital law.

Again we shall choose cartesian coordinates, and an incremental closed path of sides Δx and Δy is selected (Fig. 8.8). We shall assume that some current, as yet unspecified, produces a reference value for **H** at the *center* of this small rectangle

$$\mathbf{H}_0 = H_{x0}\mathbf{a}_x + H_{y0}\mathbf{a}_y + H_{z0}\mathbf{a}_z$$

The closed line integral of **H** about this path is then approximately the sum of the four values of $\mathbf{H} \cdot \Delta \mathbf{L}$ on each side. Choosing the

FIG. 8.8   An incremental closed path in cartesian coordinates is selected for the application of Ampère's circuital law in order to determine the spatial rate of change of **H**.

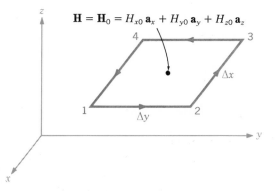

direction of traverse as 1-2-3-4-1, the first contribution is therefore

$$(\mathbf{H} \cdot \Delta \mathbf{L})_{1-2} = H_{y,1-2} \, \Delta y$$

The value of H_y *on this section* of the path may be given in terms of the reference value H_{y0} at the center of the rectangle, the rate of change of H_y with x, and the distance $\Delta x/2$ from the center to the midpoint of side 1-2:

$$H_{y,1-2} \doteq H_{y0} + \frac{\partial H_y}{\partial x} \, (\tfrac{1}{2} \, \Delta x)$$

Thus

$$(\mathbf{H} \cdot \Delta \mathbf{L})_{1-2} \doteq \left(H_{y0} + \frac{1}{2} \frac{\partial H_y}{\partial x} \, \Delta x \right) \Delta y$$

Along the next section of the path we have

$$(\mathbf{H} \cdot \Delta \mathbf{L})_{2-3} \doteq H_{x,2-3}(-\Delta x) \doteq -\left(H_{x0} + \frac{1}{2} \frac{\partial H_x}{\partial y} \, \Delta y \right) \Delta x$$

Continuing for the remaining two segments and adding the results,

$$\oint \mathbf{H} \cdot d\mathbf{L} \doteq \left(\frac{\partial H_y}{\partial x} - \frac{\partial H_x}{\partial y} \right) \Delta x \, \Delta y$$

By Ampère's circuital law, this result must be equal to the current enclosed by the path, or the current crossing the surface bounded by the path. If we assume a general current density $\mathbf{J}$, the enclosed current is then $\Delta I \doteq J_z \, \Delta x \, \Delta y$, and

$$\oint \mathbf{H} \cdot d\mathbf{L} \doteq \left(\frac{\partial H_y}{\partial x} - \frac{\partial H_x}{\partial y} \right) \Delta x \, \Delta y \doteq J_z \, \Delta x \, \Delta y$$

or

$$\frac{\oint \mathbf{H} \cdot d\mathbf{L}}{\Delta x \, \Delta y} \doteq \frac{\partial H_y}{\partial x} - \frac{\partial H_x}{\partial y} \doteq J_z$$

As we cause the closed path to shrink, the above expression becomes more nearly exact, and in the limit we have the equality

(1) $$\lim_{\Delta x, \Delta y \to 0} \frac{\oint \mathbf{H} \cdot d\mathbf{L}}{\Delta x \, \Delta y} = \frac{\partial H_y}{\partial x} - \frac{\partial H_x}{\partial y} = J_z$$

After beginning with Ampère's circuital law equating the closed line integral of $\mathbf{H}$ to the current enclosed, we have now arrived at a relationship involving the closed line integral of $\mathbf{H}$ *per unit area* enclosed and the current *per unit area* enclosed, or current density. We performed a similar analysis in passing from the integral form of Gauss's law, involving flux through a closed surface and charge enclosed, to the point form, relating flux through a closed surface *per unit volume* enclosed and charge *per unit volume* enclosed, or volume charge density. In each case a limit is necessary to produce an equality.

If we choose closed paths which are oriented perpendicularly to each of the remaining two coordinate axes, analogous processes lead to expressions for the y and z components of the current density,

$$(2) \quad \lim_{\Delta y, \Delta z \to 0} \frac{\oint \mathbf{H} \cdot d\mathbf{L}}{\Delta y \, \Delta z} = \frac{\partial H_z}{\partial y} - \frac{\partial H_y}{\partial z} = J_x$$

, and

$$(3) \quad \lim_{\Delta z, \Delta x \to 0} \frac{\oint \mathbf{H} \cdot d\mathbf{L}}{\Delta z \, \Delta x} = \frac{\partial H_x}{\partial z} - \frac{\partial H_z}{\partial x} = J_y$$

Comparing (1), (2), and (3) we see that a component of the current density is given by the limit of the quotient of the closed line integral of $\mathbf{H}$ about a small path in a plane normal to that component and of the area enclosed as the path shrinks to zero. This limit has its counterpart in other fields of science and long ago received the name of *curl*. The curl of any vector is a vector, and any component of the curl is given by the limit of the quotient of the closed line integral of the vector about a small path in a plane normal to that component desired and the area enclosed, as the path shrinks to zero. It should be noted that the above definition of curl does not refer specifically to a particular coordinate system. The mathematical form of the definition is

$$(4) \quad \boxed{(\text{curl } \mathbf{H})_n = \lim_{\Delta S_n \to 0} \frac{\oint \mathbf{H} \cdot d\mathbf{L}}{\Delta S_n}}$$

where ΔS_n is the area enclosed by the closed line integral, and n represents any component in any coordinate system. This subscript also indicates that the component of the curl is that component which is *normal* to the surface enclosed by the closed path.

In cartesian coordinates the definition (4) shows that the x, y, and z components of the curl of $\mathbf{H}$ are given by (1), (2), and (3), and therefore

$$(5) \quad \boxed{\text{curl } \mathbf{H} = \left(\frac{\partial H_z}{\partial y} - \frac{\partial H_y}{\partial z}\right)\mathbf{a}_x + \left(\frac{\partial H_x}{\partial z} - \frac{\partial H_z}{\partial x}\right)\mathbf{a}_y \\ + \left(\frac{\partial H_y}{\partial x} - \frac{\partial H_x}{\partial y}\right)\mathbf{a}_z}$$

This result may be written in the form of a determinant,

$$
(6) \quad \text{curl } \mathbf{H} = \begin{vmatrix} \mathbf{a}_x & \mathbf{a}_y & \mathbf{a}_z \\ \dfrac{\partial}{\partial x} & \dfrac{\partial}{\partial y} & \dfrac{\partial}{\partial z} \\ H_x & H_y & H_z \end{vmatrix}
$$

and may also be written in terms of the vector operator,

$$
(7) \quad \boxed{\text{curl } \mathbf{H} = \nabla \times \mathbf{H}}
$$

Equation (5) is the result of applying the definition (4) to the cartesian coordinate system. We obtained the z component of this expression by evaluating Ampère's circuital law about an incremental path of sides Δx and Δy, and we could have obtained the other two components just as easily by choosing the appropriate paths. Equation (6) is a neat method of storing the cartesian coordinate expression for curl; the form is symmetrical and easily remembered. Equation (7) is even more concise and leads to (5) upon applying the definitions of the cross product and vector operator.

The expressions for curl $\mathbf{H}$ in cylindrical and spherical coordinates are derived in the Appendix by applying the definition (4). We then have

$$
(5) \quad \nabla \times \mathbf{H} = \left(\frac{\partial H_z}{\partial y} - \frac{\partial H_y}{\partial z}\right)\mathbf{a}_x + \left(\frac{\partial H_x}{\partial z} - \frac{\partial H_z}{\partial x}\right)\mathbf{a}_y
$$
$$
+ \left(\frac{\partial H_y}{\partial x} - \frac{\partial H_x}{\partial y}\right)\mathbf{a}_z \quad \text{(cartesian)}
$$

$$
(8) \quad \nabla \times \mathbf{H} = \left(\frac{1}{r}\frac{\partial H_z}{\partial \phi} - \frac{\partial H_\phi}{\partial z}\right)\mathbf{a}_r + \left(\frac{\partial H_r}{\partial z} - \frac{\partial H_z}{\partial r}\right)\mathbf{a}_\phi
$$
$$
+ \left[\frac{1}{r}\frac{\partial (rH_\phi)}{\partial r} - \frac{1}{r}\frac{\partial H_r}{\partial \phi}\right]\mathbf{a}_z \quad \text{(cylindrical)}
$$

$$
(9) \quad \nabla \times \mathbf{H} = \frac{1}{r \sin \theta}\left[\frac{\partial (H_\phi \sin \theta)}{\partial \theta} - \frac{\partial H_\theta}{\partial \phi}\right]\mathbf{a}_r
$$
$$
+ \frac{1}{r}\left[\frac{1}{\sin \theta}\frac{\partial H_r}{\partial \phi} - \frac{\partial (rH_\phi)}{\partial r}\right]\mathbf{a}_\theta + \frac{1}{r}\left[\frac{\partial (rH_\theta)}{\partial r} - \frac{\partial H_r}{\partial \theta}\right]\mathbf{a}_\phi
$$
$$
\text{(spherical)}
$$

Although we have described curl as a line integral per unit area, this does not provide everyone with a satisfactory physical picture of the nature of the curl operation, for the closed line integral itself requires physical interpretation. The closed line integral was first met in the electrostatic field, where we saw that $\oint \mathbf{E} \cdot d\mathbf{L} = 0$. Inasmuch as the integral was zero, we did not belabor the physical picture. Since then we have discussed recently the closed line integral of $\mathbf{H}$, $\oint \mathbf{H} \cdot d\mathbf{L} = I$. Either of these closed line integrals is also known by the name of "circulation," a term obviously borrowed from the field of hydraulics.

The circulation of $\mathbf{H}$, or $\oint \mathbf{H} \cdot d\mathbf{L}$, is obtained by multiplying the component of $\mathbf{H}$ parallel to the specified path at each point along the path by the differential path lengths and summing the results as the differential lengths approach zero and as their number becomes infinite. We do not require a vanishingly small path. Ampère's circuital law tells us that if $\mathbf{H}$ does possess circulation about a given path, then current passes through this path. In electrostatics we see that the circulation of $\mathbf{E}$ is zero about every path, a direct consequence of the fact that zero work is required to carry a charge around a closed path.

We may now describe curl as *circulation per unit area*. The closed path is vanishingly small, and curl is defined at a point. The curl of $\mathbf{E}$ must be zero, for the circulation is zero. The curl of $\mathbf{H}$ is not zero, however; the circulation of $\mathbf{H}$ per unit area is the current density by Ampère's circuital law [or (1), (2), and (3)].

Skilling[1] suggests the use of a very small paddle wheel as a "curl meter." Our vector quantity, then, must be thought of as capable of applying a force to each blade of the paddle wheel, the force being proportional to the component of the field normal to the surface of that blade. In order to test a field for curl we dip our paddle wheel into the field, with the axis of the paddle wheel lined up with the direction of the component of curl desired, and note the action of the field on the paddle. No rotation means no curl; larger angular velocities mean greater values of the curl; a reversal in the direction of spin means a reversal in the sign of the curl. In order to find the direction of the vector curl and not merely to establish the presence of any particular component, we should place our paddle wheel in the field and hunt around for the orientation which produces the greatest torque. The direction of the curl is then along the axis of the paddle wheel, as given by the right-hand rule.

As an example, consider the flow of water in a river. Figure 8.9a shows the longitudinal section of a wide river taken at the middle of the river. The water velocity is zero at the bottom and increases

---

[1] See the bibliography at the end of the chapter.

FIG. 8.9 (a) The curl meter shows a component of the curl of the water velocity into the page. (b) The curl of the magnetic field intensity about an infinitely long filament is zero.

(a)   (b)

linearly as the surface is approached. A paddle wheel placed in the position shown, with its axis perpendicular to the paper, will turn in a clockwise direction, showing the presence of a component of curl in the direction of an inward normal to the surface of the page. If the velocity of the water does not change as we go up- or downstream and also shows no variation as we go across the river (or even if it decreases in the same fashion toward either bank), then this component is the only component present at the center of the stream, and the curl of the water velocity has a direction into the page.

In Fig. 8.9b the streamlines of the magnetic field intensity about an infinitely long filamentary conductor are shown. The curl meter placed in this field of curved lines shows that a larger number of blades have a clockwise force exerted on them but that this force is in general smaller than the counterclockwise force exerted on the smaller number of blades closer to the wire. It seems possible that if the curvature of the streamlines is correct and also if the variation of the field strength is just right, the net torque on the paddle wheel may be zero. Actually, the paddle wheel does not rotate in this case, for since $\mathbf{H} = I\mathbf{a}_\phi/2\pi r$, we may substitute into (8), obtaining

$$\text{curl } \mathbf{H} = -\frac{\partial H_\phi}{\partial z}\mathbf{a}_r + \frac{1}{r}\frac{\partial (rH_\phi)}{\partial r}\mathbf{a}_z = 0$$

Returning now to complete our original examination of the application of Ampère's circuital law to a differential-sized path, we may combine (1), (2), (3), (5), and (7),

$$(10) \quad \text{curl } \mathbf{H} = \nabla \times \mathbf{H} = \left(\frac{\partial H_z}{\partial y} - \frac{\partial H_y}{\partial z}\right)\mathbf{a}_x + \left(\frac{\partial H_x}{\partial z} - \frac{\partial H_z}{\partial x}\right)\mathbf{a}_y$$

$$+ \left(\frac{\partial H_y}{\partial x} - \frac{\partial H_x}{\partial y}\right)\mathbf{a}_z = \mathbf{J}$$

The Steady Magnetic Field   226

and write the *point form of Ampère's circuital law*,

(11)

$$\nabla \times \mathbf{H} = \mathbf{J}$$

This is the second of Maxwell's four equations as they apply to non-time-varying conditions. We may also write the third of these equations at this time; it is the point form of $\oint \mathbf{E} \cdot d\mathbf{L} = 0$, or

$$\nabla \times \mathbf{E} = 0$$

The fourth equation appears in Sec. 8.5.

D 8.5 The values of $\mathbf{H}$ at 6 points in the neighborhood of the origin are tabulated below in amperes per meter.

Point, mm	H_x	H_y	H_z
(1,0,0)	161	166	153
(−1,0,0)	161	156	169
(0,1,0)	156	161	155
(0,−1,0)	166	161	167
(0,0,1)	169	167	161
(0,0,−1)	153	155	161

Use Sec. 8.3, Eq. (1), to approximate the value of

(a) J_z at (0,0,0) by evaluating the left side of the equation
(b) J_z at (0,0,0) by evaluating the central part of the equation
(c) J_x at (0,0,0)

Ans. 10^4; 10^4; -1.2×10^4 A/m²

D 8.6 Find $|\nabla \times \mathbf{H}|$ at the origin if

(a) $\mathbf{H} = 2y\mathbf{a}_x - (x^2 - z^2)\mathbf{a}_y + 3y\mathbf{a}_z$
(b) $\mathbf{H} = (2 - 1/r^2)\cos\phi\, \mathbf{a}_r + [(2 + 1/r^2)(-\sin\phi) + 2r]\mathbf{a}_\phi$ (in cylindrical coordinates)
(c) $\mathbf{H} = r\sin\theta\, \mathbf{a}_\phi$ (in spherical coordinates)

Ans.   2; 3.61; 4   A/m²

8.4 STOKES' THEOREM

Although the last section was devoted primarily to a discussion of the curl operation, the contribution to the subject of magnetic fields should not be overlooked. From Ampère's circuital law we derived one of Maxwell's equations, $\nabla \times \mathbf{H} = \mathbf{J}$. This latter equation should be considered the point form of Ampère's circuital law and applies on a "per-unit-area" basis. In this section we shall

FIG. 8.10 The sum of the closed line integrals about the perimeter of every ΔS is the same as the closed line integral about the perimeter of S because of cancellation on every interior path.

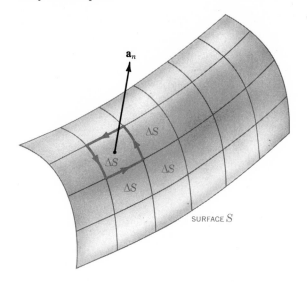

again devote a major share of the material to the mathematical theorem known as Stokes' theorem, but in the process we shall show that we may obtain Ampère's circuital law from $\nabla \times \mathbf{H} = \mathbf{J}$. In other words, we are then prepared to obtain the integral form from the point form or to obtain the point form from the integral form.

Consider the surface S of Fig. 8.10, which is broken up into incremental surfaces of area ΔS. If we apply the definition of the curl to one of these incremental surfaces, then

$$\frac{\oint \mathbf{H} \cdot d\mathbf{L}_{\Delta S}}{\Delta S} \doteq (\nabla \times \mathbf{H})_n$$

where the n subscript again indicates the right-hand normal to the surface. The subscript on $d\mathbf{L}_{\Delta S}$ indicates the closed path is the perimeter of an incremental area ΔS. This result may also be written

$$\frac{\oint \mathbf{H} \cdot d\mathbf{L}_{\Delta S}}{\Delta S} \doteq (\nabla \times \mathbf{H}) \cdot \mathbf{a}_n$$

or

$$\oint \mathbf{H} \cdot d\mathbf{L}_{\Delta S} \doteq (\nabla \times \mathbf{H}) \cdot \mathbf{a}_n \, \Delta S = (\nabla \times \mathbf{H}) \cdot \Delta \mathbf{S}$$

where $\mathbf{a}_n$ = a unit vector in direction of right-hand normal to $\Delta \mathbf{S}$.

The Steady Magnetic Field 228

Now let us determine this circulation for every ΔS comprising S and sum the results. As we evaluate the closed line integral for each ΔS, some cancellation will occur because every *interior* wall is covered once in each direction. The only boundaries on which cancellation cannot occur form the outside boundary, the path enclosing S. Therefore we have

(1) $$\boxed{\oint \mathbf{H} \cdot d\mathbf{L} \equiv \int_s (\boldsymbol{\nabla} \times \mathbf{H}) \cdot d\mathbf{S}}$$

where $d\mathbf{L}$ is taken only on the perimeter of S.

Equation (1) is an identity, holding for any vector field, and is known as *Stokes' theorem*.

It is now very easy to obtain Ampère's circuital law from $\boldsymbol{\nabla} \times \mathbf{H} = \mathbf{J}$, for we merely have to dot each side by $d\mathbf{S}$, integrate each side over the same (open) surface S, and apply Stokes' theorem:

$$\int_s (\boldsymbol{\nabla} \times \mathbf{H}) \cdot d\mathbf{S} = \int_s \mathbf{J} \cdot d\mathbf{S} = \oint \mathbf{H} \cdot d\mathbf{L}$$

The integral of the current density over the surface S is the total current I passing through the surface, and therefore

$$\oint \mathbf{H} \cdot d\mathbf{L} = I$$

This short derivation shows clearly that the current I, described as being "enclosed by the closed path," is also the current passing through any of the infinite number of surfaces which have the closed path as a perimeter.

Stokes' theorem relates a surface integral to a closed line integral. It should be recalled that the divergence theorem relates a volume integral to a closed surface integral. Both theorems find their greatest use in general vector proofs. As an example, let us find another expression for $\boldsymbol{\nabla} \cdot \boldsymbol{\nabla} \times \mathbf{A}$, where $\mathbf{A}$ represents any vector field. The result must be a scalar (why?), and we may let this scalar be T, or

$$\boldsymbol{\nabla} \cdot \boldsymbol{\nabla} \times \mathbf{A} = T$$

Multiplying by dv and integrating throughout any volume v,

$$\int_{vol} (\boldsymbol{\nabla} \cdot \boldsymbol{\nabla} \times \mathbf{A}) \, dv = \int_{vol} T \, dv$$

we first apply the divergence theorem to the left side, obtaining

$$\oint_s (\boldsymbol{\nabla} \times \mathbf{A}) \cdot d\mathbf{S} = \int_{vol} T \, dv$$

The left side is the surface integral of the curl of **A** over the *closed* surface surrounding the volume v. Stokes' theorem relates the surface integral of the curl of **A** over the *open* surface enclosed by a given closed path. If we think of the path as the opening of a laundry bag and the open surface as the surface of the bag itself, we see that as we gradually approach a closed surface by pulling on the drawstrings, the closed path becomes smaller and smaller and finally disappears as the surface becomes closed. Hence the application of Stokes' theorem to a *closed* surface produces a zero result, and we have

$$\int_{vol} T \, dv = 0$$

Since this is true for any volume, it is true for the differential volume dv,

$$T \, dv = 0$$

and therefore

$$T = 0$$

or

(2)
$$\boxed{\nabla \cdot \nabla \times \mathbf{A} \equiv 0}$$

Equation (2) is a useful identity of vector calculus. We may apply it immediately to the non-time-varying magnetic field for which

$$\nabla \times \mathbf{H} = \mathbf{J}$$

and then show that

$$\nabla \cdot \mathbf{J} = 0$$

which is the same result we obtained earlier in the chapter by using the continuity equation.

Before introducing several new magnetic field quantities in the following section, we may review our accomplishments at this point. We initially accepted the Biot-Savart law as an experimental result,

$$d\mathbf{H} = \frac{I \, d\mathbf{L} \times \mathbf{a}_R}{4\pi R^2}$$

and tentatively accepted Ampère's circuital law, subject to later proof,

$$\oint \mathbf{H} \cdot d\mathbf{L} = I$$

From Ampère's circuital law the definition of curl led to the point form of this same law,

$$\nabla \times \mathbf{H} = \mathbf{J}$$

We now see that Stokes' theorem enables us to obtain the integral form of Ampère's circuital law from the point form.

D 8.7 Make use of Stokes' theorem to evaluate, in the easiest way, the circulation of $\mathbf{A}$ about the specified path:

(a) $\mathbf{A} = 5 \cos \pi x \sin \pi y \, \mathbf{a}_x - 5 \sin \pi x \cos \pi y \, \mathbf{a}_y - 5 \cos \pi x \cos \pi y \, \mathbf{a}_z$; straight line segments from $(0,0,0)$ to $(0,1,0)$ to $(-1,1,0)$ to $(-1,0,0)$ to $(0,0,0)$

(b) $\mathbf{A} = r^2 e^{-r} \mathbf{a}_r$, in spherical coordinates; straight line from origin to $(1,0,0)$, quadrant of circle to $(0,1,0)$, straight line to $(0,0.5,0)$, quadrant of circle to $(-0.5,0,0)$, straight line to origin

(c) $\mathbf{A} = 2re^{\sin \phi} \mathbf{a}_r + r \cos \phi \, e^{\sin \phi} \mathbf{a}_\phi$, in cylindrical coordinates; circle $r = 1, z = 0$ in $\mathbf{a}_\phi$ direction

Ans. 0; 0; 0

8.5 MAGNETIC FLUX AND MAGNETIC FLUX DENSITY

In free space, let us define the *magnetic flux density* $\mathbf{B}$ as

(1)
$$\boxed{\mathbf{B} = \mu_0 \mathbf{H}}$$

where $\mathbf{B}$ is measured in webers per square meter (Wb/m²), or in a newer unit adopted in the International System of units, tesla (T). In both systems of units the constant μ_0 is not dimensionless and has the *defined* value for free space, in henrys per meter (H/m), of

(2)
$$\boxed{\mu_0 = 4\pi \times 10^{-7} \quad \text{H/m}}$$

The name given to μ_0 is the *permeability* of free space.

We should note that since $\mathbf{H}$ is measured in amperes per meter, the weber is dimensionally equal to the product of henrys and amperes. Considering the henry as a new unit, the weber is merely a convenient abbreviation for the product of henrys and amperes. When time-varying fields are introduced, it will be shown that a weber is also equivalent to the product of volts and seconds.

The magnetic-flux-density vector $\mathbf{B}$, as the name implies, is a member of the flux-density family of vector fields. One of the possible analogies between electric and magnetic fields compares the laws of Biot-Savart and Coulomb, thus establishing an analogy between $\mathbf{H}$ and $\mathbf{E}$. The relations $\mathbf{B} = \mu_0 \mathbf{H}$ and $\mathbf{D} = \epsilon_0 \mathbf{E}$ then serve to relate $\mathbf{B}$ and $\mathbf{D}$. If $\mathbf{B}$ is measured in webers per square meter, then magnetic flux should be measured in webers. Let us represent magnetic flux by Φ and define Φ as the flux passing through any designated area,

$$(3) \qquad \boxed{\Phi = \int_s \mathbf{B} \cdot d\mathbf{S} \qquad \text{Wb}}$$

Our analogy should now remind us of the electric flux Ψ, measured in coulombs, and of Gauss's law, which states that the total flux passing through any *closed* surface is equal to the charge enclosed,

$$\Psi = \oint_s \mathbf{D} \cdot d\mathbf{S} = Q$$

The charge Q is the source of the lines of electric flux, and these lines begin and terminate on positive and negative charge, respectively.

No such source has ever been discovered for the lines of magnetic flux. In the example of the infinitely long straight filament carrying a direct current I, the $\mathbf{H}$ field formed concentric circles about the filament. Since $\mathbf{B} = \mu_0\mathbf{H}$, the $\mathbf{B}$ field is of the same form. The magnetic flux lines are closed and do not terminate on a "magnetic charge." For this reason Gauss's law for the magnetic field is

$$(4) \qquad \boxed{\oint_s \mathbf{B} \cdot d\mathbf{S} = 0}$$

and application of the divergence theorem shows us that

$$(5) \qquad \boxed{\nabla \cdot \mathbf{B} = 0}$$

We have not proved (4) or (5) but have only suggested the truth of these statements by considering the single field of the infinite filament. It is possible to show that (4) or (5) follows from the Biot-Savart law and the definition of $\mathbf{B}$, $\mathbf{B} = \mu_0\mathbf{H}$, but this is another proof which we shall postpone to Sec. 8.7.

Equation (5) is the last of Maxwell's four equations as they apply to static electric fields and steady magnetic fields. Collecting these equations, we then have

$$(6) \qquad \boxed{\begin{aligned} \nabla \cdot \mathbf{D} &= \rho \\ \nabla \times \mathbf{E} &= 0 \\ \nabla \times \mathbf{H} &= \mathbf{J} \\ \nabla \cdot \mathbf{B} &= 0 \end{aligned}}$$

To these equations we may add the two expressions relating **D** to **E** and **B** to **H** in free space,

(7) $$\boxed{\mathbf{D} = \epsilon_0 \mathbf{E}}$$

(8) $$\boxed{\mathbf{B} = \mu_0 \mathbf{H}}$$

We have also found it helpful to define an electrostatic potential,

(9) $$\boxed{\mathbf{E} = -\nabla V}$$

and we shall discuss a potential for the steady magnetic field in the following section. In addition, we have extended our coverage of electric fields to include conducting materials and dielectrics, and we have introduced the polarization **P**. A similar treatment will be applied to magnetic fields in the next chapter.

Returning to (6), it may be noted that these four equations specify the divergence and curl of an electric and a magnetic field. They should be recognized, in the order given above, as the point forms of these integral equations:

(10)
$$
\boxed{
\begin{aligned}
&\oint_s \mathbf{D} \cdot d\mathbf{S} = Q = \int_{\text{vol}} \rho \, dv \\
\\
&\oint_s \mathbf{E} \cdot d\mathbf{L} = 0 \\
\\
&\oint_s \mathbf{H} \cdot d\mathbf{L} = I = \int_s \mathbf{J} \cdot d\mathbf{S} \\
\\
&\oint_s \mathbf{B} \cdot d\mathbf{S} = 0
\end{aligned}
}
$$

Our study of electric and magnetic fields would have been much simpler if we could have assumed either set of equations, (6) or (10). With a good knowledge of vector analysis, such as we should now have, either set may be readily obtained from the other by applying the divergence theorem or Stokes' theorem. The various experimental laws could have been obtained readily from these equations.

As an example of the use of flux and flux density in magnetic fields, let us find the flux between the conductors of the coaxial line of Fig. 8.5. The magnetic field intensity was found to be

$$H_\phi = \frac{I}{2\pi r} \qquad (a < r < b)$$

and therefore

$$\mathbf{B} = \mu_0\mathbf{H} = \frac{\mu_0 I}{2\pi r}\,\mathbf{a}_\phi$$

The magnetic flux contained between the conductors in a length L is the flux crossing any radial plane extending from $r = a$ to $r = b$ and from, say, $z = 0$ to $z = L$

$$\Phi = \int_s \mathbf{B}\cdot d\mathbf{S} = \int_0^L \int_a^b \frac{\mu_0 I}{2\pi r}\,\mathbf{a}_\phi \cdot dr\,dz\mathbf{a}_\phi$$

or

$$(11) \qquad \Phi = \frac{\mu_0 I L}{2\pi}\ln\frac{b}{a}$$

This expression will be used later to obtain the inductance of the coaxial transmission line.

D 8.8 A current sheet $\mathbf{K}_1 = 10\mathbf{a}_x$ A/m is present at the $z = 0$ plane, and current sheets $\mathbf{K}_2 = \mathbf{K}_3 = -5\mathbf{a}_x$ A/m are established in the planes $z = h$ and $z = -h$. Find the magnetic flux crossing the $y = 0$ plane in the $\mathbf{a}_y$ direction between $x = 0$, $x = L$,

(a) $z = 0$, and $z = h$
(b) $z = -h$, and $z = h$
(c) $z = h$, and $z = 2h$

Ans. $0; 0; -5\mu_0 h L$ Wb

8.6   THE SCALAR AND VECTOR MAGNETIC POTENTIALS

The solution of electrostatic field problems is greatly simplified by the use of the scalar electrostatic potential V. Although this potential possesses a very real physical significance for us, it is mathematically no more than a steppingstone which allows us to solve a problem by several smaller steps. Given a charge configuration, we may first find the potential and then later the electric field intensity.

We should question whether or not such assistance is available in magnetic fields. Can we define a potential function which may be found from the current distribution and from which the magnetic fields may be easily determined? Can a scalar magnetic potential be defined, similar to the scalar electrostatic potential? We shall show in the next few pages that the answer to the first question is "yes," but the second must be answered "sometimes." Let us attack the last question first by assuming the existence of a scalar magnetic potential which we may designate V_m, whose negative gradient gives the magnetic field intensity

(1)
$$\mathbf{H} = -\nabla V_m$$

The selection of the negative gradient will provide us with a closer analogy to the electric potential and to problems which we have already solved.

This definition must not conflict with our previous results for the magnetic field, and therefore

$$\nabla \times \mathbf{H} = \mathbf{J} = \nabla \times (-\nabla V_m)$$

However, the curl of the gradient of any scalar is identically zero, a vector identity the proof of which is left for a leisure moment. Therefore we see that if $\mathbf{H}$ is to be defined as the gradient of a scalar magnetic potential, then current density must be zero throughout the region in which the scalar magnetic potential is so defined. Since many magnetic problems involve geometries in which the current-carrying conductors occupy a relatively small fraction of the total region of interest, it is evident that a scalar magnetic potential can be useful. The scalar magnetic potential is also applicable in the case of permanent magnets. The dimensions of V_m are obviously amperes.

This scalar potential also satisfies Laplace's equation. In free space,

$$\nabla \cdot \mathbf{B} = \mu_0 \nabla \cdot \mathbf{H} = 0$$

and hence

$$\mu_0 \nabla \cdot (-\nabla V_m) = 0$$

or

(2)
$$\nabla^2 V_m = 0 \qquad (\mathbf{J} = 0)$$

We shall see later that V_m continues to satisfy Laplace's equation in homogeneous magnetic materials; it does not satisfy Laplace's equation in any region in which current density is present.

Although we shall consider the scalar magnetic potential to a much greater extent in the next chapter, when we introduce magnetic materials and discuss the magnetic circuit, one difference between V and V_m is worth investigating now: V_m is not a single-valued function of position. The electric potential V is single-valued; once a zero reference is assigned, there is one and only one value of V associated with each point in space. Such is not the case with V_m. Consider the cross section of the coaxial line shown

FIG. 8.11 The scalar magnetic potential V_m is a multivalued function of ϕ in the region $a < r < b$. The electrostatic potential is always single-valued.

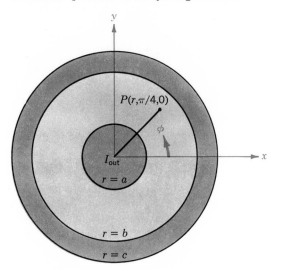

in Fig. 8.11. In the region $a < r < b$, $\mathbf{J} = 0$, and we may establish a scalar magnetic potential. The value of $\mathbf{H}$ is

$$\mathbf{H} = \frac{I}{2\pi r}\,\mathbf{a}_\phi$$

where I is the total current flowing in the $\mathbf{a}_z$ direction in the inner conductor. Applying (1),

$$\frac{I}{2\pi r} = -\nabla V_m\big|_\phi = -\frac{1}{r}\frac{\partial V_m}{\partial \phi}$$

or

$$\frac{\partial V_m}{\partial \phi} = -\frac{I}{2\pi}$$

Thus

$$V_m = -\frac{I}{2\pi}\phi$$

where the constant of integration has been set equal to zero. What value of potential do we associate with point P, where $\phi = \pi/4$? If we let V_m be zero at $\phi = 0$ and proceed counterclockwise around the circle, the magnetic potential linearly becomes more negative. When we have made one circuit the potential is $-I$, but that was the point at which we said the potential was zero a moment ago. At

P, then, $\phi = \pi/4, 9\pi/4, 17\pi/4, \ldots$, or $-7\pi/4, -15\pi/4, -23\pi/4$, $\ldots$, or

$$V_{mP} = \frac{I}{2\pi}(2n - \tfrac{1}{4})\pi \qquad (n = 0, \pm 1, \pm 2, \ldots)$$

or

$$V_{mP} = I(n - \tfrac{1}{8}) \qquad (n = 0, \pm 1, \pm 2, \ldots)$$

The reason for this multi-valuedness may be shown by a comparison with the electrostatic case. There, we know that

$$\nabla \times \mathbf{E} = 0$$

$$\oint \mathbf{E} \cdot d\mathbf{L} = 0$$

and therefore the line integral

$$V_{ab} = \int_a^b \mathbf{E} \cdot d\mathbf{L}$$

is independent of the path. In the magnetostatic case, however,

$$\nabla \times \mathbf{H} = 0 \qquad (\text{wherever } \mathbf{J} = 0)$$

but

$$\oint \mathbf{H} \cdot d\mathbf{L} = I$$

even if $\mathbf{J}$ is zero along the path of integration. Every time we make another complete lap around the current, the result of the integration increases by I. If no current I is enclosed by the path, then a single-valued potential function may be defined. In general, however,

$$\boxed{V_{m,ab} = \int_a^b \mathbf{H} \cdot d\mathbf{L} \qquad \text{(specified path)}}$$

where a specific path or type of path must be selected. We should remember that the electrostatic potential V is a conservative field; the magnetic scalar potential V_m is not a conservative field. In our coaxial problem let us erect a barrier at $\phi = \pi$; we agree not to select a path which crosses this plane. Therefore we cannot encircle I, and a single-valued potential is possible. The result is seen to be

$$V_m = -\frac{I}{2\pi}\phi \qquad (-\pi < \phi < \pi)$$

and

$$V_{mP} = -I/8$$

at $\phi = \pi/4$.

The scalar magnetic potential is evidently the quantity whose equipotential surfaces will form curvilinear squares with the stream-lines of **H** in Fig. 8.3. This is one more facet of the analogy between electric and magnetic fields about which we will have more to say in the next chapter.

Let us temporarily leave the scalar magnetic potential now and investigate a vector magnetic potential. This will prove to be a concept that is valid in regions for which the current density is zero or nonzero, and we shall also be able to extend it to the time-varying case later. Our choice of a vector magnetic potential is indicated by noting that

$$\boldsymbol{\nabla} \cdot \mathbf{B} = 0$$

Next, a vector identity which we proved in Sec. 8.4 shows that the divergence of the curl of any vector field is zero. Therefore we select

(3) $$\boxed{\mathbf{B} = \boldsymbol{\nabla} \times \mathbf{A}}$$

where **A** signifies a *vector magnetic potential*, and automatically satisfy the condition that the magnetic flux density shall have zero divergence. The **H** field is

(4) $$\mathbf{H} = \frac{1}{\mu_0} \boldsymbol{\nabla} \times \mathbf{A}$$

and

$$\boldsymbol{\nabla} \times \mathbf{H} = \mathbf{J} = \frac{1}{\mu_0} \boldsymbol{\nabla} \times \boldsymbol{\nabla} \times \mathbf{A}$$

The curl of the curl of a vector field is not zero and is given by a fairly complicated expression,[1] which we need not know now in general form. In specific cases for which the form of **A** is known, the curl operation may with no difficulty be applied twice to determine the current density.

Equation (3) serves as a useful definition of the *vector magnetic potential* **A**. Since the curl operation implies differentiation with respect to a length, the units of **A** are webers per meter.

As yet we have seen only that the definition for **A** does not conflict with any previous results. It still remains to show that this

[1] $\boldsymbol{\nabla} \times \boldsymbol{\nabla} \times \mathbf{A} \equiv \boldsymbol{\nabla}(\boldsymbol{\nabla} \cdot \mathbf{A}) - \boldsymbol{\nabla}^2 \mathbf{A}$. In cartesian coordinates, it may be shown that

$$\boldsymbol{\nabla}^2 \mathbf{A} \equiv \boldsymbol{\nabla}^2 A_x \mathbf{a}_x + \boldsymbol{\nabla}^2 A_y \mathbf{a}_y + \boldsymbol{\nabla}^2 A_z \mathbf{a}_z$$

particular definition can help us to determine magnetic fields more easily. We certainly cannot identify $\mathbf{A}$ with any easily measured quantity or history-making experiment.

We shall show in the following section that, given the Biot-Savart law, the definition of $\mathbf{B}$, and the definition of $\mathbf{A}$, then $\mathbf{A}$ may be determined from the differential current elements by

(5)
$$\boxed{\mathbf{A} = \oint \frac{\mu_0 I \, d\mathbf{L}}{4\pi R}}$$

The significance of the terms in (5) is the same as in the Biot-Savart law; a direct current I flows along a filamentary conductor of which any differential length $d\mathbf{L}$ is R m from the point at which $\mathbf{A}$ is to be found. Since we have defined $\mathbf{A}$ only through specification of its curl, it is possible to add the **grad**ient of any scalar field to (5) without changing $\mathbf{B}$ or $\mathbf{H}$, for the curl of the gradient is identically zero. In steady magnetic fields, it is customary to set this possible added term equal to zero.

The fact that $\mathbf{A}$ is a vector magnetic *potential* is more apparent when (5) is compared with the similar expression for the electrostatic potential,

$$V = \int \frac{\rho_L \, dL}{4\pi\epsilon_0 R}$$

Each expression is the integral along a line source, in one case line charge and in the other line current; each integrand is inversely proportional to the distance from the source to the point of interest; and each involves a characteristic of the medium, here free space, the permeability or the permittivity.

Equation (5) may be written in differential form,

(6) $\qquad d\mathbf{A} = \dfrac{\mu_0 I \, d\mathbf{L}}{4\pi R}$

if we again agree not to attribute any physical significance to any magnetic fields we obtain from (6) until the *entire closed path in which the current flows is considered.* With this reservation, let us go right ahead and consider the vector magnetic potential field about a differential filament. Locating the filament at the origin and allowing it to extend in the positive z direction, $d\mathbf{L} = dz\mathbf{a}_z$, and we use cylindrical coordinates to determine $d\mathbf{A}$ at the point (r,ϕ,z):

$$d\mathbf{A} = \frac{\mu_0 I \, dz\mathbf{a}_z}{4\pi\sqrt{r^2 + z^2}}$$

or

(7) $\qquad dA_z = \dfrac{\mu_0 I \, dz}{4\pi\sqrt{r^2 + z^2}} \qquad dA_\phi = 0 \qquad dA_r = 0$

We note first that the direction of $d\mathbf{A}$ is the same as that of $I\,d\mathbf{L}$. Each small section of a current-carrying conductor produces a contribution to the total vector magnetic potential which is in the same direction as the current flow in the conductor. The magnitude of the vector magnetic potential varies inversely as the distance to the current element, being strongest in the neighborhood of the current and gradually falling off to zero at distant points. Skilling[1] describes the vector magnetic potential field as "like the current distribution but fuzzy around the edges, or like a picture of the current out of focus."

In order to find the magnetic field intensity we must take the curl of (7) in cylindrical coordinates, leading to

$$d\mathbf{H} = \frac{1}{\mu_0}\,\boldsymbol{\nabla}\times d\mathbf{A} = \frac{1}{\mu_0}\left(-\frac{\partial\,dA_z}{\partial r}\right)\mathbf{a}_\phi$$

or

$$d\mathbf{H} = \frac{I\,dz}{4\pi}\frac{r}{(r^2+z^2)^{3/2}}\mathbf{a}_\phi$$

which is easily shown to be the same as the value given by the Biot-Savart law.

Expressions for the vector magnetic potential $\mathbf{A}$ can also be obtained for a current source which is distributed. For a surface current $\mathbf{K}$, the differential current element becomes

$$I\,d\mathbf{L} = \mathbf{K}\,dS$$

In the case of current flow throughout a volume with a density $\mathbf{J}$, we have

$$I\,d\mathbf{L} = \mathbf{J}\,dv$$

In each of these two expressions the vector character has been given to the current; for the filamentary element it is customary, although not necessary, to use $I\,d\mathbf{L}$ instead of $\mathbf{I}\,dL$. Since the magnitude of the filamentary current is constant, we have chosen the form which allows us to remove one quantity from the integral. The alternative expressions for $\mathbf{A}$ are then

(8)
$$\mathbf{A} = \int_s \frac{\mu_0\mathbf{K}\,dS}{4\pi R}$$

and

(9)
$$\mathbf{A} = \int_{vol} \frac{\mu_0\mathbf{J}\,dv}{4\pi R}$$

[1] See the bibliography at the end of the chapter.

Equations (5), (8), and (9) express the vector magnetic potential as an integration over all of its sources. From a comparison of the form of these integrals with those which yield the electrostatic potential, it is evident that once again the zero reference for **A** is at infinity, for no finite current element can produce any contribution as $R \rightarrow \infty$. We should remember that we very seldom used the similar expressions for V; too often our theoretical problems included charge distributions which extended to infinity and the result would be an infinite potential everywhere. Actually, we calculated very few potential fields until the differential form of the potential equation was obtained, $\nabla^2 V = -\rho/\epsilon$, or better yet, $\nabla^2 V = 0$. We were then at liberty to select our own zero reference.

The analogous expressions for **A** will be derived in the next section, and an example of the calculation of a vector magnetic potential field will be completed.

D 8.9 The inner conductor of a coaxial cable, with $a = 2$ and $b = 5$ mm, carries a uniform current density in the $\mathbf{a}_z$ direction of $10^6/\pi$ A/m².

(a) Find I_{total}.
(b) For $a < r < b$ let $V_m = 0$ at $\phi = 0$. If a barrier is placed at $\phi = \pi$, find V_m at $\phi = 2\pi/3$.
(c) If the barrier is placed at $\phi = \pi/2$, find V_m at $\phi = 2\pi/3$.

Ans. $-1.333; 2.67; 4.00$ A

D 8.10 The vector magnetic potential within a solid conductor of radius a carrying a total current I in the $\mathbf{a}_z$ direction may be found easily. Using the known value of **H** or **B** for $r < a$, then (3) may be solved for **A**. After selecting **A** = 0 at $r = a$, find **A** at

(a) $r = 0$

(b) $r = \dfrac{a}{3}$

(c) $r = \dfrac{2a}{3}$, and plot $|\mathbf{A}|$ versus r

Ans. $5.56 \times 10^{-8} I\mathbf{a}_z; 8.89 \times 10^{-8} I\mathbf{a}_z; 10 \times 10^{-8} I\mathbf{a}_z$ Wb/m

8.7 DERIVATION OF STEADY-MAGNETIC-FIELD LAWS

We shall now carry out our threat to supply the promised proofs of the several relationships between the magnetic field quantities. All these relationships may be obtained from the definitions of **H**,

(1) $\mathbf{H} = \displaystyle\oint \frac{I\, d\mathbf{L} \times \mathbf{a}_R}{4\pi R^2}$

of **B**,

(2) $\mathbf{B} = \mu_0\mathbf{H}$

and of **A**,

(3) $\mathbf{B} = \nabla \times \mathbf{A}$

Let us first assume that we may express **A** by

(4) $\mathbf{A} = \displaystyle\int_{\text{vol}} \frac{\mu_0\mathbf{J}\, dv}{4\pi R}$

and then demonstrate the correctness of (4) by showing that (1) follows. First we should add subscripts to indicate the point at which the current element is located, (x_1,y_1,z_1), and the point at which **A** is given, (x_2,y_2,z_2). The differential volume element dv is then written dv_1 and in cartesian coordinates would be $dx_1\, dy_1\, dz_1$. The variables of integration are x_1, y_1, and z_1. Using these subscripts, then,

(5) $\mathbf{A}_2 = \displaystyle\int_{\text{vol}} \frac{\mu_0\mathbf{J}_1\, dv_1}{4\pi R_{12}}$

From (2) and (3) we have

(6) $\mathbf{H} = \dfrac{\mathbf{B}}{\mu_0} = \dfrac{\nabla \times \mathbf{A}}{\mu_0}$

In order to show that (1) follows from (5) it is necessary to substitute (5) into (6). This step involves taking the curl of $\mathbf{A}_2$, a quantity expressed in terms of the variables x_2, y_2, and z_2, and the curl therefore involves partial derivatives with respect to x_2, y_2, and z_2. We do this, placing a subscript on the del operator to remind us of the variables involved in the partial differentiation process,

$$\mathbf{H}_2 = \frac{\nabla_2 \times \mathbf{A}_2}{\mu_0} = \frac{1}{\mu_0}\, \nabla_2 \times \int_{\text{vol}} \frac{\mu_0\mathbf{J}_1\, dv_1}{4\pi R_{12}}$$

The order of partial differentiation and integration is immaterial, and $\mu_0/4\pi$ is assumed constant, allowing us to write

$$\mathbf{H}_2 = \frac{1}{4\pi}\int_{\text{vol}} \nabla_2 \times \frac{\mathbf{J}_1\, dv_1}{R_{12}}$$

The curl operation within the integrand represents partial differentiation with respect to x_2, y_2, and z_2. The differential volume element dv_1 is a scalar and a function only of x_1, y_1, and z_1. Consequently, it may be factored out of the curl operation as any other constant, leaving

$$(7) \quad \mathbf{H}_2 = \frac{1}{4\pi} \int_{\text{vol}} \left(\boldsymbol{\nabla}_2 \times \frac{\mathbf{J}_1}{R_{12}} \right) dv_1$$

The curl of the product of a scalar and a vector is given by an identity which may be checked by expansion in cartesian coordinates,

$$(8) \quad \boldsymbol{\nabla} \times (S\mathbf{V}) \equiv (\boldsymbol{\nabla}S) \times \mathbf{V} + S(\boldsymbol{\nabla} \times \mathbf{V})$$

This identity is used to expand the integrand of (7),

$$(9) \quad \mathbf{H}_2 = \frac{1}{4\pi} \int_{\text{vol}} \left[\left(\boldsymbol{\nabla}_2 \frac{1}{R_{12}} \right) \times \mathbf{J}_1 + \frac{1}{R_{12}} (\boldsymbol{\nabla}_2 \times \mathbf{J}_1) \right] dv_1$$

The second term of this integrand is zero, because $\boldsymbol{\nabla}_2 \times \mathbf{J}_1$ indicates partial derivatives of a function of x_1, y_1, and z_1 taken with respect to the variables x_2, y_2, and z_2. The first set of variables is not a function of the second set, and all partial derivatives are zero.

The first term of the integrand may be determined by expressing R_{12} in terms of the coordinate values,

$$R_{12} = \sqrt{(x_2 - x_1)^2 + (y_2 - y_1)^2 + (z_2 - z_1)^2}$$

and taking the gradient of its reciprocal. Problem 34 shows that the result is

$$\boldsymbol{\nabla}_2 \left(\frac{1}{R_{12}} \right) = -\frac{\mathbf{R}_{12}}{R_{12}{}^3} = -\frac{\mathbf{a}_{R12}}{R_{12}{}^2}$$

Substituting this result into (9), we have

$$\mathbf{H}_2 = -\frac{1}{4\pi} \int_{\text{vol}} \frac{\mathbf{a}_{R12} \times \mathbf{J}_1}{R_{12}{}^2} dv_1$$

or

$$\mathbf{H}_2 = \int_{\text{vol}} \frac{\mathbf{J}_1 \times \mathbf{a}_{R12}}{4\pi R_{12}{}^2} dv_1$$

which is the equivalent of (1) in terms of current density. Replacing $\mathbf{J}_1 \, dv_1$ by $I_1 \, d\mathbf{L}_1$, we may rewrite the volume integral as ·

$$\mathbf{H}_2 = \oint \frac{I_1 \, d\mathbf{L}_1 \times \mathbf{a}_{R12}}{4\pi R_{12}{}^2}$$

Equation (4) is therefore correct and agrees with the three definitions (1), (2), and (3).

Next we shall prove Ampère's circuital law in point form,

$$(10) \quad \boldsymbol{\nabla} \times \mathbf{H} = \mathbf{J}$$

Combining (2) and (3), we obtain

(11) $\nabla \times \mathbf{H} = \nabla \times \dfrac{\mathbf{B}}{\mu_0} = \dfrac{1}{\mu_0} \nabla \times \nabla \times \mathbf{A}$

We now need the expansion in cartesian coordinates for $\nabla \times \nabla \times \mathbf{A}$. Performing the indicated partial differentiations and collecting the resulting terms, we may write the result as

(12) $$\boxed{\nabla \times \nabla \times \mathbf{A} \equiv \nabla(\nabla \cdot \mathbf{A}) - \nabla^2 \mathbf{A}}$$

where

(13) $$\boxed{\nabla^2 \mathbf{A} \equiv \nabla^2 A_x \mathbf{a}_x + \nabla^2 A_y \mathbf{a}_y + \nabla^2 A_z \mathbf{a}_z}$$

Equation (13) is the definition (in cartesian coordinates) of the *Laplacian of a vector.*

Substituting (12) into (11), we have

(14) $\nabla \times \mathbf{H} = \dfrac{1}{\mu_0} [\nabla(\nabla \cdot \mathbf{A}) - \nabla^2 \mathbf{A}]$

and now require expressions for the divergence and the Laplacian of $\mathbf{A}$.

We may find the divergence of $\mathbf{A}$ by applying the divergence operation to (5),

(15) $\nabla_2 \cdot \mathbf{A}_2 = \dfrac{\mu_0}{4\pi} \displaystyle\int_{\mathrm{vol}} \nabla_2 \cdot \dfrac{\mathbf{J}_1}{R_{12}} \, dv_1$

and using the vector identity (5) of Sec. 4.8,

$\nabla \cdot (S\mathbf{V}) \equiv \mathbf{V} \cdot (\nabla S) + S(\nabla \cdot \mathbf{V})$

producing

(16) $\nabla_2 \cdot \mathbf{A}_2 = \dfrac{\mu_0}{4\pi} \displaystyle\int_{\mathrm{vol}} \left[\mathbf{J}_1 \cdot \left(\nabla_2 \dfrac{1}{R_{12}} \right) + \dfrac{1}{R_{12}} (\nabla_2 \cdot \mathbf{J}_1) \right] dv_1$

The second part of the integrand is zero, because $\mathbf{J}_1$ is not a function of x_2, y_2, and z_2.

We have already used the result that $\nabla_2(1/R_{12}) = -\mathbf{R}_{12}/R_{12}^3$, and it is just as easily shown that

$\nabla_1 \dfrac{1}{R_{12}} = \dfrac{\mathbf{R}_{12}}{R_{12}^3}$

or that

$\nabla_1 \dfrac{1}{R_{12}} = -\nabla_2 \dfrac{1}{R_{12}}$

Equation (16) can therefore be written as

$$\nabla_2 \cdot \mathbf{A}_2 = \frac{\mu_0}{4\pi} \int_{\text{vol}} \left[-\mathbf{J}_1 \cdot \left(\nabla_1 \frac{1}{R_{12}} \right) \right] dv_1$$

and the vector identity applied again,

(17) $\quad \nabla_2 \cdot \mathbf{A}_2 = \dfrac{\mu_0}{4\pi} \displaystyle\int_{\text{vol}} \left[\dfrac{1}{R_{12}} (\nabla_1 \cdot \mathbf{J}_1) - \nabla_1 \cdot \left(\dfrac{\mathbf{J}_1}{R_{12}} \right) \right] dv_1$

Since we are concerned only with steady magnetic fields, the continuity equation shows that the first term of (17) is zero. Application of the divergence theorem to the second term gives

$$\nabla_2 \cdot \mathbf{A}_2 = -\frac{\mu_0}{4\pi} \oint_{S_1} \frac{\mathbf{J}_1}{R_{12}} \cdot d\mathbf{S}_1$$

where the surface S_1 encloses the volume throughout which we are integrating. This volume must include all the current, for the original integral expression for $\mathbf{A}$ was an integration such as to include the effect of all the current. Since there is no current outside this volume (otherwise we should have had to increase the volume to include it), we may integrate over a slightly larger volume or a slightly larger enclosing surface without changing $\mathbf{A}$. On this larger surface the current density $\mathbf{J}_1$ must be zero, and therefore the closed surface integral is zero, since the integrand is zero. Hence the divergence of $\mathbf{A}$ is zero.

In order to find the Laplacian of the vector $\mathbf{A}$ let us compare the x component of (4) with the similar expression for electrostatic potential,

$$A_x = \int_{\text{vol}} \frac{\mu_0 J_x \, dv}{4\pi R} \qquad V = \int_{\text{vol}} \frac{\rho \, dv}{4\pi\epsilon_0 R}$$

We note that one expression can be obtained from the other by a straightforward change of variable, J_x for ρ, μ_0 for $1/\epsilon_0$, and A_x for V. However, we have derived some additional information about the electrostatic potential which we shall not have to repeat now for the x component of the vector magnetic potential. This takes the form of Poisson's equation.

$$\nabla^2 V = -\frac{\rho}{\epsilon_0}$$

which becomes, after the change of variables.

$$\nabla^2 A_x = -\mu_0 J_x$$

Similarly, we have

$$\nabla^2 A_y = -\mu_0 J_y$$

and

$$\nabla^2 A_z = -\mu_0 J_z$$

or

(18)
$$\boxed{\nabla^2 \mathbf{A} = -\mu_0 \mathbf{J}}$$

Returning to (14), we can now substitute for the divergence and Laplacian of $\mathbf{A}$ and obtain the desired answer,

(10) $$\nabla \times \mathbf{H} = \mathbf{J}$$

We have already shown the use of Stokes' theorem in obtaining the integral form of Ampère's circuital law from (10) and need not repeat that labor here.

We thus have succeeded in showing that every result we have essentially "pulled from free space" for magnetic fields follows from the basic definitions of $\mathbf{H}$, $\mathbf{B}$, and $\mathbf{A}$. The derivations are not simple, but they should be understandable on a step-by-step basis. It is hoped that the procedure need never be committed to memory.

Finally, let us return to (18) and make use of this formidable second-order vector partial differential equation to find the vector magnetic potential in one simple example. We select the field between conductors of a coaxial cable, with radii of a and b as usual, and current I in the $\mathbf{a}_z$ direction. Between the conductors, $\mathbf{J} = 0$, and therefore

$$\nabla^2 \mathbf{A} = 0$$

We have already been told (and Prob. 35 gives us the opportunity to check the results for ourselves) that the vector Laplacian may be expanded as the vector sum of the scalar Laplacians of the three components in cartesian coordinates,

$$\nabla^2 \mathbf{A} = \nabla^2 A_x \, \mathbf{a}_x + \nabla^2 A_y \, \mathbf{a}_y + \nabla^2 A_z \, \mathbf{a}_z$$

but such a relatively simple result is not possible in other coordinate systems. That is, in cylindrical coordinates, for example,

$$\nabla^2 \mathbf{A} \neq \nabla^2 A_r \, \mathbf{a}_r + \nabla^2 A_\phi \, \mathbf{a}_\phi + \nabla^2 A_z \, \mathbf{a}_z$$

However, it is not difficult to show for cylindrical coordinates that the z component of the vector Laplacian is the scalar Laplacian of the z component of $\mathbf{A}$, or

(19) $$\nabla^2 \mathbf{A}|_z = \nabla^2 A_z$$

and since the current is entirely in the z direction in this problem,

A has only a z component.   Therefore

$$\nabla^2 A_z = 0$$

or

$$\frac{1}{r}\frac{\partial}{\partial r}\left(r\frac{\partial A_z}{\partial r}\right) + \frac{1}{r^2}\frac{\partial^2 A_z}{\partial \phi^2} + \frac{\partial^2 A_z}{\partial z^2} = 0$$

Thinking symmetrical thoughts about (4) shows us that A_z is a function only of r, and thus

$$\frac{1}{r}\frac{d}{dr}\left(r\frac{dA_z}{dr}\right) = 0$$

We have solved this equation before, and the result is

$$A_z = C_1 \ln r + C_2$$

If we choose a zero reference at $r = b$, then

$$A_z = C_1 \ln \frac{r}{b}$$

In order to relate C_1 to the sources in our problem, we may take the curl of **A**,

$$\nabla \times \mathbf{A} = -\frac{\partial A_z}{\partial r}\mathbf{a}_\phi = -\frac{C_1}{r}\mathbf{a}_\phi = \mathbf{B}$$

obtain **H**,

$$\mathbf{H} = -\frac{C_1}{\mu_0 r}\mathbf{a}_\phi$$

and evaluate the line integral,

$$\oint \mathbf{H}\cdot d\mathbf{L} = I = \int_0^{2\pi} -\frac{C_1}{\mu_0 r}\mathbf{a}_\phi\cdot r\,d\phi\,\mathbf{a}_\phi = -\frac{2\pi C_1}{\mu_0}$$

Thus

$$C_1 = -\frac{\mu_0 I}{2\pi}$$

or

(20) $$A_z = \frac{\mu_0 I}{2\pi}\ln\frac{b}{r}$$

and

$$H_\phi = \frac{I}{2\pi r}$$

FIG. 8.12 The vector magnetic potential is shown within the inner conductor and in the region between conductors for a coaxial cable with $b = 5a$ carrying I in the $\mathbf{a}_z$ direction. $A_z = 0$ is arbitrarily selected at $r = b$.

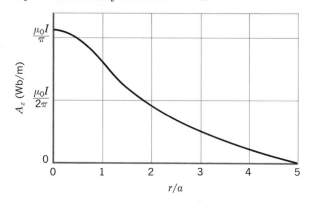

as before. A plot of A_z versus r for $b = 5a$ is shown in Fig. 8.12; the decrease of $|\mathbf{A}|$ with distance from the concentrated current source which the inner conductor represents is evident. The results of Prob. D8.10 (with an appropriate change of zero reference) have also been added to the graph of Fig. 8.12. The extension of the curve into the outer conductor is left as Prob. 37.

D 8.11 Equation (20) is obviously also applicable to the exterior of any conductor of circular cross section carrying I in the specified direction. The zero reference is arbitrarily set at $r = b$. Two parallel conductors, each of circular cross section with radius 1 cm, are separated 20 cm center to center and carry equal and opposite currents of 200 A. Select the mid-plane as the zero reference for the vector magnetic potential and then compute $|\mathbf{A}|$ at

(a) That portion of the surface of either wire which is closest to the other wire

(b) The portion farthest from the other wire

(c) Infinity

Ans.   0; 0.118; 0.121   mWb/m

SUGGESTED REFERENCES

1   Boast, W. B.: (see Suggested References for Chap. 2). The scalar magnetic potential is defined on p. 220, and its use in mapping magnetic fields is discussed on p. 444.

2   Jordan, E. C.: "Electromagnetic Waves and Radiating Systems," Prentice-Hall, Inc., Englewood Cliffs, N.J., 1950. Vector magnetic potential is discussed on pp. 82–91.

3   Skilling, H. H.: (see Suggested References for Chap. 3). The "paddle wheel" is introduced on pp. 23–25.

PROBLEMS

1 A current element $I\,d\mathbf{L}$ is located at the origin of a spherical coordinate system and directed in the $\mathbf{a}_z$ direction. Plot the locus of r versus θ in the $\phi = 0$ plane on which the magnitude of $d\mathbf{H}$ is constant.

2 Show that the incremental magnetic field intensity produced at P (x,y,z) by a current element $I\,dL\,\mathbf{a}_z$ located at the origin may be expressed (a) in cartesian coordinates as

$$d\mathbf{H} = \frac{I\,dL(-y\mathbf{a}_x + x\mathbf{a}_y)}{4\pi(x^2 + y^2 + z^2)^{3/2}}$$

and (b) in cylindrical coordinates as

$$d\mathbf{H} = \frac{I\,dL}{4\pi}\frac{r\mathbf{a}_\phi}{(r^2 + z^2)^{3/2}}$$

3 (a) A differential current $K_\phi\,dz\,\mathbf{a}_\phi$ flows around a circular path which is a differential length of a circular cylinder. The cylinder has a radius a and is centered on the z axis; the circular element is centered at $(0,0,z)$. Find $d\mathbf{H}$ at $z = h, r = 0$. (b) Now find $\mathbf{H}$ at $z = h, r = 0$ caused by the surface current $\mathbf{K} = K_\phi\mathbf{a}_\phi$ flowing on the cylinder $r = a$.

4 A filament lying on the line $z = 0$, $y = d/2$ carries a current I in the $\mathbf{a}_x$ direction. A second filament at $z = 0$, $y = -d/2$ carries I in the $-\mathbf{a}_x$ direction. (a) Find $\mathbf{H}$ at P (x,y,z); (b) simplify the result to obtain $\mathbf{H}$ at $(x,y,0)$.

5 A current I is present in a rectangular filamentary path connecting the points $(a/2,b/2,0)$, $(a/2,-b/2,0)$, $(-a/2,-b/2,0)$, and $(-a/2,b/2,0)$. If $I\,d\mathbf{L} \times \mathbf{a}_z$ is directed away from the origin, find $\mathbf{H}$ (a) at a general point in the $z = 0$ plane within the loop; (b) at a general point on the z axis.

6 Two filamentary current loops are centered on the z axis at $z = \pm h$. Each has a radius a and carries a current I in the $\mathbf{a}_\phi$ direction. (a) Find $\mathbf{H}$ on the z-axis, $-h < z < h$. Assume $I = 1$ A, $a = 1$ m. (b) Plot $|\mathbf{H}|$ versus z if $h = a/4$. (c) Plot $|\mathbf{H}|$ versus z if $h = a/2$. (d) Plot $|\mathbf{H}|$ versus z if $h = a$. Which choice for h gives the more uniform field? These are called Helmholtz coils and are used in providing uniform fields.

7 A filamentary conductor is formed into an equilateral triangle with sides of length a carrying a current I. Find the magnetic field intensity at the center of the triangle.

8 A filamentary conductor carrying I in the $\mathbf{a}_z$ direction extends along the entire negative z axis. At $z = 0$ it connects to a copper sheet filling the $x > 0$, $y > 0$ quadrant of the $z = 0$ plane. Find $\mathbf{H}$ at $(0,0,h)$. [GIFT: $\mathbf{a}_\phi = f(\phi)$, $\mathbf{a}_x \neq f(\phi)$, $\mathbf{a}_y \neq f(\phi)$.]

9 The strip $z = 0$, $-a < y < a$ carries a current sheet $\mathbf{K} = K_0\mathbf{a}_x$. (a) Find $\mathbf{H}$ at $(0,0,h)$. (b) Show that this expression for $\mathbf{H}$ approaches that of an infinite current sheet as $a \to \infty$ [Sec. 8.2, Eq. (2)].

10 For the current strip of Prob. 9 (a) find $\mathbf{H}$ at $(0,b,0)$, $b > a$. (b) If $b > a$, show that $\mathbf{H}$ is closely equal to $\mathbf{H}$ for an infinite straight filament.

FIG. 8.13   See Prob. 11.

11 Find the contribution to the magnetic field intensity at point P in Fig. 8.13 caused by (a) the semicircular section; (b) the two horizontal conductors; (c) the short vertical section.

12 A current filament carrying I in the $-\mathbf{a}_z$ direction lies along the entire positive z axis. At the origin it connects to a conducting sheet forming the $z = 0$ plane. (a) Find $\mathbf{K}$ in the conducting sheet. (b) Use Ampère's circuital law to find $\mathbf{H}$ everywhere for $z > 0$. (c) Find $\mathbf{H}$ for $z < 0$.

13 The curve $x = a(1 + 0.5 \sin z)$ is rotated about the z axis to form a surface of revolution that looks something like a newel post. Let this surface be the surface of a solid conductor, whose axis is the z axis. The conductor carries a total current I in the $\mathbf{a}_z$ direction. Is $\mathbf{H} = (I/2\pi r)\mathbf{a}_\phi$ everywhere outside the conductor? Why, or why not?

14 Two coaxial hollow cylindrical shells of radius a and b, $b > a$, are centered on the z axis. The inner cylinder has a uniform surface current density of $K_0\mathbf{a}_z$. This current may be assumed to return in the outer cylinder. Find $\mathbf{H}$ for (a) $r < a$; (b) $a < r < b$; (c) $r > b$.

15 A hollow cylindrical shell of radius a is centered on the z axis and carries a uniform surface current density of $K_a\mathbf{a}_\phi$. (a) Show that H is not a function of ϕ or z. (b) Show that H_ϕ and H_r are everywhere zero. (c) Show that $H_z = 0$ for $r > a$. (d) Show that $H_z = K_a$ for $r < a$. (e) A second shell, $r = b$, carries a current $K_b\mathbf{a}_\phi$. Find $\mathbf{H}$ everywhere.

16 The rectangle $x = a$, $x = b$, $z = c/2$, $z = -c/2$ ($b > a$) is rotated about the z axis, forming a toroid with a rectangular cross section. Assume that the toroidal surface is conducting, that it is slit along the circle $r = a$, $z = 0$, and that a distributed current generator is inserted to provide a surface current $\mathbf{K} = K_0\mathbf{a}_z$ across the slit. Consider the symmetry of the problem carefully and show that $\mathbf{H} = K_0(a/r)\mathbf{a}_\phi$ within the toroid and zero outside it.

17 Infinitely long filamentary conductors are located in the $y = 0$ plane at $x = n$, $n = 0, \pm1, \pm2, \ldots$. Each carries 1 A in the $\mathbf{a}_z$ direction. (a) Find $\mathbf{H}$ at $(0,1,0)$ and $(0,2,0)$. As a help,

$$\sum_{n=1}^{\infty} \frac{y}{y^2 + n^2} = \frac{\pi}{2} - \frac{1}{2y} + \frac{\pi}{e^{2\pi y} - 1}$$

(b) What value would be obtained by approximating the array of filaments with a current sheet of 1 A/m?

18 A balanced coaxial cable contains three coaxial conductors of negligible resistance. Assume a solid inner conductor of radius 2 mm, an intermediate conductor of inner radius 4 mm and outer radius 4.9 mm, and an outer conductor of inner radius 9.8 mm and outer radius 10 mm. Assume that

The Steady Magnetic Field   250

the intermediate conductor $(4 \text{ mm} < r < 4.9 \text{ mm})$ carries a current of 2 A in the $\mathbf{a}_z$ direction and is at a potential of 25 V, whereas each of the other two conductors is at zero potential and carries 1 A in the opposite direction. Assume also that the current distribution in each conductor is uniform. Find and sketch (a) $\mathbf{J}$ in each conductor; (b) $\mathbf{H}$ for $0 < r < 11$ mm; (c) $\mathbf{E}$ for $0 < r < 11$ mm.

19 Evaluate $\nabla \times \nabla \times \mathbf{A}$ if (a) $\mathbf{A} = r^2\mathbf{a}_z$, cylindrical coordinates; (b) $\mathbf{A} = r \sin \theta \, \mathbf{a}_r$, spherical coordinates.

20 Show that $\nabla \times \mathbf{H} = \mathbf{J}$ for the field in each conductor of the coaxial-cable example discussed in Sec. 8.2.

21 In a cylindrical coordinate system, the current density is $\mathbf{J} = J_0 e^{-r/a}\mathbf{a}_z$ for all r. (a) Find the total I crossing the $z = 0$ plane within $r = r_0$. (b) Find $\mathbf{H}$ at $r = r_0$. (c) Show that $\nabla \times \mathbf{H} = \mathbf{J}$.

22 The line integral $\oint \mathbf{F} \cdot d\mathbf{L}$ is evaluated about a circular path of radius r centered at the origin in the $z = 0$ plane. For travel in the $\mathbf{a}_\phi$ direction, use the definition of curl to determine curl $\mathbf{F}$ at the origin if the value of the line integral is (a) Kr^2; (b) $K \sin^2 \pi r$; (c) K.

23 Show that solution of the differential equations

$$\frac{dx}{(\nabla \times \mathbf{H})_x} = \frac{dy}{(\nabla \times \mathbf{H})_y} = \frac{dz}{(\nabla \times \mathbf{H})_z}$$

gives the equations of the streamlines of the current density, and find these streamlines if $\mathbf{H} = xy\mathbf{a}_x + \frac{1}{2}(x^2 + y^2)\mathbf{a}_z$.

24 Prove that $\oint \nabla T \cdot d\mathbf{L} = 0$

25 Show that the circulation of the vector magnetic potential is equal to the total flux enclosed by the path.

26 Consider a sphere of radius $r = 4$ centered at $(0,0,3)$. Let S_1 be that portion of the spherical surface on which $z > 0$. Find $\int_{S_1} (\nabla \times \mathbf{H}) \cdot d\mathbf{S}$ if $\mathbf{H} = 3r\mathbf{a}_\phi$ in cylindrical coordinates.

27 The region $0 < z < a$ is a conductor carrying $\mathbf{J} = J_0\mathbf{a}_y$ A/m^2; the region $(d - a) < z < d$ is also a conductor and carries $\mathbf{J} = -J_0\mathbf{a}_y$ A/m^2. Find the total magnetic flux crossing a plane area extending between $y = 0$, $y = L$, (a) $z = -\infty$, and $z = 0$; (b) $z = 0$, and $z = a$; (c) $z = a$, and $z = d - a$; (d) $z = d - a$, and $z = d$; (e) $z = d$, and $z = \infty$.

28 Find the total flux Φ flowing through the interior of the toroid of Prob. 16.

29 A current filament carrying I in the $\mathbf{a}_z$ direction lies along the z axis. Consider a rectangular path of sides a and b in the $y = 0$ plane, with the side of length a parallel to and d m from the z axis. If $b = 2a = 2d$, by what percentage does the magnetic flux passing through the rectangle decrease as it rotates about its center of gravity a quarter-turn in the $y = 0$ plane?

30 A planar transmission line consists of two very thin conducting planes at $z = 0$ and $z = d$, carrying current sheets of $-K_x\mathbf{a}_x$ and $K_x\mathbf{a}_x$, respectively. Each extends from $y = -b/2$ to $y = b/2$, where b may be assumed to be large compared to d. (a) Find $\mathbf{B}$ and $\mathbf{H}$ between the planes. (b) Find the scalar magnetic potential V_m for $0 < z < d$ such that $V_m = 0$ at $y = 0$. (c) By using the definition of $\mathbf{A}$, find the vector magnetic potential between the planes such that $\mathbf{A} = 0$ at $z = 0$. (d) Find Φ crossing the plane $y = 0$

between $x = 0$ and L and $z = 0$ and d. (e) Use the line integral of Prob. 25 to check the result of (d) above.

31 A square filamentary differential current loop, dL on a side, is centered at the origin in the $z = 0$ plane. The current I flows generally in the $\mathbf{a}_\phi$ direction. (a) Assuming $r \gg dL$, show that

$$d\mathbf{A} = \frac{\mu_0 I \, dL^2 \sin\theta}{4\pi r^2} \, \mathbf{a}_\phi$$

(b) show that

$$d\mathbf{H} = \frac{I \, dL^2}{4\pi r^3} \, (2\mathbf{a}_r \cos\theta + \mathbf{a}_\theta \sin\theta)$$

32 Two circular cylindrical conductors of 1-m radius in air are parallel to the z axis with axes in the plane $y = 0$ at $x = 2$ and $x = -2$, carrying currents of I in the $\mathbf{a}_z$ and $-\mathbf{a}_z$ directions, respectively. (a) Find the unit vector in the direction of $\mathbf{H}$ at $(2,1,0)$ on one conductor surface. (b) Outside the conductor, $\mathbf{H} = -\nabla V_m$ and $\nabla^2 V_m = 0$. In the $z = 0$ plane, are the lines $V_m = $ constant perpendicular to $\mathbf{H}$ outside the conductor? (c) What is the direction of the $V_m = $ constant line at $(2,1,0)$? (d) May either the streamlines of $\mathbf{H}$ or the lines on which $V_m = $ constant be identified with the equipotentials in the problem of the electric fields between two parallel circular cylinders?

33 Show that Sec. 8.7, Eq. (8), is correct.

34 Following Sec. 8.7, Eq. (9), the statement is made that $\nabla_2(1/R_{12}) = -R_{12}/\mathbf{R}_{12}{}^3$. Prove it.

35 By expanding Sec. 8.7, Eq. (12), in cartesian coordinates, show that (13) is correct.

36 Find $\mathbf{A}$ within a cylindrical conductor of radius a, axis on the z axis, carrying I in the $\mathbf{a}_z$ direction, by using $\nabla^2 \mathbf{A} = -\mu_0 \mathbf{J}$. Let $\mathbf{A} = 0$ at $r = a$.

37 Compute the vector magnetic potential within the outer conductor for the coaxial line whose magnetic field intensity is shown in Fig. 8.12 if the outer radius of the outer conductor is $6a$. Select the proper zero reference and sketch the results on the figure.

38 Use the article by J. H. Miller, Magnetic Field Strength in Oersteds Near Large Rectangular Conductors: Part I, *Trans. AIEE*, vol. 77, p. 726, November, 1958, to compute H in amperes per meter at a point 5 cm distant (in a direction perpendicular to a face) from the axis of a conductor of square cross section, 5 cm on a side, carrying 1,000 A. Conductors and currents of these magnitudes are used in the production of aluminum.

39 Refer to Maxwell's "Treatise" (see Suggested References for Chap. 5), art. 684, and use his Eq. (17) to calculate and plot A_z versus r, $a_2 < r < a_1$, if the constant A is selected so that $A_z = 0$ at $r = a_1$, $I = 1$ A, $a_2 = 1$ cm, and $a_1 = 2$ cm. Maxwell uses emu units here, and A_z is naturally in maxwells per centimeter, I is in abamperes, and μ and μ_0 are dimensionless. Conversion of these units to the rationalized mks system or International System may be accomplished with the help of Sec. B.2. You may also want to read the previous two pages to find his symbols for $\mathbf{A}$, $\mathbf{H}$, $\mathbf{B}$, I, $\mathbf{J}$, and V_m.

9 MAGNETIC FORCES, MATERIALS, AND INDUCTANCE

The magnetic field quantities $\mathbf{H}$, $\mathbf{B}$, Φ, V_m, and $\mathbf{A}$ introduced in the last chapter have not as yet been given any physical significance. Each of these quantities is merely defined in terms of the distribution of current sources throughout space. If the current distribution is known, we should feel that $\mathbf{H}$, $\mathbf{B}$, and $\mathbf{A}$ are determined at every point in space, even though we may not be able to evaluate the defining integrals because of mathematical complexity.

We are now ready to undertake the second half of the magnetic field problem, that of determining the forces and torques exerted by the magnetic field on other charges. The electric field causes a force to be exerted on a charge which may be either stationary or in motion; we shall see that the steady magnetic field is capable of exerting a force only on a *moving* charge. This result appears logical; a magnetic field may be produced by moving charges and may exert forces on moving charges; a magnetic field cannot arise from stationary charges and cannot exert any force on a stationary charge.

This chapter initially considers the forces and torques on current-carrying conductors which may either be of a filamentary nature or possess a finite cross section with a known current density distribution. The problems associated with the motion of particles in a vacuum are largely avoided.

With an understanding of the fundamental effects produced by the magnetic field, we may then consider the varied types of magnetic materials, the analysis of elementary magnetic circuits, forces on magnetic materials, and finally, the important electrical circuit concept of inductance.

9.1 FORCE ON A MOVING CHARGE

In an electric field the definition of the electric field intensity shows us that the force on a charged particle is

(1)
$$\boxed{\mathbf{F} = Q\mathbf{E}}$$

The force is in the same direction as the electric field intensity (for a positive charge) and is directly proportional to both $\mathbf{E}$ and Q. If the charge is in motion, the force at any point in its trajectory is then given by (1).

A charged particle in motion in a magnetic field of flux density $\mathbf{B}$ is found experimentally to experience a force which is proportional to the charge Q, its velocity U, the flux density B, and to the sine of the angle between the vectors $\mathbf{U}$ and $\mathbf{B}$. The direction of the force is perpendicular to both $\mathbf{U}$ and $\mathbf{B}$ and is given by a unit vector in the direction of $\mathbf{U} \times \mathbf{B}$. The force may therefore be expressed as

$$(2) \qquad \boxed{\mathbf{F} = Q\mathbf{U} \times \mathbf{B}}$$

A fundamental difference in the effect of the electric and magnetic fields on charged particles is now apparent, for a force which is always applied in a direction at right angles to the direction in which the particle is proceeding can never change the magnitude of the particle velocity. In other words, the *acceleration* vector is always normal to the velocity vector. The kinetic energy of the particle thus remains unchanged, and the steady magnetic field is therefore incapable of transferring energy to the moving charge. The electric field, on the other hand, exerts a force on the particle which is independent of the direction in which the particle is progressing and therefore effects an energy transfer between field and particle in general.

The force on a moving particle due to combined electric and magnetic fields is obtained easily by superposition,

$$(3) \qquad \boxed{\mathbf{F} = Q(\mathbf{E} + \mathbf{U} \times \mathbf{B})}$$

This equation is known as the *Lorentz force equation*, and its solution is required in determining electron orbits in the magnetron, proton paths in the cyclotron, or, in general, charged-particle motion in combined electric and magnetic fields.

D 9.1 A charged particle in a *uniform* magnetic field must move in a circular path. Assume that $\mathbf{B} = 10^{-3}\,\mathbf{a}_z$ Wb/m^2 and that the initial velocity at $t = 0$ is $\mathbf{U}_0 = 2{,}000\mathbf{a}_x$ m/s. If the particle is an electron,

(a) Find $\mathbf{F}$ at $t = 0$.
(b) Find $\mathbf{F}$ when $\mathbf{U} = -2{,}000\mathbf{a}_x$.
(c) By equating centrifugal and centripetal forces, it is quite simple to determine the radius of the path and the time required for one revolution. Using these results, find $\mathbf{F}$ at $t = 6$ ns.

Ans. $-3.2 \times 10^{-19}\mathbf{a}_y$; $(-2.79\mathbf{a}_x + 1.58\mathbf{a}_y) \times 10^{-19}$; $\quad 3.2 \times 10^{-19}\mathbf{a}_y \quad$ N

9.2 FORCE ON A DIFFERENTIAL CURRENT ELEMENT

The force on a charged particle moving through a steady magnetic field,

$$(1) \qquad \mathbf{F} = Q\mathbf{U} \times \mathbf{B}$$

may be used to obtain the expression for the differential amount of force exerted on a differential element of charge,

(2) $\qquad d\mathbf{F} = dQ\ \mathbf{U} \times \mathbf{B}$

Physically, the differential element of charge consists of a large number of very small discrete charges occupying a volume which, although small, is much larger than the average separation between the charges. The differential force expressed by (2) is thus merely the sum of the forces on the individual charges. This sum, or resultant force, is not a force applied to a single object. In an analogous way, we might consider the differential gravitational force experienced by a small volume taken in a shower of falling sand. The small volume contains a large number of sand grains, and the differential force is the sum of the forces on the individual grains within the small volume.

If our charges are electrons in motion in a conductor, however, we can show that the force is transferred to the conductor and that the sum of this extremely large number of extremely small forces is of practical importance. Within the conductor electrons are in motion throughout a region of immobile positive ions which form a crystalline array giving the conductor its solid properties. A magnetic field which exerts forces on the electrons tends to cause them to shift position slightly and produces a small displacement between the centers of "gravity" of the positive and negative charges. The Coulomb forces between electrons and positive ions, however, tend to resist such a displacement. Any attempt to move the electrons, therefore, results in an attractive force between electrons and the positive ions of the crystalline lattice. The magnetic force is thus transferred to the crystalline lattice, or to the conductor itself. The Coulomb forces are so much greater than the magnetic forces in good conductors that the actual displacement of the electrons is almost immeasurable. The charge separation that does result, however, is disclosed by the presence of a slight potential difference across the conductor sample in a direction perpendicular to both the magnetic field and the velocity of the charges. The voltage is known as the *Hall voltage,* and the effect itself is called the *Hall effect.* Devices employ the Hall effect to measure the magnetic flux density and, in some applications where the current through the device can be made proportional to the magnetic field across it, to serve as electronic wattmeters, squaring elements, and so forth.

Returning to (2), we may therefore say that if we are considering an element of moving charge in an electron beam, the force is merely the sum of the forces on the individual electrons in that small volume element, but if we are considering an element of moving charge within a conductor, the total force is applied to the solid conductor itself. We shall now limit our attention to the forces on current-carrying conductors.

In Chap. 5 we defined current density in terms of the velocity of the volume charge density,

$$\boxed{\mathbf{J} = \rho\mathbf{U}}$$

The differential element of charge in (2) may also be expressed in terms of volume charge density,

$$dQ = \rho\, dv$$

Thus

$$d\mathbf{F} = \rho\, dv\ \mathbf{U} \times \mathbf{B}$$

or

(3)
$$\boxed{d\mathbf{F} = \mathbf{J} \times \mathbf{B}\, dv}$$

We saw in the previous chapter that $\mathbf{J}\, dv$ may be interpreted as a differential current element; that is,

$$\mathbf{J}\, dv = \mathbf{K}\, dS = I\, d\mathbf{L}$$

and thus the Lorentz force equation may be applied to surface current density,

(4)
$$\boxed{d\mathbf{F} = \mathbf{K} \times \mathbf{B}\, dS}$$

or to a differential current filament,

(5)
$$\boxed{d\mathbf{F} = I\, d\mathbf{L} \times \mathbf{B}}$$

Each of the expressions for the differential force on a current element, (3), (4), or (5), leads to results that may be verified experimentally only when the entire physical current distribution is considered. This is exactly analogous to the interpretation of the expressions for the differential field $d\mathbf{H}$ produced by differential current elements, as discussed in Sec. 8.1.

Integrating (3), (4), or (5) over a volume, a surface which may be either open or closed (why?), or a closed path, respectively, leads to the integral formulations

(6) $$\mathbf{F} = \int_{\text{vol}} \mathbf{J} \times \mathbf{B}\, dv$$

(7) $$\mathbf{F} = \int_{s} \mathbf{K} \times \mathbf{B}\, dS$$

and

(8)

$$\mathbf{F} = \oint I \, d\mathbf{L} \times \mathbf{B} = -I \oint \mathbf{B} \times d\mathbf{L}$$

One simple result is obtained by applying (5) or (8) to a straight conductor in a uniform magnetic field,

(9)

$$\mathbf{F} = I\mathbf{L} \times \mathbf{B}$$

The magnitude of the force is given by the familiar equation

(10) $F = BIL \sin \theta$

where the angle between the vectors representing the direction of the current flow and the direction of the magnetic flux density is θ. Equation (9) or (10) applies only to a portion of the closed circuit, and the remainder of the circuit must be considered in any practical problem.

D 9.2 A circular current loop $r = 8$ cm, $z = 0$ carries a current of 30 A in the $\mathbf{a}_\phi$ direction. A uniform magnetic field of $2\mathbf{a}_z$ Wb/m² is present; the field is partly produced by the loop itself. Find the magnitude of the force

(a) On a short 1-cm length of the loop at the positive x axis
(b) On a 1-cm length at the positive y axis
(c) Of tension acting to break the loop apart

Ans.   0.6; 0.6; 9.6   N

D 9.3 A "filamentary" conductor on the z axis carries a current of 50 A in the $\mathbf{a}_z$ direction in air. A differential current element $I \, d\mathbf{L} = 10^{-6}\mathbf{a}_L$ is located at $(0.1,0,0)$. Specify $\mathbf{a}_L$ in cartesian coordinates such that

(a) There is no force on the current element.
(b) There is a maximum force on the current element.
(c) The magnitude of the force on the current element is 5×10^{-11} N.

Ans. $\pm\mathbf{a}_y;\ l\mathbf{a}_x + n\mathbf{a}_z,\ l^2 + n^2 = 1;\ l\mathbf{a}_x \pm 0.866\mathbf{a}_y + n\mathbf{a}_z,\ l^2 + n^2 = 0.25$

9.3   FORCE BETWEEN DIFFERENTIAL CURRENT ELEMENTS

The concept of the magnetic field was introduced to break into two parts the problem of finding the interaction of one current distribution on a second current distribution. It is possible to express the force on one current element directly in terms of a second current element without finding the magnetic field. Since we have claimed that the magnetic-field concept simplifies our work, it then behooves us to show that avoidance of this intermediate step leads to more complicated expressions.

The magnetic field at point 2 due to a current element at point 1 has been found to be

$$d\mathbf{H}_2 = \frac{I_1 \, d\mathbf{L}_1 \times \mathbf{a}_{R12}}{4\pi R_{12}^2}$$

Now, the differential force on a differential current element is

$$d\mathbf{F} = I \, d\mathbf{L} \times \mathbf{B}$$

and we apply this to our problem by letting $\mathbf{B}$ be $d\mathbf{B}_2$, the differential flux density at point 2 caused by current element 1, by identifying $I \, d\mathbf{L}$ as $I_2 \, d\mathbf{L}_2$, and by symbolizing the differential amount of our differential force on element 2 as $d(d\mathbf{F}_2)$:

$$d(d\mathbf{F}_2) = I_2 \, d\mathbf{L}_2 \times d\mathbf{B}_2$$

Since $d\mathbf{B}_2 = \mu_0 \, d\mathbf{H}_2$, we obtain the force between two differential current elements,

(1) $$\quad d(d\mathbf{F}_2) = \mu_0 \frac{I_1 I_2}{4\pi R_{12}^2} \, d\mathbf{L}_2 \times (d\mathbf{L}_1 \times \mathbf{a}_{R12})$$

The total force between the two filamentary circuits is obtained by integrating twice:

(2) $$\quad \mathbf{F}_2 = \mu_0 \frac{I_1 I_2}{4\pi} \oint \left[d\mathbf{L}_2 \times \oint \frac{d\mathbf{L}_1 \times \mathbf{a}_{R12}}{R_{12}^2} \right]$$

$$= \mu_0 \frac{I_1 I_2}{4\pi} \oint \left[\oint \frac{\mathbf{a}_{R12} \times d\mathbf{L}_1}{R_{12}^2} \right] \times d\mathbf{L}_2$$

Equation (2) is quite formidable, but the familiarity gained in the last chapter with the magnetic field should enable us to recognize the inner integral as the integral necessary to find the magnetic field at point 2 due to the current element at point 1.

Although we shall not do so, it is not very difficult to make use of (2) to find the force of repulsion between two infinitely long, straight parallel filamentary conductors, separated d m, and carrying equal but opposite currents of I A. The integrations are simple, and most errors are made in determining suitable expressions for $\mathbf{a}_{R12}$, $d\mathbf{L}_1$, and $d\mathbf{L}_2$. However, since the magnetic field intensity at either wire caused by the other is already known to be $I/2\pi d$, it is readily apparent that the answer is a force of $\mu_0 I^2/2\pi d$ N per meter length.

D 9.4   Two conducting filaments extend along the x and y axes, carrying currents I_1 and I_2 in the $\mathbf{a}_x$ and $\mathbf{a}_y$ directions, respectively. Find the differential force exerted on the differential current element

(a) $I_2\,dL_2$ at $(0,1,0)$ by the differential element $I_1\,dL_1$ at $(1,0,0)$
(b) $I_2\,dL_2$ at $(0,-1,0)$ by $I_1\,dL_1$ at $(1,0,0)$
(c) $I_1\,dL_1$ at $(1,0,0)$ by $I_2\,dL_2$ at $(0,1,0)$

Ans. $-\dfrac{\mu_0 I_1 I_2\,dL_1\,dL_2}{8\sqrt{2}\,\pi}\,\mathbf{a}_x;\qquad \dfrac{\mu_0 I_1 I_2\,dL_1\,dL_2}{8\sqrt{2}\,\pi}\,\mathbf{a}_y;\qquad \dfrac{\mu_0 I_1 I_2\,dL_1\,dL_2}{8\sqrt{2}\,\pi}\,\mathbf{a}_x \qquad$ N

9.4 FORCE AND TORQUE ON A CLOSED CIRCUIT

We have already obtained general expressions for the forces exerted on current systems. One special case is easily disposed of, for if we take our relationship for the force on a filamentary closed circuit, as given by Sec. 9.2, Eq. (8),

$$\mathbf{F} = -I \oint \mathbf{B} \times d\mathbf{L}$$

and assume a *uniform* magnetic flux density, then $\mathbf{B}$ may be removed from the integral:

$$\mathbf{F} = -I\mathbf{B} \times \oint d\mathbf{L}$$

However, we discovered during our investigation of closed line integrals in any electrostatic potential field that $\oint d\mathbf{L} = 0$, and therefore the force on a closed filamentary circuit in a uniform magnetic field is zero.

If the field is not uniform, the total force need not be zero.

This result for uniform fields does not have to be restricted to filamentary circuits only. The circuit may contain surface currents or volume current density as well. If the total current is divided into filaments, the force on each one is zero, as we showed above, and the total force is again zero. Therefore any real closed circuit carrying direct currents experiences a total vector force of zero in a uniform magnetic field.

Although the force is zero, the torque is generally not equal to zero.

The *torque*, or *moment*, of a force is a vector whose magnitude is the product of the magnitudes of the vector force, the vector lever arm, and the sine of the angle between these two vectors. The direction of the vector torque is normal to both the force and lever arm and is in the direction of progress of a right-handed screw as the lever arm is rotated into the force vector through the smaller angle. The torque is expressible as a cross product,

$$\mathbf{T} = \mathbf{R} \times \mathbf{F}$$

Let us assume that two forces $\mathbf{F}_1$ and $\mathbf{F}_2$ with lever arms $\mathbf{R}_1$ and $\mathbf{R}_2$ are applied to an object of fixed shape and that the object does not undergo any translation. Then

$$\mathbf{T} = \mathbf{R}_1 \times \mathbf{F}_1 + \mathbf{R}_2 \times \mathbf{F}_2$$

where

$$\mathbf{F}_1 + \mathbf{F}_2 = 0$$

and therefore

$$\mathbf{T} = (\mathbf{R}_1 - \mathbf{R}_2) \times \mathbf{F}_1 = \mathbf{R}_{21} \times \mathbf{F}_1$$

The vector $\mathbf{R}_{21} = (\mathbf{R}_1 - \mathbf{R}_2)$ joins the point of application of $\mathbf{F}_2$ to that of $\mathbf{F}_1$ and is independent of the choice of origin for the two vectors $\mathbf{R}_1$ and $\mathbf{R}_2$. We are therefore free to choose any common origin for the lever arms $\mathbf{R}_1$ and $\mathbf{R}_2$, provided that the total force is zero. This may be extended to any number of forces.

Consider the application of a vertically upward force at the end of a horizontal crank handle on an elderly automobile. This cannot be the only applied force, for if it were, the entire handle would be accelerated in an upward direction. A second force, equal in magnitude to that exerted at the end of the handle, is applied in a downward direction by the bearing surface at the axis of rotation. For

FIG. 9.1 A differential current loop in a magnetic field $\mathbf{B}$. The torque on the loop is $d\mathbf{T} = I(dx\,dy\,\mathbf{a}_z) \times \mathbf{B}_0 = I\,d\mathbf{S} \times \mathbf{B}$.

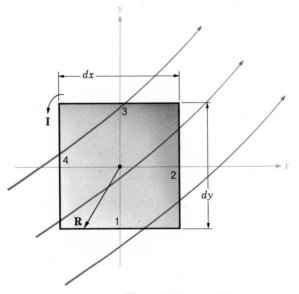

a 40-N force on a crank handle 0.3 m in length, the torque is 12 N-m. This figure is obtained regardless of whether the origin is considered to be on the axis of rotation (leading to 12 N-m plus 0 N-m), at the midpoint of the handle (leading to 6 N-m plus 6 N-m), or at some point not even on the handle or an extension of the handle.

We may therefore choose the most convenient origin, and this is usually on the axis of rotation and in the plane containing the applied forces if the several forces are coplanar.

With this introduction to the concept of torque, let us now consider the torque on a differential current loop in a magnetic field $\mathbf{B}$. The loop lies in the xy plane (Fig. 9.1); the sides of the loop are parallel to the x and y axes and are of length dx and dy. The value of the magnetic field at the center of the loop is taken as $\mathbf{B}_0$. Since the loop is of differential size, the value of $\mathbf{B}$ at all points on the loop may be taken as $\mathbf{B}_0$. (Why was this not possible in the discussion of curl and divergence?) The total force on the loop is therefore zero, and we are free to choose the origin for the lever arms at the center of the loop.

The vector force on side 1 is

$$d\mathbf{F}_1 = I\,dx\,\mathbf{a}_x \times \mathbf{B}_0$$

or

$$d\mathbf{F}_1 = I\,dx\,(B_{0y}\mathbf{a}_z - B_{0z}\mathbf{a}_y)$$

For this side of the loop the average lever arm $\mathbf{R}$ extends from the origin to the midpoint of the side, $\mathbf{R}_1 = -\tfrac{1}{2}dy\,\mathbf{a}_y$, and the contribution to the total torque is

$$
\begin{aligned}
d\mathbf{T}_1 &= \mathbf{R}_1 \times d\mathbf{F}_1 \\
&= -\tfrac{1}{2}dy\,\mathbf{a}_y \times I\,dx\,(B_{0y}\mathbf{a}_z - B_{0z}\mathbf{a}_y) \\
&= -\tfrac{1}{2}dx\,dy\,IB_{0y}\mathbf{a}_x
\end{aligned}
$$

Similarly, the torque contribution on side 3 is found to be equal to the above expression,

$$d\mathbf{T}_3 = d\mathbf{T}_1$$

and

$$d\mathbf{T}_1 + d\mathbf{T}_3 = -dx\,dy\,IB_{0y}\mathbf{a}_x$$

Evaluating the torque on sides 2 and 4, we find

$$d\mathbf{T}_2 + d\mathbf{T}_4 = dx\,dy\,IB_{0x}\mathbf{a}_y$$

and the total torque is then

$$d\mathbf{T} = I\,dx\,dy\,(B_{0x}\mathbf{a}_y - B_{0y}\mathbf{a}_x)$$

The quantity within the parentheses may be represented by a cross product,

$$d\mathbf{T} = I\,dx\,dy\,(\mathbf{a}_z \times \mathbf{B}_0)$$

or

(1) $$\boxed{d\mathbf{T} = I\,d\mathbf{S} \times \mathbf{B}}$$

where $d\mathbf{S}$ is the vector area of the differential current loop and the subscript on $\mathbf{B}_0$ has been dropped.

Now, the differential torque on a differential electric dipole (discussed in Sec. 4.7) in an electric field $\mathbf{E}$ is easily shown to be

$$d\mathbf{T} = d\mathbf{p} \times \mathbf{E}$$

It is therefore logical that we define the product of the loop current and the vector area of the loop as the differential *magnetic dipole moment* $d\mathbf{m}$. Thus

(2) $$\boxed{d\mathbf{m} = I\,d\mathbf{S}}$$

and hence we may express the differential torque on the current loop as

(3) $$d\mathbf{T} = d\mathbf{m} \times \mathbf{B}$$

Equations (1) or (3) are general results which hold for differential loops of any shape, not just rectangular ones. The torque on a circular or triangular loop is also given in terms of the vector surface or the moment by (1) or (3).

Since we selected a differential current loop so that we might assume $\mathbf{B}$ was constant throughout it, it follows that the torque on a *planar* loop of any size in a *uniform* magnetic field is given by the same expression,

(4) $$\boxed{\mathbf{T} = I\mathbf{S} \times \mathbf{B} = \mathbf{m} \times \mathbf{B}}$$

We should note that the torque on the current loop is in such a direction as to align the magnetic field produced by the loop with the applied magnetic field that is causing the torque. This is perhaps the easiest way to determine the direction of the torque.

D 9.5 An electric dipole with $\mathbf{p} = 10^{-16}\mathbf{a}_z$ and a magnetic dipole with $\mathbf{m} = 10^{-12}\mathbf{a}_x$ are rigidly connected at the origin. Find the torque on the combination if

(*a*) $\mathbf{E} = 2\mathbf{a}_z,\ \mathbf{B} = 2 \times 10^{-4}\mathbf{a}_z$
(*b*) $\mathbf{E} = 2\mathbf{a}_x,\ \mathbf{B} = 2 \times 10^{-4}\mathbf{a}_y$
(*c*) $\mathbf{E} = 2\mathbf{a}_x,\ \mathbf{B} = 2 \times 10^{-4}\mathbf{a}_z$

Ans. $0;\ -2 \times 10^{-16}\mathbf{a}_y;\ 2 \times 10^{-16}(\mathbf{a}_y + \mathbf{a}_z)$ N-m

We are now in a position to combine our knowledge of the action of a magnetic field on a current loop with a simple model of an atom and obtain some appreciation of the difference in behavior of various materials in magnetic fields.

Although accurate quantitative results can only be predicted through the use of quantum theory, the simple atomic model which assumes that there is a central positive nucleus surrounded by electrons in various circular orbits yields reasonable quantitative results and provides a satisfactory qualitative theory. An electron in an orbit is analogous to a small current loop (in which the current is directed oppositely to the direction of electron travel) and as such experiences a torque in an external magnetic field, the torque tending to align the magnetic field produced by the orbiting electron with the external magnetic field. If there were no other magnetic moments to consider, we would then conclude that all the orbiting electrons in the material would shift in such a way as to add their magnetic fields to the applied field, and thus that the resultant magnetic field at any point in the material would be greater than it would be at that point if the material were not present.

A second moment, however, is attributed to *electron spin*. Although it is tempting to model this phenomenon by considering the electron as spinning about its own axis and thus generating a magnetic dipole moment, satisfactory quantitative results are not obtained from such a theory. Instead, it is necessary to digest the mathematics of relativistic quantum theory to show that an electron may have a spin magnetic moment of $\pm 9.27 \times 10^{-24}$ A-m^2; the plus and minus signs indicate that alignment aiding or opposing an external magnetic field is possible. In an atom with many electrons present, only the spins of those electrons in shells which are not completely filled will contribute to a magnetic moment for the atom.

A third contribution to the moment of an atom is caused by *nuclear spin*, but this factor provides a negligible contribution to the over-all magnetic properties of materials and we shall not consider it further.

Thus each atom contains many different component moments, and their combination determines the magnetic characteristics of the material and provides its general magnetic classification. We shall describe briefly six different types of material: diamagnetic, paramagnetic, ferromagnetic, antiferromagnetic, ferrimagnetic, and superparamagnetic.

Let us first consider those atoms in which the small magnetic fields produced by the motion of the electrons in their orbits and those produced by the electron spin combine to produce a net field of zero. Note that we are considering here the fields produced by the electron motion itself in the absence of any external magnetic field; we might also describe this material as one in which the permanent magnetic moment $\mathbf{m}_0$ of each atom is zero. Such a material is termed *diamagnetic*. It would seem, therefore, that an external magnetic field would produce no torque on the atom, no realignment of the dipole fields, and consequently an internal magnetic field that is the same as the applied field. To an accuracy of about one part in a hundred thousand, this is correct. However, the action of the externally applied field on an orbiting electron whose moment, for example, is in the same direction as the applied field, can be shown[1] to effectively increase the centrifugal force. Since the opposing force (Coulomb attraction) is unchanged, the electron must therefore have a somewhat smaller velocity if the radius of the orbit is assumed constant. A smaller velocity means a smaller dipole moment. Initially this orbital moment was canceled by a spin moment, and hence the spin moment now predominates. Since that moment opposes the applied field, the net result is a slight reduction in the internal field as compared with the external field.

Metallic bismuth shows a greater diamagnetic effect[2] than most other diamagnetic materials, among which are hydrogen, helium, the other "inert" gases, sodium chloride, copper, gold, silicon, germanium, graphite, and sulfur. We should also realize that the diamagnetic effect is present in all materials, because it arises from an interaction of the external magnetic field with every orbiting electron; however, it is overshadowed by other effects in the materials we shall consider next.

Now let us discuss an atom in which the effects of the electron spin and orbital motion do not quite cancel. The atom as a whole has a small magnetic moment, but the random orientation of the atoms in a larger sample produces an *average* magnetic moment of zero. The material shows no magnetic effects in the absence of an external field. When an external field is applied, however, there is a small torque on each atomic moment, and these moments tend to become aligned with the external field. This alignment acts to increase the value of **B** within the material over the external value. However, the diamagnetic effect is still operating on the orbiting electrons and may counteract the above increase. If the net result is a decrease in **B**, the material is still called diamagnetic. However, if there is an increase in **B**, the material is termed *paramagnetic*. Potassium, oxygen, tungsten, and the rare

[1] At least we hope it can be shown. Try Prob. 19 at the end of this chapter.
[2] A sensitive compass having a bismuth needle would be ideal for the young man going west (or east), for it always aligns itself at right angles to the magnetic field.

earth elements and many of their salts, such as erbium chloride, neodymium oxide, and yttrium oxide, one of the materials used in masers, are examples of paramagnetic substances.

The remaining four classes of material, ferromagnetic, antiferromagnetic, ferrimagnetic, and superparamagnetic, all have strong atomic moments. Moreover, the interaction of adjacent atoms causes an alignment of the magnetic moments of the atoms in either an aiding or exactly opposing manner.

In *ferromagnetic* materials each atom has a relatively large dipole moment, caused primarily by uncompensated electron spin moments. Interatomic forces cause these moments to line up in a parallel fashion over regions containing a large number of atoms. These regions are called *domains*, and they may have a variety of shapes and sizes ranging from one micron (10^{-6} m) to several centimeters, depending on the size, shape, material, and magnetic history of the sample. Virgin ferromagnetic materials will have domains which each have a strong magnetic moment; the domain moments, however, vary in direction from domain to domain. The over-all effect is therefore one of cancellation, and the material as a whole has no magnetic moment. Upon application of an external magnetic field, however, those domains which have moments in the direction of the applied field increase their size at the expense of their neighbors, and the internal magnetic field increases greatly over that of the external field alone. When the external field is removed, a completely random domain alignment is not usually attained, and a residual, or remnant, dipole field remains in the macroscopic structure. The fact that the magnetic moment of the material is different after the field has been removed, or that the magnetic state of the material is a function of its magnetic history is called *hysteresis*, a subject which will be discussed again when magnetic circuits are studied a few pages from now. Ferromagnetic materials are not isotropic in single crystals, and we shall therefore limit our discussion to polycrystalline materials, except for mentioning that one of the characteristics of anisotropic magnetic materials is magnetostriction, or the change in dimensions of the crystal when a magnetic field is impressed on it. The only elements that are ferromagnetic at room temperature are iron, nickel, and cobalt. Some alloys of these metals with each other and with other metals are also ferromagnetic, as for example alnico, an aluminum-nickel-cobalt alloy with a small amount of copper. At lower temperatures some of the rare earth elements, such as gadolinium and dysprosium, are ferromagnetic. It is also interesting that some alloys of nonferromagnetic metals are ferromagnetic, such as bismuth-manganese and copper-manganese-tin.

In *antiferromagnetic* materials, the forces between adjacent atoms cause the atomic moments to line up in an antiparallel fashion.

The net magnetic moment is zero, and antiferromagnetic materials are affected only slightly by the presence of an external magnetic field. This effect, first discovered in manganese oxide, is not of engineering importance at present.

The *ferrimagnetic* substances also show an antiparallel alignment of adjacent atomic moments, but the moments are not equal. A large response to an external magnetic field therefore occurs, although not as large as that in ferromagnetic materials. The most important group of ferrimagnetic materials are the *ferrites*, in which the conductivity is low, several orders of magnitude less than that of semiconductors. The fact that these substances have greater resistance than the ferromagnetic materials results in much smaller induced currents in the material when alternating fields are applied, as for example in transformer cores which operate at the higher frequencies. The reduced currents (eddy currents) lead to lower ohmic losses in the transformer core. The iron oxide magnetite (Fe_3O_4), a nickel-zinc ferrite $(Ni_{1/2}Zn_{1/2}Fe_2O_4)$, and a nickel ferrite $(NiFe_2O_4)$ are examples of this class of materials.

Superparamagnetic materials are composed of an assemblage of ferromagnetic particles in a nonferromagnetic matrix. Although domains exist within the individual particles, the domain walls cannot penetrate the intervening matrix material to the adjacent particle. An important example is the magnetic tape used in audio or video tape recorders.

9.6 MAGNETIZATION AND PERMEABILITY

In order to place our description of magnetic materials on a more quantitative basis we shall now devote a page or so to showing how the magnetic dipoles act as sources of the magnetic field. Our result will be an equation that looks very much like the point form of Ampère's circuital law, $\nabla \times \mathbf{H} = \mathbf{J}$. The current, however, will be the movement of *bound* charges (orbital electrons, electron spin, and nuclear spin), and the field, which has the dimensions of $\mathbf{H}$, will be called the magnetization $\mathbf{M}$. The current produced by the bound charges is called a *bound current*, or *Amperian current*.

Let us begin by defining the magnetization $\mathbf{M}$ in terms of the magnetic dipole moment $\mathbf{m}$. We remember that a current I circulating about a path enclosing a differential vector area $d\mathbf{S}$ defines the magnetic dipole moment,

$$\mathbf{m} = I \, d\mathbf{S}$$

If there are n *identical* magnetic dipoles per unit volume, then

(1) $$\mathbf{M} = nI \, d\mathbf{S}$$

where the *magnetization* $\mathbf{M}$ is obviously the magnetic dipole moment per unit volume. In general, however, we must think of $\mathbf{M}$ as being obtained by an averaging process over some given

FIG. 9.2 A section $d\mathbf{L}$ of a closed path along which magnetic dipoles have been partially aligned by some external magnetic field. The alignment has caused the bound current crossing the surface defined by the closed path to increase by $nI\,d\mathbf{S}\cdot d\mathbf{L}$ amperes.

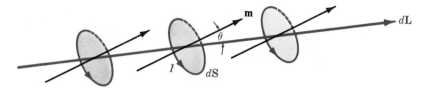

volume, because identical moments can not be assumed. Thus

$$(2) \qquad \mathbf{M} = \frac{1}{V} \sum_{i=1}^{nV} I_i\, d\mathbf{S}_i$$

The units of magnetization are seen to agree with those of $\mathbf{H}$, amperes per meter.

Now let us consider the effect of some alignment of the magnetic dipoles as the result of the application of a magnetic field. We shall investigate this alignment along a closed path, a short portion of which is shown in Fig. 9.2. The figure shows several magnetic moments $\mathbf{m}$ that make an angle θ with the element of path $d\mathbf{L}$; each moment consists of a current I circulating about an area $d\mathbf{S}$. We are therefore considering a small volume, $dS \cos \theta\, dL$, or $d\mathbf{S}\cdot d\mathbf{L}$, within which there are $n\,d\mathbf{S}\cdot d\mathbf{L}$ magnetic dipoles. In changing from a random orientation to this partial alignment, the bound current crossing the surface enclosed by the path (to our left as we travel in the $\mathbf{a}_L$ direction in Fig. 9.2) has increased I A for each of the $n\,d\mathbf{S}\cdot d\mathbf{L}$ dipoles. Thus

$$dI_b = nI\,d\mathbf{S}\cdot d\mathbf{L} = \mathbf{M}\cdot d\mathbf{L}$$

and within an entire closed contour,

$$(3) \qquad I_b = \oint \mathbf{M}\cdot d\mathbf{L}$$

Equation (3) merely says that if we go around a closed path and find dipole moments going our way more often than not, there will be a corresponding current composed of, for example, orbiting electrons crossing the interior surface.

Our desired result is now obtained readily. We express (3) in terms of bound current density,

$$\oint \mathbf{M}\cdot d\mathbf{L} = \int_s \mathbf{J}_b\cdot d\mathbf{S}$$

and apply Stokes' theorem to the closed line integral,

$$\int_s \nabla \times \mathbf{M} \cdot d\mathbf{S} = \int_s \mathbf{J}_b \cdot d\mathbf{S}$$

Since this is true for any surface $d\mathbf{S}$, it therefore follows that

(4)
$$\boxed{\nabla \times \mathbf{M} = \mathbf{J}_b}$$

The bound currents, therefore, are active in producing the magnetization field in the same way that the motion of the free charges gives rise to an **H** field in vacuum.

Now let us use this result to relate **B**, **H**, and **M**. We already have the free-space relationship

$$\nabla \times \mathbf{H} = \mathbf{J} \qquad \text{(free space)}$$

where **J** must represent all current-density sources, free or bound,

$$\nabla \times \mathbf{H} = \mathbf{J}_f + \mathbf{J}_b \qquad \text{(free space)}$$

In terms of **B**, we may write

$$\nabla \times \frac{\mathbf{B}}{\mu_0} = \mathbf{J}_f + \mathbf{J}_b$$

Using (4),

$$\nabla \times \frac{\mathbf{B}}{\mu_0} = \mathbf{J}_f + \nabla \times \mathbf{M}$$

Now, in order to avoid direct consideration of the bound current density, we may absorb **M** in the left side of this equation and define the relationship between **B** and **H** in a more general manner:

$$\nabla \times \left(\frac{\mathbf{B}}{\mu_0} - \mathbf{M}\right) = \mathbf{J}_f$$

or

(5)
$$\boxed{\nabla \times \mathbf{H} = \mathbf{J}_f}$$

where

(6)
$$\mathbf{H} = \frac{\mathbf{B}}{\mu_0} - \mathbf{M}$$

or

(7)
$$\boxed{\mathbf{B} = \mu_0(\mathbf{H} + \mathbf{M})}$$

Thus (5) is our new improved version of Maxwell's equation for steady fields when magnetic materials are present. Only the motion of the *free* charges appears explicitly on the right side of the equation; the effect of the bound charges appears in **H**, as expressed by (6) or (7). The relationship may be simplified for linear isotropic media where a *magnetic susceptibility* can be defined:

(8)
$$\mathbf{M} = \chi_m \mathbf{H}$$

Thus we have

$$\mathbf{B} = \mu_0(\mathbf{H} + \chi_m \mathbf{H})$$
$$= \mu_0 \mu_R \mathbf{H}$$

or

(9)
$$\mathbf{B} = \mu \mathbf{H}$$

where the *permeability* μ,

(10)
$$\mu = \mu_0 \mu_R$$

is defined in terms of a *relative permeability* μ_R,

(11)
$$\mu_R = 1 + \chi_m$$

that is related to the susceptibility.

Just as we found for anisotropic dielectric materials, an anisotropic magnetic material must be described in terms of a tensor permeability:

$$B_x = \mu_{xx}H_x + \mu_{xy}H_y + \mu_{xz}H_z$$
$$B_y = \mu_{yx}H_x + \mu_{yy}H_y + \mu_{yz}H_z$$
$$B_z = \mu_{zx}H_x + \mu_{zy}H_y + \mu_{zz}H_z$$

For anisotropic materials, then, μ is a tensor in the relationship $\mathbf{B} = \mu\mathbf{H}$; however, $\mathbf{B} = \mu_0(\mathbf{H} + \mathbf{M})$ remains valid, although **B**, **H**, and **M** are no longer parallel in general. The most common anisotropic magnetic material is a single ferromagnetic crystal, although thin magnetic films also exhibit anisotropy. Most applications of ferromagnetic materials, however, involve polycrystalline arrays that are much easier to make.

Our definitions of susceptibility and permeability are also dependent upon the assumption of linearity. Unfortunately, this is true only in the less interesting paramagnetic and diamagnetic materials for which the relative permeability rarely differs from unity by more than one part in a thousand. Some typical values of the susceptibility for diamagnetic materials are hydrogen, -2×10^{-5}; copper, -0.9×10^{-5}; germanium, -0.8×10^{-5}; silicon, -0.3×10^{-5}; and graphite, -12×10^{-5}. Several representative paramagnetic susceptibilities are oxygen, 2×10^{-6}; tungsten, 6.8×10^{-5}; ferric oxide (Fe_2O_3), 1.4×10^{-3}; and yttrium oxide (Y_2O_3), 0.53×10^{-6}. If we simply take the ratio of B to $\mu_0 H$ as the relative permeability of a ferromagnetic material, typical values of μ_R would range from 10 to 100,000. Superparamagnetic materials have relative permeabilities ranging from 1 to 10.

As we leave this section, we shall adopt the standard practice of dropping the subscript f on the current density. It should not be too difficult to remember that the $\mathbf{J}$ in

(12) $\quad \nabla \times \mathbf{H} = \mathbf{J}$

or the I in

(13) $\quad \oint \mathbf{H} \cdot d\mathbf{L} = I$

are caused by the motion of free charges, for we only introduced the bound currents in this section. Their effects are now included through the use of a relative permeability,

(14) $\quad \mathbf{B} = \mu_R \mu_0 \mathbf{H}$

D 9.6 Find the magnitude of the magnetization in a material in which

(a) There are 8.1×10^{28} atoms/m³ and the atoms have equal dipole moments of 1.7×10^{-33} A-m².

(b) The relative permeability is 1.00038 and the magnetic field intensity is 0.31 A/m.

(c) $B = 3 \times 10^{-5}$ Wb/m² and the magnetic susceptibility is -4×10^{-6}.

Ans. 0.0956; 0.138; 0.118   mA/m

D 9.7 In a certain magnetic material $\mathbf{H} = 100r^2 \mathbf{a}_\phi$ and $\mathbf{M} = 25r^2 \mathbf{a}_\phi$. At $r = 0.2$ m, find

(a) $\mathbf{J}_f$
(b) $\mathbf{J}_b$
(c) $\mathbf{J}_{\text{total}}$

Ans. $15\mathbf{a}_z$; $60\mathbf{a}_z$; $75\mathbf{a}_z$ A/m²

9.7 MAGNETIC BOUNDARY CONDITIONS

We should have no difficulty in arriving at the proper boundary conditions to apply to $\mathbf{B}$, $\mathbf{H}$, and $\mathbf{M}$ at the interface between two

FIG. 9.3 A Gaussian surface and a closed path are constructed at the boundary between media 1 and 2, having permeabilities of μ_1 and μ_2, respectively. From this we determine the boundary conditions, $B_{n1} = B_{n2}$ and $H_{t1} - H_{t2} = K$.

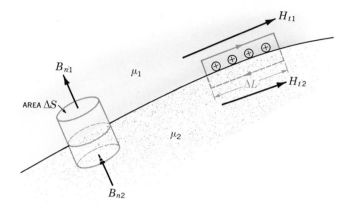

different magnetic materials, for we have solved similar problems for both conducting materials and dielectrics. We need develop no new techniques.

Figure 9.3 shows a boundary between two isotropic homogeneous linear materials with permeabilities μ_1 and μ_2. The boundary condition on the normal components is determined by allowing the surface to cut a small cylindrical Gaussian surface. Applying Gauss's law for the magnetic field [Sec. 8.5, Eq. (4)],

$$\oint_s \mathbf{B} \cdot d\mathbf{S} = 0$$

we find that

$$B_{n1}\, \Delta S - B_{n2}\, \Delta S = 0$$

or

(1) $\boxed{B_{n2} = B_{n1}}$

and

(2) $H_{n2} = \dfrac{\mu_1}{\mu_2} H_{n1}$

The normal component of **B** is continuous, and the normal component of **H** is discontinuous by the ratio μ_1/μ_2.

The relationship between the normal components of **M**, of course, is fixed once those for **B** and **H** are known. The result is written simply as

(3) $\quad M_{n2} = \dfrac{\chi_{m2}\mu_1}{\chi_{m1}\mu_2} M_{n1}$

Application of Ampère's circuital law

$$\oint \mathbf{H} \cdot d\mathbf{L} = I$$

to a small closed path in a plane normal to the boundary surface indicates that

$$H_{t1}\,\Delta L - H_{t2}\,\Delta L = K\,\Delta L$$

where K is the component of the surface current normal to the plane of the closed path. Thus

(4) $\quad \boxed{H_{t1} - H_{t2} = K}$

and

(5) $\quad \dfrac{B_{t1}}{\mu_1} - \dfrac{B_{t2}}{\mu_2} = K$

The boundary condition on the tangential component of the magnetization is therefore

(6) $\quad M_{t2} = \dfrac{\chi_{m2}}{\chi_{m1}} M_{t1} - \chi_{m2}K$

The last three boundary conditions on the tangential components are much simpler, of course, if the surface current density is zero. This is a free current density, and it must be zero if neither material is a conductor.

D 9.8 The plane $x = 0$ separates two isotropic linear homogeneous magnetic materials. The relative permeability is 5 for $x > 0$ and 2 for $x < 0$. If $\mathbf{B}/\mu_0 = -2\mathbf{a}_x + 3\mathbf{a}_y - \mathbf{a}_z$ for $x < 0$, find

(a) **H** for $x < 0$
(b) **H** for $x > 0$
(c) **M** for $x > 0$

Ans. $\quad -\mathbf{a}_x + 1.5\mathbf{a}_y - 0.5\mathbf{a}_z; \ -1.6\mathbf{a}_x + 6\mathbf{a}_y - 2\mathbf{a}_z; \ -0.4\mathbf{a}_x + 1.5\mathbf{a}_y - 0.5\mathbf{a}_z \qquad$ A/m

D 9.9 Repeat Prob. D9.8 assuming the $x = 0$ plane carries a surface current density $\mathbf{K} = 2\mathbf{a}_y$ A/m.

Ans. $\quad -\mathbf{a}_x + 1.5\mathbf{a}_y - 0.5\mathbf{a}_z; \ -1.6\mathbf{a}_x + 6\mathbf{a}_y - 10\mathbf{a}_z; \ -0.4\mathbf{a}_x + 1.5\mathbf{a}_y - 2.5\mathbf{a}_z$ A/m

In this section we shall digress briefly to discuss the fundamental techniques involved in solving a class of magnetic problems known as magnetic circuits. As we shall see shortly, the name arises from the great similarity to the d-c-resistive-circuit analysis with which it is assumed we are all facile. The only important difference lies in the nonlinear nature of the ferromagnetic portions of the magnetic circuit; the methods which must be adopted are similar to those required in nonlinear electric circuits which contain diodes, thermistors, incandescent filaments, and other nonlinear elements.

As a convenient starting point, let us identify those field equations upon which resistive circuit analysis is based. At the same time we shall point out or derive the analogous equations for the magnetic circuit. We begin with the electrostatic potential and its relationship to electric field intensity,

(1a) $\mathbf{E} = -\nabla V$

The scalar magnetic potential has already been defined, and its analogous relation to the magnetic field intensity is

(1b) $$\boxed{\mathbf{H} = -\nabla V_m}$$

In dealing with magnetic circuits it is convenient to call V_m the *magnetomotive force*, or mmf, and we shall acknowledge the analogy to the electromotive force, or emf, by doing so. The units of the mmf are, of course, amperes, but it is customary to recognize that coils with many turns are often employed by using the term "ampere-turns."

The electric potential difference between points A and B may be written as

(2a) $V_{AB} = \displaystyle\int_A^B \mathbf{E} \cdot d\mathbf{L}$

and the corresponding relationship between the mmf and the magnetic field intensity,

(2b) $$\boxed{V_{mAB} = \int_A^B \mathbf{H} \cdot d\mathbf{L}}$$

was developed in Chap. 8, where we learned that the path selected must not cross the chosen barrier surface.

Ohm's law for the electric circuit has the point form

(3a) $\mathbf{J} = \sigma\mathbf{E}$

and we see that the magnetic flux density will be the analog of the current density,

(3b) $\mathbf{B} = \mu\mathbf{H}$

To find the total current, we must integrate:

(4a) $I = \displaystyle\int_s \mathbf{J}\cdot d\mathbf{S}$

A corresponding operation is necessary to determine the total magnetic flux flowing through the cross section of a magnetic circuit:

(4b) $\boxed{\Phi = \displaystyle\int_s \mathbf{B}\cdot d\mathbf{S}}$

We then defined resistance as the ratio of potential difference and current, or

(5a) $V = IR$

and we shall now define *reluctance* as the ratio of the magnetomotive force to the total flux; thus

(5b) $\boxed{V_m = \Phi\mathfrak{R}}$

where reluctance is measured in ampere-turns per weber (A-t/Wb). In resistors which are made of linear isotropic homogeneous material of conductivity σ and have a uniform cross section of area S and length L, the total resistance is

(6a) $R = \dfrac{L}{\sigma S}$

If we are fortunate enough to have such a linear isotropic homogeneous magnetic material of length L and uniform cross section S, then the total reluctance is

(6b) $\boxed{\mathfrak{R} = \dfrac{L}{\mu S}}$

The only such material to which we shall commonly apply this relationship is air.

Finally, let us consider the analog of the source voltage in an electric circuit. We know that the closed line integral of $\mathbf{E}$ is zero,

$$\oint \mathbf{E}\cdot d\mathbf{L} = 0$$

In other words, Kirchhoff's voltage law states that the rise in potential through the source is exactly equal to the fall in potential through the load. The expression for magnetic phenomena takes on a slightly different form,

$$\oint \mathbf{H} \cdot d\mathbf{L} = I_{\text{total}}$$

for the closed line integral is not zero. Since the total current is usually obtained by allowing a current I to flow through an N-turn coil, we may express this result as

(7)
$$\oint \mathbf{H} \cdot d\mathbf{L} = NI$$

In an electric circuit the voltage source is a part of the closed path; in the magnetic circuit the current-carrying coil will surround the magnetic circuit. In tracing a magnetic circuit, we shall not be able to identify a pair of terminals at which the magnetomotive force is applied. The analogy is closer here to a pair of coupled circuits in which induced voltages exist (and in which we shall see in Chap. 10 that the closed line integral of $\mathbf{E}$ is also not zero).

Let us try out some of these ideas on a simple magnetic circuit. In order to avoid the complications of ferromagnetic materials at this time we shall assume that we have an air-core toroid with 500 turns, a cross-sectional area of 6 cm², a mean radius of 15 cm, and a coil current of 4 A. As we already know, the magnetic field is confined to the interior of the toroid, and if we consider the closed path of our magnetic circuit along the mean radius, we link 2,000 A-t,

$$V_{m,\text{source}} = 2{,}000 \text{ A-t}$$

Although the field in the toroid is not quite uniform, we may assume that it is for all practical purposes and calculate the total reluctance of the circuit as

$$\Re = \frac{L}{\mu S} = \frac{2\pi 0.15}{4\pi 10^{-7} \times 6 \times 10^{-4}}$$

$$= 1.25 \times 10^{9} \text{ A-t/Wb}$$

Thus

$$\Phi = \frac{V_{m,s}}{\Re} = \frac{2{,}000}{1.25 \times 10^{9}} = 1.6 \times 10^{-6} \text{ Wb}$$

This value of the total flux is in error by less than $\frac{1}{4}$ per cent, in comparison with the value obtained when the exact distribution of flux over the cross section is used.

Hence

$$B = \frac{\Phi}{S} = \frac{1.6 \times 10^{-6}}{6 \times 10^{-4}} = 2.67 \times 10^{-3} \, \text{Wb/m}^2$$

and finally,

$$H = \frac{B}{\mu} = \frac{2.67 \times 10^{-3}}{4\pi 10^{-7}} = 2,120 \, \text{A-t/m}$$

As a check, we may apply Ampère's circuital law directly in this symmetrical problem,

$$H_\phi 2\pi r = NI$$

and obtain

$$H_\phi = \frac{NI}{2\pi r} = \frac{500 \times 4}{6.28 \times 0.15} = 2,120 \, \text{A/m}$$

at the mean radius.

Our magnetic circuit in this example does not give us any opportunity to find the mmf across different elements in the circuit, for there is only one. The analogous electric circuit is, of course, a single source and a single resistor. We could make it look just as long as the above analysis, however, if we found the current density, the electric field intensity, the total current, the resistance, and the source voltage.

More interesting and more practical problems arise when ferromagnetic materials are present in the circuit. Let us begin by considering the relationship between B and H in such a material. We may assume that we are establishing a curve of B versus H for a sample of ferromagnetic material which is completely demagnetized;

FIG. 9.4 Magnetization curve of a sample of silicon sheet steel.

FIG. 9.5 A hysteresis loop for silicon steel. The coercive
force H_c and remnant flux density B_r are indicated.

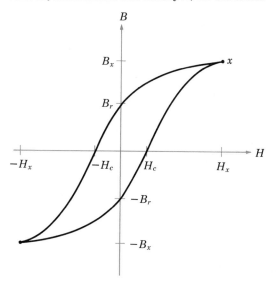

both B and H are zero. As we begin to apply an mmf, the flux
density also rises, but not linearly, as the experimental data of Fig.
9.4 show near the origin. After H reaches a value of about 100
A-t/m, the flux density rises more slowly and begins to saturate
when H is several hundred A-t/m. Having reached partial saturation, let us now turn to Fig. 9.5, where we may continue our experiment at point X by reducing H. As we do so, the effects of hysteresis begin to show, and we do not retrace our original curve. Even
after H is zero, $B = B_r$, the remnant flux density. As H is reversed,
then brought back to zero, and the complete cycle traced several
times, the hysteresis loop of Fig. 9.5 is obtained. The mmf required to reduce the flux density to zero is identified as H_c, the
coercive "force." For smaller maximum values of H smaller
hysteresis loops are obtained and the locus of the tips is about the
same as the virgin magnetization curve of Fig. 9.4.

Let us make use of the magnetization curve for silicon steel to
solve a magnetic circuit problem slightly different from our previous
example. We shall use a steel core in the toroid, except for an air
gap of 2 mm. Magnetic circuits with air gaps occur because gaps
are deliberately introduced in some devices, such as inductors which
must carry large direct currents, because they are unavoidable in
other devices such as rotating machines, or because of unavoidable
problems in assembly. There are still 500 turns about the toroid,
but we desire to know the current required to establish a flux
density of 1 Wb/m² everywhere in the core. This magnetic circuit

is analogous to an electric circuit containing a voltage source and two resistors, one of which is nonlinear. Since we are given the "current" it is easy to find the "voltage" across each series element, and hence the total "emf." In the air gap,

$$\mathcal{R}_{air} = \frac{L_{air}}{\mu S} = \frac{2 \times 10^{-3}}{4\pi 10^{-7} \times 6 \times 10^{-4}} = 2.65 \times 10^6 \text{ A-t/Wb}$$

Knowing the total flux,

$$\Phi = BS = 1(6 \times 10^{-4}) = 6 \times 10^{-4} \text{ Wb}$$

which is the same in both steel and air, we may find the mmf required for the gap,

$$V_{m,air} = (6 \times 10^{-4})(2.65 \times 10^6) = 1,590 \text{ A-t}$$

Referring to Fig. 9.4, a magnetic field strength of 200 A-t/m is required to produce a flux density of 1 Wb/m² in the steel. Thus

$$H_{steel} = 200 \text{ A-t}$$

$$V_{m,steel} = H_{steel}L_{steel} = 200 \times 0.30\pi$$

$$= 188 \text{ A-t}$$

The total mmf is therefore 1,778 A-t and a coil current of 3.56 A is required.

We should realize that we have made several approximations in obtaining this answer. We have already mentioned the lack of a completely uniform cross section, or cylindrical symmetry; the path of every flux line is not of the same length. The choice of a "mean" path length can help compensate for this error in problems in which it may be more important than it is in our example. Fringing flux in the air gap is another source of error, and formulas are available by which we may calculate an effective length and cross-sectional area for the gap which will yield more accurate results. There is also a leakage flux between the turns of wire, and in devices containing coils concentrated on one section of the core a few flux lines bridge the interior of the toroid. Fringing and leakage are problems which seldom arise in the electric circuit because the ratio of the conductivities of air and the conductive or resistive materials used is so high. In contrast, the magnetization curve for silicon steel shows that the ratio of H to B in the steel is about 200; this compares with a ratio in air of about 800,000. Thus, although flux prefers steel to air by the commanding ratio of 4,000 to 1, this is not very close to the ratio of conductivities of, say, 10^{15} for a good conductor and a fair insulator.

As a last example, let us consider the reverse problem. Given a coil current of 4 A in the previous magnetic circuit, what will the

FIG. 9.6 See Prob. D9.10.

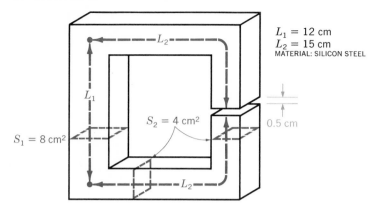

$L_1 = 12$ cm
$L_2 = 15$ cm
MATERIAL: SILICON STEEL

0.5 cm

$S_2 = 4$ cm²

$S_1 = 8$ cm²

L_1

L_2

L_2

flux density be? First let us try to linearize the magnetization curve by a straight line from the origin to $B = 1$, $H = 200$. We then have $B = H/200$ in steel and $B = \mu_0 H$ in air. The two reluctances are found to be 0.314×10^6 for the steel path and 2.65×10^6 for the air gap, or 2.96×10^6 A-t/Wb total. Since V_m is 2,000 A-t, the flux is 6.76×10^{-4} Wb, and $B = 1.13$ Wb/m². A more accurate solution may be obtained by assuming several values of B and calculating the necessary mmf. Plotting the results enables us to determine the true value of B by interpolation. With this method we obtain $B = 1.10$ Wb/m². The good accuracy of the linear model results from the fact that the reluctance of the air gap in a magnetic circuit is often much greater than the reluctance of the ferromagnetic portion of the circuit. A relatively poor approximation for the iron or steel can thus be tolerated.

D 9.10 Given the magnetic circuit of Fig. 9.6, assume $B = 0.8$ Wb/m² at the midpoint of the upper leg and find

(a) $V_{m,\text{air}}$
(b) $V_{m,\text{steel}}$
(c) The number of ampere-turns required in the coil

Ans. 49.2; 3,180; 3,230 A-t

D 9.11 Assume that silicon steel may be represented, up to the "knee" of the magnetization curve, by $H = 200\,B$. A core that is shaped like that in Fig. 9.7 has areas of 2 cm² and lengths of 10 cm in each outer leg, and an area of 3 cm² and a length of 4 cm in the central leg. A coil of 1,000 turns carrying 20 mA is placed on the center leg.

(a) Find B in an outer leg.
(b) Find B in the center leg.

The Magnetic Circuit 279

FIG. 9.7   See Prob. D9.11.

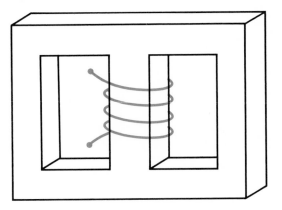

(c) If an air gap of 0.1 mm is introduced into the center leg and the coil current is increased to 60 mA, find B in the air gap.

Ans.   0.585; 0.652; 0.870 Wb/m²

9.9   POTENTIAL ENERGY AND FORCES ON MAGNETIC MATERIALS

In the electrostatic field we first introduced the point charge and the experimental law of force between point charges.   After defining electric field intensity, electric flux density, and electric potential, we were able to find an expression for the energy in an electrostatic field by establishing the work necessary to bring the prerequisite point charges from infinity to their final resting places.   The general expression for energy is

$$(1) \quad W_E = \frac{1}{2} \int_{\text{vol}} \mathbf{D} \cdot \mathbf{E} \, dv$$

where a linear relationship between $\mathbf{D}$ and $\mathbf{E}$ is assumed.

This is not as easily done for the steady magnetic field.   It would seem that we might assume two simple sources, perhaps two current sheets, find the force on one due to the other, move the sheet a differential distance against this force, and equate the necessary work to the change in energy.   If we did, we should be wrong, because Faraday's law (coming up in the next chapter) shows that there will be a voltage induced in the moving current sheet against which the current must be maintained.   Whatever source is supplying the current sheet turns out to receive half the energy we are putting into the circuit by moving it.

In other words, energy density in the magnetic field may be determined more easily after time-varying fields are discussed. We shall develop the appropriate expression in discussing Poynting's theorem in Chap. 11.

An alternate approach would be possible at this time, however, for we might define a magnetostatic field based on assumed magnetic poles (or "magnetic charges"). Using the scalar magnetic potential, we could then develop an energy expression by methods similar to those used in obtaining the electrostatic energy relationship. These new magnetostatic quantities we should have to introduce would be too great a price to pay for one simple result, and we shall therefore merely present the result at this time and show that the same expression arises in the Poynting theorem later. The total energy stored in a steady magnetic field in which $\mathbf{B}$ is linearly related to $\mathbf{H}$ is

(2)
$$W_H = \frac{1}{2} \int_{\text{vol}} \mathbf{B} \cdot \mathbf{H} \, dv$$

Letting $\mathbf{B} = \mu \mathbf{H}$, we have the equivalent formulations

(3)
$$W_H = \frac{1}{2} \int_{\text{vol}} \mu H^2 \, dv$$

or

(4)
$$W_H = \frac{1}{2} \int_{\text{vol}} \frac{B^2}{\mu} \, dv$$

It is again convenient to think of this energy as being distributed throughout the volume with an energy density of $\frac{1}{2}\mathbf{B} \cdot \mathbf{H}$ J/m³, although we have no mathematical justification for such a statement.

In spite of the fact that these results are valid only for linear media, we may use them to calculate the forces on nonlinear magnetic materials if we focus our attention on the linear media (usually air) which may surround them. For example, suppose that we have a long solenoid with a silicon-steel core. A coil containing n turns/m and carrying I A surrounds it. The magnetic field intensity in the core is therefore nI A-t/m, and the magnetic flux density can be obtained from the magnetization curve for silicon steel. Let us call this value B_{st}. Suppose that the core is composed of two semi-infinite cylinders[1] which are just touching. We now apply a mechanical force to separate these two sections of the core. We apply a force F over a distance dL, thus doing work $F \, dL$. Faraday's law does not apply here, as we shall see shortly, for the fields in the core have not changed, and we can therefore use the principle of virtual work to determine that the work we have done in moving one core appears as stored energy in the air gap we

[1] A semi-infinite cylinder is a cylinder of infinite length having one end located in finite space.

have created. By (4) above, this increase is

$$dW_H = F\,dL = \tfrac{1}{2}\,\frac{B_{st}^2}{\mu_0}\,S\,dL$$

where S is the core cross-sectional area. Thus

$$F = \frac{B_{st}^2 S}{2\mu_0}$$

If, for example, the magnetic field intensity is sufficient to produce saturation in the steel, $B_{st} = 1.4$ Wb/m², approximately, the force is

$$F = 7.80 \times 10^5 S \qquad N$$

or about 113lbf/in.² of area.

D 9.12 A relay has a magnetic circuit of high-permeability material, including the movable bar. A force of 1.5 lbf is required to give rapid closure. The air-gap cross section is 0.6 cm². If a 1,000-turn coil is provided, find the required coil current if the air-gap spacing is

(*a*) 2 mm, and the reluctance of the ferromagnetic portions of the magnetic circuit may be neglected
(*b*) 1 mm, and the ferromagnetic reluctance is neglected
(*c*) 1 mm, and the material is silicon steel with a mean length of 6 cm and cross section of 0.6 cm²

Ans. 0.421; 0.426; 0.842 A

9.10 INDUCTANCE

Inductance is the last of the three familiar constants from circuit theory which we should now define in more general terms. Resistance was defined in Chap. 5 as the ratio of the potential difference between two equipotential surfaces of a conducting material to the total current crossing either equipotential surface. The resistance is a function of conductor geometry and conductivity only. Capacitance was defined in the same chapter as the ratio of the total charge on either of two equipotential conducting surfaces to the potential difference between the surfaces. Capacitance is a function only of the geometry of the two conducting surfaces and the permittivity of the dielectric medium between or surrounding them.

Let us now use the dual of the capacitance definition to define inductance.[1] Since the dual of charge is flux linkage and the dual

---

[1] Duality is discussed in most texts on circuit theory. For example, see Hayt and Kemmerly, in the bibliography at the end of the chapter.

of electric potential difference is current, then *inductance* (or self-inductance) is the ratio of the total flux linkages to the current which they link,

(1)
$$L = \frac{N\Phi}{I}$$

The current I flowing in the N-turn coil produces the total flux Φ and $N\Phi$ flux linkages, where we assume for the moment that Φ Wb link each turn. This definition is applicable only to magnetic media which are linear, so that the flux is proportional to the current. If ferromagnetic materials are present there is no single definition of inductance which is useful in all cases, and we shall restrict our attention to linear materials.

The unit of inductance is the henry (H), equivalent to one weber per ampere.

Let us apply (1) in a straightforward way to calculate the inductance per meter length of a coaxial cable of inner radius a and outer radius b. We may take the expression for total flux developed as Eq. (7) in Sec. 8.7,

$$\Phi = \frac{\mu_0 I l}{2\pi} \ln \frac{b}{a}$$

and obtain the inductance rapidly for a length l,

$$L = \frac{\mu_0 l}{2\pi} \ln \frac{b}{a} \quad \text{H}$$

or, on a per-meter basis,

(2) $L = \frac{\mu_0}{2\pi} \ln \frac{b}{a} \quad \text{H/m}$

In this case $N = 1$ turn, and all the flux links all the current.

In the problem of a toroidal coil of N turns and I A, since the fields have been requested in several problems in the past, we now know that

$$B_\phi = \frac{\mu_0 N I}{2\pi r}$$

If the dimensions of the cross section are small compared with the mean radius of the toroid R, then the total flux is

$$\Phi = \frac{\mu_0 N I S}{2\pi R}$$

Multiplying the total flux by N, we have the flux linkages, and

FIG. 9.8 A portion of a coil showing partial flux linkages. The total flux linkages are obtained by adding the fluxes linking each turn.

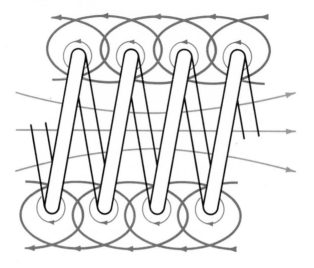

dividing by I, we have the inductance,

$$(3) \quad L = \frac{\mu_0 N^2 S}{2\pi R}$$

Once again we have assumed that all the flux links all the turns, and this is a good assumption for a toroidal coil of many turns packed closely together. Suppose, however, that our toroid has an appreciable spacing between turns, a short part of which might look like Fig. 9.8. The flux linkages are no longer the product of the flux at the mean radius times the total number of turns. In order to obtain the total flux linkages we must look at the coil on a turn-by-turn basis,

$$(N\Phi)_{\text{total}} = \Phi_1 + \Phi_2 + \cdots + \Phi_i + \cdots + \Phi_N$$

$$= \sum_{i=1}^{N} \Phi_i$$

where Φ_i is the flux linking the ith turn. Rather than doing this, we usually rely on experience, winding factors, and pitch factors to adjust the basic formula to apply to the real physical world.

An equivalent definition for inductance may be made using an energy point of view,

$$(4) \quad \boxed{L = \frac{2W_H}{I^2}}$$

where I is the total current flowing in the closed path and W_H is the energy in the magnetic field produced by the current. After using (4) to obtain several other expressions for inductance we shall show that it is equivalent to (1). Let us first express the potential energy W_H in terms of the magnetic fields,

$$(5) \quad L = \frac{\displaystyle\int_{\text{vol}} \mathbf{B} \cdot \mathbf{H} \, dv}{I^2}$$

and replace $\mathbf{B}$ by $\nabla \times \mathbf{A}$,

$$L = \frac{1}{I^2} \int_{\text{vol}} \mathbf{H} \cdot (\nabla \times \mathbf{A}) \, dv$$

The vector identity

$$(6) \quad \nabla \cdot (\mathbf{A} \times \mathbf{H}) \equiv \mathbf{H} \cdot (\nabla \times \mathbf{A}) - \mathbf{A} \cdot (\nabla \times \mathbf{H})$$

may be proved by expansion in cartesian coordinates. The inductance is then

$$(7) \quad L = \frac{1}{I^2} \left[\int_{\text{vol}} \nabla \cdot (\mathbf{A} \times \mathbf{H}) \, dv + \int_{\text{vol}} \mathbf{A} \cdot (\nabla \times \mathbf{H}) \, dv \right]$$

After applying the divergence theorem to the first integral and letting $\nabla \times \mathbf{H} = \mathbf{J}$, we have

$$L = \frac{1}{I^2} \left[\oint_s (\mathbf{A} \times \mathbf{H}) \cdot d\mathbf{S} + \int_{\text{vol}} \mathbf{A} \cdot \mathbf{J} \, dv \right]$$

The surface integral is zero, since the surface encloses the volume containing all the magnetic energy, and this requires that $\mathbf{A}$ and $\mathbf{H}$ be zero on the bounding surface. The inductance may therefore be written as

$$(8) \quad L = \frac{1}{I^2} \int_{\text{vol}} \mathbf{A} \cdot \mathbf{J} \, dv$$

Equation (8) expresses the inductance in terms of an integral of the values of $\mathbf{A}$ and $\mathbf{J}$ at every point. Since current density exists only within the conductor, the integrand is zero at all points *outside* the conductor and the vector magnetic potential need not be determined there. The vector potential is that which arises from the current $\mathbf{J}$, and any other current source contributing a vector potential field in the region of the original current density is to be ignored for the present. Later we shall see that this leads to a *mutual inductance*.

The vector magnetic potential **A** due to **J** is given by Sec. 8.6, Eq. (9),

$$\mathbf{A} = \int_{\text{vol}} \frac{\mu \mathbf{J}}{4\pi R}\, dv$$

and the inductance may therefore be expressed more basically as a rather formidable double volume integral,

(9) $\quad L = \dfrac{1}{I^2} \displaystyle\int_{\text{vol}} \left(\int_{\text{vol}} \frac{\mu \mathbf{J}}{4\pi R}\, dv \right) \cdot \mathbf{J}\, dv$

A slightly simpler integral expression is obtained by restricting our attention to current filaments of small cross section for which **J** dv may be replaced by $I\, d\mathbf{L}$ and the volume integral by a closed line integral along the axis of the filament,

(10) $\quad L = \dfrac{1}{I^2} \oint \left(\oint \dfrac{\mu I\, d\mathbf{L}}{4\pi R} \right) \cdot I\, d\mathbf{L}$

$\qquad\quad = \dfrac{\mu}{4\pi} \oint \left(\oint \dfrac{d\mathbf{L}}{R} \right) \cdot d\mathbf{L}$

Our only present interest in Eqs. (9) and (10) lies in their implication that the inductance is a function of the distribution of the current in space or the geometry of the conductor configuration.

In order to obtain our original definition of inductance (1) let us hypothesize a uniform current distribution in a filamentary conductor of small cross section so that **J** dv in (8) becomes $I\, d\mathbf{L}$,

(11) $\quad L = \dfrac{1}{I} \oint \mathbf{A} \cdot d\mathbf{L}$

For a small cross section $d\mathbf{L}$ may be taken along the center of the filament. We now apply Stokes' theorem and obtain

$$L = \frac{1}{I} \int_s (\nabla \times \mathbf{A}) \cdot d\mathbf{S}$$

or

$$L = \frac{1}{I} \int_s \mathbf{B} \cdot d\mathbf{S}$$

or

(12) $\quad L = \dfrac{\Phi}{I}$

Retracing the steps by which (12) has been obtained, we should see that the flux Φ is that portion of the total flux which passes through any and every open surface whose perimeter is the filamentary current path.

If we now let the filament make N identical turns about the total flux, an idealization which may be closely realized in some types of inductors, the closed line integral must consist of N laps about this common path and (12) becomes

$$(13) \qquad L = \frac{N\Phi}{I}$$

The flux Φ is now the flux crossing any surface whose perimeter is the path occupied by any one of the N turns. The inductance of an N-turn coil may still be obtained from (12), however, if we realize that the flux is that which crosses the complicated surface[1] whose perimeter consists of all N turns.

Use of any of the inductance expressions for a true filamentary conductor (having zero radius) leads to an infinite value of inductance, regardless of the configuration of the filament. Near the conductor Ampère's circuital law shows that the magnetic field intensity varies inversely with the distance from the conductor, and a simple integration soon shows that an infinite amount of energy and an infinite amount of flux are contained within any finite cylinder about the filament. This difficulty is eliminated by specifying a small but finite filamentary radius.

The interior of any conductor also contains magnetic flux, and this flux links a variable fraction of the total current, depending on its location. These flux linkages lead to an *internal inductance*, which must be combined with the external inductance to obtain the total inductance. The internal inductance of a long straight wire of circular cross section with uniform current distribution is $\mu/8\pi$ H/m, a result requested in a problem at the end of this chapter.

In Chap. 11 it will be seen that the current distribution in a conductor at high frequencies tends to be concentrated near the surface. The internal flux is reduced, and it is usually sufficient to consider only the external inductance. At lower frequencies, however, internal inductance may become an appreciable part of the total inductance.

We conclude by defining the *mutual inductance* between circuits 1 and 2, L_{12}, in terms of mutual flux linkages,

$$(14) \qquad \boxed{L_{12} = \frac{N_2 \Phi_{12}}{I_1}}$$

[1] Sort of like a spiral ramp.

where Φ_{12} signifies the flux produced by I_1 which links the path of the filamentary current I_2 and N_2 is the number of turns in circuit 2. The mutual inductance, therefore, depends upon the magnetic interaction between two currents. With either current alone, the total energy stored in the magnetic field can be found in terms of a single inductance, or self-inductance; with both currents having nonzero values, the total energy is a function of the two self-inductances and the mutual inductance. In terms of a mutual energy, it can be shown that (14) is equivalent to

(15) $\qquad L_{12} = \dfrac{1}{I_1 I_2} \displaystyle\int_{\mathrm{vol}} (\mathbf{B}_1 \cdot \mathbf{H}_2)\, dv$

or

(16) $\qquad L_{12} = \dfrac{1}{I_1 I_2} \displaystyle\int_{\mathrm{vol}} (\mu \mathbf{H}_1 \cdot \mathbf{H}_2)\, dv$

where $\mathbf{B}_1$ is the field resulting from I_1 (with $I_2 = 0$) and $\mathbf{H}_2$ is the field due to I_2 (with $I_1 = 0$). Interchange of the subscripts does not change the right-hand side of (16), and therefore

(17) $\qquad \boxed{L_{12} = L_{21}}$

As an example of the calculation of a mutual inductance, let us assume two coaxial solenoids of radius R_1 and R_2, $R_2 > R_1$, carrying currents I_1 and I_2 with n_1 and n_2 turns/m, respectively. From Sec. 8.2, Eq. (5), we approximate the surface current density by $n_1 I_1$, obtaining

$\mathbf{H}_1 = n_1 I_1 \mathbf{a}_z \qquad (0 < r < R_1)$

$\quad\;\; = 0 \qquad\qquad (R_1 < r)$

and

$\mathbf{H}_2 = n_2 I_2 \mathbf{a}_z \qquad (0 < r < R_2)$

$\quad\;\; = 0 \qquad\qquad (R_2 < r)$

Thus, for this uniform field

$\Phi_{12} = \mu_0 n_1 I_1 \pi R_1^2$

and

$L_{12} = \mu_0 n_1 n_2 \pi R_1^2$

Similarly,

$\Phi_{21} = \mu_0 n_2 I_2 \pi R_1^2$

$L_{21} = \mu_0 n_1 n_2 \pi R_1^2 = L_{12}$

If $n_1 = 50$ t/cm, $n_2 = 80$ t/cm, $R_1 = 2$ cm, and $R_2 = 3$ cm, then

$$L_{12} = L_{21} = 63.0 \, \text{mH/m}$$

whereas,

$$L_1 = 39.4 \, \text{mH/m} \quad \text{and} \quad L_2 = 227 \, \text{mH/m}$$

We see, therefore, that there are many methods available for the calculation of self-inductance and mutual inductance. Unfortunately, even problems possessing a high degree of symmetry present very challenging integrals for evaluation, and only a few problems are available for us to try our skill on.

Inductance will be discussed in circuit terms in Chap. 13.

D 9.13 Find the self-inductance of

(a) A 100-m length of coaxial cable with polyethylene dielectric ($\epsilon_R = 2.26$, $\mu_R = 1$) of inner radius 1 mm and outer radius 7 mm
(b) A toroid with a 2×2-cm-square cross section, an inner radius of 9 cm, an outer radius of 11 cm, and 400 turns, in air
(c) A solenoid, 60 cm long with a 2-cm radius, containing 500 turns

Ans. 38.9; 128; 236 μH

D 9.14 Find the mutual inductance between a square filamentary loop in the $x = 0$ plane with corners at $(0,1,0)$, $(0,1.5,0)$, $(0,1.5,0.5)$, and $(0,1,0.5)$ and

(a) An infinite filament on the z axis
(b) A solid cylindrical conductor, centered on the line $x = 0$, $y = 0.5$, with a radius of 5 cm
(c) An infinite filament on the line $x = 0.25$, $y = 1.25$

Ans. 0; 0.0405; 0.0693 μH

SUGGESTED REFERENCES

1 Azároff, L. V., and J. J. Brophy: "Electronic Processes in Materials," McGraw-Hill Book Company, New York, 1963. Magnetic materials are discussed in chap. 13.

2 Fano, R. M., L. J. Chu, and R. B. Adler: (see Suggested References for Chap. 5). Magnetic materials are covered in chap. 5.

3 Hayt, W. H., Jr., and J. E. Kemmerly: (see Suggested References for Chap. 7). Duality is defined on p. 128, and the dual nature of charge and flux linkages is described on p. 211.

4 Matsch, L. W.: (see Suggested References for Chap. 5). Chapter 3 is devoted to magnetic circuits and ferromagnetic materials.

PROBLEMS

1 Assume that an electron enters a uniform electric field $E_x = -V_0/d$ at $x = 0$ and $t = 0$ with no initial velocity. Use Newton's force equation to determine (a) $U_x(t)$; (b) $x(t)$; (c) the potential energy as a function of x if the zero reference is at $x = 0$; (d) the velocity at $x = d$ as a function of V_0.

2 Compare the magnitudes of the electric and magnetic forces on an electron that has attained a velocity of 10^7 m/s. Assume an electric field intensity of 10^5 V/m and let the magnetic flux density be approximately that caused by the earth's magnetic field in temperate latitudes, 0.5 gauss.

3 Show that a charged particle in a uniform magnetic field describes a circular orbit with an orbital period that is independent of the radius. Find the relationship between the angular velocity and the magnetic flux density for an electron (the *cyclotron frequency*).

4 A long strip of material has a rectangular cross section in the $x = 0$ plane, $0 < z < a$, $0 < y < b$. A magnetic field $B_0\mathbf{a}_z$ is present and a current I flows in the $-\mathbf{a}_x$ direction. If we assume that the current is composed solely of positive charges moving with an average velocity U_d, show that the Hall coefficient, $R_H = 1/\rho$ m^3/C, is (a) equal to aV_y/B_0I, where V_y is the voltage developed between the edges at $y = b$ and $y = 0$; (b) equal to the ratio of the mobility of the carrier to the conductivity. (c) If $a = 1$ mm, $b = 1$ cm, $B_0 = 0.1$ Wb/m^2, and $I = 0.1$ A, find V_y if the material is copper with electrons being the carriers ($R_H = -5.5 \times 10^{-11}$ m^3/C); (d) find V_y if the material is p-type germanium for which $R_H = 4 \times 10^{-4}$ m^3/C.

5 Show that the differential work done in moving a current element $I \, d\mathbf{L}$ a distance $d\mathbf{l}$ in a magnetic field $\mathbf{B}$ is the negative of that done moving the element $I \, d\mathbf{l}$ a distance $d\mathbf{L}$ in the same field.

6 A planar transmission line consists of two conducting planes of width b, separated d m in air, carrying equal and opposite currents of I A. If $b \gg d$, find the force of repulsion per meter length between the two conductors.

7 Find the force of repulsion between the two strips of Prob. 6 for any ratio of b to d. Show that the limit as $b \to 0$ is $F = \mu_0 I^2/2\pi d$.

8 Two conducting strips lie in the $y = 0$ plane; the one between $x = d/2$ and $x = b + (d/2)$ carries $\mathbf{K} = K_0\mathbf{a}_z$ and the other is located in the region $-b - (d/2) < x < -d/2$ and carries $-K_0\mathbf{a}_z$. (a) Find the force per meter length tending to separate the two strips. (b) Let b approach zero as $K_0 b$ remains constant and show that the force per unit length approaches $\mu_0 K_0^2 b^2/2\pi d$, or $\mu_0 I^2/2\pi d$ N/m.

9 If $\mathbf{A} = \mathbf{a}_x + \mathbf{a}_y - \mathbf{a}_z$ and $\mathbf{B} = -2\mathbf{a}_x + \mathbf{a}_y + \mathbf{a}_z$, and if $\mathbf{A} \times (\mathbf{B} \times \mathbf{C}) + (\mathbf{A} \times \mathbf{B}) \times \mathbf{C} = -\mathbf{a}_x - 9\mathbf{a}_y - 5\mathbf{a}_z$, find $\mathbf{C}$.

10 A strip $-b/2 < y < b/2$, $z = 0$ carries I A in the $\mathbf{a}_x$ direction. A filament at $y = 0$, $z = d$ carries I A in the $-\mathbf{a}_x$ direction. (a) Find $\mathbf{B}$ at the filament due to the strip, and from this find the force per meter length on the filament. (b) Show that this force approaches $\mu_0 I^2/2\pi d$ as b approaches zero. (c) Find $\mathbf{B}$ at the strip due to the filament, and from this find the force per meter length on the strip.

11 Two filamentary current rings are parallel, each has a 1-m radius, and each is centered on the z axis, one at $z = 0$ and the other at $z = 10^{-3}$. What identical currents should the rings carry to produce a force of repulsion of 1 lbf?

12 A differential current loop of radius a lies at the origin in the $z = 0$ plane and carries a current I in the $\mathbf{a}_\phi$ direction. Assume a uniform magnetic field $\mathbf{B}_0 = B_{0x}\mathbf{a}_x + B_{0y}\mathbf{a}_y + B_{0z}\mathbf{a}_z$. (a) What torque will be produced on the current loop by $B_{0z}\mathbf{a}_z$? (b) How will the torque produced by $B_{0y}\mathbf{a}_y$ compare with that caused by $B_{0x}\mathbf{a}_x$? (c) Use the answers to (a) and (b) to simplify the work and show that the torque on the loop is given by $\mathbf{m} \times \mathbf{B}$.

13 A rectangular filamentary current loop in the $z = 0$ plane has corners at $(0,0,0)$, $(1,0,0)$, $(1,2,0)$, and $(0,2,0)$. The loop carries a current of 5 A (in the $\mathbf{a}_x$ direction on the x axis). Find the total force on the loop produced by the magnetic field (a) $\mathbf{B} = 5\mathbf{a}_x + 2\mathbf{a}_y - 4\mathbf{a}_z$ Wb/m²; (b) $\mathbf{B} = 2x\mathbf{a}_x - 2y\mathbf{a}_y$ Wb/m²; (c) $\mathbf{B} = 2z\mathbf{a}_x + 2x\mathbf{a}_z$ Wb/m².

14 Find the torque on the loop in Prob. 13 for each of the three given fields. Give the torque about the midpoint of the rectangle.

15 An infinitely long filament carrying a current I lies on the positive x and y axes. Find the torque on the 1-m length of wire adjacent to the corner, using an axis which passes through the corner.

16 Find the energy which must be expended in a magnetic field $\mathbf{B}$ to rotate a current loop of moment $\mathbf{m}$ from a position where $\mathbf{m}$ is parallel to $\mathbf{B}$ to one in which $\mathbf{m} \cdot \mathbf{B} = 0$.

17 If the armature of a rotating machine is assumed to be a cylinder $r = a$, L m long and carrying a current sheet $\mathbf{K} = K_0\mathbf{a}_z$ A/m, find the torque produced in a magnetic field $\mathbf{B} = 0.1\mathbf{a}_r/r$ Wb/m². Evaluate the torque and power if $a = 10$ cm, $L = 20$ cm, $K_0 = 3{,}000$ A/m, and the speed of rotation is 3,000 rpm.

18 Assume that an electron is describing a circular orbit of radius a about a positively charged nucleus. (a) By selecting an appropriate current and area, show that the equivalent orbital dipole moment is $ea^2\omega/2$, where ω is the electron's angular velocity. (b) By equating the Coulomb and centrifugal forces, show that ω is $(e^2/4\pi\epsilon_0 ma^3)^{1/2}$. (c) Find values for the angular velocity and the orbital magnetic moment for a hydrogen atom, where a is about 6×10^{-11} m.

19 The hydrogen atom described in Prob. 18 is now subjected to a magnetic field $\mathbf{B}$, parallel to the orbital magnetic moment of the atom. Show that the forces caused by $\mathbf{B}$ result in a decrease of the angular velocity by $eB/2m$ and a decrease in the orbital moment by $e^2a^2B/4m$. What are these decreases for the hydrogen atom in parts per million for the relatively large magnetic flux density of 1 Wb/m²?

20 A square current loop, a on a side, has a certain dipole moment $\mathbf{m}_1$. If we now think of two coincident conductors, carrying equal and opposite currents, which bisect the loop into two identical rectangles, we have two current loops. How does the total moment of this combination compare with $\mathbf{m}_1$?

21 Under some conditions it is possible to approximate the effects of ferromagnetic materials by assuming linearity in the relationship of **B** and **H**. Let $\mu_R = 1,000$ for a certain material of which a cylindrical wire of 1 mm radius is made. If $I_{(f)}$ is 1 A and the current distribution is uniform, find **B**, **H**, **M**, $\mathbf{J}_f$, and $\mathbf{J}_b$ within the wire.

22 Two parallel filaments are buried in a powdered ferrite for which we shall assume $\mu_R = 100$. If the wires carry equal and opposite currents, how does the force of repulsion compare with that between the same wires in air?

23 Use Ampère's circuital law to determine **B**, **H**, and **M** for all r for a copper conductor of radius a carrying I A in the $\mathbf{a}_z$ direction if the conductor has a layer of nonconducting material with $\mu_R = 5$ surrounding it from $r = a$ to $r = 2a$. Plot B, H, and M as functions of r.

24 Show that Sec. 9.7, Eqs. (1) and (4), may be written as the vector equations $\mathbf{a}_n \times (\mathbf{H}_1 - \mathbf{H}_2) = \mathbf{K}$ and $\mathbf{a}_n \cdot (\mathbf{B}_1 - \mathbf{B}_2) = 0$, where $\mathbf{a}_n$ is directed from region 2 to region 1 at the boundary.

25 Derive Sec. 9.7, Eqs. (3) and (6).

26 Define region 1 as $x < 0$ and let $\mu_{R1} = 2.5$ and $\mathbf{B}_1 = (\mathbf{a}_x + 2\mathbf{a}_y - 3\mathbf{a}_z)\mu_0$. Region 2 is described by $x > 0$, and $\mu_{R2} = 5$. Find $|\mathbf{B}_2/\mathbf{B}_1|$ and the angle between the vectors $\mathbf{B}_2$ and $\mathbf{B}_1$.

27 Two current sheets, $8\mathbf{a}_y$ A/m at $z = 0$ and $-8\mathbf{a}_y$ A/m at $z = 1$, are separated by an inhomogeneous material for which $\mu_R = 4z + 1$. Find **H** and **B** within the material and also the total flux crossing an area 1 m square on the $x = 0$ plane.

28 Two current sheets, $K_0\mathbf{a}_y$ at $z = 0$ and $-K_0\mathbf{a}_y$ at $z = d$, are separated by two slabs of magnetic material, μ_{R1} for $0 < z < a$ and μ_{R2} for $a < z < d$. If $\mu_{R2} = 3\mu_{R1}$, find a/d such that (a) 10 per cent of the total flux is in the region $0 < z < a$; (b) the scalar magnetic potential difference across each region is the same.

29 Determine the boundary conditions on the scalar magnetic potential V_m at the boundary between two materials with permeabilities μ_1 and μ_2. Assume that there are no surface currents on the boundary.

30 Determine the boundary conditions on the normal and tangential components of the vector magnetic potential **A** at the boundary between two materials with permeabilities μ_1 and μ_2. Some helpful relations are $\nabla \cdot \mathbf{A} = 0$ and $\oint \mathbf{A} \cdot d\mathbf{L} = \Phi$ (easily derived from $\mathbf{B} = \nabla \times \mathbf{A}$.)

31 In Prob. D9.11c the approximation suggested in the statement of the problem leads to a value of flux density in the central leg of 0.585 Wb/m². Using this value, find the actual current required in the coil if the material is accurately represented by the BH curve of Fig. 9.4.

32 For flux densities in the saturation region a piecewise linear model will yield better accuracy than a single straight-line approximation. Assume that the magnetization curve for silicon steel, Fig. 9.4, can be represented by a straight line from the origin to $B = 1$, $H = 200$, a second straight line from that point to $B = 1.4$, $H = 700$, and a third horizontal line at $B = 1.4$ for $H > 700$. Use this approximation to find the total flux in a series magnetic circuit containing (a) 2 m of path length in steel with a 0.16-m² cross section, 3 m in steel with a 0.1-m² cross section, and an mmf of 1,800

FIG. 9.9 See Prob. 35.

A-t; (b) the same two steel sections, plus a 1-cm air gap in the 0.16-m²
portion and an mmf of 7,500 A-t; (c) the same steel and the same air gap,
but an mmf of 10,000 A-t.

33 The magnetic circuit shown in Fig. 9.7 has the dimensions given in Prob.
D9.11.   The flux density in a 0.1-mm air gap in the center leg is 1.3 Wb/m².
What current is required in the 1,000-turn coil?

34 A toroid of cross section 1 cm² and mean path length 20 cm is composed of a
half-ring of ferrite, for which $\mu_R = 800$, and a half-ring of silicon steel.   Assume that the two butt joints are equivalent to one 0.2-mm air gap.   The
coil has 500 turns and carries 0.5 A.   Find the total flux in the core.

35 Find the flux density in each of the three legs of the magnetic circuit shown
in Fig. 9.9.   Assume that $H = 200B$ in the steel.

36 Two parallel current sheets carrying equal and opposite currents of K_0 A/m
are separated h m in air.   Find the energy stored in the magnetic field
between the sheets in a length L and width b.

37 Find the energy stored per unit length within the nonmagnetic conducting
material of a cylindrical shell of inner radius b and outer radius c carrying
a uniformly distributed total current I.

38 A magnetic material which is linear and has a relative permeability of 1,000
is used to construct a magnetic circuit with a length of 10 cm and a cross-
sectional area of 1.5 cm².   An air gap of 1 mm is included in the circuit.   If
a 300-turn coil carrying 1.1 A is provided, find the total energy stored
(a) in the air; (b) in the magnetic material.   (c) What is the ratio of the
energy density in the air to that in the magnetic material?

39 Show that the internal inductance of a nonmagnetic cylindrical wire of
radius a carrying a uniformly distributed current I is $\mu_0/8\pi$ H/m.

40 A flux density of 0.04 Wb/m² is established in a magnetic circuit of uniform
2-cm² cross section containing a 2-mm air gap and a 5-cm length of material
for which $\mathbf{B} = 200\mu_0\mathbf{H}$.   What is the inductance of the 500-turn coil producing the mmf?

41 Find an approximate value for the self-inductance of a square loop of wire, b on a side, if the wire radius a is much smaller than b. Neglect internal inductance. What is the inductance if $b = 2$ in. and $a = 0.0025$ in. (#36 wire)?

42 A toroidal coil containing 1,000 turns has a square cross section and an inner radius of 4 cm and outer radius of 6 cm. Concentric with this toroid and completely enclosing it is a second toroid of 500 turns with a square cross section and an inner radius of 3 cm and an outer radius of 7 cm. The permeability is unity everywhere. (a) Find the self-inductance of each toroid and the mutual inductance between them, assuming a uniform field. (b) Repeat the calculations, taking into account the variation of H and B with r.

43 Find an approximate value for the mutual inductance between concentric filamentary square loops of wire of sides a and b, $b > a$. The wires are in air and the sides of the two squares are parallel. As a check, L_{12} is exactly 1.27×10^{-7} H if $b = 40$ cm and $a = 20$ cm.

44 Four filamentary conductors are located in the $z = 0$ plane at $x = -a - b$, $x = -a$, $x = a$, and $x = a + b$. They carry currents in the $\mathbf{a}_y$ direction of I_1, $-I_1$, I_2, and $-I_2$, respectively. Find L_{12}.

45 Two coaxial solenoids, one of radius 2 cm with 30 turns/cm and the other of radius 3 cm with 50 turns/cm, surround a coaxial core of radius 1 cm and relative permeability 100. Find the self-inductance of each solenoid and the mutual inductance between them for a 50-cm length.

46 Two rigid parallel horizontal conducting plates of width b and separation d are each carrying I A in opposite directions. Midway between the plates is a filamentary conductor of mass m kg per meter length. Assume that $b \gg d$, and (a) find the magnitude and direction of the current that must be maintained in the filament to hold it in its centered position against the force of gravity; (b) evaluate the filament current if $b = 0.2$ m, $d = 0.01$ m, $I = 100$ A, and $m = 1$ gram per meter (g/m).

47 Refer to one of the handbooks for electrical engineers and compute the inductance of a single rectangular loop of wire of the following dimensions: length, 12 cm; breadth, 9 cm; wire radius, 1 mm.

48 In Oliver Heaviside, "Electrical Papers," vol. II, Copley Publishers, Boston, 1925, pp. 25–27, Heaviside suggests the use of pere, mac, tom, bob, and dick as names for electrical units. What use did he have in mind for pere and tom?

49 Use the paper by H. A. Wheeler, Inductance Chart for Solenoid Coil, *Proc. IRE*, vol. 38, no. 12, pp. 1398–1400, December, 1950, to find the inductance of a solenoid with a mean radius $a = 0.5$ in. and an axial length b of 2 in., using 100 turns of wire having a diameter of 0.01 in. Compare with the value obtained from the approximate formula $L = \mu_0 N^2 \pi a^2 / b$, which we have used several times previously.

50 What permanent effects does radiation have on the magnetic properties of nickel-zinc and manganese-zinc ferrites? This question is answered in R. E. Alley, Jr., In-pile Measurements of Radiation Effects in Magnetic Materials, *J. Appl. Phys.*, suppl. to vol. 30, pp. 284S–285S, April, 1959.

10 TIME-VARYING FIELDS AND MAXWELL'S EQUATIONS

The basic relationships of the electrostatic and the steady magnetic field have been obtained in the previous nine chapters, and we are now ready to discuss time-varying fields. The discussion will be short, for vector analysis and vector calculus should now be more familiar tools, some of the relationships are unchanged, and most of the relationships are changed only slightly.

Two new concepts will be introduced: the electric field produced by a changing magnetic field and the magnetic field produced by a changing electric field. The first of these concepts resulted from directed experimental research by Michael Faraday, and the second from the theoretical efforts of James Clerk Maxwell. Maxwell was also responsible for collecting and unifying previously known relationships, and the four basic equations of electromagnetic theory presented in this chapter bear his name.

10.1 FARADAY'S LAW

After Oersted demonstrated in 1820 that an electric current affected a compass needle, Faraday professed his belief that if a current could produce a magnetic field, then a magnetic field should be able to produce a current. The concept of the "field" was not available at that time, and Faraday's goal was to show that a current could be produced by "magnetism."

He worked on this problem intermittently over a period of ten years, until he was finally successful in 1831. He wound two separate windings on an iron toroid and placed a galvanometer in one circuit and a battery in the other. Upon closing the battery circuit, he noted a momentary deflection of the galvanometer; a similar deflection in the opposite direction occurred when the battery was disconnected. This, of course, was the first experiment he had made involving a *changing* current, and he followed it with a demonstration that either a *moving* magnetic field or a moving coil could also produce a galvanometer deflection.

In terms of fields, we now say that a time-varying magnetic field produces an *electromotive force* which may establish a current in a suitable closed circuit. An electromotive force is merely a voltage that arises from conductors moving in a magnetic field or from changing magnetic fields, and we shall define it below. Faraday's law is customarily stated as

$$(1) \qquad \text{emf} = -\frac{d\Phi}{dt} \quad \text{V}$$

Equation (1) implies a closed path, although not necessarily a closed conducting path; the closed path, for example, might include a capacitor, or it might be a purely imaginary line in space. The magnetic flux is that flux which passes through any and every surface whose perimeter is the closed path, and $d\Phi/dt$ is the time rate of change of this flux. A nonzero value of $d\Phi/dt$ may result from either a time-changing flux linking a stationary closed path, relative motion between a steady flux and a closed path, or a combination of the two. The minus sign is an indication that the emf is in such a direction as to produce a current whose flux, if added to the original flux, would reduce the magnitude of the emf. This statement that the induced voltage acts to produce an opposing flux is known as *Lenz's law*.

If the closed path is that taken by an N-turn filamentary conductor, it may be sufficiently accurate to consider the turns as coincident and let

$$(2) \qquad \text{emf} = -N\frac{d\Phi}{dt}$$

Φ is then interpreted as the flux passing through any one of N coincident paths.

We must now define emf as used in (1) or (2). The emf is obviously a scalar, and (perhaps not so obviously) a dimensional check shows that it is measured in volts. We shall define the emf as

$$(3) \qquad \text{emf} = \oint \mathbf{E} \cdot d\mathbf{L}$$

and note that it is the potential difference about a specific *closed path*. If any part of the path is changed, the emf in general changes. The departure from static results is clearly shown by (3), for an electric field intensity resulting from a static charge distribution must lead to zero potential difference about a closed path.

Replacing Φ in (1) by the surface integral of $\mathbf{B}$, we have

$$(4) \qquad \oint \mathbf{E} \cdot d\mathbf{L} = -\frac{d}{dt}\int_s \mathbf{B} \cdot d\mathbf{S}$$

where the fingers of our right hand indicate the direction of the closed path, and our thumb indicates the direction of $d\mathbf{S}$. A flux density $\mathbf{B}$ in the direction of $d\mathbf{S}$ and increasing with time thus produces an average value of $\mathbf{E}$ which is *opposite* to the positive direction about the closed path.

Let us divide our investigation into two parts by first finding the contribution to the total emf made by a changing field within a stationary path; a moving path within a constant field will be treated later. We first consider a stationary path; the magnetic flux is the only time-varying quantity on the right side of (4), and a partial derivative may be taken under the integral sign,

$$(5) \quad \text{emf} = \oint \mathbf{E} \cdot d\mathbf{L} = -\int_s \frac{\partial \mathbf{B}}{\partial t} \cdot d\mathbf{S}$$

Before we apply this simple result to an example, let us obtain the point form of this integral equation. Applying Stokes' theorem to the left side of this equation, we have

$$\int_s (\boldsymbol{\nabla} \times \mathbf{E}) \cdot d\mathbf{S} = -\int_s \frac{\partial \mathbf{B}}{\partial t} \cdot d\mathbf{S}$$

where the surface integrals may be taken over identical surfaces. The surfaces are perfectly general and may be chosen as differentials,

$$(\boldsymbol{\nabla} \times \mathbf{E}) \cdot d\mathbf{S} = -\frac{\partial \mathbf{B}}{\partial t} \cdot d\mathbf{S}$$

and

$$(6) \quad \boxed{\boldsymbol{\nabla} \times \mathbf{E} = -\frac{\partial \mathbf{B}}{\partial t}}$$

This is one of Maxwell's four equations as written in differential, or point, form, the form in which they are most generally used. Equation (5) is the integral form of this equation and is equivalent to Faraday's law as applied to a fixed path. If $\mathbf{B}$ is not a function of time, (5) and (6) evidently reduce to the equations obtained in electrostatics,

$$\oint \mathbf{E} \cdot d\mathbf{L} = 0$$

and

$$\boldsymbol{\nabla} \times \mathbf{E} = 0$$

As an example of the interpretation of (5) and (6), let us assume a simple magnetic field which increases exponentially with time,

$$(7) \quad \mathbf{B} = B_0 e^{bt} \mathbf{a}_z$$

where B_0 = constant. Choosing a circular path of radius a in the $z = 0$ plane, along which E_ϕ must be constant by symmetry, we then have from (5)

$$\text{emf} = 2\pi a E_\phi = -bB_0 e^{bt} \pi a^2$$

The emf around this closed path is $-bB_0 e^{bt} \pi a^2$. It is proportional to a^2, since the magnetic flux density is uniform and the flux passing through the surface at any instant is proportional to the area. The emf is evidently the same for any other path in the $z = 0$ plane enclosing the same area.

If we now replace a by r, the electric field intensity at any point is

(8)
$$\mathbf{E} = -\tfrac{1}{2}bB_0 e^{bt} r \mathbf{a}_\phi$$

Let us now attempt to obtain the same answer from (6), which becomes

$$(\nabla \times \mathbf{E})_z = -bB_0 e^{bt} = \frac{1}{r}\frac{\partial(rE_\phi)}{\partial r}$$

Multiplying by r and integrating from 0 to r (treating t as a constant, since the derivative is a partial derivative),

$$-\tfrac{1}{2}bB_0 e^{bt} r^2 = rE_\phi + K$$

or

$$\mathbf{E} = -\tfrac{1}{2}bB_0 e^{bt} r \mathbf{a}_\phi$$

once again.

If B_0 is considered positive, a filamentary conductor of resistance R would have a current flowing in the negative $\mathbf{a}_\phi$ direction, and this current would establish a flux within the circular loop in the negative $\mathbf{a}_z$ direction. Since E_ϕ increases exponentially with time, the current and flux do also, and thus tend to reduce the time rate of increase of the applied flux and the resultant emf in accordance with Lenz's law.

Before leaving this example, it is well to point out that the given field $\mathbf{B}$ does not satisfy all of Maxwell's equations. Such fields are often assumed (*always* in a-c-circuit problems) and cause no difficulty when they are interpreted properly. They occasionally cause surprise, however. This particular field is discussed further in Prob. 12 at the end of the chapter.

Now let us consider the case of a time-constant flux and a moving closed path. Before we derive any special results from Faraday's law (1), let us use it to analyze the specific problem outlined in Fig. 10.1. The closed circuit consists of two parallel conductors which are connected at one end by a high-resistance voltmeter of negligible dimensions and at the other end by a sliding bar moving at a velocity $\mathbf{U}$. The magnetic flux density is constant (in space and time) and is normal to the plane containing the closed path.

Let the position of the shorting bar be given by y; the flux passing through the surface within the closed path at any time t is then

$$\Phi = BLy$$

From (1),

$$\text{emf} = -\frac{d\Phi}{dt}$$

we obtain

(9) $\qquad \text{emf} = -BL\frac{dy}{dt} = -BLU$

Since the emf is defined as $\oint \mathbf{E} \cdot d\mathbf{L}$ and we have a conducting path, we may actually determine $\mathbf{E}$ at every point along the closed path. But we found in electrostatics that the tangential component of $\mathbf{E}$ is zero at the surface of a conductor, and we shall show in Sec. 10.4 that the tangential component is zero at the surface of a *perfect* conductor ($\sigma = \infty$) for all time-varying conditions. This is equivalent to saying that a perfect conductor is a "short circuit." The entire closed path in Fig. 10.1 may be considered as a perfect conductor, with the exception of the voltmeter. The actual computation of $\oint \mathbf{E} \cdot d\mathbf{L}$ then must involve no contribution along the entire moving bar, both rails, and the voltmeter leads. Since we

FIG. 10.1   An example illustrating the application of Faraday's law to the case of a constant magnetic flux density and a moving path. The shorting bar moves to the right with a velocity $\mathbf{U}$, and the circuit is completed through the two rails and an extremely small high-resistance voltmeter. The voltmeter reading is $V_{12} = -BLU$.

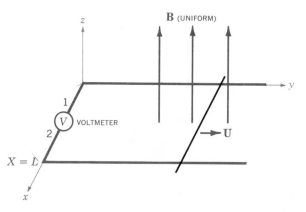

are integrating in a counterclockwise direction (keeping the interior of the positive side of the surface on our left), the contribution $E \Delta L$ across the voltmeter must be $-BLU$, showing that the electric field intensity in the instrument is directed from terminal 2 to terminal 1. For an up-scale reading, the positive terminal of the voltmeter should therefore be terminal 2.

The direction of the resultant small current flow may be confirmed by noting that the enclosed flux is reduced by a clockwise current in accordance with Lenz's law. The voltmeter terminal 2 is again seen to be the positive terminal.

Let us now consider this example using the concept of *motional emf*. The force on a charge Q moving at a velocity $\mathbf{U}$ in a magnetic field $\mathbf{B}$ is

$$\boxed{\mathbf{F} = Q\mathbf{U} \times \mathbf{B}}$$

or

$$(10) \qquad \frac{\mathbf{F}}{Q} = \mathbf{U} \times \mathbf{B}$$

The sliding conducting bar is composed of positive and negative charges, and each experiences this force. The force per unit charge, as given by (10), is called the *motional* electric field intensity $\mathbf{E}_m$,

$$(11) \qquad \boxed{\mathbf{E}_m = \mathbf{U} \times \mathbf{B}}$$

If the moving conductor were lifted off the rails, this electric field intensity would force electrons to one end of the bar until the *static field* due to these charges just balanced the field induced by the motion of the bar. The resultant tangential electric field intensity would then be zero along the length of the bar.

The motional emf produced by the moving conductor is then

$$(12) \qquad \text{emf} = \oint \mathbf{E}_m \cdot d\mathbf{L} = \oint (\mathbf{U} \times \mathbf{B}) \cdot d\mathbf{L}$$

where the last integral may have a nonzero value only along that portion of the path which is in motion, or along which $\mathbf{U}$ has some nonzero value. Evaluating the right side of (12), we obtain

$$\oint (\mathbf{U} \times \mathbf{B}) \cdot d\mathbf{L} = \int_L^0 UB\, dx = -BLU$$

as before. This is the total emf, since $\mathbf{B}$ is not a function of time.

In the case of a conductor moving in a uniform constant magnetic field we may therefore ascribe an induced electric field intensity

$$\mathbf{E}_m = \mathbf{U} \times \mathbf{B}$$

FIG. 10.2 An apparent increase in flux linkages does not lead to an induced voltage when one part of a circuit is simply substituted for another by opening the switch above. No indication will be observed on the voltmeter.

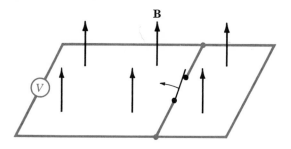

to every portion of the moving conductor and evaluate the resultant emf by

(13) $\quad \text{emf} = \oint \mathbf{E} \cdot d\mathbf{L} = \oint \mathbf{E}_m \cdot d\mathbf{L} = \oint (\mathbf{U} \times \mathbf{B}) \cdot d\mathbf{L}$

If the magnetic flux density is also changing with time, then we must include both contributions (5) and (12) to the emf,

(14) $\quad \text{emf} = \oint \mathbf{E} \cdot d\mathbf{L} = -\int_s \frac{\partial \mathbf{B}}{\partial t} \cdot d\mathbf{S} + \oint (\mathbf{U} \times \mathbf{B}) \cdot d\mathbf{L}$

This expression is equivalent to the simple statement

(1) $\quad \text{emf} = -\frac{d\Phi}{dt}$

and either can be used to determine these induced voltages. Although (1) appears simple, there are a few contrived examples in which its proper application is quite difficult. These usually involve sliding contacts or switches; they always involve the substitution of one part of a circuit by a new part.[1] As an example, consider the simple circuit of Fig. 10.2, containing several perfectly conducting wires, an ideal voltmeter, a uniform constant field **B**, and a switch. When the switch is opened, there is obviously more flux enclosed in the voltmeter circuit; however, it continues to read zero. The change in flux has not been produced by either a time-changing **B** [first term of (14)] or a conductor moving through a magnetic field [second part of (14)]. Instead, a new circuit has been substituted for the old. Thus it is necessary to use care in evaluating the change in flux linkages. There are several interesting problems

[1] See Bewley, in the bibliography at the end of the chapter, particularly pp. 12–19.

included at the end of the chapter to try these ideas on; some of the circuits have no induced emf.

The separation of the emf into the two parts indicated by (14), one due to the time rate of change of **B** and the other to the motion of the circuit, is somewhat arbitrary in that it is dependent on the relative velocity of the *observer* and the system. A field that is changing with both time and space may look constant to an observer moving with the field. This line of reasoning is developed more fully in applying the special theory of relativity to electromagnetic theory.[1]

D 10.1 Find the emf developed about the path $r = 0.5$, $z = 0$, at $t = 0$ if

(a) $\mathbf{B} = 0.1\mathbf{a}_z \sin 377t$

(b) $\mathbf{B} = 0.1\mathbf{a}_r \dfrac{\sin 377t}{r}$

(c) $\mathbf{B} = 10^{-7}\mathbf{a}_z \sin\left(2\pi 10^8 t - \dfrac{2\pi r}{3}\right)$

Ans. $0; -29.6; -36.6$ V

D 10.2 In Fig. 10.1 let **B** be constant with time but not necessarily uniform in space. Find the voltmeter reading at $t = 0.2$ s if $L = 0.4$ m, $U = dy/dt$, and

(a) $y = 10t$ m, $\mathbf{B} = \dfrac{y\mathbf{a}_z}{2}$ Wb/m²

(b) $y = 50t^2$ m, $\mathbf{B} = \dfrac{y\mathbf{a}_z}{2}$ Wb/m²

(c) $y = 50t^2$ m, $\mathbf{B} = \frac{1}{2}(x + y)\mathbf{a}_z$ Wb/m²

Ans. $-4; -8; -8.8$ V

10.2 DISPLACEMENT CURRENT

Faraday's experimental law has been used to obtain one of Maxwell's equations,

(1) $\nabla \times \mathbf{E} = -\dfrac{\partial \mathbf{B}}{\partial t}$

which shows us that a time-changing magnetic field produces an electric field. Remembering the definition of curl, we see that this electric field has the special property of circulation; its line integral

---

[1] This is discussed in several of the references listed in the bibliography at the end of the chapter. See Panofsky and Phillips, pp. 142–151; Owen, pp. 231–245; and Harman in several places.

about a general closed path is not zero. Now let us turn our attention to the time-changing electric field.

We should first look at the point form of Ampère's circuital law as it applies to steady magnetic fields,

(2) $\quad \nabla \times \mathbf{H} = \mathbf{J}$

and show its inadequacy for time-varying conditions by taking the divergence of each side,

$$\nabla \cdot \nabla \times \mathbf{H} \equiv 0 = \nabla \cdot \mathbf{J}$$

Since the divergence of the curl is identically zero, $\nabla \cdot \mathbf{J}$ is also zero. However, the equation of continuity,

(3) $\quad \nabla \cdot \mathbf{J} = -\dfrac{\partial \rho}{\partial t}$

then shows us that (2) can be true only if $\partial \rho / \partial t = 0$. This is an unrealistic limitation, and (2) must be amended before we can accept it for time-varying fields. Suppose we add an unknown term $\mathbf{G}$ to (2),

$$\nabla \times \mathbf{H} = \mathbf{J} + \mathbf{G}$$

Again taking the divergence, we have

$$0 = \nabla \cdot \mathbf{J} + \nabla \cdot \mathbf{G}$$

or

$$\nabla \cdot \mathbf{G} = \dfrac{\partial \rho}{\partial t}$$

Replacing ρ by $\nabla \cdot \mathbf{D}$,

$$\nabla \cdot \mathbf{G} = \dfrac{\partial}{\partial t} (\nabla \cdot \mathbf{D}) = \nabla \cdot \dfrac{\partial \mathbf{D}}{\partial t}$$

from which we obtain the simplest solution for $\mathbf{G}$,

$$\mathbf{G} = \dfrac{\partial \mathbf{D}}{\partial t}$$

Ampère's circuital law in point form therefore becomes

(4) $\quad \boxed{\nabla \times \mathbf{H} = \mathbf{J} + \dfrac{\partial \mathbf{D}}{\partial t}}$

Equation (4) has not been derived. It is merely a form we have obtained which does not disagree with the continuity equation. It is also consistent with all our other results, and we accept it as we did each experimental law and the equations derived from it. We are building a theory, and we have every right to our equations *until they are proved wrong*. This has not yet been done.

We now have a second one of Maxwell's equations and shall investigate its significance. The additional term $\partial \mathbf{D}/\partial t$ has the dimensions of current density, amperes per square meter. Since it results from a time-varying electric flux density (or displacement density), Maxwell termed it a *displacement current density*. We sometimes denote it by $\mathbf{J}_d$:

$$\nabla \times \mathbf{H} = \mathbf{J} + \mathbf{J}_d$$

$$\mathbf{J}_d = \frac{\partial \mathbf{D}}{\partial t}$$

This is the third type of current density we have met. Conduction current density,

$$\mathbf{J} = \sigma \mathbf{E}$$

the motion of charge (usually electrons) in a region of zero net charge density, and convection current density,

$$\mathbf{J} = \rho \mathbf{U}$$

the motion of volume charge density, are both represented by $\mathbf{J}$ in (4). Bound current density is, of course, included in $\mathbf{H}$. In a nonconducting medium in which no volume charge density is present, $\mathbf{J} = 0$, and then

(5) $$\nabla \times \mathbf{H} = \frac{\partial \mathbf{D}}{\partial t}$$

Notice the symmetry between (5) and (1):

(1) $$\nabla \times \mathbf{E} = -\frac{\partial \mathbf{B}}{\partial t}$$

Again the analogy between the intensity vectors $\mathbf{E}$ and $\mathbf{H}$ and the flux density vectors $\mathbf{D}$ and $\mathbf{B}$ is apparent. Too much faith cannot be placed in this analogy, however, for it fails when we investigate forces on particles. The force on a charge is related to $\mathbf{E}$ and to $\mathbf{B}$, and some good arguments may be presented showing an analogy between $\mathbf{E}$ and $\mathbf{B}$ and between $\mathbf{D}$ and $\mathbf{H}$. We shall omit them, however, and merely say that the concept of displacement current was probably suggested to Maxwell by the symmetry first mentioned above.

FIG. 10.3 A filamentary conductor forms a loop connecting the two plates of a parallel-plate capacitor. Within the closed path a time-varying magnetic field produces an emf of $V_0 \cos \omega t$. The conduction current I is equal to the displacement current between the capacitor plates.

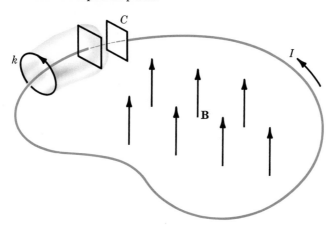

The total displacement current crossing any given surface is given by the surface integral,

$$\int_s \mathbf{J}_d \cdot d\mathbf{S} = \int_s \frac{\partial \mathbf{D}}{\partial t} \cdot d\mathbf{S}$$

and we may obtain the time-varying version of Ampère's circuital law from (4) by integrating over the surface S,

$$\int_s (\nabla \times \mathbf{H}) \cdot d\mathbf{S} = \int_s \mathbf{J} \cdot d\mathbf{S} + \int_s \frac{\partial \mathbf{D}}{\partial t} \cdot d\mathbf{S}$$

and applying Stokes' theorem,

(6)
$$\oint \mathbf{H} \cdot d\mathbf{L} = I + I_d = I + \int_s \frac{\partial \mathbf{D}}{\partial t} \cdot d\mathbf{S}$$

What is the nature of displacement current density? Let us study the simple circuit of Fig. 10.3, containing a filamentary loop and a parallel-plate capacitor. Within the loop a magnetic field varying sinusoidally with time is applied to produce an emf about the closed path (the filament plus the dashed portion between the capacitor plates) which we shall take as

$$\text{emf} = V_0 \cos \omega t$$

Using elementary circuit theory, we may obtain the current in the loop as

$$I = -\omega C V_0 \sin \omega t$$

$$= -\omega \frac{\epsilon S}{d} V_0 \sin \omega t$$

where the quantities ϵ, S, and d pertain to the capacitor. Let us apply Ampère's circuital law about the smaller closed circular path k and neglect displacement current for the moment:

$$\oint_k \mathbf{H} \cdot d\mathbf{L} = I_k$$

The path and the value of $\mathbf{H}$ along the path are both definite quantities (although difficult to determine), and $\oint_k \mathbf{H} \cdot d\mathbf{L}$ is a definite quantity. The current I_k is that current through every surface whose perimeter is the path k. If we choose a simple surface punctured by the filament, such as the plane circular surface defined by the path k, the current is evidently the conduction current. Suppose now we consider the closed path k as the mouth of a paper bag whose bottom passes between the capacitor plates. The bag is not pierced by the filament, and the conduction current is zero. Now we need to consider displacement current, for within the capacitor

$$D = \frac{\epsilon V_0}{d} \cos \omega t$$

and therefore

$$I_d = -\omega \frac{\epsilon S}{d} V_0 \sin \omega t$$

This is the same value as that of the conduction current in the filamentary loop. Therefore the application of Ampère's circuital law including displacement current to the path k leads to a definite value for the line integral of $\mathbf{H}$. This value must be equal to the total current crossing the chosen surface. For some surfaces the current is almost entirely conduction current, but for those surfaces passing between the capacitor plates the conduction current is zero and it is the displacement current which is now equal to the closed line integral of $\mathbf{H}$.

Physically, we should note that a capacitor stores charge and that the electric field between the capacitor plates is much greater than the small leakage fields outside. We therefore introduce little error when we neglect displacement current on all those surfaces which do not pass between the plates.

Displacement current is associated with time-varying electric fields and therefore exists in all imperfect conductors carrying a conduction current. The second part of the drill problem below indicates the reason why this additional current was never discovered experimentally.

D 10.3 Find the displacement current at $t = 0$ flowing

    (a) Between plates of a 10-pF capacitor if the voltage across the capacitor is $0.1 \sin 120\pi t$ V
    (b) In a copper conductor of circular cross section having a total resistance of 0.1 Ω and a voltage of $200 \sin 50,000\pi t$ V across it ($\epsilon \doteq \epsilon_0$ for copper)
    (c) In a polystyrene cylinder of 3-mm radius if the value of **H** at the surface of the cylinder is $H_\phi = 5 \times 10^{-9}$ A/m at $t = 0$

Ans.   0.0479; 0.0942; 0.377 nA

10.3 MAXWELL'S EQUATIONS IN POINT FORM

We have already obtained two of Maxwell's equations for time-varying fields,

(1)
$$\nabla \times \mathbf{E} = -\frac{\partial \mathbf{B}}{\partial t}$$

and

(2)
$$\nabla \times \mathbf{H} = \mathbf{J} + \frac{\partial \mathbf{D}}{\partial t}$$

The remaining two equations are unchanged from their non-time-varying form:

(3)
$$\nabla \cdot \mathbf{D} = \rho$$

(4)
$$\nabla \cdot \mathbf{B} = 0$$

Equation (3) essentially states that charge density is a source (or sink) of electric flux lines. Note that we can no longer say that *all* electric flux begins and terminates on charge, because the point form of Faraday's law (1) shows that **E**, and hence **D**, may have circulation if a changing magnetic field is present. Thus the lines of electric flux may form closed loops. However, the converse is still true, and every coulomb of charge must have one coulomb of electric flux diverging from it.

Equation (4) again acknowledges the fact that "magnetic charges," or poles, are not known to exist. Magnetic flux is always found in closed loops and never diverges from a point source.

These four equations form the basis of all electromagnetic theory. They are partial differential equations and relate the electric and magnetic fields to each other and to their sources, charge and current density. The auxiliary equations relating $\mathbf{D}$ and $\mathbf{E}$,

$$(5) \quad \boxed{\mathbf{D} = \epsilon\mathbf{E}}$$

relating $\mathbf{B}$ and $\mathbf{H}$,

$$(6) \quad \boxed{\mathbf{B} = \mu\mathbf{H}}$$

defining conduction current density,

$$(7) \quad \boxed{\mathbf{J} = \sigma\mathbf{E}}$$

and defining convection current density,

$$(8) \quad \boxed{\mathbf{J} = \rho\mathbf{U}}$$

are also required to define and relate the quantities appearing in Maxwell's equations.

The potentials V and $\mathbf{A}$ have not been included above because they are not strictly necessary, although they are extremely useful. They will be discussed at the end of this chapter.

If we do not have "nice" materials to work with, then we will find it necessary to include the polarization and magnetization fields,

$$(9) \quad \boxed{\mathbf{D} = \epsilon_0\mathbf{E} + \mathbf{P}}$$

$$(10) \quad \boxed{\mathbf{B} = \mu_0(\mathbf{H} + \mathbf{M})}$$

Finally, because of its fundamental importance we should include the Lorentz force equation, written in point form as the force per unit volume,

$$(11) \quad \boxed{\mathbf{f} = \rho(\mathbf{E} + \mathbf{U} \times \mathbf{B})}$$

The following chapters are devoted to the application of Maxwell's equations to several simple problems.

D 10.4 Determine whether or not the following fields satisfy Maxwell's equations in a linear isotropic homogeneous material for which $\epsilon_R = 8$, $\mu_R = 2$, and $\sigma = 0$:

(a) $\mathbf{B} = 4x\mathbf{a}_z$, $\mathbf{E} = 2\mathbf{a}_y$
(b) $\mathbf{H} = 1/\pi \cos{(3 \times 10^8 t - 4x)}\mathbf{a}_z$, $\mathbf{E} = 60 \cos{(3 \times 10^8 t - 4x)}\mathbf{a}_y$
(c) $\mathbf{B} = (8 \times 10^{-6}y^2 + 4 \times 10^9 t^2)\mathbf{a}_z$; $\mathbf{E} = 9 \times 10^{10}yt\mathbf{a}_x$

Ans. No; no; yes

10.4 MAXWELL'S EQUATIONS IN INTEGRAL FORM

The integral forms of Maxwell's equations are usually easier to recognize in terms of the experimental laws from which they have been obtained by a generalization process. Experiments must treat physical macroscopic quantities, and their results therefore are expressed in terms of integral relationships. A differential equation always represents a theory. Let us now collect the integral forms of Maxwell's equations of the previous section.

Integrating Sec. 10.3, Eq. (1), over a surface and applying Stokes' theorem, we obtain Faraday's law,

(1)
$$\oint \mathbf{E} \cdot d\mathbf{L} = -\int_s \frac{\partial \mathbf{B}}{\partial t} \cdot d\mathbf{S}$$

and the same process applied to Sec. 10.3, Eq. (2), yields Ampère's circuital law,

(2)
$$\oint \mathbf{H} \cdot d\mathbf{L} = I + \int_s \frac{\partial \mathbf{D}}{\partial t} \cdot d\mathbf{S}$$

Gauss's laws for the electric and magnetic fields are obtained by integrating Sec. 10.3, Eqs. (3) and (4), throughout a volume and using the divergence theorem:

(3)
$$\oint_s \mathbf{D} \cdot d\mathbf{S} = \int_{\text{vol}} \rho \, dv$$

(4)
$$\oint_s \mathbf{B} \cdot d\mathbf{S} = 0$$

These four integral equations enable us to find the boundary conditions on $\mathbf{B}$, $\mathbf{D}$, $\mathbf{H}$, and $\mathbf{E}$ which are necessary to evaluate the constants obtained in solving Maxwell's equations in partial differential form. These boundary conditions are in general unchanged from their forms for static or steady fields, and the same methods may be used to obtain them. Between any two real physical media, (1) enables us to relate the tangential **E**-field components,

(5) $E_{t1} = E_{t2}$

and from (2),

(6) $H_{t1} = H_{t2}$

The surface integrals produce the boundary conditions on the normal components,

(7) $D_{n1} - D_{n2} = \rho_s$

and

(8) $B_{n1} = B_{n2}$

It is often desirable to idealize a physical problem by assuming a perfect conductor for which σ is infinite but **J** is finite. From Ohm's law, then, in a perfect conductor,

$\mathbf{E} = 0$

and it follows from the point form of Faraday's law that

$\mathbf{H} = 0$

for time-varying fields. The point form of Ampère's circuital law then shows that the finite value of **J** is

$\mathbf{J} = 0$

and current must be carried on the conductor surface as a surface current. Thus, if region 2 is a perfect conductor, (5) to (8) become, respectively,

(9) $E_{t1} = 0$

(10) $H_{t1} = K$

(11) $D_{n1} = \rho_s$

(12) $B_{n1} = 0$

Note that surface charge density is considered a physical possibility for either dielectrics, perfect conductors, or imperfect conductors, but that surface *current* density is assumed only in conjunction with perfect conductors.

The boundary conditions stated above are a very necessary part of Maxwell's equations. All real physical problems have boundaries and require the solution of Maxwell's equations in two or more regions and the matching of these solutions at the boundaries. In the case of perfect conductors, the solution of the equations within the conductor is trivial (all time-varying fields are zero), but the application of the boundary conditions (9) to (12) may be very difficult.

Certain fundamental properties of wave propagation are evident when Maxwell's equations are solved for an *unbounded* region. This problem is treated in the following chapter. It represents the simplest application of Maxwell's equations, because it is the only problem which does not require the application of any boundary conditions.

D 10.5 Two nonconducting materials with $\epsilon_{R1} = 8$, $\epsilon_{R2} = 3$, $\mu_{R1} = 2$, and $\mu_{R2} = 3$ have an interface at which the normal from region 1 to 2 is given by the unit vector $\mathbf{a}_{n12} = (-2\mathbf{a}_x - \mathbf{a}_y + 2\mathbf{a}_z)/3$. At the boundary in region 1, $\mathbf{B}_1 = (2\mathbf{a}_x - 3\mathbf{a}_y + \mathbf{a}_z) \cos 1{,}000t$. Find at $t = 0$

(a) $|\mathbf{B}_{t1}|$
(b) $|\mathbf{B}_{t2}|$
(c) $|\mathbf{B}_{n2}|$

Ans. 0.333; 3.73; 5.59 Wb/m²

D 10.6 The fields inside an air-filled rectangular box with perfectly conducting walls are $E_y = 1{,}130 \sin 2x \sin 3z \cos \omega t$ V/m, $H_x = 3 \sin 2x \cos 3z \sin \omega t$ A/m, and $H_z = -2 \cos 2x \sin 3z \sin \omega t$ A/m. Show that possible walls for the cavity are located at $x = 0$, $x = \pi/2$, $y = 0$, $y = 0.7316$, $z = 0$, and $z = \pi/3$. Then find the crest amplitude of the surface current density at

(a) $x = 0, y = 0.216, z = \dfrac{\pi}{10}$

(b) $x = \dfrac{\pi}{8}, y = 0.1247, z = 0$

(c) $x = \dfrac{\pi}{8}, y = 0.7316, z = \dfrac{\pi}{12}$

Ans. 1.618; 1.803, 2.121 A/m

10.5 THE RETARDED POTENTIALS

The time-varying potentials, usually called *retarded* potentials for a reason which we shall see shortly, find their greatest application in radiation problems in which the distribution of the source is known approximately. We should remember that the scalar electric potential V may be expressed in terms of a static charge distribution,

$$(1) \quad V = \int_{\text{vol}} \frac{\rho \, dv}{4\pi\epsilon R} \quad \text{(static)}$$

and the vector magnetic potential may be found from a current distribution which is constant with time,

(2) $\quad \mathbf{A} = \displaystyle\int_{\text{vol}} \frac{\mu \mathbf{J} \, dv}{4\pi R} \quad$ (d-c)

The differential equations satisfied by V,

(3) $\quad \nabla^2 V = -\dfrac{\rho}{\epsilon} \quad$ (static)

and $\mathbf{A}$,

(4) $\quad \nabla^2 \mathbf{A} = -\mu \mathbf{J} \quad$ (d-c)

may be regarded as the point forms of the integral equations (1) and (2), respectively.

Having found V and $\mathbf{A}$, the fundamental fields are then simply obtained from

(5) $\quad \mathbf{E} = -\nabla V \quad$ (static)

and

(6) $\quad \mathbf{B} = \nabla \times \mathbf{A} \quad$ (d-c)

We now wish to define suitable time-varying potentials which are consistent with the above expressions when only static charges and direct currents are involved. Equation (6) apparently is still consistent with Maxwell's equations. These equations state that $\nabla \cdot \mathbf{B} = 0$ and the divergence of (6) leads to the divergence of the curl which is identically zero. Let us therefore tentatively accept (6) as satisfactory for time-varying fields and turn our attention to (5).

The inadequacy of (5) is obvious, because application of the curl operation to each side and recognition of the curl of the gradient as being identically zero confront us with $\nabla \times \mathbf{E} = 0$. The point form of Faraday's law states that $\nabla \times \mathbf{E}$ is not generally zero. Let us try to effect an improvement by adding an unknown term to (5),

$$\mathbf{E} = -\nabla V + \mathbf{N}$$

taking the curl,

$$\nabla \times \mathbf{E} = 0 + \nabla \times \mathbf{N}$$

using the point form of Faraday's law,

$$\nabla \times \mathbf{N} = -\frac{\partial \mathbf{B}}{\partial t}$$

and using (6), giving us

$$\nabla \times \mathbf{N} = -\frac{\partial}{\partial t}(\nabla \times \mathbf{A})$$

or

$$\nabla \times \mathbf{N} = -\nabla \times \frac{\partial \mathbf{A}}{\partial t}$$

The simplest solution of this equation is

$$\mathbf{N} = -\frac{\partial \mathbf{A}}{\partial t}$$

and therefore

(7) $\quad \mathbf{E} = -\nabla V - \dfrac{\partial \mathbf{A}}{\partial t}$

We still must check (6) and (7) by substituting them into the remaining two of Maxwell's equations:

$$\nabla \times \mathbf{H} = \mathbf{J} + \frac{\partial \mathbf{D}}{\partial t}$$

$$\nabla \cdot \mathbf{D} = \rho$$

Doing this, we obtain the more complicated expressions

$$\frac{1}{\mu}\nabla \times \nabla \times \mathbf{A} = \mathbf{J} + \epsilon\left(-\nabla\frac{\partial V}{\partial t} - \frac{\partial^2 \mathbf{A}}{\partial t^2}\right)$$

and

$$\epsilon\left(-\nabla \cdot \nabla V - \frac{\partial}{\partial t}\nabla \cdot \mathbf{A}\right) = \rho$$

or

(8) $\quad \nabla(\nabla \cdot \mathbf{A}) - \nabla^2 \mathbf{A} = \mu\mathbf{J} - \mu\epsilon\left(\nabla\dfrac{\partial V}{\partial t} + \dfrac{\partial^2 \mathbf{A}}{\partial t^2}\right)$

and

(9) $\quad \nabla^2 V + \dfrac{\partial}{\partial t}(\nabla \cdot \mathbf{A}) = -\dfrac{\rho}{\epsilon}$

There is no apparent inconsistency in (8) and (9). Under static or d-c conditions $\nabla \cdot \mathbf{A} = 0$, and (8) and (9) reduce to (4) and (3), respectively. We shall therefore assume that the time-varying potentials may be defined in such a way that $\mathbf{B}$ and $\mathbf{E}$ may be obtained from them through (6) and (7). These latter two equations do not serve, however, to define **A** and V *completely*. They represent necessary, but not sufficient, conditions. Our initial assumption was merely that $\mathbf{B} = \nabla \times \mathbf{A}$, and a vector cannot be defined by giving its curl alone. Suppose, for example, that we have a very simple vector potential field in which A_y and A_z are zero. Expansion of (6) leads to

$$B_x = 0$$

$$B_y = \frac{\partial A_x}{\partial z}$$

$$B_z = -\frac{\partial A_x}{\partial y}$$

and we see that no information is available about the manner in which A_x varies with x. This information could be found if we also knew the value of the divergence of **A**, for in our example

$$\nabla \cdot \mathbf{A} = \frac{\partial A_x}{\partial x}$$

Finally, we should note that our information about **A** is given only as partial derivatives and that a space-constant term might be added. In all physical problems in which the region of the solution extends to infinity, this constant term must be zero, for there can be no fields at infinity.

Generalizing from this simple example, we may say that a vector field is defined completely when both its curl and divergence are given and when its value is known at any one point (including infinity). We are therefore at liberty to specify the divergence of **A**, and we do so with an eye on (8) and (9), seeking the simplest expressions. We define

$$(10) \quad \nabla \cdot \mathbf{A} = -\mu\epsilon \frac{\partial V}{\partial t}$$

and (8) and (9) become

$$(11) \quad \nabla^2 \mathbf{A} = -\mu \mathbf{J} + \mu\epsilon \frac{\partial^2 \mathbf{A}}{\partial t^2}$$

and

$$(12) \quad \nabla^2 V = -\frac{\rho}{\epsilon} + \mu\epsilon \frac{\partial^2 V}{\partial t^2}$$

These equations are related to the wave equation, which will be discussed in the following chapter. They show considerable symmetry, and we should be highly pleased with our definitions of V and $\mathbf{A}$,

(6) $\qquad \mathbf{B} = \nabla \times \mathbf{A}$

(10) $\qquad \nabla \cdot \mathbf{A} = -\mu\epsilon \dfrac{\partial V}{\partial t}$

(7) $\qquad \mathbf{E} = -\nabla V - \dfrac{\partial \mathbf{A}}{\partial t}$

The integral equivalents of (1) and (2) for the time-varying potentials follow from the definitions (6), (7), and (10), but we shall merely present the final results and indicate their general nature. In the next chapter a study of the uniform plane wave will introduce the concept of *propagation*, in which any electromagnetic disturbance is found to travel at a velocity

$$U = \frac{1}{\sqrt{\mu\epsilon}}$$

through any homogeneous medium described by μ and ϵ. In the case of free space this velocity turns out to be the velocity of light, approximately 3×10^8 m/s. It is logical, then, to suspect that the potential at any point is due not to the value of the charge density at some distant point at the same instant, but to its value at some previous time, since the effect propagates at a finite velocity. Thus (1) becomes

(13) $\qquad \boxed{V = \int_{\text{vol}} \frac{[\rho]}{4\pi\epsilon R}\, dv}$

where $[\rho]$ indicates that every t appearing in the expression for ρ has been replaced by a *retarded* time,

$$t' = t - \frac{R}{U}$$

Thus, if the charge density throughout space were given by

$$\rho = e^{-r} \cos \omega t$$

then

$$[\rho] = e^{-r} \cos\left[\omega\left(t - \frac{R}{U}\right)\right]$$

where R is the distance between the differential element of charge being considered and the point at which the potential is to be determined.

The retarded vector magnetic potential is given by

(14)
$$\mathbf{A} = \int_{\text{vol}} \frac{\mu[\mathbf{J}]}{4\pi R} \, dv$$

The use of a retarded time has resulted in the time-varying potentials being given the name of retarded potentials. In the last chapter we shall apply (14) to the simple situation of a differential current element in which I is a sinusoidal function of time. Other simple applications of (13) and (14) are considered in the problems at the end of this chapter.

We may summarize the use of the potentials by stating that a knowledge of the distribution of ρ and $\mathbf{J}$ throughout space theoretically enables us to determine V and $\mathbf{A}$ from (13) and (14). The electric and magnetic fields are then obtained by applying (6) and (7). If the charge and current distributions are unknown, or reasonable approximations cannot be made for them, these potentials usually offer no easier path toward the solution than does the direct application of Maxwell's equations.

SUGGESTED REFERENCES

1 Bewley, L. V.: "Flux Linkages and Electromagnetic Induction," The Macmillan Company, New York, 1952. This little book discusses many of the paradoxical examples involving induced (?) voltages.

2 Faraday, M.: "Experimental Researches in Electricity," B. Quaritch, London, 1839, 1855. Very interesting reading of early scientific research. A more recent and available source is "Great Books of the Western World," vol. 45, Encyclopaedia Britannica, Inc., Chicago, 1952.

3 Harman, W. W.: "Fundamentals of Electronic Motion," McGraw-Hill Book Company, New York, 1953. Relativistic effects are discussed in a clear and interesting manner.

4 Langmuir, R. V.: "Electromagnetic Fields and Waves," McGraw-Hill Book Company, New York, 1961. Maxwell's equations are developed in chap. 6.

5 Nussbaum, A.: "Electromagnetic Theory for Engineers and Scientists," Prentice-Hall, Inc., Englewood Cliffs, N.J., 1965. See the rocket-generator example beginning on p. 211.

6 Owen, G. E.: "Electromagnetic Theory," Allyn and Bacon, Inc., Englewood Cliffs, N.J., 1963. Faraday's law is discussed in terms of the frame of reference in chap. 8.

7 Panofsky, W. K. H., and M. Phillips: "Classical Electricity and Magnetism," Addison-Wesley Publishing Company, Inc., Reading, Mass., 1955. Relativity is treated at a moderately advanced level in chap. 14.

PROBLEMS

1 A filament is formed into a rectangular loop as shown in Fig. 10.4. A d-c voltmeter is included in the circuit. If $\mathbf{B} = B_0 e^{cx} e^{at} \mathbf{a}_z$, find the voltmeter reading at $t = 0$.

2 Refer to the example illustrated in Fig. 10.1 and replace the voltmeter with a resistance R. (*a*) Find the clockwise current I that flows as a result of the motion of the sliding bar. (*b*) This current in the bar causes a force to be exerted on the bar as it moves. Determine this force. (*c*) Calculate the mechanical power required to maintain a velocity U and show that this power is equal to the power absorbed by R.

3 Refer to Fig. 10.5, where a current filament carrying a current of 12 A lies along the z axis. The rectangular loop is approaching the filament at a velocity of 1,000 m/s when it is in the position shown. Find I_x if $R = 1,000\,\Omega$.

4 A perfectly conducting filament is formed into a circular ring of radius a. At one point a resistance R is inserted into the circuit and at another a battery of potential difference V_0 is inserted. Assume that the loop current itself produces a negligible magnetic field. (*a*) Apply Faraday's law, Sec. 10.1, Eq. (4), evaluating each side of the equation carefully and independently to show the equality. (*b*) Repeat (*a*) assuming the battery removed, the ring closed again, and a linearly increasing $\mathbf{B}$ field applied in a direction normal to the loop surface.

5 Replace the constant field in Fig. 10.1 with $\mathbf{B} = B_0 e^{bt} \mathbf{a}_z$ and determine the voltmeter reading.

6 Replace the uniform field in Fig. 10.1 with $\mathbf{B} = B_0 e^{ay} \mathbf{a}_z$ and determine the voltmeter reading.

7 Let $\mathbf{B} = B_0 \cos(\omega t - \beta y)\, \mathbf{a}_z$ replace the constant uniform field in Fig. 10.1 and determine the voltmeter reading.

8 The conducting sheet of Fig. 10.6 is moving at a constant velocity of U m/s. A fixed voltmeter makes sliding contact with the sheet. Given the uniform $\mathbf{B}$ field, find the voltmeter reading.

FIG. 10.4 See Prob. 1.

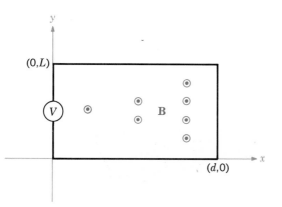

FIG. 10.5 See Prob. 3.

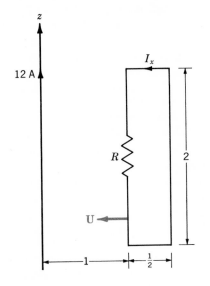

9 In Fig. 10.6, let the voltmeter leads and sheet both move with a constant velocity **U** through the uniform field **B** and find the voltmeter reading.

10 In Fig. 10.7 a sliding contact is made at two points with a fixed slab of high-permeability high-conductivity material. A uniform **B** field is confined to the slab and directed out of the paper. If the voltmeter leads are moved to the left at a uniform velocity (we may assume that they were stretched and are now contracting; the voltmeter itself is stationary), find the voltmeter reading.

11 The device shown in Fig. 10.8 contains two windings on a high-permeability nonconducting core. The left winding has a constant current and produces a uniform flux density **B** in the core. The right winding is soldered to a slip ring at its left end, and the right end is free. As the mass M falls (at constant velocity **U** due to friction in the system), the coil unwinds, and the

FIG. 10.6 See Prob. 8.

FIG. 10.7 See Prob. 10.

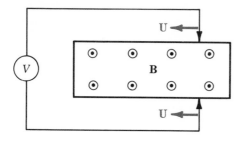

voltmeter leads unfold. What does the voltmeter read in terms of the diameter a of the core, the velocity $\mathbf{U}$, and the field $\mathbf{B}$?

12 In finding the electric field intensity produced by the changing flux density of Sec. 10.1, Eq. (7), Maxwell's equation, $\nabla \times \mathbf{E} = -\partial\mathbf{B}/\partial t$, was used (in its integral form) to obtain Sec. 10.1, Eq. (8). However, another of Maxwell's equations, Sec. 10.2, Eq. (4), also relates electric and magnetic fields. Use this latter equation in an attempt to find $\mathbf{E}$ and show that the given magnetic flux density is not a proper solution of Maxwell's equations.

13 In a certain region of free space an approximate expression for $\mathbf{H}$ is given as $10^{-5}r\mathbf{a}_\phi \cos \omega t$ in cylindrical coordinates. Find the crest amplitudes of the displacement current density and the electric field intensity at $r = 2$ if $f = 1$ megahertz (MHz).

14 Show that the displacement current flowing in the air between two concentric spherical conducting shells of radii a and b, $b > a$, is exactly the same as the conduction current flowing in the external circuit if the applied source is an emf of $V_0 \cos \omega t$.

FIG. 10.8 See Prob. 11.

15 A parallel-plate capacitor contains a lossy dielectric of conductivity σ and permittivity ϵ. Show that the ratio of the total conduction current amplitude flowing between the plates to the total displacement current amplitude there is $\sigma/\omega\epsilon$, where the internal field is $E = E_m \cos \omega t$.

16 Find the displacement current density associated with the magnetic field $\mathbf{H} = A_1 \sin 4x \cos (\omega t - \beta z) \mathbf{a}_x + A_2 \cos 4x \sin (\omega t - \beta z) \mathbf{a}_z$.

17 Starting with Maxwell's equations in point form, assume $\mathbf{E} = E_x \mathbf{a}_x$, $\mathbf{H} = H_y \mathbf{a}_y$, where E_x and H_y are functions only of z and t, let $\mu = \mu_0$, $\epsilon = \epsilon_0$, $\mathbf{J} = 0$, and $\rho = 0$, and obtain the two simple scalar partial differential equations which result. These will be solved in the next chapter.

18 In the cylindrical region $r < 2$ the approximate magnetic flux density in air is $\mathbf{B} = 10^{-8} [1 - (r^2/4)] \sin 3 \times 10^8 t \mathbf{a}_z$. (a) Find $\mathbf{E}$ in this region using $\nabla \times \mathbf{H} = \mathbf{J} + (\partial\mathbf{D}/\partial t)$; (b) Repeat, using $\nabla \times \mathbf{E} = -\partial\mathbf{B}/\partial t$; (c) Repeat, using $\oint \mathbf{E} \cdot d\mathbf{L} = -d\Phi/dt$. (d) The difference in the answers is due to the fact that the given $\mathbf{B}$ field is only an approximate solution to Maxwell's equations. Is $r < 2$ a reasonable restriction to make a good approximation?

19 Derive the continuity equation from Maxwell's equations.

20 Given Maxwell's equations in point form, assume that all fields vary as e^{st} and write the equations without explicitly involving time.

21 The region $z < 0$ is a perfect conductor. On its surface at the origin, $\mathbf{K} = 50\mathbf{a}_x - 120\mathbf{a}_y$ A/m and $\rho_s = 3 \times 10^{-7}$ C/m² at $t = t_0$. Find $\mathbf{D}, \mathbf{E}, \mathbf{B}$, and $\mathbf{H}$ at the origin at $t = t_0$ if the region $z \geq 0$ is free space.

22 Given a boundary between two linear isotropic homogeneous materials described by $\epsilon_1, \epsilon_2, \mu_1, \mu_2, \sigma_1$, and σ_2, (a) obtain the ratios H_{n2}/H_{n1}, D_{t2}/D_{t1}, B_{t2}/B_{t1}, and J_{t2}/J_{t1} at the boundary in terms of these six parameters. (b) Use the continuity equation to help show that $\sigma_1 E_{n1} - \sigma_2 E_{n2} = (\epsilon_2 \partial E_{n2}/\partial t) - (\epsilon_1 \partial E_{n1}/\partial t)$, and determine the remaining boundary conditions on D_n and J_n when this equation is solved.

23 Region 1, $z < 0$, is a perfect dielectric, where $\mathbf{E}_1 = [200 \cos (3 \times 10^{10}t - 200z) - 100 \cos (3 \times 10^{10}t + 200z)] \mathbf{a}_x$. (a) Find $\mathbf{H}_1$. (b) In region 2, $z > 0$, $\mathbf{E}_2 = A \cos (\omega t - \beta z) \mathbf{a}_x$. Use Maxwell's equations and the proper boundary conditions at $z = 0$ to evaluate A, ω, and β. (c) Find $\mathbf{H}_2$.

24 A point charge $Q = Q_0 \cos \omega t$ is located in free space at the origin of a spherical coordinate system. Describe all surfaces on which $V = 0$ at $t = 0$ if $\omega = 10^{10}\pi$ rad/s.

25 If the vector potential $\mathbf{A} = A_0 \cos (\omega t - kz) \mathbf{a}_y$ find $\mathbf{H}, \mathbf{E}$, and V. Assume as many components as possible are zero. Specify k in terms of A_0, ω, and the constants of the lossless medium, ϵ and μ.

26 Two identical current elements, $I \, d\mathbf{L} = 10^{-6}\mathbf{a}_z \cos(3 \times 10^8\pi t)$, are located in free space at $(0,0,-1)$ and $(0,0,1)$. The relative values of $\mathbf{A}$ are desired at $r = 1,000,000$ as a function of θ. Only a few steps are required to obtain the answer, but it may help to point out that the R in the denominator of Sec. 10.5, Eq. (14), may be assumed the same for the two elements, whereas that in the cosine argument may not. Also, $\cos (A + B) + \cos (A - B) = 2 \cos A \cos B$. Plot the crest amplitude of A_z versus θ on polar graph paper.

27 A filamentary ring of radius 2 m in free space is centered at the origin in the $z = 0$ plane and carries a current $I = 10 \cos{(10^8 t + \phi)}$ in the $\mathbf{a}_\phi$ direction. (a) Find $\mathbf{A}$ at $z = h$ on the z axis at $t = 0$. (b) What is the smallest value of h for which $\mathbf{A}$ has no y component there at $t = 0$?

28 In the article by S. A. Schelkunoff, Some Equivalence Theorems of Electromagnetics and Their Application to Radiation Problems, *Bell System Tech. J.*, vol. 15, pp. 92–112, 1936, note the author's definitions of $\mathbf{M}$ and $\mathbf{M_1}$, and show that his eq. (14) follows from Maxwell's equations.

29 Refer to the paper by G. Goubau, Surface Waves and Their Applications to Transmission Lines, *J. Appl. Phys.*, vol. 21, pp. 1119–1128, November, 1950, and demonstrate that his eq. (27) follows from "Faraday's induction law." Note the definition of Φ.

11 THE UNIFORM PLANE WAVE

In this chapter we shall apply Maxwell's equations to introduce the fundamental theory of wave motion. The uniform plane wave represents one of the simplest applications of Maxwell's equations, and yet it illustrates the principles behind the propagation of energy. We shall introduce the velocity of propagation, wavelength, wave impedance, the phase and attenuation constants, and the use of the Poynting theorem in finding the power density. Finally, we shall consider the reflection and transmission of a uniform plane wave at the boundary between two different media. The use of the standing-wave ratio and input impedance will enable us to consider many of the practical problems of the guided transmission of power and information.

11.1 WAVE MOTION IN FREE SPACE

As we indicated in our discussion of boundary conditions in the previous chapter, the solution of Maxwell's equations without the application of any boundary conditions at all represents a very special type of problem. Although we restrict our attention to a solution in cartesian coordinates, it may seem even then that we are solving several different problems as we consider various special cases in this chapter. Solutions are obtained first for free-space conditions, then for perfect dielectrics, next for lossy dielectrics, and finally for the good conductor. We do this to take advantage of the approximations that are applicable to each special case and to emphasize the special characteristics of wave propagation in these media, but it is not necessary to use a separate treatment; it is possible (and not very difficult) to solve the general problem once and for all. Our discussion of propagation in the lossy dielectric begins with a consideration of the general case, but we shall then simplify the analysis by confining our attention to dielectrics with relatively small losses.

To consider wave motion in free space first, Maxwell's equations may be written in terms of $\mathbf{E}$ and $\mathbf{H}$ only as

$$(1) \qquad \boxed{\nabla \times \mathbf{H} = \epsilon_0 \frac{\partial \mathbf{E}}{\partial t}}$$

(2)
$$\nabla \times \mathbf{E} = -\mu_0 \frac{\partial \mathbf{H}}{\partial t}$$

(3)
$$\nabla \cdot \mathbf{E} = 0$$

(4)
$$\nabla \cdot \mathbf{H} = 0$$

Now let us see whether wave motion can be inferred from these four equations without actually solving them. The first equation states that if **E** is changing with time at some point, then **H** has curl at that point and thus can be considered as forming a small closed loop linking the changing **E** field. Also, if **E** is changing with time, then **H** will in general also change with time, although not necessarily in the same way. Next, we see from the second equation that this changing **H** produces an electric field which forms small closed loops about the **H** lines. We now have once more a changing electric field, our original hypothesis, but this field is present a small distance away from the point of the original disturbance. We might guess (correctly) that the velocity with which the effect moves away from the original point is the velocity of light, but this must be checked by a more quantitative examination of Maxwell's equations.

Let us first write Maxwell's four equations above for the special case of sinusoidal (more strictly, *cosinusoidal*) variation with time. This is accomplished by complex notation and phasors. Let us assume that some component, such as E_x, is given as

(5) $\quad E_x = E_{xyz} \cos (\omega t + \psi)$

where E_{xyz} is a real function of x, y, z, and perhaps ω, but not of time, and ψ is a phase angle which may also be a function of x, y, z, and ω. Making use of Euler's identity,

$$e^{j\omega t} = \cos \omega t + j \sin \omega t$$

we let

(6) $\quad E_x = \mathrm{Re}\, E_{xyz} e^{j(\omega t + \psi)} = \mathrm{Re}\, E_{xyz} e^{j\psi} e^{j\omega t}$

where Re signifies that the *real* part of the following quantity is to be taken. If we then drop Re and suppress $e^{j\omega t}$, the field quantity E_x becomes a *phasor*, or a complex quantity, which we identify by use of an s subscript, E_{xs}. Thus

(7) $\quad E_{xs} = E_{xyz} e^{j\psi}$

The s can be thought of as signifying "static" or non-time-varying, or it may be interpreted more exactly as indicating a frequency-domain quantity expressed as a function of the complex frequency s, even though we shall consider only those cases in which s is a pure imaginary, $s = j\omega$.

Given a phasor, the corresponding real quantity may always be obtained by multiplying by $e^{j\omega t}$ and taking the real part of the resultant expression.

Now, since

$$\frac{\partial E_x}{\partial t} = \frac{\partial}{\partial t}\left[E_{xyz}\cos{(\omega t + \psi)}\right] = -\omega E_{xyz}\sin{(\omega t + \psi)}$$

$$= \operatorname{Re} j\omega E_{xs}e^{j\omega t}$$

it is evident that taking the partial derivative of any field quantity with respect to time is equivalent to multiplying the corresponding phasor by $j\omega$. As an example, if

$$\frac{\partial E_x}{\partial t} = -\frac{1}{\epsilon_0}\frac{\partial H_y}{\partial z}$$

the corresponding phasor equation is

$$j\omega E_{xs} = -\frac{1}{\epsilon_0}\frac{\partial H_{ys}}{\partial z}$$

where E_{xs} and H_{ys} may both be complex quantities.

Expressing a vector as a phasor is no more complicated than expressing a single component as a phasor. Thus, given Maxwell's equation,

$$\nabla \times \mathbf{H} = \epsilon_0\frac{\partial \mathbf{E}}{\partial t}$$

the corresponding relationship in terms of phasor-vectors is

(8) $$\boxed{\nabla \times \mathbf{H}_s = j\omega\epsilon_0\mathbf{E}_s}$$

Equation (8) and the three equations

(9) $$\boxed{\nabla \times \mathbf{E}_s = -j\omega\mu_0\mathbf{H}_s}$$

(10) $$\boxed{\nabla \cdot \mathbf{E}_s = 0}$$

(11) $$\boxed{\nabla \cdot \mathbf{H}_s = 0}$$

are Maxwell's four equations in phasor notation for sinusoidal time variation in free space. It should be noted that (10) and (11) are no longer independent relationships, for they can be obtained by taking the divergence of (8) and (9), respectively.

Our next step is to obtain the wave equation, a step we could omit because the simple problem we are going to solve yields easily to simultaneous solution of the four equations above. The wave equation is an important equation, however, and it is a convenient starting point for many other investigations.

The method by which the wave equation is obtained could be accomplished in one line (using four equals signs on a wider sheet of paper):

$$\mathbf{\nabla} \times \mathbf{\nabla} \times \mathbf{E}_s = \mathbf{\nabla}(\mathbf{\nabla} \cdot \mathbf{E}_s) - \nabla^2 \mathbf{E}_s = -j\omega\mu_0 \mathbf{\nabla} \times \mathbf{H}_s$$
$$= \omega^2\mu_0\epsilon_0 \mathbf{E}_s = -\nabla^2 \mathbf{E}_s$$

since $\mathbf{\nabla} \cdot \mathbf{E}_s = 0$. Thus

(12)
$$\boxed{\nabla^2 \mathbf{E}_s = -\omega^2\mu_0\epsilon_0 \mathbf{E}_s}$$

This concise phasor-vector equation is fairly formidable when expanded, even in cartesian coordinates, for three scalar phasor equations result, and each has four terms. The x component of (12) becomes, still using the del-operator notation,

(13) $\nabla^2 E_{xs} = -\omega^2\mu_0\epsilon_0 E_{xs}$

and the expansion of the operator leads to the second-order partial differential equation

(14)
$$\frac{\partial^2 E_{xs}}{\partial x^2} + \frac{\partial^2 E_{xs}}{\partial y^2} + \frac{\partial^2 E_{xs}}{\partial z^2} = -\omega^2\mu_0\epsilon_0 E_{xs}$$

Let us attempt a solution of (14) by assuming that a simple solution is possible in which E_{xs} does not vary with x or y, so that the two corresponding derivatives are zero, leading to the ordinary differential equation

(15)
$$\frac{d^2 E_{xs}}{dz^2} = -\omega^2\mu_0\epsilon_0 E_{xs}$$

By inspection, we may write down one solution of (15),

(16) $E_{xs} = Ae^{-j\omega\sqrt{\mu_0\epsilon_0}\,z}$

reinsert the $e^{j\omega t}$ factor, and reduce to trigonometric form by taking the real part,

(17) $E_x = A \cos\left[\omega(t - z\sqrt{\mu_0\epsilon_0})\right]$

where the arbitrary amplitude factor may be replaced by E_{x0}, the value of E_x at $z = 0$, $t = 0$,

(18)
$$\boxed{E_x = E_{x0} \cos\left[\omega(t - z\sqrt{\mu_0\epsilon_0})\right]}$$

Looking back, it is almost obvious that this is a solution to (15). Problem 1 at the end of the chapter indicates that

(19)
$$E'_x = E'_{x0} \cos\left[\omega(t + z\sqrt{\mu_0\epsilon_0})\right]$$

is also a solution of (15).

Before we find any other field components we should understand the physical nature of the single component of the electric field we have obtained in Eq. (18). We see that it is an x component, which we might describe as directed upward at the surface of a plane earth. The radical $\sqrt{\mu_0\epsilon_0}$ has the value $1/(3 \times 10^8)$ s/m, which is the reciprocal of U_0, the velocity of light in free space,

$$U_0 = \frac{1}{\sqrt{\mu_0\epsilon_0}} = 3 \times 10^8 \text{ m/s}$$

Let us also allow the z axis to point east and take $z = 0$ in Chicago. In Chicago, then, the field is given by

$$E_x = E_{x0} \cos \omega t$$

which is a simple and familiar variation with time. A free charge (perhaps in a vertical receiving antenna) is accelerated up and down $\omega/2\pi$ times a second. In Cleveland, about 500 km east, we would find

$$E_x = E_{x0} \cos\left[\omega\left(t - \frac{5 \times 10^5}{3 \times 10^8}\right)\right] = E_{x0} \cos\left[\omega(t - 0.00167)\right]$$

indicating that the field strength in Cleveland is identical to that which existed in Chicago 0.00167 s earlier. In general terms, we should then expect the field at any point z m east of Chicago to lag the reference field by $z\sqrt{\mu_0\epsilon_0}$, or $z/(3 \times 10^8)$ s.

Let us change our viewpoint now and inspect the field everywhere at $t = 0$,

$$E_x = E_{x0} \cos\left(-\omega z\sqrt{\mu_0\epsilon_0}\right) = E_{x0} \cos\frac{\omega z}{U_0}$$

finding a periodic variation with distance. The period of this cosine wave as measured along the z axis is called the wavelength λ,

$$\frac{\omega\lambda}{U_0} = 2\pi$$

$$\lambda = \frac{U_0}{f} = \frac{3 \times 10^8}{f}$$

At any point we find a sinusoidal variation with time of period $T = 1/f$; at any time we find a sinusoidal variation with distance of period λ; at every point and at every instant of time E_x is directed vertically upward. Now let us consider the response as both time and location are varied. Certainly we may say that E_x is unchanged if $t - z\sqrt{\mu_0\epsilon_0}$ is unchanged, or

$$t - \frac{z}{U_0} = \text{constant}$$

and taking differentials, we have

$$dt - \frac{1}{U_0}dz = 0$$

$$\frac{dz}{dt} = U_0$$

The field is therefore moving in the z direction with the velocity of light U_0. Whatever the value of the field instantaneously at $z = z_1$, $t = t_1$, it will have the identical value at z_2 at a time $(z_2 - z_1)/U_0$ later; it will also have the identical value at $t = t_2$, a distance $(t_2 - t_1)U_0$ farther to the east. The electric field is in motion and is logically termed a *traveling wave*.

Equation (19), which was also a solution to our wave equation, obviously represents a wave traveling in the $-z$ direction, or west. For simplicity, we are considering only the positively traveling wave.

Let us now return to Maxwell's equations, (8) to (11), and determine the form of the **H** field. Given $\mathbf{E}_s$, $\mathbf{H}_s$ is most easily obtained from (9),

(9) $\quad \mathbf{\nabla} \times \mathbf{E}_s = -j\omega\mu_0\mathbf{H}_s$

which is greatly simplified for a single E_{xs} component varying only with z,

$$\frac{\partial E_{xs}}{\partial z} = -j\omega\mu_0 H_{ys}$$

Using (16) for E_{xs} with $A = E_{x0}$, we have

$$H_{ys} = -\frac{1}{j\omega\mu_0}E_{x0}(-j\omega\sqrt{\mu_0\epsilon_0})e^{-j\omega\sqrt{\mu_0\epsilon_0}z}$$

and

(20) $\quad \boxed{H_y = E_{x0}\sqrt{\frac{\epsilon_0}{\mu_0}}\cos\left[\omega(t - z\sqrt{\mu_0\epsilon_0})\right]}$

We therefore find that this vertical **E** component traveling to the east is accompanied by a horizontal (north-south) magnetic field. Moreover, the ratio of electric to magnetic field intensities, given by the ratio of (18) to (20),

(21)
$$\frac{E_x}{H_y} = \sqrt{\frac{\mu_0}{\epsilon_0}}$$

is constant. Using the language of circuit theory, we would say that E_x and H_y are "in phase," but this in-phase relationship refers to space as well as to time. We are accustomed to taking this for granted in a circuit problem in which a current $I_m \cos \omega t$ is assumed to have its maximum amplitude I_m throughout the entire circuit at $t = 0$. Both (18) and (20) clearly show, however, that the maximum value of either E_x or H_y occurs when $\omega(t - z\sqrt{\mu_0\epsilon_0})$ is an integral multiple of 2π rad; neither field is a maximum everywhere at the same instant. It is remarkable, then, that the ratio of these two components, both changing in space and time, should be everywhere a constant.

The square root of the ratio of the permeability to the permittivity is called the *intrinsic impedance* η (eta),

(22)
$$\eta = \sqrt{\frac{\mu}{\epsilon}}$$

where η has the dimensions of ohms. The intrinsic impedance of free space is

$$\eta_0 = \sqrt{\frac{\mu_0}{\epsilon_0}} = 377 \ \Omega$$

This wave is called a *uniform plane wave* because its value is uniform throughout any plane, $z = $ constant. It represents an energy flows in the positive z direction. Both the electric and magnetic fields are perpendicular to the direction of propagation, or both lie in a plane that is transverse to the direction of propagation; the uniform plane wave is a *transverse electromagnetic* wave, or a TEM wave.

Some feeling for the way in which the fields vary in space may be obtained from Figs. 11.1a and 11.1b. The electric field intensity in Fig. 11.1a is shown at $t = 0$ and the instantaneous value of the field is depicted along three lines, the z axis and arbitrary lines parallel to the z axis in the $x = 0$ and $y = 0$ planes. Since the field is uniform in planes perpendicular to the z axis, the variation along all three of the lines is the same. One complete cycle of the variation occurs in a wavelength λ. The values of H_y at the same time and positions are shown in Fig. 11.1b.

FIG. 11.1 (a) Arrows represent the instantaneous value of $E_x \cos \left[\omega(t - z\sqrt{\mu_0\epsilon_0}) \right]$ at $t = 0$ along the z axis, along an arbitrary line in the $x = 0$ plane parallel to the z axis, and along an arbitrary line in the $y = 0$ plane parallel to the z axis. (b) Corresponding values of H_y are indicated. Note that E_x and H_y are in phase at any point at any time.

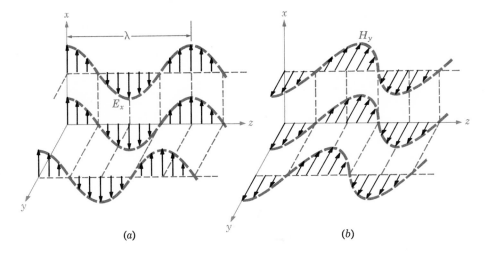

(a)   (b)

A uniform plane wave cannot exist physically, for it extends to infinity in two dimensions at least and represents an infinite amount of energy. The distant field of a transmitting antenna, however, is essentially a uniform plane wave in some limited region. A wave reaching a receiving antenna in Cleveland from Chicago is analyzed as a uniform plane wave in the vicinity of the antenna; a radar signal impinging on a distant target is also closely a uniform plane wave.

Although we have considered only a wave varying sinusoidally in time and space, a suitable combination of solutions to the wave equation may be made to achieve a wave of any desired form. The summation of an infinite number of harmonics through the use of a Fourier series can produce a periodic wave of square or triangular shape in both space and time. Nonperiodic waves may be obtained from our basic solution by Fourier integral methods. Finally, waves in other directions may also be included, representing perhaps a wave propagating slightly south of east. These topics are among those considered in the more advanced books on electromagnetic theory.

D 11.1 Find the magnitude of **H** at $z = 10$ m, $t = 10^{-6}$ s for the wave in air described by

(a) $\mathbf{E}_s = 500e^{-jz/300}\mathbf{a}_x$

(b) $\mathbf{E}_s = j400e^{-jz/300}\mathbf{a}_x$

(c) $\mathbf{E}_s = 300e^{-jz/300}\mathbf{a}_x + 200e^{-jz/300}\mathbf{a}_y$

Ans.   0.544; 0.753; 0.874   A/m

11.2 WAVE MOTION IN PERFECT DIELECTRICS

Let us now extend our analytical treatment of the uniform plane wave to propagation in a perfect (lossless) dielectric of permittivity ϵ and permeability μ. The medium is isotropic and homogeneous, and the wave equation is now

(1) $\quad \nabla^2\mathbf{E}_s = -\omega^2\mu\epsilon\mathbf{E}_s$

For E_{xs} we have

(2) $\quad \dfrac{\partial^2 E_{xs}}{\partial z^2} = -\omega^2\mu\epsilon E_{xs}$

Instead of writing down the solution of (2) immediately, let us hypothesize a solution of more general form and use (2) to specify appropriate values for our assumed parameters. We allow for exponential attenuation by assuming

(3) $\quad E_x = E_{x0}e^{-\alpha z}\cos(\omega t - \beta z)$

or its equivalent in complex exponential notation,

(4) $\quad E_{xs} = E_{x0}e^{-\alpha z}e^{-j\beta z}$

The real exponential factor now allows us to consider cases in which the wave may be attenuated as it propagates in the $+z$ direction; α is called the *attenuation constant*. Since our medium is lossless, we should be able to show that α is zero. If we next note that βz must be measured in radians (assuming β to be real), then it is logical that β be termed the *phase constant*. It is a measure of the radian phase shift per meter. In general, we often combine α and β into the complex *propagation constant* γ (gamma),

(5) $\quad \boxed{\gamma = \alpha + j\beta}$

and then (4) may be written as

(6) $\quad E_{xs} = E_{x0}e^{-\gamma z}$

Now let us substitute back into (2):

$$\gamma^2 E_{x0}e^{-\gamma z} = -\omega^2\mu\epsilon E_{x0}e^{-\gamma z}$$

and thus we must require

$$\gamma^2 = -\omega^2\mu\epsilon$$

or

$$\boxed{\gamma = \pm j\omega\sqrt{\mu\epsilon}}$$

Hence

$$\boxed{\alpha = 0}$$

and

(7)
$$\boxed{\beta = \omega\sqrt{\mu\epsilon}}$$

where we have selected the root which yields propagation in the positive z direction. Thus

(8) $\quad E_x = E_{x0}\cos\left[\omega(t - z\sqrt{\mu\epsilon})\right]$

and we may interpret this as a wave traveling in the $+z$ direction at a velocity U,

(9) $\quad U = \dfrac{1}{\sqrt{\mu\epsilon}} = \dfrac{U_0}{\sqrt{\mu_R\epsilon_R}}$

The wavelength is the ratio of velocity to frequency,

(10) $\quad \lambda = \dfrac{U}{f} = \dfrac{U_0}{f\sqrt{\mu_R\epsilon_R}} = \dfrac{\lambda_0}{\sqrt{\mu_R\epsilon_R}}$

where λ_0 is the free-space wavelength. Note that $\mu_R\epsilon_R > 1$, and therefore the wavelength is shorter and the velocity is lower in all real media than in free space. From (7) and (10) we also have the important relationship

(11)
$$\boxed{\beta = \dfrac{2\pi}{\lambda}}$$

Associated with E_x is the magnetic field intensity

(12)
$$\boxed{H_y = \dfrac{E_{x0}}{\eta}\cos\left(\omega t - \beta z\right)}$$

where the intrinsic impedance is

(13)
$$\boxed{\eta = \sqrt{\dfrac{\mu}{\epsilon}}}$$

The two fields E_x and H_y are perpendicular to each other, perpendicular to the direction of propagation, and in phase with each other everywhere. Note that when **E** is crossed into **H**, the resultant vector is in the direction of propagation. We shall see the reason for this when we discuss the Poynting vector.

Let us apply these results to a 300-MHz[1] wave propagating

---

[1] MHz is the abbreviation for megahertz, or 10^6 hertz. The hertz (abbreviated Hz, and pronounced as if it were spelled "hurts") is one of the units in the International System and has been adopted by the Institute of Electric and Electronic Engineers as the standard unit of frequency; it replaces the cycle per second. Most of the current periodical literature and manufacturers' catalogs have begun using the new unit, and we might as well do so too.

through fresh water. Although we do not have a lossless medium, we shall neglect the attenuation at this time and assume that $\alpha = 0$. Therefore $\mu_R = 1$, $\epsilon_R = 78$ (at 300 MHz), and

$$U = \frac{U_0}{\sqrt{\mu_R \epsilon_R}} = \frac{3 \times 10^8}{\sqrt{78}} = 0.340 \times 10^8 \text{ m/s}$$

$$\lambda = \frac{U}{f} = \frac{0.340 \times 10^8}{3 \times 10^8} = 0.113 \text{ m}$$

whereas the wavelength in air would have been 1 m. Continuing to calculate the other parameters, we find that

$$\beta = \frac{2\pi}{\lambda} = 55.4 \text{ rad/m}$$

or 80.6°/in., and

$$\eta = \eta_0 \sqrt{\frac{\mu_R}{\epsilon_R}} = \frac{377}{\sqrt{78}} = 42.7 \ \Omega$$

If we let the electric field intensity have a maximum amplitude of 0.1 V/m, then

$$E_x = 0.1 \cos (6\pi 10^8 t - 55.4z)$$

$$H_y = \frac{E_x}{\eta} = 2.34 \times 10^{-3} \cos (6\pi 10^8 t - 55.4z)$$

D 11.2 Find the relative dielectric constant of a nonmagnetic material through which a uniform plane wave is propagating if

(a) The intrinsic impedance is 180 Ω.
(b) The wavelength at 10 GHz (gigahertz) is 2 cm.
(c) $\mathbf{E}_s = (2\mathbf{a}_x + j3\mathbf{a}_y)e^{-j0.001z}$, $f = 25,000$ Hz.

Ans. 2.25; 3.65; 4.38

D 11.3 Two lossless materials are described by μ_{R1}, ϵ_{R1}, μ_{R2}, and ϵ_{R2}. Determine μ_{R2} and ϵ_{R2} if $\mu_{R1} = 3$, $\epsilon_{R1} = 2$, and

(a) $U_2 = U_1$, $\eta_2 = \dfrac{\eta_1}{2}$

(b) $\eta_2 = \eta_1$, $\lambda_2 = \dfrac{\lambda_1}{2}$

(c) $\eta_2 = 3 \eta_1$, $\beta_2 = 2 \beta_1$

Ans. (1.5,4); (6,4); (18,1.333)

All dielectric materials have some conductivity, and while it may be neglected in many cases, even then it is necessary to establish the criteria for doing so.   We shall continue to confine our attention to a sinusoidal time variation, and thus Maxwell's curl equations are

$$\nabla \times \mathbf{H}_s = \mathbf{J}_s + j\omega\epsilon\mathbf{E}_s$$

or

(1) $\nabla \times \mathbf{H}_s = (\sigma + j\omega\epsilon)\mathbf{E}_s$

and

(2) $\nabla \times \mathbf{E}_s = -j\omega\mu\mathbf{H}_s$

The only effect of including the conductivity σ is that the factor $j\omega\epsilon$ has now become $\sigma + j\omega\epsilon$. We may therefore immediately calculate the new value of the propagation constant,

$$\gamma^2 = (\sigma + j\omega\epsilon)j\omega\mu$$

$$\gamma = \pm\sqrt{(\sigma + j\omega\epsilon)j\omega\mu}$$

or dividing throughout by a familiar group of constants,

(3) $\gamma = j\omega\sqrt{\mu\epsilon}\sqrt{1 - j\dfrac{\sigma}{\omega\epsilon}}$

where we have retained only the plus sign of the radical for a reason which will be evident shortly.   This expression differs from the lossless case in the presence of the second radical factor, which becomes unity as σ vanishes.   In the general case values for σ, μ, ϵ, and ω may be inserted into (3), the real and imaginary parts of γ calculated,

(4) $\gamma = \alpha + j\beta$

and the x component of the electric field intensity propagating in the $+z$ direction obtained,

(5) $E_{xs} = E_{x0}e^{-\alpha z}e^{-j\beta z}$

The use of the plus sign for the radical in (3) leads to positive numerical values for α and β, and hence corresponds to propagation in the $+z$ direction.

Using (2), it is easily shown that H_{ys} is

(6) $H_{ys} = \dfrac{E_{x0}}{\eta} e^{-\alpha z}e^{-j\beta z}$

where the intrinsic impedance is now a complex quantity,

$$(7) \qquad \eta = \sqrt{\frac{j\omega\mu}{\sigma + j\omega\epsilon}} = \sqrt{\frac{\mu}{\epsilon}} \frac{1}{\sqrt{1 - j(\sigma/\omega\epsilon)}}$$

The electric and magnetic fields are no longer in time phase.

Before we consider an example illustrating these calculations the nature of the exponential factor $e^{-\alpha z}$ bears some investigation. For a wave propagating in the $+z$ direction this factor causes an exponential decrease in amplitude with increasing values of z. The attenuation constant is measured in nepers per meter (nep/m) in order that the exponent of e be measured in the dimensionless units of nepers.[1] Thus, if $\alpha = 0.01$ nep/m, the crest amplitude of the wave at $z = 50$ m will be $e^{-0.5}/e^{-0} = 0.607$ of its value at $z = 0$. In traveling a distance of $1/\alpha$ m in the $+z$ direction, the amplitude of the wave is reduced by the familiar factor of e^{-1}, or 0.368.

Some numerical results may be calculated for distilled water, which is quite a poor dielectric. At $\omega = 10^{11}$ rad/s, or $f = 15.9$ GHz, representative values of the parameters are $\mu_R = 1$, $\epsilon_R = 50$, and $\sigma = 20$ ℧/m. Thus

$$\frac{\sigma}{\omega\epsilon} = \frac{20 \times 10^{12}}{10^{11} \times 50 \times 8.85} = 0.452$$

and

$$\gamma = j\frac{10^{11}\sqrt{1 \times 50}}{3 \times 10^8}\sqrt{1 - j0.452}$$

$$= j2,360\sqrt{1.098/\underline{-24.3°}}$$

$$= 2,480/\underline{77.8°} = 522 + j2,420 \qquad \text{m}^{-1}$$

Therefore

$$\alpha = 522 \text{ nep/m}$$

and the amplitude of E_x or H_y will attenuate by a factor of 0.368 for every $1/522$ m of propagation in the water. The term "propagates" is thus being used quite loosely. The large attenuation indicates the reason why radar is ineffective under water and sonar is used instead; it also suggests that water or rain in the atmosphere will cause propagation problems at high frequencies.

The phase constant is

$$\beta = 2,420 \text{ rad/m}$$

and this has been affected only slightly by the nonzero conductivity, for the numerical calculations above show that it would have been

---

[1] The term *neper* was selected (by some poor speller) to honor John Napier, a Scottish mathematician who first proposed the use of logarithms.

2,360 rad/m if σ were zero. The wavelength at this frequency is 1.88 cm in air, and since $\beta = 2\pi/\lambda$, it is 2.60 mm in water.

The intrinsic impedance is found to be

$$\eta = \frac{377}{\sqrt{50}} \frac{1}{\sqrt{1 - j0.452}} = 50.8\underline{/12.2°} = 49.6 + j10.7 \qquad \Omega$$

and E_x leads H_y by 12.2° at every point.

Let us now turn our attention to the more practical case of a dielectric material that has some small loss. The criterion by which we should judge whether or not the loss is small is the magnitude of $\sigma/\omega\epsilon$ as compared to unity, as shown by (3) and (7). The term $\sigma/\omega\epsilon$ is referred to as the *loss tangent* for a reason that becomes clear when we consider Maxwell's curl $\mathbf{H}$ equation, which formed the starting point for our analysis,

$$\nabla \times \mathbf{H}_s = (\sigma + j\omega\epsilon)\mathbf{E}_s = \mathbf{J}_{\sigma s} + \mathbf{J}_{ds}$$

The ratio of conduction current density to displacement current density is

$$(8) \qquad \frac{\mathbf{J}_{\sigma s}}{\mathbf{J}_{ds}} = \frac{\sigma}{j\omega\epsilon}$$

That is, these two vectors point in the same direction in space, but they are 90° out of phase in time. Displacement current density leads conduction current density by 90°, just as the current through a capacitor leads the current through a resistor in parallel with it by 90° in an ordinary electrical circuit. This phase relationship is shown in Fig. 11.2. The angle θ (not to be confused with the polar

FIG. 11.2 The time-phase relationship between $\mathbf{J}_{ds}$, $\mathbf{J}_{\sigma s}$, $\mathbf{J}_s$, and $\mathbf{E}_s$. The tangent of θ is equal to $\sigma/\omega\epsilon$, and $90° - \theta$ is the common power-factor angle, or the angle by which $\mathbf{J}_s$ leads $\mathbf{E}_s$.

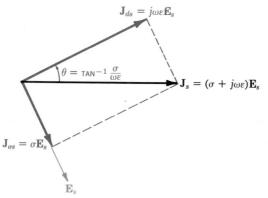

angle in spherical coordinates) may therefore be identified as the angle by which the displacement current density leads the total current density, and

(9)
$$\tan \theta = \frac{\sigma}{\omega\epsilon}$$

This relationship has led to the name of "loss tangent" for $\sigma/\omega\epsilon$. Problem 12 at the end of the chapter indicates that the Q of a capacitor (its quality factor, not its charge) which incorporates a lossy dielectric is the reciprocal of the loss tangent.

If the loss tangent is small, then we may obtain useful approximations for the attenuation and phase constants, and the intrinsic impedance. Since

(3)
$$\gamma = j\omega\sqrt{\mu\epsilon}\sqrt{1 - j\frac{\sigma}{\omega\epsilon}}$$

we may expand the second radical by the binomial theorem,

$$(1 + x)^n = 1 + nx + \frac{n(n-1)}{2!}x^2 + \frac{n(n-1)(n-2)}{3!}x^3 + \cdots$$

where $|x| < 1$. We identify x as $-j\sigma/\omega\epsilon$ and n as $\frac{1}{2}$, and thus

$$\gamma = j\omega\sqrt{\mu\epsilon}\left[1 - j\frac{\sigma}{2\omega\epsilon} + \frac{1}{8}\left(\frac{\sigma}{\omega\epsilon}\right)^2 + \cdots\right]$$

Hence

(10)
$$\alpha \doteq j\omega\sqrt{\mu\epsilon}\left(-j\frac{\sigma}{2\omega\epsilon}\right) = \frac{\sigma}{2}\sqrt{\frac{\mu}{\epsilon}}$$

and

(11a)
$$\beta \doteq \omega\sqrt{\mu\epsilon}\left[1 + \frac{1}{8}\left(\frac{\sigma}{\omega\epsilon}\right)^2\right]$$

or in many cases,

(11b)
$$\beta \doteq \omega\sqrt{\mu\epsilon}$$

In a similar way, we find

(12a)
$$\eta \doteq \sqrt{\frac{\mu}{\epsilon}}\left[1 - \frac{3}{8}\left(\frac{\sigma}{\omega\epsilon}\right)^2 + j\frac{\sigma}{2\omega\epsilon}\right]$$

or

(12b)
$$\eta \doteq \sqrt{\frac{\mu}{\epsilon}}\left(1 + j\frac{\sigma}{2\omega\epsilon}\right)$$

In order to illustrate the accuracy of our approximations let us recalculate α, β, and η for the distilled-water example discussed earlier, even though the loss tangent has the relatively large value of 0.452. With $\epsilon_R = 50$, $\sigma = 20$ ℧/m, $\omega = 10^{11}$, and $\mu_R = 1$, we have from (10)

$$\alpha = 533 \text{ nep/m}$$

as compared with the exact value of 522 nep/m. Using (11a), the phase constant is

$$\beta = 2,420 \text{ rad/m}$$

which is the same as the exact value, while (11b) yields the lossless value

$$\beta = 2,360 \text{ rad/m}$$

Finally, the intrinsic impedance is found by (12a) to be

$$\eta = 50.3\underline{/13.7^\circ} = 49.2 + j12.0 \quad \Omega$$

as compared to an exact value of $50.8\underline{/12.2^\circ} = 49.6 + j10.7$ Ω, and a greater error is introduced by (12b),

$$\eta = 54.7\underline{/12.7^\circ} = 53.3 + j12.0 \quad \Omega$$

Although the loss tangent in this example is 0.452, the errors involved in using the more approximate formulations are not excessive, because the conductivity and relative dielectric constant are seldom known to any great accuracy. We shall, however, recommend use of the approximations only when $\sigma/\omega\epsilon < 0.1$; any further approximations should be based on engineering judgment.

In most physical dielectrics the loss tangent is more constant with frequency than is the conductivity. That is, conductivity tends to increase with frequency, although not linearly. There may also be relatively rapid changes of conductivity, permittivity, and loss tangent in the infrared region and again in the ultraviolet region.[1] A sketch of the variation of σ, ϵ_R, and $\sigma/\omega\epsilon$ with frequency for Pyranol 1467 and polystyrene is shown in Fig. 11.3 on a logarithmic frequency scale.

D 11.4 If the loss tangent for a certain material is 0.1 and it is assumed to be constant with frequency, find the fraction by which the amplitude of $\mathbf{E}_s$ is reduced when propagating 200 m in the material. Use $\epsilon_R = 9$, $\mu_R = 1$ and determine the fraction at

(a) $\omega = 10^4$
(b) $\omega = 10^6$
(c) $\omega = 10^8$

Ans. 4.54×10^{-5}; 0.905; 0.999

[1] The variation of all these parameters with frequency is given for many materials in von Hippel. See the bibliography at the end of the chapter.

FIG. 11.3 The variation of σ, ϵ_R, and $\sigma/\omega\epsilon$ is shown in (a), (b), and (c), respectively, for Pyranol 1467 and polystyrene. Note the use of logarithmic scales for all axes except ϵ_R.

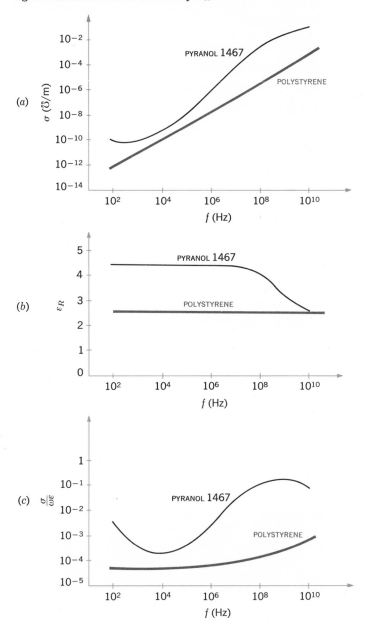

D 11.5 Determine the wavelength in a material for which $\epsilon_R = 4$, $\mu_R = 1$, and $f = 3 \times 10^8$ Hz and the loss tangent is

(a) 0.01

(b) 0.1

(c) 1

Ans. 0.455; 0.499; 0.500   m

11.4 THE POYNTING VECTOR AND POWER CONSIDERATIONS

In order to find the power in a uniform plane wave it is necessary to develop a power theorem for the electromagnetic field known as the Poynting theorem. It was originally postulated in 1884 by an English physicist, John H. Poynting.

Let us begin with Maxwell's equation,

$$\nabla \times \mathbf{H} = \mathbf{J} + \frac{\partial \mathbf{D}}{\partial t}$$

and dot each side of the equation with $\mathbf{E}$,

$$\mathbf{E} \cdot \nabla \times \mathbf{H} = \mathbf{J} \cdot \mathbf{E} + \mathbf{E} \cdot \frac{\partial \mathbf{D}}{\partial t}$$

We now make use of the vector identity,

$$\nabla \cdot (\mathbf{E} \times \mathbf{H}) = -\mathbf{E} \cdot \nabla \times \mathbf{H} + \mathbf{H} \cdot \nabla \times \mathbf{E}$$

which may be proved by expansion in cartesian coordinates. Thus

$$\mathbf{H} \cdot \nabla \times \mathbf{E} - \nabla \cdot (\mathbf{E} \times \mathbf{H}) = \mathbf{J} \cdot \mathbf{E} + \mathbf{E} \cdot \frac{\partial \mathbf{D}}{\partial t}$$

But

$$\nabla \times \mathbf{E} = -\frac{\partial \mathbf{B}}{\partial t}$$

and therefore

$$-\mathbf{H} \cdot \frac{\partial \mathbf{B}}{\partial t} - \nabla \cdot (\mathbf{E} \times \mathbf{H}) = \mathbf{J} \cdot \mathbf{E} + \mathbf{E} \cdot \frac{\partial \mathbf{D}}{\partial t}$$

or

$$-\nabla \cdot (\mathbf{E} \times \mathbf{H}) = \mathbf{J} \cdot \mathbf{E} + \epsilon \mathbf{E} \cdot \frac{\partial \mathbf{E}}{\partial t} + \mu \mathbf{H} \cdot \frac{\partial \mathbf{H}}{\partial t}$$

However,

$$\epsilon \mathbf{E} \cdot \frac{\partial \mathbf{E}}{\partial t} = \frac{\epsilon}{2} \frac{\partial E^2}{\partial t} = \frac{\partial}{\partial t} \left(\frac{\epsilon E^2}{2} \right)$$

and

$$\mu\mathbf{H}\cdot\frac{\partial\mathbf{H}}{\partial t} = \frac{\partial}{\partial t}\left(\frac{\mu H^2}{2}\right)$$

Thus

$$-\boldsymbol{\nabla}\cdot(\mathbf{E}\times\mathbf{H}) = \mathbf{J}\cdot\mathbf{E} + \frac{\partial}{\partial t}\left(\frac{\epsilon E^2}{2} + \frac{\mu H^2}{2}\right)$$

Finally, we integrate throughout a volume,

$$-\int_{\text{vol}}\boldsymbol{\nabla}\cdot(\mathbf{E}\times\mathbf{H})\,dv = \int_{\text{vol}}\mathbf{J}\cdot\mathbf{E}\,dv + \frac{\partial}{\partial t}\int_{\text{vol}}\left(\frac{\epsilon E^2}{2} + \frac{\mu H^2}{2}\right)dv$$

and apply the divergence theorem to obtain

(1)
$$-\oint_s(\mathbf{E}\times\mathbf{H})\cdot d\mathbf{S} = \int_{\text{vol}}\mathbf{J}\cdot\mathbf{E}\,dv + \frac{\partial}{\partial t}\int_{\text{vol}}\left(\frac{\epsilon E^2}{2} + \frac{\mu H^2}{2}\right)dv$$

The first integral on the right is the total (but instantaneous) ohmic power dissipated within the volume. The integral in the second term on the right is the total energy stored in the electric and magnetic fields,[1] and the partial derivatives with respect to time cause this term to be the time rate of increase of energy stored within this volume, or the instantaneous power going to increase the stored energy within this volume. The sum of the expressions on the right must therefore be the total power flowing *into* this volume, and thus the total power flowing *out* of the volume is

$$\oint_s(\mathbf{E}\times\mathbf{H})\cdot d\mathbf{S}$$

where the integral is over the closed surface surrounding the volume. The cross product $\mathbf{E}\times\mathbf{H}$ is known as the Poynting vector $\boldsymbol{\mathcal{P}}$,

(2)
$$\boldsymbol{\mathcal{P}} = \mathbf{E}\times\mathbf{H}$$

which is interpreted as an instantaneous power density, measured in watts per square meter (W/m²). This interpretation is subject to the same philosophical considerations as was the description of $\frac{1}{2}\mathbf{D}\cdot\mathbf{E}$ or $\frac{1}{2}\mathbf{B}\cdot\mathbf{H}$ as energy densities. We can show rigorously only that the integration of the Poynting vector over a closed surface yields the total power crossing the surface in an outward sense. This interpretation as a power density does not lead us astray, however, especially when applied to sinusoidally varying fields. Problem 20 indicates that strange results may be found when the Poynting vector is applied to time-constant fields.

---

[1] This is the expression for magnetic field energy we have been anticipating since chap. 9.

The direction of the vector $\mathcal{P}$ indicates the direction of the instantaneous power flow at the point, and many of us think of the Poynting vector as a "pointing" vector. This homonym, while accidental, is correct.

Since $\mathcal{P}$ is given by the cross product of $\mathbf{E}$ and $\mathbf{H}$, the direction of power flow at any point is normal to both the $\mathbf{E}$ and $\mathbf{H}$ vectors. This certainly agrees with our experience with the uniform plane wave, for propagation in the $+z$ direction was invariably associated with an E_x and H_y component. Moreover,

$$E_x\mathbf{a}_x \times H_y\mathbf{a}_y = \mathcal{P}_z\mathbf{a}_z$$

In a perfect dielectric these $\mathbf{E}$ and $\mathbf{H}$ fields are given by

$$E_x = E_{x0} \cos (\omega t - \beta z)$$

$$H_y = \frac{E_{x0}}{\eta} \cos (\omega t - \beta z)$$

and thus

$$\mathcal{P}_z = \frac{E_{x0}^2}{\eta} \cos^2 (\omega t - \beta z)$$

To find the time-average power density, we integrate over one cycle and divide by the period $T = 1/f$,

$$\mathcal{P}_{z,\text{av}} = f \int_0^{1/f} \frac{E_{x0}^2}{\eta} \cos^2 (\omega t - \beta z) \, dt$$

$$= \frac{f}{2} \frac{E_{x0}^2}{\eta} \int_0^{1/f} [1 + \cos (2\omega t - 2\beta z)] \, dt$$

$$= \frac{f}{2} \frac{E_{x0}^2}{\eta} \left[t + \frac{1}{2\omega} \sin (2\omega t - 2\beta z) \right]_0^{1/f}$$

and

(3) $$\boxed{\mathcal{P}_{z,\text{av}} = \frac{1}{2} \frac{E_{x0}^2}{\eta}}$$

If we were using root-mean-square values instead of peak amplitudes, the factor of $\frac{1}{2}$ would not be present.

Finally, the average power flowing through any area S normal to the z axis is[1]

$$P_{z,\text{av}} = \frac{1}{2} \frac{E_{x0}^2}{\eta} S$$

[1] We shall use P for power as well as for polarization. If they both appear in the same equation in this book, it is an error.

In the case of a lossy dielectric E_x and H_y are not in time phase, and the integration is a step or two longer. The result is

$$(4) \quad \mathcal{P}_{z,\text{av}} = \frac{1}{2} \frac{E_{x0}^2}{\eta_m} e^{-2\alpha z} \cos \theta_\eta$$

where η is expressed in polar form,

$$\eta = \eta_m \underline{/\theta_\eta}$$

D 11.6 Find the time-average power density, at $x = 1$, associated with a uniform plane wave $\mathbf{E} = 30e^{-\alpha x} \cos(10^8 t - \beta x) \, \mathbf{a}_z$ V/m propagating through

(a) Free space
(b) Polyethylene ($\epsilon_R = 2.26$, $\sigma \doteq 0$)
(c) Neoprene ($\epsilon_R = 3.40$, $\sigma/\omega\epsilon = 0.2$)

Ans. $1.19\mathbf{a}_x; 1.79\mathbf{a}_x; 1.96\mathbf{a}_x \quad$ W/m²

11.5 PROPAGATION IN GOOD CONDUCTORS: SKIN EFFECT

As our final example of unbounded propagation we shall investigate the behavior of a good conductor when a uniform plane wave is established in it. Rather than thinking of a source embedded in a block of copper and launching a wave in that material, we should be more interested in a wave that is established by an electromagnetic field existing in some external dielectric that adjoins the conductor surface. We shall see that energy must be transmitted in the region *outside* the conductor, because all time-varying fields attenuate very quickly *within* a good conductor.

The good conductor has a high conductivity and large conduction currents. The energy represented by the wave traveling through the material therefore decreases as the wave propagates because ohmic losses are continuously present. When we discussed the loss tangent, we saw that the ratio of conduction current density to the displacement current density in a material is given by $\sigma/\omega\epsilon$. Choosing a poor metallic conductor and a very high frequency as a conservative example, this ratio for nichrome ($\sigma \doteq 10^6$) at 100 MHz is about 2×10^8. Thus we have a situation where $\sigma/\omega\epsilon \gg 1$, and we should be able to make several very good approximations to find α, β, and η for a good conductor.

The general expression for the propagation constant is

$$\gamma = j\omega\sqrt{\mu\epsilon} \sqrt{1 - j\frac{\sigma}{\omega\epsilon}}$$

which we immediately simplify to obtain

$$\gamma = j\omega\sqrt{\mu\epsilon} \sqrt{-j\frac{\sigma}{\omega\epsilon}}$$

or

$$\gamma = j\sqrt{-j\omega\mu\sigma}$$

But

$$-j = 1\underline{/-90^\circ}$$

and

$$\sqrt{1\underline{/-90^\circ}} = 1\underline{/-45^\circ} = \frac{1}{\sqrt{2}} - j\frac{1}{\sqrt{2}}$$

Therefore

$$\gamma = j\left(\frac{1}{\sqrt{2}} - j\frac{1}{\sqrt{2}}\right)\sqrt{\omega\mu\sigma}$$

or

(1) $$\gamma = (j1 + 1)\sqrt{\pi f\mu\sigma}$$

Hence

(2) $$\alpha = \beta = \sqrt{\pi f\mu\sigma}$$

Regardless of the parameters μ and σ of the conductor or of the frequency of the applied field, α and β are equal. If we again assume only an E_x component traveling in the $+z$ direction, then

(3) $$E_x = E_{x0}e^{-z\sqrt{\pi f\mu\sigma}}\cos\left(\omega t - z\sqrt{\pi f\mu\sigma}\right)$$

We may tie this field in the conductor to an external field at the conductor surface. We let the region $z > 0$ be the good conductor and the region $z < 0$ be a perfect dielectric. At the boundary surface $z = 0$, (3) becomes

$$E_x = E_{x0}\cos\omega t \qquad (z = 0)$$

This we shall consider as the source field that establishes the fields within the conductor. Since displacement current is negligible,

$$\mathbf{J} = \sigma\mathbf{E}$$

and the conduction current density at any point within the conductor is directly related to $\mathbf{E}$:

(4) $$J_x = \sigma E_x = \sigma E_{x0}e^{-z\sqrt{\pi f\mu\sigma}}\cos\left(\omega t - z\sqrt{\pi f\mu\sigma}\right)$$

The form of J_x is the same as that of E_x.

Equations (3) and (4) contain a wealth of information. Considering first the negative exponential term, we find an exponential decrease in the conduction current density and electric field intensity with penetration into the conductor (away from the source).

The exponential factor is unity at $z = 0$ and decreases to $e^{-1} = 0.368$ when

$$z = \frac{1}{\sqrt{\pi f \mu \sigma}}$$

This distance is denoted by δ and is termed the *depth of penetration*, or the *skin depth*,

(5)
$$\delta = \frac{1}{\sqrt{\pi f \mu \sigma}} = \frac{1}{\alpha} = \frac{1}{\beta}$$

It is an important parameter in describing conductor behavior in electromagnetic fields. To get some idea of the magnitude of the skin depth, let us consider copper, $\sigma = 5.8 \times 10^7$ ℧/m, at several different frequencies. We have

$$\delta_{cu} = \frac{0.0661}{\sqrt{f}}$$

At a power frequency of 60 Hz, $\delta_{cu} = 8.53$ mm, or about ⅓ in. Remembering that the power density carries an exponential term $e^{-2\alpha z}$, we see that the power density decreases by a factor of $0.368^2 = 0.135$ with every 8.53 mm of distance into the copper. At a microwave frequency of 10,000 MHz, δ is 6.61×10^{-4} mm, or about one-eighth the wavelength of visible light.

We see then that any current density or electric field intensity established at the surface of a good conductor decays rapidly as we progress into the conductor. Electromagnetic energy is not transmitted in the interior of a conductor; it travels in the region surrounding the conductor, while the conductor merely guides the waves. The currents established at the conductor surface propagate into the conductor in a direction perpendicular to the direction of the current density, and they are attenuated by ohmic losses. This power loss is the price exacted by the conductor for acting as a guide. We shall consider guided propagation in more detail in the following chapter.

Suppose we have a copper bus bar in the substation of an electric utility company which we wish to have carry large currents, and we therefore select dimensions of 2 by 4 in. Then much of the copper is wasted, for the fields are greatly reduced in one skin depth, about ⅓ in. A hollow conductor with a wall thickness of about ½ in. would be a much better design. Although we are applying the results of an analysis for an infinite planar conductor to one of finite dimensions, the fields are attenuated in the finite-size conductor in a similar fashion.

The extremely short skin depth at microwave frequencies shows that only the surface coating of the guiding conductor is important. A piece of glass with an evaporated silver surface 0.0001 in. thick is an excellent conductor at these frequencies.

Next, let us determine expressions for the velocity and wavelength within a good conductor. Since

$$\beta = \frac{2\pi}{\lambda}$$

we have, from Eq. (5),

(6) $\lambda = 2\pi\delta$

Also,

$$U = f\lambda$$

and therefore

(7) $U = 2\pi f\delta = \omega\delta$

For copper at 60 Hz, $\lambda = 5.36$ cm and $U = 3.22$ m/s, or about 7.2 mph. Most of us can run faster than that. In free space, of course, a 60-Hz wave has a wavelength of 3,110 miles and travels at the velocity of light.

In order to find H_y we need an expression for the intrinsic impedance of a good conductor. We begin with Sec. 11.3, Eq. (7),

$$\eta = \sqrt{\frac{j\omega\mu}{\sigma + j\omega\epsilon}}$$

Since $\sigma \gg \omega\epsilon$, we have

$$\eta = \sqrt{\frac{j\omega\mu}{\sigma}}$$

which may be written as

(8) $\eta = \dfrac{\sqrt{2}\underline{/45^\circ}}{\sigma\delta} = \dfrac{1}{\sigma\delta} + j\dfrac{1}{\sigma\delta}$

Thus, if we rewrite (3) in terms of the skin depth,

(9) $E_x = E_{x0}e^{-z/\delta} \cos\left(\omega t - \dfrac{z}{\delta}\right)$

then

(10) $H_y = \dfrac{\sigma\delta E_{x0}}{\sqrt{2}} e^{-z/\delta} \cos\left(\omega t - \dfrac{z}{\delta} - \dfrac{\pi}{4}\right)$

and we see that the maximum amplitude of the magnetic field intensity occurs one-eighth of a cycle later than the maximum amplitude of the electric field intensity at every point.

From (9) and (10) we may obtain the time-average Poynting vector by applying Sec. 11.4, Eq. (4),

$$\mathcal{P}_{z,\text{av}} = \frac{1}{2} \frac{\sigma \delta E_{x0}{}^2}{\sqrt{2}} e^{-2z/\delta} \cos \frac{\pi}{4}$$

or

$$\mathcal{P}_{z,\text{av}} = \tfrac{1}{4} \sigma \delta E_{x0}{}^2 e^{-2z/\delta}$$

We again note that in a distance of one skin depth the power density is reduced by a factor of $e^{-2} = 0.135$.

The total power loss in a width $0 < y < b$ and length $0 < x < L$ (in the direction of the current) is obtained by finding the power crossing the conductor surface within this area,

$$P_{L,\text{av}} = \int_0^b \int_0^L \tfrac{1}{4}\sigma \delta E_{x0}{}^2 e^{-2z/\delta} \Bigg]_{z=0} dx\, dy$$

$$= \tfrac{1}{4}\sigma \delta b L E_{x0}{}^2 \quad \text{W}$$

or in terms of the current density J_{x0} at the surface,

$$J_{x0} = \sigma E_{x0}$$

we have

(11) $\quad P_{L,\text{av}} = \dfrac{1}{4}\dfrac{1}{\sigma}\,\delta b L J_{x0}{}^2$

Now let us see what power loss would result if the *total* current in a width b were distributed uniformly in one skin depth. To find the total current we integrate the current density over the infinite depth of the conductor,

$$I = \int_0^\infty \int_0^b J_x\, dy\, dz$$

where

$$J_x = J_{x0} e^{-z/\delta} \cos\left(\omega t - \frac{z}{\delta}\right)$$

or in complex exponential notation to simplify the integration,

$$J_{xs} = J_{x0} e^{-z/\delta} e^{-jz/\delta}$$

$$= J_{x0} e^{-(1+j1)z/\delta}$$

Therefore

$$I_s = \int_0^\infty \int_0^b J_{x0} e^{-(1+j1)\,z/\delta} \, dy \, dz$$

$$= J_{x0} b e^{-(1+j1)\,z/\delta} \left. \frac{-\delta}{1+j1} \right]_0^\infty$$

$$= \frac{J_{x0} b \delta}{1+j1}$$

and

$$I = \frac{J_{x0} b \delta}{\sqrt{2}} \cos\left(\omega t - \frac{\pi}{4}\right)$$

If this is distributed uniformly in the cross section $0 < y < b$, $0 < z < \delta$, then

$$J' = \frac{J_{x0}}{\sqrt{2}} \cos\left(\omega t - \frac{\pi}{4}\right)$$

The ohmic power loss per unit volume is $\mathbf{J} \cdot \mathbf{E}$, and thus the total instantaneous power dissipated in the volume under consideration is

$$P_L = \frac{1}{\sigma}(J')^2 bL\delta = \frac{J_{x0}^2}{2\sigma} bL\delta \cos^2\left(\omega t - \frac{\pi}{4}\right)$$

The time-average power loss is easily obtained, since the average value of the cosine-squared factor is one-half,

(12) $$P_L = \frac{1}{4}\frac{1}{\sigma} J_{x0}^2 bL\delta$$

Comparing (11) and (12), we see that they are identical. Thus the average power loss in a conductor with skin effect present is the same as the average power loss that would be produced by having the total current distributed uniformly in one skin depth. In terms of resistance, we may say that the resistance of a width b and length L of an infinitely thick slab with skin effect is the same as the resistance of a rectangular slab of width b, length L, and thickness δ without skin effect, or with uniform current distribution.

We may apply this to a conductor of circular cross section with little error, provided that the radius a is much greater than the skin depth. The resistance at a high frequency where there is a well-developed skin effect is therefore found by considering a slab of width equal to the circumference $2\pi a$ and thickness δ. Hence

(13) $$R = \frac{L}{\sigma S} = \frac{L}{2\pi a \sigma \delta}$$

A round copper wire of 1-mm radius and 1-km length has a resistance at direct current of

$$R_{\text{dc}} = \frac{10^3}{\pi 10^{-6}(5.8 \times 10^7)} = 5.48 \; \Omega$$

At 1 MHz the skin depth is 0.0661 mm. Thus $\delta \ll a$, and the resistance at 1 MHz is found by (13),

$$R = \frac{10^3}{2\pi 10^{-3}(5.8 \times 10^7)(0.0661 \times 10^{-3})} = 41.5 \; \Omega$$

D 11.7 Using conductivity values given in Appendix C, find the skin depth in millimeters at 1,000 Hz in

(a) Silver
(b) Brass
(c) Nichrome

Ans.   2.02; 4.11; 16.9   mm

D 11.8 Find the factor by which the resistance of a copper wire 2 mm in radius increases as the frequency goes from direct current to

(a) 250 kHz
(b) 25 MHz
(c) 2,500 MHz

Ans.   7.57; 75.7; 757

11.6   REFLECTION OF UNIFORM PLANE WAVES

In order to treat problems of practical interest we must turn our attention to regions of *finite* size.   In this section we shall consider the phenomenon of reflection which occurs when a uniform plane wave is incident on the boundary between regions composed of two different materials.   We shall establish expressions for the wave that is reflected from the interface and for that which is transmitted from one region into the other.   These results will be directly applicable to matching problems in ordinary transmission lines as well as to waveguides and other more exotic transmission systems.

We shall again assume that we have only a single component of the electric field intensity.   Let us select region 1 $(\epsilon_1, \mu_1, \sigma_1)$ as $z < 0$ and region 2 $(\epsilon_2, \mu_2, \sigma_2)$ as $z > 0$.   Initially we establish the wave traveling in the $+z$ direction in region 1,

(1) $\quad E_{xs1}^+ = E_{x10}^+ e^{-\gamma_1 z}$

The subscript 1 identifies the region and the superscript $+$ indicates a positively traveling wave. Associated with $\mathbf{E}_1^+$ is a magnetic field

(2) $\quad H_{ys1}^+ = \dfrac{1}{\eta_1} E_{x10}^+ e^{-\gamma_1 z}$

This uniform plane wave in region 1 which is traveling toward the boundary surface at $z = 0$ is called the *incident* wave. Since the direction of propagation of the incident wave is perpendicular to the boundary plane, we describe it as *normal incidence*.

We now recognize that energy will be transmitted across the boundary surface at $z = 0$ into region 2 by providing a wave moving in the $+z$ direction in that medium,

(3) $\quad E_{xs2}^+ = E_{x20}^+ e^{-\gamma_2 z}$

(4) $\quad H_{ys2}^+ = \dfrac{1}{\eta_2} E_{x20}^+ e^{-\gamma_2 z}$

This wave which moves away from the boundary surface into region 2 is called the *transmitted* wave; note the use of a different propagation constant γ_2 and intrinsic impedance η_2.

Now we must try to satisfy the boundary conditions at $z = 0$ with these assumed fields. E_x is a tangential field; therefore the **E** fields in regions 1 and 2 must be equal at $z = 0$. Setting $z = 0$ in (1) and (3), this would require that $E_{x10}^+ = E_{x20}^+$. However, H_y is also a tangential field and must be continuous across the boundary (no current sheets are present in real media). When we let $z = 0$ in (2) and (4), however, we find that we must have $E_{x10}^+/\eta_1 = E_{x20}^+/\eta_2$; since $E_{x10}^+ = E_{x20}^+$, then $\eta_1 = \eta_2$. But this is a very special condition that we cannot afford to assume in general, and we are therefore unable to satisfy the boundary conditions with only an incident and a transmitted wave. We also need a wave that is traveling away from the boundary in region 1, as shown in Fig. 11.4; this is called a *reflected* wave,

(5) $\quad E_{xs1}^- = E_{x10}^- e^{\gamma_1 z}$

(6) $\quad H_{ys1}^- = -\dfrac{E_{x10}^-}{\eta_1} e^{\gamma_1 z}$

where E_{x10}^- may be a complex quantity. Since this field is traveling in the $-z$ direction, $E_{xs1}^- = -\eta_1 H_{ys1}^-$, for the Poynting vector shows that $\mathbf{E}_1^- \times \mathbf{H}_1^-$ must be in the $-\mathbf{a}_z$ direction.

FIG. 11.4 A wave $\mathbf{E}_1^+$ incident on a plane
boundary establishes a reflected
wave $\mathbf{E}_1^-$ and a transmitted wave
$\mathbf{E}_2^+$.

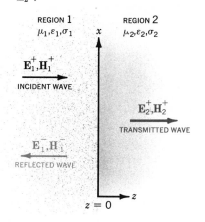

The boundary conditions are now easily satisfied, and in the
process the amplitudes of the transmitted and reflected waves may
be found in terms of E_{x10}^+. The total electric field intensity is continuous at $z = 0$,

$$E_{xs1} = E_{xs2} \qquad (z = 0)$$

or

$$E_{xs1}^+ + E_{xs1}^- = E_{xs2}^+ \qquad (z = 0)$$

Therefore

$$(7) \qquad E_{x10}^+ + E_{x10}^- = E_{x20}^+$$

Furthermore,

$$H_{ys1} = H_{ys2} \qquad (z = 0)$$

or

$$H_{ys1}^+ + H_{ys1}^- = H_{ys2}^+ \qquad (z = 0)$$

and therefore

$$(8) \qquad \frac{E_{x10}^+}{\eta_1} - \frac{E_{x10}^-}{\eta_1} = \frac{E_{x20}^+}{\eta_2}$$

Solving (8) for E_{x20}^+ and substituting into (7), we find

$$E_{x10}^+ + E_{x10}^- = \frac{\eta_2}{\eta_1} E_{x10}^+ - \frac{\eta_2}{\eta_1} E_{x10}^-$$

or

$$E_{\overline{x}10} = E_{x10}^{+} \frac{\eta_2 - \eta_1}{\eta_2 + \eta_1}$$

The ratio of the amplitudes of the reflected and incident electric fields is called the *reflection coefficient* and designated by Γ (gamma),

(9)
$$\Gamma = \frac{E_{\overline{x}10}}{E_{x10}^{+}} = \frac{\eta_2 - \eta_1}{\eta_2 + \eta_1}$$

The reflection coefficient may be complex, in which case there is a phase shift in the reflected wave.

The amplitude of the transmitted electric field intensity is found by combining (9) and (7),

(10)
$$\frac{E_{x20}^{+}}{E_{x10}^{+}} = \frac{2\eta_2}{\eta_2 + \eta_1}$$

This is known as the transmission coefficient, but we shall not use it enough to justify designating it by a special symbol.

Let us see how these results may be applied to several special cases. We first let region 1 be a perfect dielectric and region 2 be a perfect conductor. Then, since σ_2 is infinite,

$$\eta_2 = \sqrt{\frac{j\omega\mu_2}{\sigma_2 + j\omega\epsilon_2}} = 0$$

and from (10),

$$E_{x20}^{+} = 0$$

No time-varying fields can exist in the *perfect* conductor. An alternate way of looking at this is to note that the skin depth is zero. Since $\eta_2 = 0$, then (9) shows that

$$\Gamma = -1$$

and

$$E_{\overline{x}10} = -E_{x10}^{+}$$

The reflected wave is equal in amplitude and opposite in sign to the incident wave. All the incident energy is reflected by the perfect conductor, and the total **E** field in region 1 is

$$E_{xs1} = E_{xs1}^{+} + E_{\overline{x}s1}$$

$$= E_{x10}^{+}e^{-j\beta_1 z} - E_{x10}^{+}e^{j\beta_1 z}$$

where we have let $\gamma_1 = 0 + j\beta_1$ in the perfect dielectric. These terms may be combined and simplified,

$$E_{xs1} = (e^{-j\beta_1 z} - e^{j\beta_1 z})E_{x10}^+$$

$$= -j2 \sin \beta_1 z \; E_{x10}^+$$

or multiplying by $e^{j\omega t}$ and taking the real part to obtain the trigonometric form,

(11) $$\boxed{E_{x1} = 2E_{x10}^+ \sin \beta_1 z \sin \omega t}$$

This total field in region 1 is not a traveling wave, although it was obtained by combining two waves of equal amplitude traveling in opposite directions. Let us compare its form with that of the incident wave,

(12) $$\boxed{E_{x1}^+ = E_{x10}^+ \cos (\omega t - \beta_1 z)}$$

Here we see the term $\omega t - \beta_1 z$ or $\omega(t - z/U_1)$, which characterizes a wave traveling in the $+z$ direction at a velocity $U_1 = \omega/\beta_1$. In (11), however, the factors involving time and distance are separate trigonometric terms. At all planes for which $\beta_1 z = n\pi$, E_{x1} is zero for all time. Furthermore, whenever $\omega t = n\pi$, E_{x1} is zero everywhere. A field of the form of (11) is known as a *standing wave*.

The planes on which $E_{x1} = 0$ are located where

$$\beta_1 z = n\pi \qquad (n = 0, \pm 1, \pm 2, \; \ldots)$$

Thus

$$\frac{2\pi}{\lambda_1} z = n\pi$$

and

$$z = n\frac{\lambda_1}{2}$$

Thus $E_{x1} = 0$ at the boundary $z = 0$ and every half wavelength from the boundary in region 1, $z < 0$, as illustrated in Fig. 11.5. Since $E_{xs1}^+ = H_{ys1}^+\eta_1$ and $E_{xs1}^- = -H_{ys1}^-\eta_1$, the magnetic field is

$$H_{ys1} = \frac{E_{x10}^+}{\eta_1}(e^{-j\beta_1 z} + e^{j\beta_1 z})$$

or

(13) $$\boxed{H_{y1} = 2\frac{E_{x10}^+}{\eta_1} \cos \beta_1 z \cos \omega t}$$

FIG. 11.5 Instantaneous values of the total field E_{x1} are shown at $t = 0$. $E_{x1} = 0$ for all time at multiples of one-half wavelength from the conducting surface.

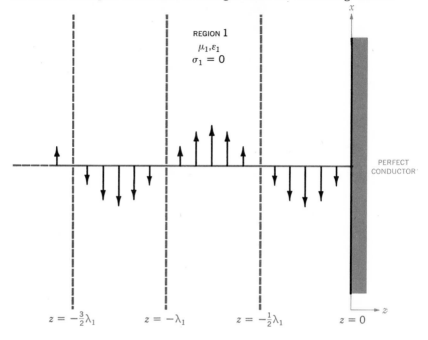

This is also a standing wave, but it shows a maximum amplitude at the positions where $E_{x1} = 0$. It is also 90° out of time phase with E_{x1} everywhere. Thus no average power is transmitted in either direction.

Let us now consider perfect dielectrics in both regions 1 and 2; η_1 and η_2 are both real positive quantities and $\alpha_1 = \alpha_2 = 0$. Equation (9) enables us to calculate the reflection coefficient and find E_{x1}^- in terms of the incident amplitude E_{x10}^+. Knowing E_{x1}^+ and E_{x1}^-, we then find H_{y1}^+ and H_{y1}^-. In region 2, E_{x2}^+ is found from (10), and this then determines H_{y2}^+. As a numerical example let us select

$$\eta_1 = 300 \ \Omega$$

$$\eta_2 = 100 \ \Omega$$

$$E_{x10}^+ = 100 \ \text{V/m}$$

Then

$$\Gamma = \frac{100 - 300}{100 + 300} = -0.5$$

$$E_{x10}^- = -50 \ \text{V/m}$$

The magnetic field intensities are

$$H_{y10}^+ = \frac{100}{300} = 0.333 \text{ A/m}$$

$$H_{y10}^- = -\frac{-50}{300} = 0.167 \text{ A/m}$$

The incident average power density is

$$P_{1,av}^+ = \tfrac{1}{2} E_{x10}^+ H_{y10}^+ = 16.67 \text{ W/m}^2$$

while

$$P_{1,av}^- = \tfrac{1}{2} E_{x10}^- H_{y10}^- = 4.17 \ W/m^2$$

In region 2

$$E_{x20}^+ = \frac{2\eta_2}{\eta_2 + \eta_1} E_{x10}^+ = 50 \text{ V/m}$$

and

$$H_{y20}^+ = \frac{50}{100} = 0.500 \text{ A/m}$$

Thus

$$P_{2,av}^+ = \tfrac{1}{2} E_{x20}^+ H_{y20}^+ = 12.5 \text{ W/m}^2$$

Note that energy is conserved:

$$P_{1,av}^+ = P_{1,av}^- + P_{2,av}^+$$

The power relationship between incident, reflected, and transmitted powers should be compared with the equation expressing the continuity of the tangential electric field intensity at the boundary surface,

$$E_{x10}^+ + E_{x10}^- = E_{x20}^+$$

The incident and reflected waves in region 1 may be combined to yield the total field there, but this will be reserved for the following section.

D 11.9 Find the percentage of the incident power that is reflected when a uniform plane wave traveling in region 1 is normally incident on region 2 if regions 1 and 2 are, respectively,

(*a*) Polystyrene and air
(*b*) Air and polystyrene
(*c*) Polystyrene and polyethylene

Ans. 0.08; 5.2; 5.2 per cent

D 11.10 A uniform plane wave in region 1, $z < 0$, for which $\mu_{R1} = 1$, $\eta_1 = 100$, is normally incident on a perfect conductor at $z = 0$. Find the distance from the conductor surface to the first plane on which

(a) $\mathbf{E}_1 = 0$ if $\lambda_1 = 2$ m
(b) $\mathbf{E}_1 = 0$ if $f = 150$ MHz
(c) $\mathbf{H}_1 = 0$ if $f = 150$ MHz

Ans. $0.133; 0.265; 1.00$ m

11.7 STANDING-WAVE RATIO

One of the measurements that is easily made on transmission systems is the *relative* amplitude of the electric or magnetic field intensity through use of a probe. A small coupling loop will give an indication of the amplitude of the magnetic field, while a slightly extended center conductor of a coaxial cable will sample the electric field. Both devices are customarily tuned to the operating frequency to provide increased sensitivity. The output of the probe is rectified and connected directly to a microammeter, or it may be delivered to a vacuum-tube voltmeter or a special amplifier. The indication is proportional to the amplitude of the sinusoidal time-varying field in which the probe is immersed.

When a uniform plane wave is traveling through the region, the probe will indicate the same amplitude at every point. Of course, the instantaneous field which the probe samples will differ in phase by $\beta(z_2 - z_1)$ rad, where the probe locations are at $z = z_1$ and $z = z_2$ but the probe is insensitive to the phase of the field. The equal-amplitude voltages are characteristic of a traveling wave.

When the traveling wave is reflected by a perfect conductor, the total field is a standing wave and the voltage probe provides no output when it is located an integral number of half-wavelengths from the reflecting surface. As the probe position is changed, its output varies as $|\sin \beta z|$, where z is the distance from the conductor. This sinusoidal-amplitude variation characterizes a standing wave.

A more complicated situation arises when the reflected field is neither 0 nor 100 per cent of the incident field. Some energy is transmitted into the second region and some is reflected. Region 1 therefore supports a field that is composed of both a traveling wave and a standing wave. It is customary to describe this field as a standing wave even though a traveling wave is also present. We shall see that the field does not have zero amplitude at any point for all time, and the degree to which the field is divided between a traveling wave and a true standing wave is expressed by the ratio of the maximum amplitude found by the probe to the minimum amplitude.

Using the same fields investigated in the previous section, we combine the incident and reflected electric field intensities,

$$E_{x1} = E_{x1}^+ + E_{x1}^-$$

The field E_{x1} is a sinusoidal function of t (generally with a nonzero phase angle), and it varies with z in a manner as yet unknown. We shall inspect all z to find the maximum and minimum amplitudes, and determine their ratio. We call this ratio the *standing-wave ratio*, and we shall symbolize it by s.

Let us now go through the mechanics of this procedure. We shall treat the case in which medium 1 is a perfect dielectric, $\alpha_1 = 0$, but region 2 may be any material. We have

$$E_{xs1}^+ = E_{x10}^+ e^{-j\beta_1 z}$$

$$E_{xs1}^- = \Gamma E_{x10}^+ e^{j\beta_1 z}$$

where

$$\Gamma = \frac{\eta_2 - \eta_1}{\eta_2 + \eta_1}$$

and η_1 is real and positive but η_2 may be complex. Thus Γ may be complex, and we allow for this possibility by letting

$$\boxed{\Gamma = |\,\Gamma\,|\, e^{j\phi}}$$

If region 2 is a perfect conductor, ϕ is equal to π; if η_2 is real and less than η_1, ϕ is also equal to π; and if η_2 is real and greater than η_1, ϕ is zero. The total field in region 1 is

(1) $\quad E_{xs1} = (e^{-j\beta_1 z} + |\,\Gamma\,|\, e^{j(\beta_1 z + \phi)}) E_{x10}^+$

We seek the maximum and minimum values of the complex quantity in the larger parentheses. We shall certainly have a maximum when each term in the larger parentheses has the same phase angle; thus

(2) $\quad E_{xs1,\max} = (1 + |\,\Gamma\,|) E_{x10}^+$

and this occurs where

$$-\beta_1 z = \beta_1 z + \phi + 2n\pi \qquad (n = 0, \pm 1, \pm 2, \ldots)$$

Thus

(3) $\quad -\beta_1 z_{\max} = \dfrac{\phi}{2} + n\pi$

Note that a voltage maximum is located at the boundary plane $(z = 0)$ if $\phi = 0$; moreover, $\phi = 0$ when Γ is real and positive. This occurs for real η_1 and η_2 when $\eta_2 > \eta_1$. Thus there is a voltage maximum at the boundary surface when the intrinsic impedance of region 2 is greater than that of region 1 and both impedances are real.

For the perfect conductor $\phi = \pi$ and these maxima are found at $-\beta_1 z = \pi/2, 3\pi/2$, and so forth, as we saw before. The minima must occur where the phase angles of the two terms in the larger parentheses differ by 180°; thus

(4) $\quad E_{xs1,min} = (1 - |\Gamma|)E_{x10}^+$

and this occurs where

$$-\beta_1 z = \beta_1 z + \phi + \pi + 2n\pi \qquad (n = 0, \pm 1, \pm 2, \ldots)$$

or

(5) $\quad -\beta_1 z_{min} = \dfrac{\phi}{2} + n\pi + \dfrac{\pi}{2}$

The minima are separated by multiples of one-half wavelength, and for the perfect conductor the first one occurs when $-\beta_1 z = 0$, or at the conducting surface. A voltage minimum is found at $z = 0$ whenever $\phi = \pi$; this occurs if $\eta_2 < \eta_1$ and both are real.

The ratio of the maximum to minimum amplitudes is

(6) $\quad \boxed{s = \dfrac{E_{xs1,max}}{E_{xs1,min}} = \dfrac{1 + |\Gamma|}{1 - |\Gamma|}}$

Since $|\Gamma| \leq 1$, s must be positive and greater than unity. If $|\Gamma| = 1$, the reflected amplitude is equal to the incident amplitude, all the incident energy is reflected, and s is infinite. Planes separated by multiples of $\lambda_1/2$ can be found on which E_{x1} is zero at all times. Midway between these planes, E_{x1} has a maximum amplitude twice that of the incident wave. If $\eta_2 = \eta_1$, then $\Gamma = 0$, no energy is reflected, and $s = 1$; the maximum and minimum amplitudes are equal. If one-half the incident power is reflected, $|\Gamma|^2 = 0.5$, $|\Gamma| = 0.707$, and $s = 5.83$.

Since the standing-wave ratio is a ratio of amplitudes, the relative amplitudes provided by a probe permit its use to determine s experimentally. For this reason the standing-wave ratio is an important transmission-line parameter, and we shall use it extensively in the following chapter.

Let us now suppose that region 1 is a lossy material for which α_1 is not zero. An incident wave coming in from the left undergoes exponential attenuation as it progresses in the $+z$ direction. The reflected wave attenuates as it propagates in the $-z$ direction. Eventually its amplitude is negligible compared to that of the incident wave. Thus maxima and minima may be discernible near

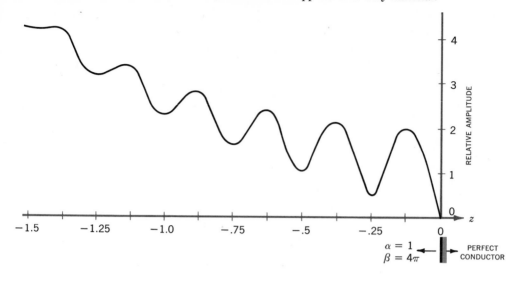

the reflecting surface, but they are smoothed out at greater distances from it.   Figure 11.6 shows a sketch of the amplitude of E_{x1} when region 2 is a perfect conductor and region 1 has a propagation constant $\gamma_1 = 1 + j4\pi$.   It should be noted that no two maxima have the same amplitude, nor do two successive minima.   The standing-wave ratio is a function of position along the line, and its value cannot be specifically defined for a case such as that shown. Unless the location at which the standing-wave ratio is measured is specified, it is much more informative to describe the behavior in terms of the reflection coefficient and the attenuation factor.

Although the case shown in Fig. 11.6 is an extreme one, we must also realize that the true lossless line does not exist in practice, and standing-wave ratio is always a function of position from the load. The value of s is meaningful only when it does not change appreciably throughout the region in which we are interested.

Again restricting our attention to a lossless medium 1, let us find the ratio of the total electric and magnetic field intensities.   For a traveling wave this is $\pm\eta_1$, with the sign depending on the direction of travel.   However, reflection from a perfect conductor has shown us that E_{xs1} or H_{ys1} may be zero at certain locations, and their ratio may thus vary from zero to an infinite value.   The total fields at $z = -L$ are

$$E_{xs1} = (e^{j\beta_1 L} + \Gamma e^{-j\beta_1 L})E_{x10}^{+}$$

$$H_{ys1} = (e^{j\beta_1 L} - \Gamma e^{-j\beta_1 L})\frac{E_{x10}^{+}}{\eta_1}$$

The Uniform Plane Wave   358

We call the ratio an *input* intrinsic impedance η_{in},

$$\eta_{in} = \frac{E_{xs1}}{H_{ys1}}\bigg|_{z=-L} = \eta_1 \frac{e^{j\beta_1 L} + \Gamma e^{-j\beta_1 L}}{e^{j\beta_1 L} - \Gamma e^{-j\beta_1 L}}$$

Letting $\Gamma = (\eta_2 - \eta_1)/(\eta_2 + \eta_1)$ and using Euler's identity, we have

$$\eta_{in} = \eta_1 \frac{(\eta_2+\eta_1)(\cos\beta_1 L + j\sin\beta_1 L) + (\eta_2-\eta_1)(\cos\beta_1 L - j\sin\beta_1 L)}{(\eta_2+\eta_1)(\cos\beta_1 L + j\sin\beta_1 L) - (\eta_2-\eta_1)(\cos\beta_1 L - j\sin\beta_1 L)}$$

This is easily simplified to yield

(7)
$$\boxed{\eta_{in} = \eta_1 \frac{\eta_2 + j\eta_1 \tan\beta_1 L}{\eta_1 + j\eta_2 \tan\beta_1 L}}$$

When η_2 equals η_1, η_{in} also equals η_1. There is no reflection, and we say that the transmission system is *matched*. If $\eta_2 = 0$ (perfect conductor), $\eta_{in} = j\eta_1 \tan\beta_1 L$. Note that the input impedance here is zero when $\beta_1 L = n\pi$ or $E_{xs1} = 0$. Also, η_{in} is infinite at those locations where $H_{ys1} = 0$.

We shall use (7) extensively in the following chapter in a form applicable to transmission lines, but we may conclude this chapter on plane waves by showing how to design a transparent window for a radar antenna. This problem arises because it is necessary to protect these antennas from the weather by appropriate covers or radomes. Let us assume that the antenna is off to the left in free space, $z < -L$. Region 1 lies between $z = -L$ and 0, where we shall locate a slab of perfect dielectric, making it as thin as we can, to keep our assumption of zero losses valid. To the right in region 2, $z > 0$, is the free-space region into which the radar signal is to be sent. In order to avoid any reflection of power back into the antenna, or in order to match the antenna to the outside world, we set $\eta_{in} = 377$. Since $\eta_2 = 377$, we have

$$377 = \eta_1 \frac{377 + j\eta_1 \tan\beta_1 L}{\eta_1 + j377 \tan\beta_1 L}$$

Multiplying out, we find

$$j377^2 \tan\beta_1 L = j\eta_1^2 \tan\beta_1 L$$

Since $\eta_1 < 377$ for all nonmagnetic materials, we can satisfy this equation only by selecting $\beta_1 L = n\pi$. The thinnest radome is obtained when $\beta_1 L = \pi$, or $L = \lambda_1/2$. Thus, if the operating frequency is 10,000 MHz, we may select a lightweight low-loss plastic for which $\epsilon_{R1} = 2.25$ and use a thickness

$$L = \frac{\lambda_1}{2} = \frac{U_1}{2f_1} = \frac{3 \times 10^8}{2\sqrt{2.25}\ 10^{10}} = 10^{-2}\ \text{m} \qquad \text{(or 1 cm)}$$

If the radome were 0.5 cm thick, it could be shown that $\eta_{in} = 167.5 \ \Omega$ and 14.8 per cent of the incident power would be reflected.

D 11.11 A wave is normally incident on a dielectric from air. Find the standing-wave ratio in the air at 10^8 Hz if

(a) $\sigma_2 = 0, \mu_{R2} = 1, \epsilon_{R2} = 9$
(b) $\sigma_2 = 0, \mu_{R2} = 9, \epsilon_{R2} = 9$
(c) $\sigma_2 = 0.05, \mu_{R2} = 9, \epsilon_{R2} = 9$

Ans. $1; 1.55; 3$

D 11.12 Find the input intrinsic impedance at $z = -1$ if the region $-1 < z < 0$ has $\eta_1 = 100$ and the region $z > 0$ has $\eta_2 = 200$ and

(a) $\lambda_1 = 2$ m
(b) $\lambda_1 = 4$ m
(c) $\lambda_1 = 8$ m

Ans. $50; 80 - j60; 200 \quad \Omega$

SUGGESTED REFERENCES

1 Stuart, R. D.: "Electromagnetic Field Theory," Addison-Wesley Publishing Company, Inc., Reading, Mass., 1965. This short book is directed toward junior electrical engineering students. Wave motion is the subject of chap. 9.

2 Von Hippel, A. R.: "Dielectric Materials and Applications," The Technology Press of the Massachusetts Institute of Technology, Cambridge, Mass., and John Wiley & Sons, Inc., New York, 1954.

PROBLEMS

1 Show that the following are also solutions of Sec. 11.1, Eq. (15): (a) $E'_{xs} = E'_{x0} e^{j\omega z \sqrt{\mu_0 \epsilon_0}}$; (b) $E''_{xs} = e^{j(\theta \pm \omega z \sqrt{\mu_0 \epsilon_0})}$; (c) Find the real functions E'_x and E''_x. (d) Show that the magnetic field associated with E'_x is $H'_y = -E'_x/\eta$.

2 If the wave $\mathbf{E} = 0.2 \sin(\omega t - 0.5x) \ \mathbf{a}_y$ is traveling in free space, find (a) ω; (b) $\mathbf{H}$.

3 Determine the real trigonometric form of the uniform plane wave $\mathbf{E}_s = (A_x + jB_x) e^{-j\beta_x z} \mathbf{a}_x + (A_y + jB_y) e^{-j\beta_y z} \mathbf{a}_y$ and its instantaneous magnitude at $t = t_1, z = z_1$.

4 Given the uniform plane wave $\mathbf{E} = \mathbf{E}_0 \cos[\omega(t - \mathbf{a}_n \cdot \mathbf{r} \sqrt{\mu_0 \epsilon_0})]$, where $\mathbf{a}_n$ is a unit vector and $\mathbf{r} = x\mathbf{a}_x + y\mathbf{a}_y + z\mathbf{a}_z$, determine (a) the general equation of the plane on which the phase angle of $\mathbf{E}$ is constant at any given instant (or $\mathbf{E}$ is "uniform"); (b) the equation of the plane of constant phase passing through the origin on which $\mathbf{E} = \mathbf{E}_0$ at $t = 0$ if $\mathbf{a}_n$ is directed from the origin toward $(1,2,-2)$. (c) Use a geometrical sketch to show that $\mathbf{a}_n$ is perpendicular to the plane $\mathbf{a}_n \cdot \mathbf{r} = $ constant. (d) Show that $\mathbf{E}_0 \cdot \mathbf{a}_n = 0$.

5 Probe measurements on a uniform plane wave show that $\mathbf{E}$ has only a z component and that the distance between positive maxima as measured along the x axis is 5 m and 3 m along the y axis. (a) Specify the direction of propagation by a unit vector. (b) Find the wavelength.

6 Refer to Sec. 11.2 and show that Eqs. (12) and (13) follow from (8).

7 The field $\mathbf{E} = 2 \cos (10^8 t - z)\, \mathbf{a}_x + 2 \sin (10^8 t - z)\, \mathbf{a}_y$ is established in a certain material. If $\mu_R = 1$, (a) determine ϵ_R; (b) find $\mathbf{H}$; (c) specify the direction of $\mathbf{E}$ at $z = 0$ by a unit vector $\mathbf{a}_E$ at $t = 0$, $T/8$, $T/4$, $3T/8, T/2$, $5T/8, 3T/4$, and $7T/8$, where T is the period $1/f$.

8 Highly directional receiving antennas may be designed by spacing several single elements one-quarter wavelength apart in a line. What separation should be used at 100 MHz for an antenna immersed in mineral oil ($\epsilon_R = 2.5$, $\mu_R = 1$)?

9 Determine the ratio of E to B for a uniform plane wave in a lossless dielectric that is supporting propagation in the $+z$ direction.

10 Very small antennas have very low efficiencies, and the efficiency increases with the size up to the point at which a critical dimension of the antenna is an appreciable fraction of a wavelength, say $\lambda/8$. (a) An antenna that is 5 in. long is operated in air at 1 MHz, the center of the radio broadcast band. What fraction of a wavelength long is it? (b) If this same antenna is embedded in a ferrite material for which $\epsilon_R = 20$ and $\mu_R = 2,000$, what fraction of a wavelength is it at 1 MHz?

11 Given a parallel-plate capacitor of plate area S and separation d, filled with a lossy dielectric, show that the power factor of the capacitor is $(\sigma/\omega\epsilon)[1 + (\sigma/\omega\epsilon)^2]^{-1/2}$ and determine the maximum value of $\sigma/\omega\epsilon$ such that the power factor is $\sigma/\omega\epsilon$ with an error less than 1 per cent.

12 Pyranol has a relative dielectric constant of 4.4 and a loss tangent of 2×10^{-3} at a frequency of 1 MHz. If R is the parallel resistance and C is the capacitance, the Q of a capacitor is ωCR. Given a coaxial capacitor with inner radius of 0.5 cm, outer radius of 2 cm, and length of 18 cm, (a) find R; (b) find C; (c) find Q; (d) show that Q is equal to the reciprocal of the loss tangent.

13 Write complete numerical expressions for a uniform plane wave propagating in the $+z$ direction in Teflon at 100 MHz. Use a loss tangent of 2×10^{-4}, $\epsilon_R = 2.1$, $\mu_R = 1$, and let $\mathbf{E} = E_x \mathbf{a}_x$. where $E_x = 2$ V/m at $t = 0$, $z = 0$.

14 The effect of the conductivity in an imperfect dielectric is often introduced by using a complex dielectric constant. That is, ϵ_R is replaced by $\epsilon_R' - j\epsilon_R''$, where ϵ_R' now serves as the common dielectric constant. Express α, β, and loss tangent in terms of ϵ_R' and ϵ_R''. The permittivity of free space ϵ_0 may be used in the expressions, but ϵ, ϵ_R, and σ should not.

15 Use the curves of Fig. 11.3 to determine α and β for polystyrene at $\omega = 10^8$ rad/s.

16 Find α, β, U, λ, and η for a ferrite having the following characteristics at 10,000 MHz: $\epsilon_R = 9$, $\sigma = 10^{-2}$ ℧/m, and $\mu_R = 4$.

17 The attenuation of a uniform plane wave in a nonmagnetic lossy dielectric is 10^{-4} decibel/m. If $\beta = 0.08$ rad/m, find the loss tangent.

FIG. 11.7 See Prob. 20.

18 Voltage breakdown in air at standard temperature and pressure occurs at a field strength of approximately 30,000 V/cm. How much power can be carried in 1 cm² of air by a uniform plane wave without causing voltage breakdown?

19 Show that Sec. 11.4, Eq. (4), is correct.

20 Apply the Poynting vector to determine the power flow about the permanent magnet and charged capacitor plates shown in Fig. 11.7.

21 An air-filled coaxial cable of inner radius a and outer radius b carries a direct current I in the $\mathbf{a}_z$ direction in the inner conductor and in the $-\mathbf{a}_z$ direction in the outer. The potential difference between the conductors is V_0, with the inner conductor positive. (a) Find $\mathbf{H}$ for $a < r < b$. (b) Find $\mathbf{E}$ for $a < r < b$. (c) Find $\mathcal{P}$ for $a < r < b$. (d) Show that the integral of $\mathcal{P}_z$ over the cross section is V_0I.

22 A round wire of radius a and conductivity σ carries a uniformly distributed total current I. (a) Find $\mathbf{J}$. (b) Find $\mathbf{E}$ within the wire. (c) Find $\mathbf{H}$ within the wire. (d) Find $\mathcal{P}$ within the wire. (e) Find the total power crossing the surface of the wire in an L-m length. (f) Express this total power in terms of the total resistance of the L-m length.

23 A uniform plane wave has a crest amplitude of 100 mV/m at $z = 0$. It is propagating in the $+z$ direction in a lossy dielectric for which $\eta = 200\ \Omega$ (approximately) and $\alpha = 0.01$ nep/m. Find the average power density at $z = 0$ and $z = 100$.

24 Show that the time-average power loss per unit volume in a good conductor is $\frac{1}{2}\sigma E_{x0}^2 e^{-2z/\delta}$, assuming the same fields as in Sec. 11.5. [HINT: Consider Sec. 11.4, Eq. (1).]

25 The current density at the surface of a thick copper plate is given by $\mathbf{J} = 10^4 \cos 1{,}000t\ \mathbf{a}_x$. The region $z > 0$ is copper. Find the value of $\mathbf{J}$ at a point in the conductor 1 cm from the surface at $t = 0$.

26 A wave propagating into a good conductor delivers 86.5 per cent of its power to heating the conductor in the first skin depth. What percentage of the incident power is supplied to the layer between δ and 2δ?

27 Find the applied frequency and the conductivity of a good conducting material for which the velocity of propagation is 0.1 per cent of the free-space velocity and in which the wavelength is 0.3 mm. Assume the material is nonmagnetic.

The Uniform Plane Wave 362

28 Use Sec. 11.6, Eqs. (11) and (13), to find $\mathcal{P}_1$ and $\mathcal{P}_{1,\mathrm{av}}$ for the total field in region 1 (incident plus reflected waves).

29 The wave $\mathbf{E}^+ = 10 \cos (3 \times 10^9 t - 30\pi z)\,\mathbf{a}_x$ is incident on a planar boundary at $z = 0$. If $\mu_R = 1$ everywhere and $\epsilon_R = 4$ for $z > 0$, find $\mathbf{E}$ and $\mathbf{H}$ for $z > 0$.

30 Find the reflection coefficient for normal incidence on an air-to-water boundary if the parameters for the water are those of Sec. 11.3: $\mu_R = 1$, $\epsilon_R = 50$, $\sigma = 20\ \mho/\mathrm{m}$.

31 If 64 per cent of the incident power is reflected when a uniform plane wave is normally incident from air on a perfect dielectric, find ϵ_R if $\mu_R = 1$.

32 In Sec. 11.6 reflection from a perfect conductor was considered as one example. Now let region 1 be air and region 2 be copper ($\epsilon_{R2} = \mu_{R2} = 1$, $\sigma_2 = 5.8 \times 10^7$) and find $\mathbf{E}_2^+$ if $E_{z10}^+ = 100\ \mathrm{V/m}$ and $\omega = 10^{11}$.

33 In Sec. 11.7, given η_1 and η_2 both real and positive, show that the standing-wave ratio in region 1 equals η_2/η_1 if $\eta_2 > \eta_1$ and η_1/η_2 if $\eta_1 > \eta_2$.

34 Show that the fraction of the incident power that is reflected is $(s - 1)^2/(s + 1)^2$.

35 A probe is used to measure the electric field intensity inside a tank of oil, where a 1,000-MHz uniform plane wave is reflected from a conducting wall. The probe gives readings of 84 at 5.8 cm from the wall, 2 at 11.7 cm from the wall, and 88 at 17.5 cm. What is the dielectric constant of the oil? (NOTE: Although there is sufficient information to determine α in the oil, the measurements are not accurate enough to be used for this purpose. However, if you wish to work a harder problem, show that the probe readings of 2 and 84 would lead to $\alpha = 0.2$.)

36 A region in which $\eta = \eta_2$ has a thickness of $\lambda_2/4$. (a) Show that if this region is placed between two semi-infinite regions in which $\eta = \eta_1$ and $\eta = \eta_3$, the input impedance at the boundary between regions 1 and 2, looking toward region 2, is η_1 if $\eta_2 = \sqrt{\eta_1\eta_3}$. (b) Find ϵ_{R2} and the thickness of the layer if $\epsilon_{R1} = 1$, $\epsilon_{R3} = 4$, $\mu_R = 1$, and $f = 10\ \mathrm{GHz}$. $\sigma = 0$ everywhere.

37 A 200-MHz wave with a peak amplitude of 2 V/m is normally incident on an air-to-polysytrene boundary. Both regions are infinitely thick. (a) Find the maximum field strength in the air and its location. (b) Repeat for the minimum. (c) Repeat (a) and (b) for the polystyrene.

38 Assume four regions with the intrinsic impedances $\eta_1 = 100$, $z < 2\ \mathrm{cm}$; $\eta_2 = 200$, $2 < z < 3\ \mathrm{cm}$; $\eta_3 = 300$, $3 < z < 5\ \mathrm{cm}$; and $\eta_4 = 100$, $z > 5\ \mathrm{cm}$. The source is in region 1, where it has a wavelength of 4 cm. If all the materials have $\mu_R = 1$, find (a) the frequency of the source; (b) the input impedance at $z = 3\ \mathrm{cm}$; (c) the input impedance at $z = 2\ \mathrm{cm}$.

39 Show that the last sentence in Sec. 11.7 is correct.

40 Resonance in a certain liquid-filled cavity is achieved when the length of the cavity is approximately one-half wavelength. The input and output connections affect the length slightly by an unknown amount. When the cavity is filled it resonates at 600 MHz. When it is empty it resonates at 804 MHz. What is the relative dielectric constant of the liquid, assuming $\sigma = 0$? At what frequency is this determination of ϵ_R most nearly correct?

41 Refer to K. Kurokawa, Electromagnetic Waves in Waveguides with Wall Impedance, *IRE Trans. Microwave Theory Tech.*, vol. MTT-10, pp. 314–320, September, 1962, and show that his eq. (5) follows from his eq. (3).

42 In C. P. Steinmetz, "Theory and Calculation of Transient Electric Phenomena and Oscillations," 3d ed., McGraw-Hill Book Company, New York, 1920, show that the numerical values in the bottom row of the table showing depths of penetration on p. 385 are correct.

43 You have just been notified that you are to be the communications officer on a space flight to one of the inner moons of the planet Jupiter. Communications between the several bases on the moon will involve bouncing a signal off the surface of the planet. The composition of the surface is ammonia slush at a temperature of about $-80°C$. Refer to National Research Council, "International Critical Tables of Numerical Data, Physics, Chemistry and Technology," McGraw-Hill Book Company, New York, 1926, to obtain suitable values for σ and ϵ_R for this material and calculate the reflection coefficient at $f = 5$ MHz.

12 TRANSMISSION LINES

The effort devoted to the uniform plane wave in the previous chapter now makes it possible to develop analogous results for the uniform transmission line easily and rapidly. The field distributions for the uniform plane wave and for the uniform transmission line are both known as transverse electromagnetic (TEM) waves because **E** and **H** are both perpendicular to the direction of propagation, or both lie in the transverse plane. The great similarity in results is a direct consequence of the fact that we are dealing with TEM waves in each case. In the transmission line, however, it is possible and customary to define a voltage and a current. These quantities are the ones for which we shall write equations, obtain solutions, and find propagation constants, reflection coefficients, and input impedances. We shall also consider power instead of power density.

An important addition to our analytical and design tools will be the use of a graphical technique for solving reflection and matching problems. This method is also applicable to the uniform plane wave.

12.1 THE TRANSMISSION-LINE EQUATIONS

We shall first obtain the differential equations which the voltage or current must satisfy on a uniform transmission line. We might do this by any of several methods. For example, an obvious method would be solving Maxwell's equations subject to the boundary conditions imposed by the particular transmission line we are considering. We could then define a voltage and a current, thus obtaining our desired equations. It is also possible to solve the general TEM-wave problem once and for all. Instead, we shall construct a circuit model for an incremental length of line, write two circuit equations, and show that the resultant equations are analogous to the fundamental equations from which the wave equation was developed in the previous chapter. By these means we shall begin to tie field theory and circuit theory together, a task which we shall take up again in the following chapter.

Our circuit model will contain the inductance, capacitance, shunt conductance, and series resistance associated with an incremental length of line. Let us do our thinking in terms of a coaxial transmission line containing a dielectric of permeability

μ (usually μ_0), permittivity ϵ, and conductivity σ. The inner and outer conductors have a high conductivity σ_c. Knowing the operating frequency and the dimensions, we can then determine the values of R, G, L, and C on a per-unit-length basis by using formulas developed in earlier chapters. We shall review these expressions and collect the information on several different types of lines in the following section.

Let us again assume propagation in the $\mathbf{a}_z$ direction. We therefore cut out a section of length Δz containing a resistance $R\,\Delta z$, an inductance $L\,\Delta z$, a conductance $G\,\Delta z$, and a capacitance $C\,\Delta z$, as shown in Fig. 12.1. Since the section of the line looks the same from either end, we divide the series elements in half to produce a symmetrical network. We could equally well have placed half the conductance and half the capacitance at each end.

Since we are already familiar with the basic characteristics of wave propagation, let us turn immediately to the case of sinusoidal time variation. We shall use the same notation for complex quantities that we did in the last chapter. The voltage V between conductors is in general a function of z and t, as, for example

$$V = V_0 \cos\,(\omega t - \beta z + \psi)$$

We may use Euler's identity to express this in complex notation,

$$V = \text{Re}\; V_0 e^{j(\omega t - \beta z + \psi)} = \text{Re}\; V_0 e^{j\psi} e^{-j\beta z} e^{j\omega t}$$

By dropping Re and suppressing $e^{j\omega t}$, we transform the voltage to a phasor, which we indicate by an s subscript,

$$V_s = V_0 e^{j\psi} e^{-j\beta z}$$

We may now write the voltage equation around the perimeter of the circuit of Fig. 12.1,

$$V_s = (\tfrac{1}{2}R\,\Delta z + j\tfrac{1}{2}\omega L\,\Delta z) I_s$$

$$+ (\tfrac{1}{2}R\,\Delta z + j\tfrac{1}{2}\omega L\,\Delta z)(I_s + \Delta I_s) + V_s + \Delta V_s$$

or

$$\frac{\Delta V_s}{\Delta z} = -(R + j\omega L) I_s - (\tfrac{1}{2}R + j\tfrac{1}{2}\omega L)\,\Delta I_s$$

As we let Δz approach zero, ΔI_s also approaches zero, and the second term on the right vanishes. In the limit,

(1)
$$\boxed{\frac{dV_s}{dz} = -(R + j\omega L) I_s}$$

FIG. 12.1 An incremental length of a uniform transmission line. R, G, L, and C are functions of the transmission-line configuration and materials.

Neglecting second-order effects, we approximate the voltage across the central branch as V_s and obtain a second equation,

$$\frac{\Delta I_s}{\Delta z} \doteq -(G + j\omega C)\,V_s$$

or

(2)
$$\frac{dI_s}{dz} = -(G + j\omega C)\,V_s$$

Instead of solving these equations, let us save some time by comparing them with the equations which arise from Maxwell's curl equations for the uniform plane wave. From

$$\nabla \times \mathbf{E}_s = -j\omega\mu\mathbf{H}_s$$

we set $\mathbf{E}_s = E_{xs}\mathbf{a}_x$, $\mathbf{H}_s = H_{ys}\mathbf{a}_y$, where E_{xs} and H_{ys} are functions of z only, and obtain the single scalar equation

$$\frac{dE_{xs}}{dz} = -j\omega\mu H_{ys} \qquad \left[\frac{dV_s}{dz} = -(R + j\omega L)I_s,\ \text{from (1)}\right]$$

with Eq. (1) shown for easy comparison. Similarly, from

$$\nabla \times \mathbf{H}_s = (\sigma + j\omega\epsilon)\mathbf{E}_s$$

we have

$$\frac{dH_{ys}}{dz} = -(\sigma + j\omega\epsilon)E_{xs} \qquad \left[\frac{dI_s}{dz} = -(G + j\omega C)V_s,\ \text{from (2)}.\right]$$

Careful comparison of these last two equations shows a direct analogy between the following pairs of quantities: I_s and H_{ys}, G and σ, C and ϵ, and V_s and E_{xs}. Replacing the variables in one equation by the corresponding quantities produces the other equation. The analogy is particularly strong in this pair of equations, for the corresponding quantities are measured in almost the same units.

Carrying this same analogy over to the first pair of equations, we see that it continues to hold and provides one additional analogous pair, L and μ. However, there is also a surprise, for the transmission-line equation is more complicated than the field equation. There is no analogue for the conductor resistance per unit length R. Although it would be good salesmanship to say that this shows that field theory is simpler than circuit theory, let us be fair in determining the reason for this omission. Conductor resistance must be determined by obtaining a separate solution to Maxwell's equations *within* the conductors and forcing the two solutions to satisfy the necessary boundary conditions at the interface. We considered steady current fields in conductors back in Chap. 5, and we have just considered the high-frequency case under the guise of "skin effect"; however, we have looked only briefly at the problem of matching two solutions at the boundary. Thus the term that is omitted in the field equation represents the problem of the fields within the conductors, and the solution of this problem enables us to obtain a value for R in the circuit equation. We maintain the analogy by agreeing to replace $j\omega\mu$ by $R + j\omega L$.[1]

The solution of our two circuit equations may therefore be obtained from a knowledge of the solution of the two field equations, as obtained in the last chapter. From

$$E_{xs} = E_{x0}e^{-\gamma z}$$

we obtain the voltage wave

(3) $\quad V_s = V_0 e^{-\gamma z}$

which propagates in the $+z$ direction with an amplitude $V_s = V_0$ at $z = 0$ (and $V = V_0$ at $z = 0, t = 0; \psi = 0$). The propagation constant for the uniform plane wave,

$$\gamma = \sqrt{j\omega\mu(\sigma + j\omega\epsilon)}$$

becomes

(4) $\quad \boxed{\gamma = \sqrt{(R + j\omega L)(G + j\omega C)}}$

For a lossless line $R = G = 0$ we see that

$$\gamma = j\beta = j\omega\sqrt{LC}$$

---

[1] When ferrite materials enter the field problem, a complex permeability $\mu = \mu' - j\mu''$ is often used to include the effect of nonohmic losses in that material. Under these special conditions $\omega\mu''$ is analogous to R.

But

$$\beta = \frac{\omega}{U}$$

and hence

(5)
$$U = \frac{1}{\sqrt{LC}}$$

From the expression for the magnetic field intensity

$$H_{ys} = \frac{E_{x0}}{\eta} e^{-\gamma z}$$

we see that the positively traveling current wave

(6)
$$I_s = \frac{V_0}{Z_0} e^{-\gamma z}$$

is related to the positively traveling voltage wave by a *characteristic impedance* Z_0 that is analogous to η. Thus

$$\eta = \sqrt{\frac{j\omega\mu}{\sigma + j\omega\epsilon}}$$

and therefore

(7)
$$Z_0 = \sqrt{\frac{R + j\omega L}{G + j\omega C}}$$

When a uniform plane wave in medium 1 strikes the interface with medium 2, the fraction of the incident wave that is reflected is called the reflection coefficient Γ,

$$\Gamma = \frac{E_{x0}^-}{E_{x0}^+} = \frac{\eta_2 - \eta_1}{\eta_2 + \eta_1}$$

Thus the fraction of the incident voltage wave that is reflected by a line with a different characteristic impedance, say Z_{02}, is

(8)
$$\Gamma = \frac{V_0^-}{V_0^+} = \frac{Z_{02} - Z_{01}}{Z_{02} + Z_{01}}$$

Knowing the reflection coefficient, we may find the standing-wave ratio,

$$(9) \qquad s = \frac{1 + |\Gamma|}{1 - |\Gamma|}$$

Finally, when $\eta = \eta_2$ for $z > 0$, the ratio of E_{xs} to H_{ys} at $z = -l$ is

$$\eta_{\text{in}} = \eta_1 \frac{\eta_2 + j\eta_1 \tan \beta_1 l}{\eta_1 + j\eta_2 \tan \beta_1 l}$$

and therefore the input impedance

$$(10) \qquad Z_{\text{in}} = Z_{01} \frac{Z_{02} + jZ_{01} \tan \beta_1 l}{Z_{01} + jZ_{02} \tan \beta_1 l}$$

is the ratio of V_s to I_s at $z = -l$ when $Z_0 = Z_{02}$ for $z > 0$. We often terminate a transmission line at $z = 0$ with a load impedance Z_L which may represent an antenna, the input circuit of a television receiver, or an amplifier on a telephone line. The input impedance at $z = -l$ is then written simply as

$$(11) \qquad Z_{\text{in}} = Z_0 \frac{Z_L + jZ_0 \tan \beta l}{Z_0 + jZ_L \tan \beta l}$$

We shall use these equations to gain some familiarity with transmission lines as soon as we are able to determine values for the pertinent parameters, R, G, L, and C.

D 12.1 Find the velocity at which a sinusoidal signal of 10^9 rad/s travels down a transmission line for which $L = 0.4$ μH/m and $C = 40$ pF/m if

(a) $R = 0, G = 0$
(b) $R = 0.1$ Ω/m, $G = 10^{-5}$ ℧/m
(c) $R = 300$ Ω/m, $G = 0$

Ans. $2.36 \times 10^8; 2.5 \times 10^8; 2.5 \times 10^8$ m/s

12.2 TRANSMISSION-LINE PARAMETERS

Let us use this section to collect previous results and develop new ones where necessary, so that values for R, G, L, and C are available for the simpler types of transmission lines. We begin by seeing how many of the necessary expressions we already have for a coaxial cable of inner radius a and outer radius b (Fig. 12.2a). The ca-

FIG. 12.2 The geometry of the (*a*) coaxial, (*b*) two-wire, and (*c*) planar transmission lines. Homogeneous dielectrics are assumed.

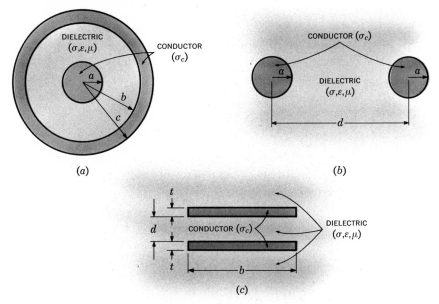

(*a*)

(*b*)

(*c*)

pacitance, obtained in Chap. 5, is

$$(1) \qquad C = \frac{2\pi\epsilon}{\ln{(b/a)}} \qquad \text{F/m}$$

The value of permittivity used should be appropriate for the range of operating frequencies considered. The conductance may be determined easily by use of the current analogy described in Sec. 6.3,

$$(2) \qquad G = \frac{2\pi\sigma}{\ln{(b/a)}} \qquad \mho/\text{m}$$

where σ is the conductivity of the dielectric between the conductors at the operating frequency. The inductance computed for the coaxial cable in the previous chapter,

$$(3) \qquad L_{\text{ext}} = \frac{\mu}{2\pi}\ln\frac{b}{a} \qquad \text{H/m}$$

is an *external* inductance, for its calculation did not take into account any flux within either conductor. This is usually an excellent approximation to the total inductance, however, for at typical operating frequencies the skin depth is so small that there is negligible flux within either conductor and negligible internal inductance. Note that $L_{ext}C = \mu\epsilon$.

In order to provide a reasonably complete story, however, let us spend a few paragraphs obtaining expressions for the internal inductance. For very low frequencies where the current distribution is uniform, the internal inductance of the center conductor is given in Chap. 9 as

(4)
$$L_{a,\text{int}} = \frac{\mu}{8\pi} \quad \text{H/m}$$

The determination of the internal inductance of the outer shell is a more difficult problem, and most of the work was requested in Chap. 9, Prob. 37. From that problem, the energy stored in a cylindrical shell of inner radius b and outer radius c with uniform current distribution is

$$W_H = \frac{\mu I^2}{16\pi(c^2 - b^2)} \left(c^2 - 3b^2 + \frac{4b^4}{c^2 - b^2} \ln \frac{c}{b} \right) \quad \text{J/m}$$

Thus the internal inductance of the outer conductor at very low frequencies is

(5) $\quad L_{bc,\text{int}} = \dfrac{\mu}{8\pi(c^2 - b^2)} \left(c^2 - 3b^2 + \dfrac{4b^4}{c^2 - b^2} \ln \dfrac{c}{b} \right) \quad \text{H/m}$

At low frequencies the total inductance is obtained by combining (3), (4), and (5):

(6) $\quad L_{\text{low}} = \dfrac{\mu}{2\pi} \left[\ln \dfrac{b}{a} + \dfrac{1}{4} + \dfrac{1}{4(c^2 - b^2)} \left(c^2 - 3b^2 + \dfrac{4b^4}{c^2 - b^2} \ln \dfrac{c}{b} \right) \right] \quad \text{H/m}$

As frequency increases, the internal inductance decreases. Let us consider an intermediate frequency, where the internal inductance may still make a significant contribution to the total inductance. We shall assume that the skin depth δ is much smaller than the radius of the inner conductor a, and we shall then have a thin layer of current at the surface of the conductor. The current is in the $\mathbf{a}_z$ direction, and the *tangential* component of $\mathbf{E}_s$ at the conductor surface is therefore in the $\mathbf{a}_z$ direction, since $\mathbf{J}_s = \sigma_c \mathbf{E}_s$, where σ_c is the conductor conductivity. The magnetic field intensity is tangential at the conductor surface, and

$$H_{\phi s} = \frac{I_s}{2\pi a}$$

Now, the ratio of E_{zs} to $H_{\phi s}$ at the surface may be taken as the intrinsic impedance of the conducting material for a uniform plane wave. Although we are working with a cylindrical geometry, the skin depth is much smaller than the radius, and the thin layer may be treated as a rolled-up plane of width $2\pi a$. From Sec. 11.5, then,

$$\left.\frac{E_{zs}}{H_{\phi s}}\right|_{r=a} = \frac{1 + j1}{\sigma_c \delta}$$

or

$$\left.\frac{E_{zs}}{I_s}\right|_{r=a} = \frac{1 + j1}{2\pi a \delta \sigma_c}$$

Since E_{zs} is the voltage per unit length in the direction of the conduction current, this quotient must be the impedance per unit length; that is,

$$Z = R + j\omega L_{\text{int}} = \frac{1}{2\pi a \delta \sigma_c} + j\frac{1}{2\pi a \delta \sigma_c}$$

The inductance is an internal one, for it depends on the conductivity σ_c of the conducting material and not on the twists and turns the wire makes in its path through space. Note that this impedance is zero for a perfect conductor. Thus we obtain the internal inductance for the inner conductor,

(7) $\qquad L_{a,\text{int}} = \dfrac{1}{2\pi a \delta \sigma_c \omega} = \dfrac{\mu \delta}{4\pi a} \qquad \text{H/m} \qquad (\delta \ll a)$

and for the outer conductor,

(8) $\qquad L_{bc,\text{int}} = \dfrac{1}{2\pi b \delta \sigma_c \omega} = \dfrac{\mu \delta}{4\pi b} \qquad \text{H/m} \qquad (\delta \ll c - b)$

at high frequencies. The total high-frequency inductance is therefore

(9) $\qquad \boxed{L_{\text{high}} = \dfrac{\mu}{2\pi}\left[\ln\dfrac{b}{a} + \dfrac{\delta}{2}\left(\dfrac{1}{a} + \dfrac{1}{b}\right)\right] \qquad (\delta \ll a, \delta \ll c - b)}$

Our expression for the impedance above also gives us a value for the resistance per unit length,

(10) $\qquad \boxed{R = \dfrac{1}{2\pi\delta\sigma_c}\left(\dfrac{1}{a} + \dfrac{1}{b}\right) \qquad \Omega/\text{m} \qquad (\delta \ll a, \delta \ll c - b)}$

when skin effect is present. This is an *internal* resistance, for the *external* resistance is called the conductance per unit length. Another loss that may contribute an additional resistance term is radiation from an unshielded transmission line or from the open end of a coaxial cable.

For the two-wire transmission line of Fig. 12.2*b* with conductors of radius a and conductivity σ_c separated d m center to center, in a medium of permeability μ, permittivity ϵ, and conductivity σ, the capacitance was found to be

$$(11) \qquad \boxed{C = \frac{\pi\epsilon}{\cosh^{-1}(d/2a)} \qquad \text{F/m}}$$

or

$$C \doteq \frac{\pi\epsilon}{\ln(d/a)} \qquad (a \ll d)$$

The external inductance is

$$(12) \qquad \boxed{L_{\text{ext}} = \frac{\mu}{\pi}\cosh^{-1}\frac{d}{2a} \qquad \text{H/m}}$$

or

$$L_{\text{ext}} \doteq \frac{\mu}{\pi}\ln\frac{d}{a} \qquad (a \ll d)$$

while the total inductance at high frequencies is

$$(13) \qquad \boxed{L_{\text{high}} = \frac{\mu}{\pi}\left(\frac{\delta}{2a} + \cosh^{-1}\frac{d}{2a}\right) \qquad \text{H/m} \qquad (\delta \ll a)}$$

The resistance per unit length is

$$(14) \qquad \boxed{R = \frac{1}{\pi a \delta \sigma_c} \qquad \Omega/\text{m} \qquad (\delta \ll a)}$$

and the conductance is again obtained from the capacitance,

$$(15) \qquad \boxed{G = \frac{\pi\sigma}{\cosh^{-1}(d/2a)} \qquad \mho/\text{m}}$$

If we have the parallel plane or planar transmission line of Fig. 12.2*c*, with two conducting planes of conductivity σ_c, separated d m by a dielectric with parameters ϵ, μ, and σ, then we may easily determine the circuit parameters per unit length for a width b.

It is necessary to assume either that $b \gg d$ or that we are considering a width b of a much wider guiding system. We have

$$(16) \qquad \boxed{C = \frac{\epsilon b}{d} \qquad \text{F/m}}$$

$$(17) \qquad \boxed{L_{\text{ext}} = \mu \frac{d}{b} \qquad \text{H/m}}$$

$$(18) \qquad \boxed{L_{\text{total}} = \mu \frac{d}{b} + \frac{2}{\sigma_c \delta b \omega} = \frac{\mu}{b}(d + \delta) \qquad \text{H/m} \qquad (\delta \ll t)}$$

Here we have assumed a well-developed skin effect such that $\delta \ll t$, the thickness of either plane. Also,

$$(19) \qquad \boxed{R = \frac{2}{\sigma_c \delta b} \qquad \Omega/\text{m} \qquad (\delta \ll t)}$$

$$(20) \qquad \boxed{G = \frac{\sigma b}{d} \qquad \mho/\text{m}}$$

D 12.2 Assume operation at a high frequency with negligible losses and calculate Z_0 for

(a) A coaxial line with $a = 1$ mm, $b = 3$ mm, $\epsilon_R = \mu_R = 1$
(b) A two-wire line with $a = 1$ mm, $d = 20$ mm, $\epsilon_R = 4$, $\mu_R = 1$
(c) A planar line with $b = 1$ cm, $d = 1$ mm, $\epsilon_R = 1.44$, $\mu_R = 1$

Ans. 31.4; 65.9; 179.6 $\quad \Omega$

D 12.3 For a coaxial cable with $a = 1$ mm, $b = 3$ mm, $c = 4$ mm, $\sigma_c = 5 \times 10^7$ $\mho/\text{m}$, $\epsilon_R = 3$, $\sigma = 10^{-6}$ $\mho/\text{m}$, $\mu_R = 1$, and $f = 200,000$ Hz find

(a) L_{ext}
(b) $L_{a,\text{int}}$
(c) $L_{bc,\text{int}}$

Ans. 5.31; 15.9; 220 $\quad$ nH/m

12.3 SOME TRANSMISSION-LINE EXAMPLES

In this section we shall apply many of the results that we have obtained in the previous two sections to several typical transmission-line problems. We shall simplify our work by restricting our attention to the lossless line.

FIG. 12.3 A transmission line that is matched at each end produces no reflections and thus delivers maximum power to the load.

300 Ω

V_s 60 V
100 MHz

$Z_0 = 300\Omega, U = 2.5 \times 10^8$ m/s

300 Ω
(R_{in} OF RECEIVER)

2 m

Let us begin by assuming a two-wire 300-Ω line ($Z_0 = 300\ \Omega$), such as the lead-in wire from the antenna to a television or FM receiver. The circuit is shown in Fig. 12.3. The line is 2 m long and the dielectric constant is such that the velocity on the line is 2.5×10^8 m/s. We shall terminate the line with a receiver having an input resistance of 300 Ω and assume an input source with an internal impedance of 300 Ω and a crest amplitude of 60 V at a frequency of 100 MHz. This antenna voltage is larger by a factor of about 10^5 than it would be in a practical case, but it also provides simpler values to work with; in order to think practical thoughts, divide currents or voltages by 10^5, and divide powers by 10^{10}.

Since the load impedance is equal to the characteristic impedance, the line is matched; the reflection coefficient is zero, and the standing-wave ratio is unity. For the given velocity and frequency the wavelength on the line is 2.5 m and the phase constant is 0.8π rad/m; the attenuation constant is zero. The electrical length of the line βl is $2 \times 0.8\pi$, or 1.6π rad. This length may also be expressed as 288°, or 0.8 wavelength.

The input impedance offered to the voltage source is 300 Ω, and since the internal impedance of the source is 300 Ω, the voltage at the input to the line is half of 60 V, or 30 V. The source is matched to the line and delivers the maximum available power to the line. Since there is no reflection and no attenuation, the voltage at the load is also 30-V crest amplitude, but it is delayed in phase by 1.6π rad. Thus

$$V_{in} = 30 \cos 2\pi 10^8 t$$

whereas

$$V_L = 30 \cos (2\pi 10^8 t - 1.6\pi)$$

The input current is

$$I_{in} = \frac{V_{in}}{300} = 0.1 \cos 2\pi 10^8 t$$

while the load current is

$$I_L = 0.1 \cos (2\pi 10^8 t - 1.6\pi)$$

The average power delivered to the input of the line by the source is equal to that delivered to the load by the line,

$$P_{in} = P_L = \tfrac{1}{2} \times 30 \times 0.1 = 1.5 \text{ W}$$

Now let us connect a second receiver, also having an input resistance of 300 Ω, across the line in parallel with the first receiver. The load impedance is now 150 Ω, the reflection coefficient is

$$\Gamma = \frac{150 - 300}{150 + 300} = -\frac{1}{3}$$

and the standing-wave ratio on the line is

$$s = \frac{1 + \tfrac{1}{3}}{1 - \tfrac{1}{3}} = 2$$

The input impedance is no longer 300 Ω, but is now

$$Z_{in} = Z_0 \frac{Z_L + jZ_0 \tan \beta l}{Z_0 + jZ_L \tan \beta l} = 300 \frac{150 + j300 \tan 288°}{300 + j150 \tan 288°}$$

$$= 510\underline{/-23.8°} = 466 - j206 \quad \Omega$$

which is a capacitive impedance. Physically, this means that this length of line stores more energy in its electric field than in its magnetic field. The current flowing through the source is thus

$$I_{s,in} = \frac{60}{766 - j206} = 0.0756\underline{/15°} \quad \text{A}$$

and the power supplied to the line by the source is

$$P_{in} = \tfrac{1}{2} \times (0.0756)^2 \times 466 = 1.333 \text{ W}$$

Since there are no losses in the line, 1.333 W must also be delivered to the load. Note that this is less than the 1.50 W which we were able to deliver to a matched load; moreover, this power must divide equally between two receivers, and thus each receiver now receives only 0.667 W. Since the input impedance of each receiver is 300 Ω, the voltage across the receiver is easily found as

$$0.667 = \frac{1}{2} \frac{|V_{Ls}|^2}{300}$$

$$|V_{Ls}| = 20 \text{ V}$$

in comparison with the 30 V obtained across the single load.

Before we leave this example, let us ask ourselves several questions about the voltages on the transmission line. Where is the voltage a maximum and a minimum, and what are these values? Does the phase of the load voltage still differ from the input voltage by 288°? Presumably, if we can answer these questions for the voltage, we could do the same for the current.

Now, we answered these questions for the uniform plane wave in the last chapter, and our analogy should therefore provide us with the corresponding information for the transmission line. In Sec. 11.7, Eq. (3) serves to locate the voltage maxima at

$$-\beta z_{\max} = \frac{\phi}{2} + n\pi \qquad (n = 0, \pm 1, \pm 2, \ldots)$$

Thus, with $\beta = 0.8\pi$ and $\phi = \pi$, we find

$$z_{\max} = -0.625 \text{ and } -1.875 \qquad \text{m} \qquad (n = 0, -1)$$

The locations of the minima are specified by Sec. 11.7, Eq. (5),

$$-\beta z_{\min} = \frac{\phi}{2} + n\pi + \frac{\pi}{2}$$

Thus

$$z_{\min} = 0 \text{ and } -1.25 \text{ m} \qquad (n = -1, 0)$$

and we find that the load voltage (at $z = 0$) is a voltage minimum. This, of course, verifies the general conclusion we reached in the last chapter: a voltage minimum occurs at the load if $Z_L < Z_0$, and a voltage maximum occurs if $Z_L > Z_0$, where both impedances are pure resistances. The maxima and minima are separated by 0.625 m, or one-quarter wavelength.

The minimum voltage on the line is thus the load voltage, 20 V; the maximum voltage must be 40 V, since the standing-wave ratio is 2. The voltage at the input end of the line is

$$V_{s,\text{in}} = I_{s,\text{in}} Z_{\text{in}} = (0.0756\underline{/15°})\,(510\underline{/-23.8°})$$

or

$$V_{s,\text{in}} = 38.6\underline{/-8.8°}$$

We find that the input voltage is almost as large as the maximum voltage anywhere on the line and recognize that the line is about three-quarters wavelength long, a length which would place the voltage maximum at the input when $Z_L < Z_0$.

The final question we posed ourselves deals with the relative phase of the input and load voltages. Although we have found the crest amplitudes of each of these voltages, we do not know the phase angle of the load voltage. From Sec. 11.7, Eq. (1), the voltage at any point on the line is

$$V_s = (e^{-j\beta z} + \Gamma e^{j\beta z}) V_0^+$$

We may use this expression to determine the voltage at any point on the line in terms of the voltage at any other point. Since we know the voltage at the input to the line, we let $z = -l$,

$$V_{s,\text{in}} = (e^{j\beta l} + \Gamma e^{-j\beta l}) V_0^+$$

and we could thus determine V_0^+, the incident voltage amplitude, if we wished. However, our present interest is the load voltage at $z = 0$,

$$V_{Ls} = (1 + \Gamma) V_0^+$$

Thus

$$\frac{V_{Ls}}{V_{s,\text{in}}} = \frac{1 + \Gamma}{e^{j\beta l} + \Gamma e^{-j\beta l}}$$

and V_{Ls} can be determined,

$$V_{Ls} = (38.6\underline{/-8.8°}) \frac{1 - \tfrac{1}{3}}{e^{j0.8\pi} - \tfrac{1}{3}e^{-j0.8\pi}}$$

or

$$V_{Ls} = 20\underline{/72°} = 20\underline{/-288°}$$

The amplitude agrees with our previous value. The presence of the reflected wave causes $V_{s,\text{in}}$ and V_{Ls} to differ in phase by about $-279°$ instead of $-288°$.

As a final example let us terminate our line with a capacitive impedance, $Z_L = -j300 \ \Omega$. Obviously, we cannot deliver any average power to the load. As a consequence, the reflection coefficient is

$$\Gamma = \frac{-j300 - 300}{-j300 + 300} = -j1 = 1\underline{/-90°}$$

and the reflected wave is equal in amplitude to the incident wave. Hence it should not surprise us to see that the standing-wave ratio is

$$s = \frac{1 + |-j1|}{1 - |-j1|} = \infty$$

and the input impedance is a pure reactance,

$$Z_{in} = 300 \frac{-j300 + j300 \tan 288°}{300 + j(-j300) \tan 288°} = j153$$

to which no average power can be delivered.

Although we could continue to find numerous other facts and figures for this example, much of the work may be done more easily for problems of this type by using graphical techniques. We shall encounter these in the following section.

D 12.4 A short air-filled coaxial cable has a characteristic impedance of 50 Ω and a length of 10 cm. Find the input impedance at 50 MHz if this lossless line is terminated in

(a) An open circuit
(b) A short circuit
(c) A 10-pF capacitor

Ans. $j5.3; -j476; -j187$ Ω

D 12.5 A voltage of $12 \cos 10^8 t$ V is maintained across the input of a lossless 60-Ω line. A 300-Ω resistor is connected to the output. What average power is delivered to the resistor if the length of the line is

(a) 1.5λ
(b) 1.75λ
(c) 1.875λ

Ans. $0.240; 0.462; 6.00$ W

12.4 GRAPHICAL METHODS

Transmission-line problems often involve manipulations with complex numbers, making the time and effort required for a solution several times greater than that needed for a similar sequence of operations on real numbers. One means of reducing the labor without seriously affecting the accuracy is by using transmission-line charts. Probably the most widely used one is the Smith chart.[1]

Basically, this diagram shows curves of constant resistance and constant reactance; these may represent either an input impedance or a load impedance. An indication of location along the line is also provided, usually in terms of the fraction of a wavelength from a voltage maximum or minimum. Although they are not specifically shown on the chart, the standing-wave ratio and the magnitude and angle of the reflection coefficient are very quickly determined. As a matter of fact, the diagram is constructed within a circle of

[1] P. H. Smith, Transmission-line Calculator, *Electronics*, vol. 12, pp. 29–31, January, 1939.

FIG. 12.4 The polar coordinates of the Smith chart are the magnitude and phase angle of the reflection coefficient; the cartesian coordinates are the real and imaginary parts of the reflection coefficient. The entire chart lies with the unit circle $|\Gamma| = 1$.

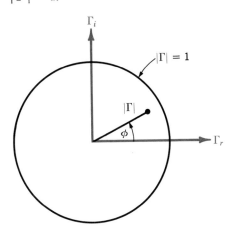

unit radius, using polar coordinates, with radius variable $|\Gamma|$ and counterclockwise angle variable ϕ, where $\Gamma = |\Gamma|e^{j\phi}$. Figure 12.4 shows this circle. Since $|\Gamma| \leq 1$, all our information must lie on or within the unit circle. Peculiarly enough, the reflection coefficient itself will not be plotted on the final chart, for these additional contours would make the chart very difficult to read.

The basic relationship upon which the chart is constructed is

$$(1) \qquad \Gamma = \frac{Z_L - Z_0}{Z_L + Z_0}$$

The impedances which we plot on the chart will be *normalized* with respect to the characteristic impedance. Let us risk possible confusion with the cartesian coordinates and use z to identify the normalized load impedance,

$$(2) \qquad z = r + jx = \frac{Z_L}{Z_0} = \frac{R_L + jX_L}{Z_0}$$

and thus

$$\Gamma = \frac{z - 1}{z + 1}$$

or

(3)
$$z = \frac{1 + \Gamma}{1 - \Gamma}$$

In polar form, we have used $|\Gamma|$ and ϕ as the magnitude and angle of Γ; let us now select Γ_r and Γ_i as the real and imaginary parts of Γ,

(4)
$$\Gamma = \Gamma_r + j\Gamma_i$$

Thus

(5) $\quad r + jx = \dfrac{1 + \Gamma_r + j\Gamma_i}{1 - \Gamma_r - j\Gamma_i}$

The real and imaginary parts of this equation are

(6) $\quad r = \dfrac{1 - \Gamma_r^2 - \Gamma_i^2}{(1 - \Gamma_r)^2 + \Gamma_i^2}$

(7) $\quad x = \dfrac{2\Gamma_i}{(1 - \Gamma_r)^2 + \Gamma_i^2}$

After several lines of elementary algebra, we may write (6) and (7) in forms which readily display the nature of the curves on Γ_r, Γ_i axes,

(8) $\quad \left(\Gamma_r - \dfrac{r}{1 + r}\right)^2 + \Gamma_i^2 = \left(\dfrac{1}{1 + r}\right)^2$

(9) $\quad (\Gamma_r - 1)^2 + \left(\Gamma_i - \dfrac{1}{x}\right)^2 = \left(\dfrac{1}{x}\right)^2$

The first equation describes a family of circles, where each circle is associated with a specific value of resistance r. For example, if $r = 0$ the radius of this zero-resistance circle is seen to be unity, and it is centered at $\Gamma_r = 0$, $\Gamma_i = 0$, the origin. This checks, for a pure reactance termination leads to a reflection coefficient of unity magnitude. However, if $r = \infty$, then $Z_L = \infty$, and we should have $\Gamma = 1$. The circle described by (8) is centered at $\Gamma_r = 1$, $\Gamma_i = 0$ and has zero radius. It is therefore the point $\Gamma = 1$, as we decided it should be. As another example, the circle for $r = 1$ is centered at $\Gamma_r = 0.5$, $\Gamma_i = 0$ and has a radius of 0.5. This circle is shown on Fig. 12.5, along with circles for $r = 0.5$ and $r = 2$. All circles are centered on the Γ_r axis and pass through the point $\Gamma_r = 1$, $\Gamma_i = 0$.

FIG. 12.5 Constant-r circles are shown on the $\Gamma_r\Gamma_i$ plane. The radius of any circle is $1/(1 + r)$.

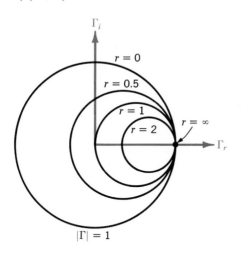

Equation (9) also represents a family of circles, but each of these circles is defined by a particular value of x, rather than r. If $x = \infty$, then $Z_L = \infty$, and Γ must be $1 + j0$ again. The circle described by (9) is centered at $\Gamma_r = 1$, $\Gamma_i = 0$ and has zero radius; it is therefore the point $\Gamma = 1$. If $x = +1$, then the circle is centered at $\Gamma_r = \Gamma_i = 1$ and has unit radius. Only one-quarter of this circle lies within the boundary curve $|\Gamma| = 1$, as shown in Fig. 12.6. A similar quarter-circle appears below the Γ_r axis for $x = -1$. The portions of other circles for $x = 0.5, -0.5, 2$, and -2 are also shown. The "circle" representing $x = 0$ is the Γ_r axis; this is also labeled on Fig. 12.6.

The two families of circles both appear on the Smith chart, as shown in Fig. 12.7. It is now evident that if we are given Z_L, we may divide by Z_0 to obtain z, locate the appropriate r and x circles (interpolating as necessary), and determine Γ by the intersection of the two circles. Since the chart does not have concentric circles showing the values of $|\Gamma|$, it is necessary to measure the radial distance from the origin to the intersection with dividers or compass and use an auxiliary scale to find $|\Gamma|$. The graduated line segment below the chart in Fig. 12.7 serves this purpose. The angle of Γ is the counterclockwise angle from the Γ_r axis. Again, radial lines showing the angle would clutter up the chart badly, so the angle is indicated on the circumference of the circle. A straight line from

FIG. 12.6 The portions of the circles of constant x lying within $|\Gamma| = 1$ are shown on the $\Gamma_r\Gamma_i$ axes. The radius of a given circle is $1/x$.

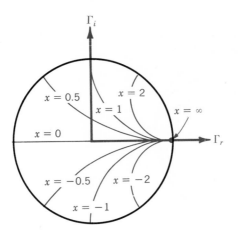

the origin through the intersection may be extended to the perimeter of the chart. As an example, if $Z_L = 25 + j50$ Ω on a 50-Ω line, $z = 0.5 + j1$, and point A on Fig. 12.7 shows the intersection of the $r = 0.5$ and $x = 1$ circles. The reflection coefficient is approximately 0.62 at an angle ϕ of 83°.

The Smith chart is completed by adding a second scale on the circumference by which distance along the line may be computed. This scale is in wavelength units, but the values placed on it are not obvious. The relationship (3) between the reflection coefficient and the normalized *load* impedance

$$(3) \quad z = \frac{1 + \Gamma}{1 - \Gamma}$$

is a special case of a more general equation relating normalized *input* impedance, reflection coefficient, and line length,

$$(10) \quad \boxed{z_{\text{in}} = \frac{1 + \Gamma e^{-j2\beta l}}{1 - \Gamma e^{-j2\beta l}}}$$

The derivation of this equation is suggested as a home exercise, even though it was essentially accomplished in Sec. 11.7. Note that when $l = 0$ we are located at the load, and $z_{\text{in}} = z$.

We use (10) to find the input impedance at a distance l from a given load impedance. Having located the load impedance z on the Smith chart, we may find the point identifying z_{in} by adding an angle $-2\beta l$ to Γ. That is,

$$\Gamma e^{-j2\beta l} \;=\; |\Gamma|\, e^{j(\phi - 2\beta l)}$$

Thus, as we proceed from the load z to the input impedance z_{in}, we move *toward* the generator a distance l on the transmission line, but we move through a *clockwise* angle of $2\beta l$ on the Smith chart. One lap around the chart is therefore accomplished whenever βl changes by π rad, or when l changes by one-half wavelength. This agrees with our earlier discovery that the input impedance of a half-wavelength lossless line is equal to the load impedance.

The Smith chart is thus completed by the addition of a scale showing a change of 0.5λ for one circumnavigation of the unit circle. For convenience, two scales are usually given, one showing an increase in distance for clockwise movement and the other an increase

FIG. 12.7 The Smith chart contains the constant-r circles and constant-x circles, an auxiliary radial scale to determine $|\Gamma|$, and an angular scale on the circumference for measuring ϕ.

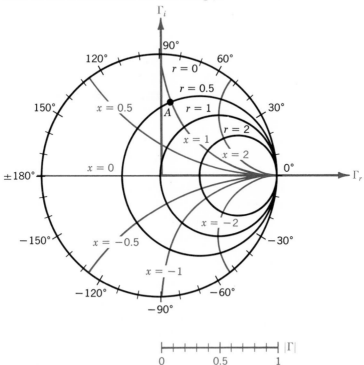

FIG. 12.9 The normalized input impedance produced by a normalized load impedance $z = 0.5 + j1$ on a line 0.3λ long is $z_{in} = 0.28 - j0.40$.

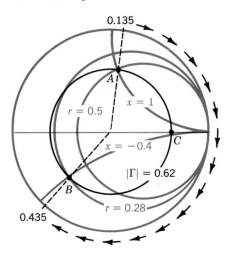

for counterclockwise travel. These two scales are shown in Fig. 12.8. Note that the one marked "wavelength toward generator" (wtg) shows increasing values of l (or βl) for clockwise travel, as described above.

The use of the transmission-line chart is best shown by example. Let us again consider the load impedance $Z_L = 25 + j50$ Ω, terminating a 50-Ω line. Thus $z = 0.5 + j1$, as marked at A on Fig. 12.7; $\Gamma = 0.62e^{j1.45} = 0.62\underline{/83°}$. If the line is 60 cm long and the operating frequency is such that the wavelength on the line is 2 m, then $\beta l = 360° \times 60/200 = 108°$. To find z_{in} we must therefore move $2 \times 108° = 216°$ in a clockwise direction about the $|\Gamma| = 0.62$ circle. Although we could accomplish this with a compass and protractor, it is easier to use the wtg scale. A straight line drawn from the origin through A intersects the wtg scale at 0.135, as shown on Fig. 12.9. Since 60 cm is 0.300 wavelength, we find z_{in} on the $|\Gamma| = 0.62$ circle opposite a wtg reading of $0.135 + 0.300 = 0.435$. This construction is shown in Fig. 12.9, and the point locating the input impedance is marked B. The normalized input impedance is read as $0.28 - j0.40$, and thus $Z_{in} = 14 - j20$. A more accurate analytical calculation gives $Z_{in} = 13.7 - j20.2$.

Information concerning the location of the voltage maxima and minima is also readily obtained on the Smith chart. We already know that a maximum or minimum must occur at the load when Z_L is a pure resistance; if $Z_L > Z_0$ there is a maximum at the load,

FIG. 12.8   The Smith chart.   (*Courtesy of The Emeloid Company, Hillside, N. J.*)

and if $Z_L < Z_0$ there is a minimum. We may extend this result now by noting that we could cut off the load end of a transmission line at a point where the input impedance is a pure resistance and replace that section with a resistance R_{in}; there would be no changes on the generator portion of the line. It follows, then, that the location of voltage maxima and minima must be at those points where Z_{in} is a pure resistance. Purely resistive input impedances must occur on the $x = 0$ line (the Γ_r axis) of the Smith chart. Voltage maxima or current minima occur when $r > 1$, and voltage minima or current maxima when $r < 1$. In the example above, we therefore see that a maximum of the voltage-standing wave occurs for a wtg reading of 0.250, or $0.250 - 0.135 = 0.115$ wavelengths from the load. This is a distance of 0.115×200, or 23 cm from the load. We should also note that since the standing-wave ratio produced by a resistive load R_L is either R_L/R_0 or R_0/R_L, whichever is greater than unity, the value of s may be read directly as the value of r at the intersection of the $|\Gamma|$ circle and the r axis, $r > 1$. In our example this intersection is marked point C, and $r = 4.2$; thus $s = 4.2$.

Transmission-line charts may also be used for normalized admittances, although there are several slight differences in such use. We let $y = Y_L/Y_0 = g + jb$ and use the r circles as g circles and the x circles as b circles. The two differences, then, are that $g > 1$, $b = 0$ corresponds to a voltage *minimum*, and 180° must be added to the angle of Γ as read from the perimeter of the chart. We shall use the Smith chart in this way in the following section.

Special charts are also available for nonnormalized lines, particularly 50-Ω charts and 20-m℧ charts.

D 12.6 Use the Smith chart of Fig. 12.8 to find the input impedance of a 300-Ω line terminated in $60 - j150\ \Omega$ and having an electrical length ($360°l/\lambda$) of

(a) 45°
(b) 72°
(c) 131.5°

Ans. $570 - j830;\ 52 + j93;\ 92 + j282 \quad \Omega$

D 12.7 A 1-m length of air-filled 72-Ω coaxial cable is terminated with the parallel combination of a 72-Ω resistor and a 10-pF capacitor. The frequency is 50 MHz. Use Fig. 12.8 to find

(a) $|\Gamma|$
(b) s
(c) The fractional part of a wavelength from the load to the first voltage maximum

Ans. 0.112; 0.367; 1.25

12.5 SEVERAL PRACTICAL PROBLEMS

In this section we shall direct our attention to two examples of practical transmission-line problems. The first is the determination of a load impedance from experimental data, and the second is the design of a single-stub matching network.

Let us assume that we have made experimental measurements on a 50-Ω air line which show that there is a standing-wave ratio of 2.5. This has been determined by moving a sliding carriage back and forth along the line to determine maximum and minimum readings. A scale provided on the track along which the carriage moves indicates that a *minimum* occurs at a scale reading of 47.0 cm, as shown in Fig. 12.10. The zero point of the scale is arbitrary and does not correspond to the location of the load. The location of the minimum is usually specified instead of the maximum because it can be determined more accurately than that of the maximum; think of the sharper minima on a rectified sine wave. The frequency of operation is 400 MHz. In order to pinpoint the location of the load we remove it and replace it with a short circuit; the position of the minimum is then determined as 26.0 cm.

We know that the short circuit must be located an integral number of half-wavelengths from the minimum; let us arbitrarily locate it

FIG. 12.10 A sketch of a coaxial slotted line. The distance scale is on the slotted line. With the load in place, $s = 2.5$, and the minimum occurs at a scale reading of 47 cm; for a short circuit the minimum is located at a scale reading of 26 cm. The wavelength is 75 cm.

FIG. 12.11 If $z_{in} = 2.5 + j0$ on a line 0.03 wavelengths long, then $z = 2.1 + j0.8$.

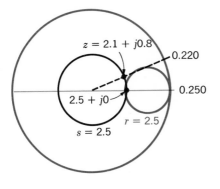

one half-wavelength away at $26.0 - 37.5 = -11.5$ cm on the scale.
Since the short circuit has replaced the load, the load is also located
at -11.5 cm. Our data thus show that the minimum is $47.0 - (-11.5) = 58.5$ cm from the load, or subtracting one-half wavelength, a minimum is 21.0 cm from the load. The voltage *maximum*
is thus $21.0 - (37.5/2) = 2.25$ cm from the load, or $2.25/75 = 0.030$
wavelengths from the load. With this information, we can now turn
to the Smith chart. At a voltage maximum the input impedance is
a pure resistance equal to sR_0; on a normalized basis, $z_{in} = 2.5$. We
therefore enter the chart at $z_{in} = 2.5$ and read 0.250 on the wtg scale.
Subtracting 0.030 wavelengths to reach the load, we find that the
intersection of the $s = 2.5$ (or $|\Gamma| = 0.429$) circle and the radial line
to 0.220 wavelengths is at $z = 2.1 + j0.8$. The construction is
sketched on the Smith chart of Fig. 12.11. Thus $Z_L = 105 + j40 \ \Omega$,
a value which assumes its location at a scale reading of -11.5 cm,
or an integral number of half-wavelengths from that position. Of
course, we may select the "location" of our load at will by placing
the short circuit at that point which we wish to consider as the
load location. Since load locations are not well defined, it is important to specify the point (or plane) at which the load impedance
is determined.

As a final example, let us try to match this load to the 50-Ω line
by placing a short-circuited stub of length d_1 at a point d m from
the load (see Fig. 12.12). The stub line has the same characteristic
impedance as the main line. The lengths d and d_1 are to be determined.

The input impedance to the stub is a pure reactance; when combined in parallel with the input impedance of the length d containing
the load, the resultant input impedance must be $1 + j0$. Of course,
it is much easier to combine admittances in parallel than imped-

FIG. 12.12 A short-circuited stub of length d_1, located d m from a load Z_L, is used to provide a matched load to the left of the stub.

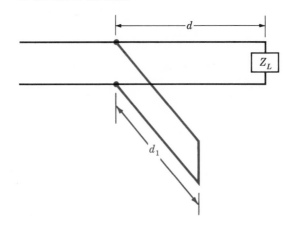

ances, so let us rephrase our goal in admittance language: the input admittance of the length d containing the load must be $1 + jb_{in}$ for the addition of the input admittance of the d-m stub jb_{stub} to produce a total admittance of $1 + j0$. Hence the stub admittance is $-jb_{in}$. We shall therefore use the Smith chart as an admittance chart instead of an impedance chart.

The impedance of the load is $2.1 + j0.8$, and its location is at -11.5 cm. The admittance of the load is therefore $1/(2.1 + j0.8)$, and this value may be determined by adding one-quarter wavelength on the Smith chart, since Z_{in} for a quarter-wavelength line is R_0^2/Z_L, or $z_{in} = 1/z$, or $y_{in} = z$. Entering the chart at $z = 2.1 + j0.8$, we read 0.220 on the wtg scale; we add (or subtract) 0.250 and find the admittance $0.41 - j0.16$ corresponding to this impedance. This point is still located on the $s = 2.5$ circle. Now, at what point or points on this circle is the real part of the admittance equal to unity? There are two answers, $1 + j0.95$ at wtg = 0.16, and $1 - j0.95$ at wtg = 0.34, as shown in Fig. 12.13. Let us select the former value and relegate to a problem the proof that this leads to the shorter stub. Hence $y_{stub} = -j0.95$, and the stub location corresponds to wtg = 0.16. Since the load admittance was found at wtg = 0.470, then 0.19 wavelengths ($= 0.16 - 0.47 + 0.50$) separate the stub and load. Hence $d = 0.19 \times 75 = 14.2$ cm.

Let us now use the chart to determine the necessary length of the short-circuited stub. The input conductance is zero for any length of short-circuited stub, so we are restricted to the perimeter; at the short circuit, $y = \infty$. We find that $b_{in} = -0.95$ is achieved at

FIG. 12.13 A normalized load $z = 2.1 + j0.8$ is matched by placing a 0.129-wavelength short-circuited stub 0.19 wavelengths from the load.

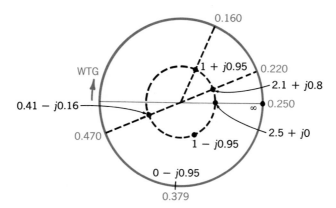

wtg = 0.379.   Since the short circuit is at wtg = 0.250, the stub is 0.129 wavelengths, or 9.67 cm long.

Although we shall conclude our introduction to transmission lines at this point, there are many important and interesting problems that we have not discussed.   Perhaps the most important involve the effects of the unavoidable losses.   Others will include the use of transmission lines as circuit elements, resonant circuits, and delay lines; the transient behavior of the lines; transmission-line equivalent circuits; nonuniform lines; other matching techniques; and special approximations that are useful in treating low-frequency high-voltage transmission lines.   Most of these topics are discussed in most of the references listed below.

D 12.8   When a short circuit is placed on a 100-Ω line, consecutive voltage minima appear at 24 and 56 cm.   Use the Smith chart to find the load impedance that produces readings of

(a) 0 at 30 cm and 27 at 46 cm
(b) 20 at 30 cm and 60 at 46 cm
(c) 20 at 46 cm and 60 at 30 cm

Ans. $-j67$; $46 - j57$; $86 + j106$ Ω

D 12.9   Find the short-circuited stub position d and shortest possible length d_1, both expressed in wavelengths, necessary to match a normalized load

(a) $z = 1 - j1$
(b) $z = 1 + j1$
(c) $z = 3 - j1$

Ans. 0.153λ, 0.105λ; 0.074λ, 0.125λ; 0.250λ, 0.125λ m

SUGGESTED REFERENCES

1 Adler, R. B., L. J. Chu, and R. M. Fano: "Electromagnetic Energy Transmission and Radiation," John Wiley & Sons, Inc., New York, 1960. Transmission lines are treated thoroughly in chaps. 3–6.

2 Brown, R. G., R. A. Sharpe, and W. L. Hughes: "Lines, Waves, and Antennas," The Ronald Press Company, New York, 1961. Transmission lines are covered in the first six chapters, with numerous examples.

3 Moore, R. K.: "Traveling-wave Engineering," McGraw-Hill Book Company, New York, 1960. This book presents plane waves and transmission lines side by side. Other types of waves are also discussed briefly.

4 Weeks, W. L.: "Electromagnetic Theory for Engineering Applications," John Wiley & Sons, Inc., New York, 1964. Several illustrative experiments with transmission lines are described beginning on p. 72.

PROBLEMS

1 A lossless transmission line with parameter values $C = 200$ pF/m and $L = \frac{1}{9}$ μH/m is operating at 300 MHz. (a) Find γ and β. (b) Calculate the velocity on the line. (c) Find the wavelength on the line. (d) Determine the characteristic impedance.

2 A transmission line with $C = 48$ pF/m, $L = \frac{1}{3}$ μH/m, $R = 1$ Ω/m, and $G = 18 \times 10^{-6}$ $\mho$/m is operated at $\omega = 1.5 \times 10^6$ rad/s. Find (a) Z_0; (b) α; (c) λ.

3 A 50-Ω transmission line is terminated with an infinitely long 150-Ω line. (a) What reflection coefficient does an incident wave on the 50-Ω line encounter at the junction? (b) What standing-wave ratio exists on the 50-Ω line? (c) What standing-wave ratio exists on the 150-Ω line?

4 A 100-MHz signal is applied to a lossless transmission line for which $Z_0 = 75$ Ω. If the wavelength on the line is 4 m, find L and C.

5 Show that the input admittance of a length l of lossless line having a characteristic impedance of $Z_0 = 1/Y_0$ and terminated in a load having an admittance Y_L is $Y_{in} = Y_0(Y_L + jY_0 \tan \beta l)/(Y_0 + jY_L \tan \beta l)$.

6 Find R, L, C, and G for a coaxial cable with $a = 0.01$ in., $b = 0.10$ in., $c = 0.13$ in., $\epsilon_R = 2$, $\mu_R = 1$, $\sigma_c = 10^7$ $\mho$/m, $\sigma = 10^{-5}$ $\mho$/m, and $\omega = 2 \times 10^9$ rad/s.

7 A shielded transmission line, half of which is shown in Fig. 6.4, is filled with polyethylene. If it were filled with air, the exact capacitance would be 55.6 pF/m. Assuming that the line is lossless, find C, L, and Z_0.

8 Derive Sec. 12.2, Eqs. (16) to (20).

9 A planar transmission line of dimensions $d = 1$ mm, $b = 1.2$ cm contains a dielectric for which $\epsilon_R = 2$, $\mu_R = 1$, and $\sigma = 10^{-4}$ $\mho$/m and utilizes conductors having a conductivity of 4×10^7 $\mho$/m. If these values are assumed constant with frequency, neglect the internal inductance and find the frequency of operation at which the characteristic impedance is a pure resistance.

10 Find R, G, L, and C for a two-wire transmission line in polyethylene at $\omega = 5 \times 10^9$. Assume copper conductors of radius 0.5 mm and separation 0.8 cm. Use $\epsilon_R = 2.26$, $\sigma/\omega\epsilon = 4 \times 10^{-4}$.

11 Find the relative magnitudes of the radii a, b, and c in a coaxial line if the internal inductance of the center conductor is twice that of the outer conductor but the internal inductance of the center conductor is equal to the external inductance. Assume low-frequency operation.

12 In Sec. 12.3 an example was discussed in which a 60-V 300-Ω source was able to deliver 0.667 W to each of two 300-Ω loads connected in parallel on a 300-Ω 0.8-wavelength line. What power would be delivered to each receiver if they were connected in series?

13 (a) Show that a transmission line with $Z_0 = Z_{01}$ may be matched to a load Z_L by inserting a quarter-wavelength section of line with $Z_0 = Z_{02} = \sqrt{Z_{01}Z_L}$ in front of the load. Assume $\alpha = 0$ for both lines. (b) Using lossless lines only, what types of load impedances may be matched with this quarter-wavelength transformer?

14 (a) Specify the necessary length and characteristic impedance of a quarter-wavelength transformer (see Prob. 13) to match a 150-Ω resistive load to a 50-Ω line at 100 MHz. Assume air lines. (b) What standing-wave ratio is present on the 50-Ω line at 100 MHz? (c) At 110 MHz?

15 A 50-Ω line is terminated with 60- and 30-Ω resistors in parallel. The voltage at the input to the line is $100 \cos (5 \times 10^9 t)$, and the line is three-eighths wavelength long. What average power is delivered to each load resistor?

16 A one-eighth-wavelength section of 100-Ω line is terminated in 200 Ω. What is the shortest length of short-circuited 100-Ω line that may be connected in parallel with this line at its input to produce a pure resistance at 300 MHz? All lines have air dielectric and are lossless.

17 A lossless 100-Ω air line with a phase shift of $\frac{1}{3}$ rad/m is terminated with a 100-pF capacitor in parallel with a 100-Ω resistor. (a) Find the standing-wave ratio. (b) Find the distance from the termination to the first voltage maximum.

18 Show that in Sec. 12.4 Eqs. (6), (7), (8), and (9) follow from Eq. (5).

19 Beginning with the definition of the reflection coefficient, develop Sec. 12.4, Eq. (10).

20 Use the Smith chart to find the input impedance of a 0.1-wavelength short-circuited line if $Z_0 = 100 \ \Omega$.

21 What length of 100-Ω open-circuited line has an input impedance magnitude of 10 Ω? Express the answer in fractional wavelength.

22 A lossless 50-Ω coaxial transmission line containing a dielectric for which $\epsilon_R = 2.25$ is 80 cm long. It is terminated in an impedance $30 - j30 \ \Omega$. What average power would be drawn from a 10-V-crest-amplitude 400-MHz source connected directly to the input of the line?

23 An air-filled 60-Ω line is three-quarters wavelength long. The input impedance is $54 - j30 \ \Omega$. Use the Smith chart to find Z_L.

24 A load consisting of a 20-Ω resistor in series with a capacitor C is placed on a 50-Ω line and produces a standing-wave ratio of 4. If the operating frequency is 600 MHz, find C.

25 Standing-wave measurements on a 50-Ω air line show that the position of the minimum shifts one-tenth wavelength away from the generator when the load is replaced by a short circuit. If $s = 1.5$, find Z_L.

26 A 50-Ω air line shows a maximum voltage amplitude of 8 V 12 cm from the load and a minimum voltage amplitude of 3 V 37 cm from the load. (*a*) What is the operating frequency? (*b*) What length of short-circuited line should be placed in parallel with the line at a point 26 cm from the load to produce a minimum standing-wave ratio between the stub and the generator? (*c*) What is s there?

27 Show that placement of a short-circuited stub at the position where the input admittance is $1 + j|b_{in}|$ leads to a stub length shorter than that which results from locating it where $y_{in} = 1 - j|b_{in}|$. Is this statement true when open-circuited stubs are used? (Short-circuited stubs are preferred because the short circuit offers support to the center conductor of air lines and also avoids radiation losses from the open end.)

28 At $f = 100$ MHz on a 72-Ω air line a 60-cm short-circuited stub is located 108 cm from the load. Find Z_L if the line to the source has unity standing-wave ratio.

29 Refer to "Reference Data for Radio Engineers," 4th ed., International Telephone and Telegraph Corp., New York, 1956, and find the characteristic impedance of a balanced two-wire line having wires of diameter 3 and 5 mm, with center-to-center spacing of 26 mm, in air.

30 In F. Assadourian and E. Rimai, Simplified Theory of Microstrip Transmission System, *Proc. IRE*, vol. 40, pp. 1651–1657, December, 1952, Fig. 5 enables the characteristic impedance of finite-width planar lines to be calculated. (*a*) Locate the error in the formula immediately below the figure and correct it. (*b*) Calculate Z_0' for a line 2 cm wide, 0.5 cm distant from the ground plane in air. (*c*) How does Z_0' compare with the characteristic impedance determined by Sec. 12.2, Eqs. (16) and (17)? (*d*) Determine Z_0 for this line.

13 SEVERAL OTHER APPLICATIONS OF MAXWELL'S EQUATIONS

We shall close our introduction to electromagnetic theory by considering several other important applications of Maxwell's equations—circuit theory, the resonant cavity, and radiation from an antenna. The coverage of these subjects is intended to indicate the application and usefulness of the fundamental equations presented in the preceding chapters and to introduce other significant areas of interest in more advanced electromagnetic theory. Certainly we shall not be able to say that we are experts on any of these subjects after these few preliminary remarks.

13.1 THE LAWS OF CIRCUIT THEORY

To indicate how Maxwell's equations, the potential definitions, and the concepts of resistance, capacitance, and inductance combine to produce the common expressions of circuit analysis, consider the configuration shown in Fig. 13.1. Between the two points 0 and 1 an external electric field is applied. These terminals are very close together, and a sinusoidal electric field may be assumed. Perhaps we could visualize a microscopic transistor oscillator, a rotating machine the size of a pinhead (complete with prime mover), or even a cooperative flea moving a mouthful of charge alternately toward point 1 and point 0. Whatever the nature of the source, it continues to produce an electric field between these two terminals which is independent of any currents which may consequently flow. Between points 2 and 3 there is a region of lossy material of small cross-sectional area S_R, length d_R, and conductivity σ. At points 4 and 5 are located two capacitor plates of area S_C, separated d_C m by a material of permittivity ϵ. These several points are connected as shown by a filamentary perfect conductor of negligible cross section. Between points 6 and 8 the filament is wound into a helix of N turns having a very fine pitch.

It is probably obvious that we are now going to develop the familiar circuit equation

$$(1) \quad V_{10} = IR + L\frac{dI}{dt} + \frac{1}{C}\int_{-\infty}^{t} I\,dt$$

from Maxwell's equations. As we do so, it is interesting to watch how each of these terms arises and what assumptions we have to

FIG. 13.1 The field version of an *RLC* circuit. The configuration and materials are arranged so that
a resistor, a capacitor, an inductor, and a
voltage source may be identified.

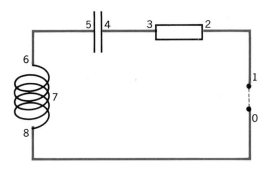

make in the process. Our beginning point is the integral form of
Faraday's law,

$$(2) \qquad \oint \mathbf{E} \cdot d\mathbf{L} = -\frac{\partial}{\partial t} \int_s \mathbf{B} \cdot d\mathbf{S}$$

We shall see that the right side of this equation provides us with
only one term in (1), that involving the inductance. The other
three terms in (1) all arise from the closed line integral.

   Let us consider the surface integral on the right side of (2). Since
the configuration of the circuit does not change with time, the
partial derivative may be replaced with the ordinary derivative.
Also, the filament between points 6 and 8, an N-turn helix, serves to
produce a much larger magnetic field within the helix than in any
other region along the filament. If we assume that a total magnetic flux Φ links all N turns, the surface integral becomes $-d\Phi/dt$,
or $-L(dI/dt)$ by the definition of inductance in Chap. 9, or

$$\oint \mathbf{E} \cdot d\mathbf{L} = -L \frac{dI}{dt}$$

where I is the filamentary current in each turn of the helix.

   The closed line integral is taken along the filament, directly between the capacitor plates and points 0 and 1, as indicated by the
dashed line. The contribution from the perfectly conducting filament is zero, because tangential $\mathbf{E}$ must be zero there; this includes
the helix, surprising as that may be. We therefore have

$$\oint \mathbf{E} \cdot d\mathbf{L} = \int_0^1 + \int_2^3 + \int_4^5$$

The first integral on the right is the negative of the voltage between points 1 and 0,

$$\int_0^1 \mathbf{E} \cdot d\mathbf{L} = -V_{10}$$

This integral is a function only of the external source and does not depend on the configuration shown in Fig. 13.1. The path is directly between the adjacent terminals, and since we are more used to considering an external source as a voltage than as an electric field intensity, we usually call V_{10} an *applied voltage*.

The second integral is taken across the lossy material, and we apply Ohm's law in point form and the definition of total resistance R,

$$\int_2^3 \mathbf{E} \cdot d\mathbf{L} = \int_2^3 \frac{\mathbf{J}}{\sigma} \cdot d\mathbf{L} = \int_2^3 \frac{J\,dL}{\sigma}$$

$$= \frac{J d_R}{\sigma} = \frac{I d_R}{\sigma S_R} = IR$$

The same total current I is assumed, and this is justified only when two conditions are met. There can be no displacement currents flowing from one portion of the filament to another (such as from point 3 to point 8), because we require the continuity of conduction plus displacement current density to be satisfied by conduction current alone. In other language, we are assuming that stray capacitances are neglected. Also, the dimensions of the filamentary path must be small compared to a wavelength. This will be amplified in the final section of this chapter, but our study of wave motion should indicate the complete reversal which may occur in a field over a distance of one-half wavelength. Here we wish to avoid radiation, but later in the chapter it will provide our main item of interest.

The third integral is evaluated across the region between the capacitor plates where conduction current is zero but where displacement current is equal to the current I, as we assumed earlier. Here we may represent the integral by

$$\int_4^5 \mathbf{E} \cdot d\mathbf{L} = \int_4^5 \frac{D}{\epsilon}\,dL = \frac{D d_C}{\epsilon} = \frac{Q d_C}{S_C \epsilon} = \frac{Q}{C}$$

or

$$\int_4^5 \mathbf{E} \cdot d\mathbf{L} = \frac{1}{C} \int_{-\infty}^t I\,dt$$

where we assume that there is no charge on the capacitor at $t = -\infty$.

Combining these results, we have

$$-V_{10} + IR + \frac{1}{C} \int_{-\infty}^{t} I \, dt = -L \frac{dI}{dt}$$

or

$$V_{10} = IR + L \frac{dI}{dt} + \frac{1}{C} \int_{-\infty}^{t} I \, dt$$

which is the familiar equation for an *RLC* series circuit that we hoped we would obtain.

The assumptions upon which this equality is based, implicitly assumed in most circuit problems, are as follows:

1. A filamentary conductor defines the closed path or circuit.
2. The maximum dimensions of the circuit are small compared to a wavelength.
3. Displacement current is confined to capacitors.
4. Magnetic flux is confined to inductors.
5. Imperfect conductivity is confined to resistors.

The first assumption simply defines what we mean by a "circuit." The second implies that any circuit ceases to obey the laws of circuit theory if the frequency is sufficiently high. The last three assumptions restrict the circuit relationships to ideal elements. If our capacitors have resistance, or our inductors have capacitance, we cannot apply the circuit equations until we have replaced the lossy capacitor or the inductor plus stray capacitance by some networks containing only ideal elements. The selection of an appropriate combination of ideal elements is made possible by our knowledge of the behavior of the electromagnetic fields in and around the devices; experience also comes in handy.

It is also possible to use a "circuits approach" to many devices which do not satisfy the conditions above, such as transmission lines. Waveguides, resonant cavities, and many antenna problems may also be treated as circuits in certain respects. When this is done, the detailed description of the electric and magnetic fields must be of secondary importance; the device is described in terms of an equivalent voltage and current at each input or output. The resonant cavity discussed in the following section is one such example.

D 13.1   (*a*) An inductance is to be wound as a tight helix on a nonmagnetic 1-cm-diameter cylindrical core of permittivity 2.25. If 1-mm-diameter wire is used, find the maximum number of turns that can be used without exceeding a wire length of 0.1 wavelength at $f = 200$ MHz.

(b) A short-circuited transmission line is 0.24 wavelength long. Find the ratio of the input inductive reactance to Z_0 $(= R_0)$ at $f = 200$ MHz.

(c) A capacitor utilizes a dielectric for which $\sigma/\omega\epsilon = 0.027$. Find the ratio of the effective parallel resistance between the terminals to the magnitude of the capacitive reactance at $f = 200$ MHz.

Ans. 15.9; 28.0; 37.0

13.2 THE RESONANT COAXIAL CAVITY

We found in the last section that the foundations of circuit theory are based on Maxwell's equations, but that we must also have a closed path (not necessarily a conducting path), circuit dimensions that are small compared with a wavelength, and identifiable circuit elements. Now let us consider a device in which, although most of these requirements are not met, certain aspects of circuit theory permit us to interpret the results in familiar terms.

We may think of a closed laboratory into which a single coaxial conductor passes. Within the laboratory there is a distributed circuit, that is, one having dimensions comparable to a wavelength with its resistive, inductive, and capacitive properties distributed throughout this region. Circuit relationships are therefore not applicable in the laboratory. At the point at which the coaxial conductor enters the laboratory, however, we are able to define a voltage between the outer and inner conductors and the current in each. This is possible because the radial dimensions of the coax are assumed to be a small fraction of a wavelength even though its length is not. The problem we wish to consider is the description of the device in the laboratory in terms of an equivalent circuit. If we are successful, then it should be impossible to determine whether the laboratory contains an equivalent circuit that satisfies all the requirements of circuit theory or a distributed circuit that does not. We shall see that within a given frequency band, this is indeed the case.

The device which we shall use as an example in developing an equivalent circuit is a coaxial resonant cavity. Such resonators are very selective with respect to frequency, and they thus find use in frequency meters, amplifiers, and oscillators; they may also be used to determine the conductivity and permittivity of dielectric materials, perhaps to control some manufacturing process.

Let us consider the coaxial cavity shown in Fig. 13.2. We assume that t, a, and b are much smaller than a wavelength; l may be any length, although we shall specifically select one-quarter wavelength. Since the constants of the dielectric and conductor are known, we could calculate R, G, L, and C for the line, and from these, Z_0 and γ.

FIG. 13.2 A coaxial cavity for which $b \ll \lambda$. This device may be represented by a parallel resonant circuit in the neighborhood of the resonant frequency.

We could then spend a few minutes obtaining an expression for the input impedance of a *lossy* transmission line, and thus determine the input impedance of the line terminated in a low-impedance load, the short-circuiting plate. Having the input impedance, we would then be able to determine the form of an equivalent circuit providing the same input impedance, at least within some desired frequency range about the resonant frequency.

Let us select a more general procedure, however, which illustrates the principles involved in determining an equivalent circuit for any microwave cavity near resonance. We shall begin by finding the fields that would exist in a *lossless* cavity. We then evaluate these fields at the conductor boundaries and calculate the losses that would occur if these fields were present. Although we could then use the results of the loss analysis to recalculate the cavity fields and use these values to improve our loss calculations, this iterative procedure is not necessary in low-loss cavities; the first approximation provides excellent accuracy.

For the lossless coaxial line terminated in a short circuit at $z = 0$, where the z axis is directed to the right, the phasor voltage at any point along the line is the sum of the incident and reflected waves,

$$V_s = V_0 e^{-j\beta z} - V_0 e^{j\beta z}$$

or

(1) $\quad V_s = -j2V_0 \sin \beta z$

and the current is

$$I_s = \frac{V_0}{Z_0} e^{-j\beta z} + \frac{V_0}{Z_0} e^{j\beta z}$$

or

(2) $\quad I_s = \dfrac{2V_0}{Z_0} \cos \beta z$

where

(3) $\quad \beta = \omega\sqrt{LC} = \omega\sqrt{\mu\epsilon}$

and

(4) $\quad Z_0 = \sqrt{\dfrac{L}{C}} = \dfrac{1}{2\pi}\sqrt{\dfrac{\mu}{\epsilon}}\ln\dfrac{b}{a}$

The magnetic field intensity is related directly to the current,

$$H_{\phi s} = \dfrac{I_s}{2\pi r}$$

and thus

(5) $\quad H_{\phi s} = \dfrac{V_0}{\pi r Z_0} \cos \beta z$

We then recall that the relationship of the electric field intensity to the voltage between conductors of a coaxial line is

(6) $\quad E_{rs} = \dfrac{V_s}{r \ln (b/a)} = \dfrac{-j2V_0}{r \ln (b/a)} \sin \beta z$

where the voltage of the outer conductor is zero and that of the inner is V_s.

Power losses in the cavity arise in several different ways: in an imperfect dielectric which might fill the cavity, and in the conductors forming the center conductor, the outer conductor, and the single end plate. Let us first assume that the power loss in the dielectric is much greater than that in the walls, as would be the case if the cavity were filled with beer, flour, or some other food the production of which we are monitoring with electrical measurements. The loss in the dielectric is determined by integrating the ohmic power density throughout the cavity. We begin by finding the conduction current density,

$$J_{rs} = \sigma E_{rs} = \dfrac{-j2\sigma V_0}{r \ln (b/a)} \sin \beta z$$

or in trigonometric form,

(7) $\quad J_r = \dfrac{2\sigma V_0}{r \ln (b/a)} \sin \beta z \sin \omega t$

The total power dissipated in the dielectric is

$$P_d = \int_{\text{vol}} \frac{1}{\sigma} J_r^2 \, dv$$

$$= \int_{-l}^0 \int_0^{2\pi} \int_a^b \frac{4\sigma V_0^2}{r[\ln (b/a)]^2} \sin^2 \beta z \sin^2 \omega t \, dr \, d\phi \, dz$$

or

$$(8) \quad P_d = \frac{4\pi\sigma V_0^2}{\ln (b/a)} \left(l - \frac{\sin 2\beta l}{2\beta}\right) \sin^2 \omega t$$

and the time-average power loss is

$$(9) \quad P_{d,\text{av}} = \frac{2\pi\sigma V_0^2}{\ln (b/a)} \left(l - \frac{\sin 2\beta l}{2\beta}\right)$$

In order to provide a *resonant* cavity let us now select the length l as one-quarter wavelength. If the cavity were truly lossless, the current at the input would be zero and the input impedance would be infinite. Instead, we shall find that the power lost in the dielectric and conducting walls causes a small input current and an input impedance which is a high resistance at resonance. If we identify the resonant frequency as f_0, then

$$(10) \quad l = \frac{\lambda_0}{4} = \frac{1}{4 f_0 \sqrt{\mu\epsilon}}$$

and

$$(11) \quad \beta_0 = \frac{2\pi}{\lambda_0} = \frac{\pi}{2l}$$

Thus the average power loss in the dielectric at the resonant frequency is

$$(12) \quad P_{d0,\text{av}} = \frac{2\pi\sigma V_0^2 l}{\ln (b/a)}$$

We may now begin to try to fit our results to an equivalent circuit of the form shown in Fig. 13.3, a parallel resonant circuit. At resonance the input impedance is a pure resistance R_e (by the definition of resonance.) From (1) we have the voltage at any point at any time,

$$V = 2V_0 \sin \beta z \sin \omega t$$

and thus the input ($z = -l$) voltage is

$$V_{\text{in}} = -2V_0 \sin \beta l \sin \omega t$$

FIG. 13.3 Suitable selections of R_e, L_e, and C_e cause this circuit to be equivalent to the resonant coaxial cavity of Fig. 13.2 near $f_0 = 1/2\pi\sqrt{L_e C_e} = 1/4l\sqrt{\mu\epsilon}$, where l is the length of the cavity.

At resonance $\beta_0 l = \pi/2$ and

$$V_{0,\text{in}} = -2V_0 \sin \omega t$$

Since the crest amplitude is $2V_0$, the average power loss

$$P_{d0,\text{av}} = \frac{1}{2}\frac{V_{0,\text{in}}^2}{R_e} = \frac{2\pi\sigma V_0^2 l}{\ln (b/a)}$$

enables us to find the equivalent resistance,

(13) $$R_e = \frac{\ln (b/a)}{\pi\sigma l}$$

This expression, of course, assumes no losses in the conductor boundaries.

In order to find expressions for C_e and L_e in Fig. 13.3 it is necessary to establish a value for the energy stored in the resonator at resonance. We may then use the general definition of Q,

(14) $$\boxed{Q = 2\pi \; \frac{\text{energy stored}}{\text{energy lost per cycle}}}$$

or

(15) $$\boxed{Q = \omega \; \frac{\text{energy stored}}{\text{average power loss}}}$$

to determine Q. If we know Q, familiar circuit equations will enable us to find L_e and C_e.

The energy stored in the cavity is the sum of the energies stored in the electric and magnetic fields. It can be shown, however, that this *total* energy is the same as the *maximum* energy stored in either the electric or magnetic fields. That is, the total energy is constant, and when the magnetic energy is zero the energy in the electric field is a maximum, and vice versa. Let us select the maximum value of the magnetic field (5),

$$H_{\phi,\max} = \frac{V_0}{\pi r Z_0} \cos \beta z$$

and thus

$$W_{H,\max} = \int_{\text{vol}} \tfrac{1}{2}\mu H^2_{\max}\, dv$$

$$= \frac{\mu V_0^2}{2\pi^2 Z_0^2} \int_{-l}^{0} \int_0^{2\pi} \int_a^b \frac{1}{r} \cos^2 \beta z\, dr\, d\phi\, dz$$

$$= \frac{\mu V_0^2 \ln (b/a)}{2\pi Z_0^2} \left(l + \frac{\sin 2\beta l}{2\beta} \right)$$

At resonance

$$(16) \quad W_{H0,\max} = W_{0,\max} = \frac{\mu l V_0^2 \ln (b/a)}{2\pi Z_0^2} = \frac{2\pi\epsilon l V_0^2}{\ln (b/a)}$$

A similar determination of the maximum energy stored in the electric field is requested in Prob. 11.

Combining our expressions for the average power loss in the dielectric (12), the definition of Q (15), and the total energy (16), all evaluated at the resonant frequency, we find the Q produced by the dielectric at resonance,

$$Q_{d0} = \omega_0 \frac{2\pi\epsilon l V_0^2/\ln (b/a)}{2\pi\sigma l V_0^2/\ln (b/a)}$$

or

$$(17) \quad Q_{d0} = \frac{\omega_0 \epsilon}{\sigma}$$

which, interestingly enough, turns out to be the reciprocal of the loss tangent, the value it would have for a coaxial capacitor at lower frequencies.

The equivalent capacitance C_e may be found either from the expression for the energy in a capacitor,

$$W_{0,\max} = \tfrac{1}{2} C_e (2V_0)^2$$

would be present. With a *finite* conductivity, this total current per unit width is distributed throughout a thin layer near the surface. As we saw in Chap. 11, the total power loss may be found by assuming a uniform current density throughout a region one skin depth thick. This uniform current density is therefore

(23) $\quad J_z = \dfrac{K_z}{\delta} = \dfrac{-V_0}{\pi b \delta Z_0} \cos \beta z \cos \omega t$

The ohmic power loss in the outer cylinder (of conductivity σ_c) is thus

$$P_b = \int_{\text{vol}} \frac{1}{\sigma_c} J_z{}^2 \, dv$$

$$= \int_{-l}^{0} \frac{1}{\sigma_c} J_z{}^2 \delta 2 \pi b \, dz$$

$$= \frac{V_0{}^2}{\sigma_c \pi b \delta Z_0{}^2} \left(l + \frac{\sin 2\beta l}{2\beta} \right) \cos^2 \omega t$$

Therefore the average power loss at resonance is

(24) $\quad P_{b0,\text{av}} = \dfrac{V_0{}^2 l}{2\pi \sigma_c b \delta Z_0{}^2}$

A similar calculation for the inner conductor gives

(25) $\quad P_{a0,\text{av}} = \dfrac{V_0{}^2 l}{2\pi \sigma_c a \delta Z_0{}^2}$

The only remaining surface is the end plate at $z = 0$. The magnetic field intensity at $z = 0$ is

$$H_\phi \big|_{z=0} = \frac{V_0}{\pi r Z_0} \cos \omega t$$

leading to a surface current

$$K_r = \frac{V_0}{\pi r Z_0} \cos \omega t$$

and a current density that is independent of z in the first skin depth,

$$J_r = \frac{K_r}{\delta} = \frac{V_0}{\pi r \delta Z_0} \cos \omega t$$

or the Q of a parallel resonant circuit,

$$(18) \quad Q_{d0} = \omega_0 C_e R_e$$

It is

$$(19) \quad C_e = \frac{\pi \epsilon l}{\ln (b/a)}$$

Knowing the capacitance, we find the inductance by

$$(20) \quad \omega_0^2 = \frac{1}{L_e C_e}$$

or from the Q,

$$Q_{d0} = \frac{R_e}{\omega_0 L_e}$$

It is

$$(21) \quad L_e = \frac{4 \mu l}{\pi^3} \ln \frac{b}{a}$$

For a cavity in which $b/a = 2.72$, or $\ln (b/a) = 1$, $f_0 = 100$ MHz $\sigma/\omega\epsilon = 0.001$, $\epsilon_R = 4$, and $\mu_R = 1$, we have

$$l = 37.5 \text{ cm}$$

$$Q_{d0} = 1{,}000$$

$$R_e = 38{,}200 \ \Omega$$

$$C_e = 41.7 \text{ pF}$$

$$L_e = 0.0609 \ \mu\text{H}$$

The cavity bandwidth is therefore $f_0/Q_{d0} = 0.1$ MHz. Also, if the dielectric constant of the material filling the cavity decreased 0.? per cent from 4 to 3.99, the resonant frequency would increa 0.125 per cent, or 125 kHz. Such a change could be recogniz easily, and thus measurement of the resonant frequency for a samj in the cavity might be used to control the dryness of flour, example.

Now let us consider the losses in the cavity walls. The va of H_ϕ at the outer cylinder $r = b$ is

$$H_{\phi b} = \frac{V_0}{\pi b Z_0} \cos \beta z \cos \omega t$$

If the conductor were *perfect*, a surface current

$$(22) \quad K_z = -H_{\phi b} = \frac{-V_0}{\pi b Z_0} \cos \beta z \cos \omega t$$

The Resonant Coaxial Cavity

Thus the power loss in the end plate is

$$P_{\text{end}} = \int_a^b \int_0^{2\pi} \frac{1}{\sigma_c} \frac{V_0^2}{\pi^2 r^2 \delta^2 Z_0^2} \delta \cos^2 \omega t \; r \; d\phi \; dr$$

$$= \frac{2V_0^2}{\pi \sigma_c \delta Z_0^2} \ln \frac{b}{a} \cos^2 \omega t$$

and therefore

(26) $$P_{\text{end},0,\text{av}} = \frac{V_0^2}{\pi \sigma_c \delta Z_0^2} \ln \frac{b}{a}$$

Combining (24), (25), and (26), the total power loss in the conducting walls at resonance is

(27) $$P_{\text{av}} = \frac{V_0^2 l}{2\pi \sigma_c \delta Z_0^2} \left(\frac{1}{a} + \frac{1}{b} + \frac{2}{l} \ln \frac{b}{a} \right)$$

Since we know the total energy stored, we may calculate the Q of the coaxial cavity having wall losses only,

(28) $$Q_{w0} = \frac{(2/\delta) \ln (b/a)}{(1/a) + (1/b) + (2/l) \ln (b/a)}$$

The elements of the equivalent circuit are now readily obtained. Since the total energy stored has not changed, C_e is unchanged. L_e may again be found from C_e and the resonant frequency ω_0; thus it is also unchanged. Hence the changed Q affects only the equivalent resistance R_e,

(29) $$R_e = \frac{Q_{w0}}{\omega_0 C_e} = \frac{4\eta [\ln (b/a)]^2}{\pi^2 \delta [(1/a) + (1/b) + (2/l) \ln (b/a)]}$$

where

$$\eta = \sqrt{\frac{\mu}{\epsilon}}$$

Using the same cavity as an example, let us assume that it is silver-plated ($\sigma_c = 6.18 \times 10^7 \; \mho/\text{m}$):

$$\delta = \frac{1}{\sqrt{\pi f \mu \sigma_c}} = 6.41 \times 10^{-6} \text{ m}$$

and thus

$$Q_{w0} = 2{,}190$$

while

$R_e = 83,700 \ \Omega$

When both losses are present the total power loss is their sum, and the equivalent resistance turns out to be the parallel combination of the resistances obtained by considering each form of loss separately. The Q of the cavity at resonance is

$$(30) \quad Q_0 = \frac{1}{(1/Q_{d0}) + (1/Q_{w0})}$$

Concluding our example, the Q at resonance of the silver-plated cavity filled with the lossy dielectric is

$$Q_0 = \frac{1}{\tfrac{1}{1,000} + \tfrac{1}{2,190}} = 697$$

and the equivalent resistance is reduced to 26,200 Ω.

By using the element values of the equivalent circuit, the input impedance of the coaxial cavity may be determined at frequencies near resonance. This is a typical circuit problem, and we shall not try to develop or use these formulas. It is worth our while however, to ask, how far from resonance the equivalence holds. Two facts must be kept in mind. First, the coaxial cavity will show a series resonance when its length is one-half wavelength, or at 200 MHz; the equivalent circuit provides no other resonances. Second, the cavity parameters, such as the conductivity and permittivity of the dielectric, vary with frequency, while no provisions have been made in the equivalent circuit for this phenomenon.

These differing characteristics cause the analogy between the circuit and the cavity to be limited to a frequency range of perhaps 20 per cent of the resonant frequency. Since our interest in the cavity behavior is probably limited to a narrow frequency band near resonance, one which contains all side bands of appreciable amplitude for a modulated signal, for example, our equivalent circuit proves to be very useful.

D 13.2 A 26 cm length of coaxial line with $a = 1.7$ mm and $b = 6.7$ mm is filled with a dielectric for which $\epsilon_R = 2$ and the conductivity is negligible. If the line is short-circuited at one end and open at the other, find the three lowest frequencies at which the input impedance at the open end is a high resistance.

Ans. 204; 612; 1,020 MHz

D 13.3 A quarter-wavelength cavity is resonant at 100 MHz. All conducting surfaces have a conductivity of 10^7 ℧/m, and the dielectric has constants

$\epsilon_R = 2.25$ and $\sigma = 10^{-5}/\pi \, \mho/\text{m}$. If $a = 2 \, \text{mm}$, $\ln (b/a) = 2$, and the crest voltage at the open end is 200 V, find the average power loss in

(a) The dielectric
(b) The inner conductor
(c) The end plate

Ans. 6.25; 50; 391   mW

13.3 RADIATION

In this last example of the application of Maxwell's equations we shall find the electromagnetic field which results from a given current distribution. For the first time, therefore, we shall have the specific field which results from a specific source. In the discussion of the uniform plane wave only the wave motion in free space was investigated. The source of this field was not considered. The current distribution in a conductor was a similar problem, although we did at least relate the current to an assumed electric field intensity at the conductor surface. This might be considered as a source, but it is not a very practical one for it is infinite in extent.

At this time, however, we shall assume a current filament as the source. The filament will be assumed to be of differential length, but we shall be able to extend the results easily to a filament which is short compared to a wavelength, specifically less than about one-quarter of a wavelength over-all. The differential filament is shown at the origin and is oriented along the z axis in Fig. 13.4. The posi-

FIG. 13.4   A differential current filament of length d carries a current $I = I_0 \cos \omega t$.

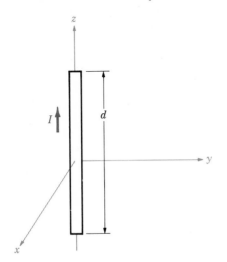

FIG. 13.5   The resolution of A_{zs} at P (r, θ, ϕ) into the two spherical components A_{rs} and $A_{\theta s}$. The sketch is arbitrarily drawn in the $\phi = 90°$ plane.

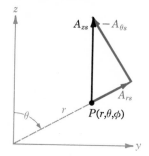

tive sense of the current is taken as upward. We shall assume a uniform current $I_0 \cos \omega t$ in this short length d and not concern ourselves at present with the apparent discontinuity at each end.

We shall not attempt at this time to discover the "source of the source," but shall merely assume that it is constant. The distribution of the current cannot be changed by any field which it produces.

The first step is the application of the retarded vector magnetic potential expression,

$$\mathbf{A} = \int \frac{\mu[I]\,d\mathbf{L}}{4\pi R}$$

which requires no integration for the very short filament assumed,

$$\mathbf{A} = \frac{\mu[I]d}{4\pi R}\,\mathbf{a}_z$$

Only the z component of $\mathbf{A}$ is present, for current flow occurs only in the z direction. At any point P, distant R m from the origin, the current is retarded by R/U and

$$I = I_0 \cos \omega t$$

$$[I] = I_0 \cos \left[\omega\left(t - \frac{R}{U}\right)\right]$$

$$[I]_s = I_0 e^{-j\omega R/U}$$

Thus

$$A_{zs} = \frac{\mu I_0 d}{4\pi R}\,e^{-j\omega R/U}$$

Using a mixed coordinate system for the moment, let us replace R by the small r of the spherical coordinate system and then determine which spherical components are represented by A_{zs}. Figure 13.5 helps to determine that

$$A_{rs} = A_{zs} \cos \theta$$

$$A_{\theta s} = -A_{zs} \sin \theta$$

and therefore

$$A_{rs} = \frac{\mu I_0 d}{4\pi r} \cos \theta \, e^{-j\omega R/U}$$

$$A_{\theta s} = -\frac{\mu I_0 d}{4\pi r} \sin \theta \, e^{-j\omega R/U}$$

From these two components of the vector magnetic potential at P we may find $\mathbf{B}_s$ or $\mathbf{H}_s$ from the definition of $\mathbf{A}_s$,

$$\mathbf{B}_s = \mu \mathbf{H}_s = \nabla \times \mathbf{A}_s$$

by merely taking the indicated partial derivatives. Thus

$$H_{\phi s} = \frac{1}{\mu r} \frac{\partial}{\partial r} (r A_{\theta s}) - \frac{1}{\mu r} \frac{\partial A_{rs}}{\partial \theta}$$

$$H_{rs} = H_{\theta s} = 0$$

and

$$H_{\phi s} = \frac{I_0 d}{4\pi} \sin \theta \, e^{-j\omega R/U} \left(j \frac{\omega}{U r} + \frac{1}{r^2} \right)$$

The components of the electric field which must be associated with this magnetic field are found from the point form of Ampère's circuital law as it applies to a region in which conduction and convection current are absent,

$$\nabla \times \mathbf{H} = \frac{\partial \mathbf{D}}{\partial t}$$

or in complex notation,

$$\nabla \times \mathbf{H}_s = j\omega\epsilon \mathbf{E}_s$$

Expansion of the curl in spherical coordinates leads to

$$E_{rs} = \frac{1}{j\omega\epsilon} \frac{1}{r \sin \theta} \frac{\partial}{\partial \theta} (H_{\phi s} \sin \theta)$$

$$E_{\theta s} = \frac{1}{j\omega\epsilon} \left(-\frac{1}{r} \right) \frac{\partial}{\partial r} (r H_{\phi s})$$

or

$$E_{rs} = \frac{I_0 d}{2\pi} \cos\theta \, e^{-j\omega R/U} \left(\frac{1}{\epsilon U r^2} + \frac{1}{j\omega\epsilon r^3} \right)$$

$$E_{\theta s} = \frac{I_0 d}{4\pi} \sin\theta \, e^{-j\omega R/U} \left(\frac{j\omega}{\epsilon U^2 r} + \frac{1}{\epsilon U r^2} + \frac{1}{j\omega\epsilon r^3} \right)$$

In order to simplify the interpretation of the enclosed terms in the expressions for $H_{\phi s}$, E_{rs}, and $E_{\theta s}$ we shall make the substitutions $\omega = 2\pi f$, $f\lambda = U$, and $U = 1/\sqrt{\mu\epsilon}$, producing

(1)
$$H_{\phi s} = \frac{I_0 d}{4\pi} \sin\theta \, e^{-j2\pi r/\lambda} \left(j\frac{2\pi}{\lambda r} + \frac{1}{r^2} \right)$$

(2)
$$E_{rs} = \frac{I_0 d}{2\pi} \sqrt{\frac{\mu}{\epsilon}} \cos\theta \, e^{-j2\pi r/\lambda} \left(\frac{1}{r^2} + \frac{\lambda}{j2\pi r^3} \right)$$

(3)
$$E_{\theta s} = \frac{I_0 d}{4\pi} \sqrt{\frac{\mu}{\epsilon}} \sin\theta \, e^{-j2\pi r/\lambda} \left(j\frac{2\pi}{\lambda r} + \frac{1}{r^2} + \frac{\lambda}{j2\pi r^3} \right)$$

These three equations are indicative of the reason that so many problems involving antennas are solved by experimental rather than theoretical methods. They have resulted from three general steps: an integration (atypically trivial) and two differentiations. These steps are sufficient to cause the simple current element and its simple current expression to "blow up" into the complicated field described by (1) to (3). In spite of this complexity, several interesting observations are possible.

We might notice first the $e^{-j2\pi r/\lambda}$ factor appearing with each component. This indicates propagation outward from the origin in the positive r direction with a wavelength λ and velocity $U = 1/\sqrt{\mu\epsilon}$. We use the term "wavelength" now in a somewhat broader sense than the original definition, which identified the wavelength of a uniform plane wave with the distance between two points, measured in the direction of propagation, at which the wave has identical instantaneous values. Here there are additional complications caused by the factor enclosed in parentheses, which is a complex function of r. This variation must now be neglected in determining the wavelength. This is equivalent to a determination of the wavelength at a large distance from the origin, and we may demonstrate this by sketching the H_ϕ component as a function of r under the following conditions:

$$I_0 d = 4\pi \qquad \theta = 90° \qquad t = 0 \qquad f = 300 \text{ MHz}$$

$$U = 3 \times 10^8 \text{ m/s (free space)} \qquad \lambda = 1 \text{ m}$$

Therefore

$$H_{\phi s} = \left(j\frac{2\pi}{r} + \frac{1}{r^2} \right) e^{-j2\pi r}$$

and the real part may be determined at $t = 0$,

$$H_\phi = \sqrt{\left(\frac{2\pi}{r}\right)^2 + \frac{1}{r^4}} \cos\left(\tan^{-1} 2\pi r - 2\pi r\right)$$

or

$$H_\phi = \frac{1}{r^2} \left(\cos 2\pi r + 2\pi r \sin 2\pi r\right)$$

Values obtained from this last equation are plotted against r in the range $1 \le r \le 2$ in Fig. 13.6a; the curve is noticeably nonsinusoidal. At $r = 1$, $H_\phi = 1$, while at $r = 2$, one wavelength greater, $H_\phi = 0.25$. Moreover, the curve crosses the axis (with positive slope) at $r = 1 - 0.0258$ and $r = 2 - 0.0127$, again a distance not equal to a wavelength. If a similar sketch is made in the range $101 \le r \le 102$, shown in Fig. 13.6b on a different amplitude scale, an essentially sinusoidal wave is obtained and the instantaneous values of H_ϕ at $r = 101$ and $r = 102$ are 0.0000998 and 0.0000996. The maximum amplitudes of the positive and negative portions of the waveform differ by less than 1 per cent, and we may say that for all practical purposes the wave in this region is a uniform plane wave having a sinusoidal variation with distance (and time, of course) and a well-defined wavelength. This wave evidently carries energy away from the differential antenna, and we shall calculate this power shortly.

Continuing the investigation of (1) to (3), let us now take a more careful look at the expressions containing terms varying as $1/r^3$,

FIG. 13.6 The instantaneous amplitude of H_θ for the special case of a current element having $I_0 d = 4\pi$ and $\lambda = 1$ is plotted at $\theta = 90°$ and $t = 0$ (a) in the region $1 \le r \le 2$ near the antenna, and (b) in the region $101 \le r \le 102$ distant from the antenna. The upper curve is noticeably nonsinusoidal.

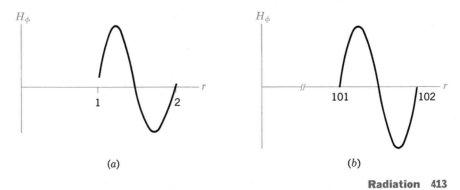

(a) (b)

$1/r^2$, and $1/r$. At points very close to the current element the $1/r^3$ term must be dominant. In the numerical example we have used the relative values of the terms in $1/r^3$, $1/r^2$, and $1/r$ in the $E_{\theta s}$ expression are about 250, 16, and 1, respectively, when r is 1 cm. The variation of an electric field as $1/r^3$ should remind us of the *electrostatic* field of the dipole (Chap. 4). This term represents energy stored in a reactive (capacitive) field, and it does not contribute to the radiated power. The inverse-square term in the $H_{\phi s}$ expression is similarly important only in the region very near to the current element and corresponds to the *induction* field of the d-c element given by the Biot-Savart law. At distances corresponding to 10 or more wavelengths from the oscillating current element, all terms except the inverse-distance ($1/r$) term may be neglected and the *distant* or *radiation* fields become

$$E_{rs} = 0$$

$$H_{\phi s} = j \frac{I_0 d}{2\lambda r} \sin \theta \, e^{-j2\pi r/\lambda}$$

$$E_{\theta s} = j \frac{I_0 d}{2\lambda r} \sqrt{\frac{\mu}{\epsilon}} \sin \theta \, e^{-j2\pi r/\lambda}$$

or

$$E_{\theta s} = \sqrt{\frac{\mu}{\epsilon}} \, H_{\phi s}$$

The relationship between $E_{\theta s}$ and $H_{\phi s}$ is thus seen to be that between the electric and magnetic fields of the uniform plane wave, thus substantiating the previous conclusion, which we reached when investigating the wavelength.

The variation of both radiation fields with the polar angle θ is the same; the fields are maximum in the equatorial plane of the current element and vanish along either extension of the element. The variation with angle may be shown by plotting a *vertical directivity pattern* (assuming a vertical orientation of the current element) in which the relative magnitude of $E_{\theta s}$ is plotted against θ for a constant r. The pattern is usually shown on polar coordinates, as in Fig. 13.7. A *horizontal directivity pattern* may also be plotted for more complicated antenna systems and shows the variation of field intensity with ϕ. The horizontal pattern of the current element is a circle centered at the origin since the field is not a function of the azimuth angle.

FIG. 13.7 The polar plot of the vertical directivity pattern of a vertical current
element. The crest amplitude of $E_{\theta s}$
is plotted as a function of the polar
angle θ at a constant distance r. The
locus is a circle.

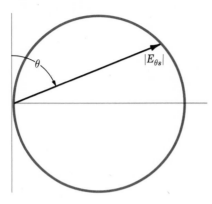

In order to obtain a quantitative expression for the power radiated we need to apply the Poynting vector $\mathcal{P}$,

(4) $\quad \mathcal{P} = \mathbf{E} \times \mathbf{H}$

developed in Sec. 11.4. The instantaneous expressions for the
radiation components of the electric and magnetic field intensities
are

$$H_\phi = -\frac{I_0 d}{2\lambda r} \sin \theta \sin \left(\omega t - \frac{2\pi r}{\lambda} \right)$$

$$E_\theta = \sqrt{\frac{\mu}{\epsilon}} H_\phi$$

and thus

$$\mathcal{P}_r = E_\theta H_\phi = \left(\frac{I_0 d}{2\lambda r} \right)^2 \sqrt{\frac{\mu}{\epsilon}} \sin^2 \theta \sin^2 \left(\omega t - \frac{2\pi r}{\lambda} \right)$$

The total (in space) instantaneous (in time) power crossing the
surface of a sphere of radius r_0 is then

$$P = \int_{\phi=0}^{2\pi} \int_{\theta=0}^{\pi} \mathcal{P}_r r_0^2 \sin \theta \, d\theta \, d\phi$$

$$= \left(\frac{I_0 d}{\lambda} \right)^2 \sqrt{\frac{\mu}{\epsilon}} \frac{2\pi}{3} \sin^2 \left(\omega t - \frac{2\pi r_0}{\lambda} \right)$$

and the time-average power is given by one-half the maximum amplitude,

$$P_{av} = \left(\frac{I_0 d}{\lambda}\right)^2 \sqrt{\frac{\mu}{\epsilon}} \frac{\pi}{3} = 40\pi^2 \left(\frac{I_0 d}{\lambda}\right)^2 \quad \text{W}$$

This is the same power as that which would be dissipated in a resistance R_{rad} by the current I_0 in the absence of any radiation, where

$$P_{av} = \frac{1}{2}I_0^2 R_{rad}$$

$$R_{rad} = \frac{2P_{av}}{I_0^2} = 80\pi^2 \left(\frac{d}{\lambda}\right)^2 \quad \Omega$$

If we assume the differential length is 0.01λ, then R_{rad} is 0.08Ω. This small resistance is probably comparable to the *ohmic* resistance of a practical antenna, and thus the efficiency of the antenna might be unsatisfactorily low. Effective matching to the source also becomes very difficult to achieve, for the input reactance is much greater in magnitude than the input resistance R_{rad}. This is the basis for the statement that an effective antenna should be an appreciable fraction of a wavelength long.

Let us now hypothesize a current distribution appropriate for short antennas by setting the current equal to zero at each end and assuming a linear increase to a maximum value I_0 at the center. Such a current distribution is found on a thin antenna having a length less than about one-quarter wavelength. Neglecting retardation effects, the average current is then $\frac{1}{2}I_0$, where the current I_0 is taken as the input current at the center terminals. Thus the electric and magnetic field intensities are about one-half the values given above. The power is one-quarter, and the radiation resistance is also one-quarter its previous value. If we try to extend these results to an antenna which is one-half wavelength over-all, we obtain a value of $20\pi^2$, or about 200Ω for the resistance. This compares to an exact value of 73.1Ω, and thus our approximation has led to too large a resistance or radiated power for the given input current. The canceling effect of retardation has been neglected, and a current distribution which is actually almost sinusoidal has been approximated by a triangular pattern.

D 13.4 Refer to Eq. (3) and determine the ratio r/λ at which the magnitudes of

(a) The "electrostatic" and "radiation" components of $E_{\theta s}$ are equal
(b) The "induction" and "radiation" components of $E_{\theta s}$ are equal
(c) The sum of the "electrostatic" and "induction" components and the "radiation" component are equal

Ans.   0.159; 0.159; 0.203

D 13.5 Find the time-average power density radiated in free space by a differential element for which $d = 0.01\lambda$, $I_0 = 10$ A, and $\lambda = 1$ m at the point

(a) $(r = 100, \theta = 30°, \phi = 0°)$
(b) $(r = 200, \theta = 90°, \phi = 90°)$
(c) $(r = 141.4, \theta = 45°, \phi = 45°)$

Ans.   11.8; 11.8; 11.8 $\mu W/m^2$

SUGGESTED REFERENCES

1   Jordan, E. C.: (see Suggested References for Chap. 8). Each of the topics covered in this chapter is thoroughly discussed.

2   Marcuvitz, N.: "Waveguide Handbook," M.I.T. Radiation Laboratory Series, vol. 10, McGraw-Hill Book Company, New York, 1951. This standard reference on transmission lines, waveguides, and resonant cavities provides both theory and numerical data.

3   Ramo, S., J. R. Whinnery, and T. Van Duzer: (see Suggested References for Chap. 6). Each of the subjects discussed in this chapter are treated in more detail.

PROBLEMS

1   In Sec. 13.1, Eq. (2), it appears that if the left side is interpreted as the sum of the potential differences or voltages around the circuit, this sum is equal to the negative time rate of change of flux linkages through the circuit, and not zero.   How is this equation reconciled with Kirchhoff's voltage law?

FIG. 13.8   See Prob. 2.

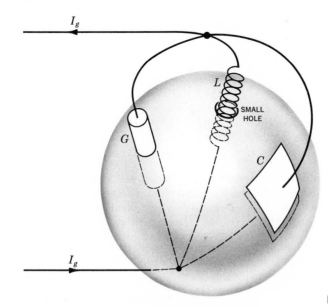

2 Assume a parallel circuit containing a resistor, a capacitor, an inductor, and a current source I_g; all elements are ideal. Construct a spherical surface containing a small hole, as shown in Fig. 13.8, and thread the inductor through the hole. The spherical surface passes between the capacitor plates, through the resistive material, and is pierced by one lead of the current source. Recall that

$$\oint \mathbf{H} \cdot d\mathbf{L} = \int_s \mathbf{J} \cdot d\mathbf{S} + \frac{\partial}{\partial t} \int_s \mathbf{D} \cdot d\mathbf{S}$$

where the clockwise perimeter of the hole is the closed path. (a) Show that the second term on the right equals $C\, dV/dt$, where V is the potential of the lower node with respect to the upper. (b) Show that the first term on the right equals $GV - I_g$, where G is the conductance of the resistor. (c) Show that the term on the left is $-I_L$, where I_L is the inductor current (flowing upward). (d) Use the results of Sec. 13.1 to show that $V = L\, dI_L/dt$. (e) Show that $I_g = GV + (C\, dV/dt) + (1/L) \int_{-\infty}^{t} V\, dt$.

3 If we agree that "much smaller than a wavelength" means "less than 0.1λ," give the maximum permissible dimension of each of the following systems for it to be treated as a circuit in free space: (a) a 60-Hz power line; (b) a 10,000-Hz audio amplifier; (c) a 1,500-kHz radio-frequency amplifier; (d) an FM amplifier stage operating at 100 MHz; (e) a microwave detector used at 15 GHz.

4 Show that the input impedance of a lossy transmission line l m long, terminated in a short circuit, is $Z_0 \tanh \gamma l$.

5 The input impedance of a lossy transmission line one-quarter wavelength long ($l = \lambda/4$) terminated in a short circuit is $Z_{\text{in}} = Z_0 \tanh (\alpha l + j\,\pi/2)$. (a) Show that $Z_{\text{in}} = Z_0 \coth \alpha l$. (b) If $\alpha l \ll 1$, show that $Z_{\text{in}} \doteq Z_0/\alpha l$.

6 (a) Find R, G, L, and C for the coaxial line shown in Fig. 13.2. Neglect the effect of the end plate. The parameters are $a = 1$ cm, $b = 2.718$ cm, $f = 100$ MHz, $\sigma/\omega\epsilon = 0.001$, $\epsilon_R = 4$, $\mu_R = 1$, and $\sigma_c = 6.17 \times 10^7\ \mho/\text{m}$. (b) Find α and Z_0. (c) Refer to Prob. 5 and find Z_{in}; neglect the small imaginary part of Z_0.

7 Using the results of Sec. 13.2, obtain an expression for the Q of an air-filled coaxial resonator that is one-half wavelength long with short-circuiting plates at each end. Find the Q of a resonator for which $\sigma_c = 6.17 \times 10^7$, $f_0 = 100$ MHz, $a = 1$ cm, and $b = 2.718$ cm.

8 A copper coaxial resonator, short-circuited at one end, has a length of 20 cm, inner radius of 0.5 cm, and outer radius of 4 cm. If it is air-filled and excited with $V = 10 \cos \omega_0 t$ V at the input, find (a) the lowest resonant frequency; (b) Q_0; (c) the input current at resonance.

9 Rework Prob. 8 for the case in which the resonator is filled with polystyrene, $\sigma/\omega\epsilon = 10^{-4}$, $\epsilon_R = 2.55$, where both values are assumed correct at the operating frequency.

10 For the circuit of Fig. 13.3 assume sinusoidal voltage excitation at the resonant frequency. Calculate the energy stored and the average power loss, and then show that Sec. 13.2, Eq. (15), leads to the expression for Q_0 given as Eq. (18).

11 Show that the maximum energy stored in the electric field of the quarter-wavelength cavity at resonance is equal to that stored in the magnetic field, Sec. 13.2, Eq. (16).

12 Show that Sec. 13.2, Eq. (19), follows from each of the two equations immediately preceding it.

13 Show that Sec. 13.2, Eq. (21), follows from each of the two equations immediately preceding it.

14 Assume that the power losses in a cavity are caused by two independent phenomena, such as P_1 from wall losses and P_2 from dielectric losses. Show that the Q_0 of the cavity with both losses present is $Q_1 Q_2 / (Q_1 + Q_2)$, where Q_1 and Q_2 are the quality factors achieved by the wall and dielectric losses independently.

15 A cavity is resonant at 600 MHz with a Q_0 of 1,000. For the level of excitation used, the power losses are 0.8 W. If a probe is now inserted into the cavity and abstracts 0.2 W without appreciably disturbing the fields in the cavity, find the new Q_0, or *loaded* Q_0.

16 An air-filled quarter-wavelength coaxial cavity is operated at 640 MHz. If $a = 0.5$ cm, $b = 1.359$ cm, and $\sigma_c = 4.9 \times 10^7$ ℧/m, find the ratio of the crest input current at 640 MHz to that at 641 MHz for equal applied voltages.

17 A copper conductor is 1 m long and 1 mm in radius. If it carries a uniform current $I_0 \cos \omega t$ at a frequency of 1 MHz, find both the radiation resistance and the ohmic resistance of this relatively short length.

18 Sketch the vertical directivity patterns for $E_{\theta s}$ and $\mathcal{P}_r$ on the same axes for the differential current element.

19 Two identical differential current elements lie along the z axis at $z = -1$ and $z = 1$. Each is one-tenth wavelength long at 300 MHz and carries a uniform current of $6 \cos \omega t$ A. Find the combined $E_{\theta s}$ field at a distant point $(r, \theta, 0°)$, and plot the vertical directivity pattern as a function of θ at $\phi = 0°$.

20 The directivity D of an antenna is defined as the ratio of the maximum value of the time-average power density found at any point on the surface of a large sphere surrounding the antenna to its average value over the sphere. Show that the directivity of the differential current element is 1.5.

21 Show that the "electrostatic" components of $E_{\theta s}$ and E_{rs} are identical to those of an electrostatic dipole for which each charge varies sinusoidally with time. Note that since $I = dQ/dt$, $I_0 d = j\omega p_s$, where p_s is the dipole moment, and that $e^{-j2\pi r/\lambda} \doteq 1$.

APPENDIX A VECTOR ANALYSIS

A.1 GENERAL CURVILINEAR COORDINATES

Let us consider a general coordinate system in which a point is located by the intersection of three mutually perpendicular surfaces (of unspecified form or shape),

$u = $ constant

$v = $ constant

$w = $ constant

where u, v, and $w = $ variables of the coordinate system. If each variable is increased by a differential amount and three additional mutually perpendicular surfaces are drawn corresponding to these new values, a differential volume is enclosed within a rectangular parallelepiped. Since u, v, and w need not be measures of length, as, for example, the angle variables of the cylindrical and spherical coordinate systems, each must be multiplied by a general function of u, v, and w in order to obtain the differential sides of the parallelepiped. Thus we define h_1, h_2, and h_3 each as a function of the three variables u, v, and w and write the lengths of the sides of the differential volume as

$dL_1 = h_1 du$

$dL_2 = h_2 dv$

$dL_3 = h_3 dw$

In the three coordinate systems discussed in Chap. 1, it is apparent that the variables and multiplying functions are

$$\text{Cartesian:} \quad u = x \quad v = y \quad w = z$$
$$h_1 = 1 \quad h_2 = 1 \quad h_3 = 1$$

(1) $\quad$ Cylindrical: $\quad u = r \quad v = \phi \quad w = z$
$$h_1 = 1 \quad h_2 = r \quad h_3 = 1$$

$$\text{Spherical:} \quad u = r \quad v = \theta \quad w = \phi$$
$$h_1 = 1 \quad h_2 = r \quad h_3 = r \sin \theta$$

The choice of u, v, and w above has been made so that $\mathbf{a}_u \times \mathbf{a}_v = \mathbf{a}_w$ in all cases. More involved expressions for h_1, h_2, and h_3 are to be expected in other less familiar coordinate systems.

A.2 DIVERGENCE, GRADIENT, AND CURL IN GENERAL CURVILINEAR COORDINATES

If the general development of the divergence in Secs. 3.4 and 3.5 is applied to the general curvilinear coordinate system, the flux of the vector $\mathbf{D}$ passing through the surface of the parallelepiped whose unit normal is $\mathbf{a}_u$ is

$$D_{u0}\, dL_2\, dL_3 + \frac{1}{2}\frac{\partial}{\partial u}\left(D_u\, dL_2\, dL_3\right)\, du$$

or

$$D_{u0}h_2h_3\, dv\, dw + \frac{1}{2}\frac{\partial}{\partial u}\left(D_u h_2 h_3\, dv\, dw\right)\, du$$

and for the opposite face is

$$-D_{u0}h_2h_3\, dv\, dw + \frac{1}{2}\frac{\partial}{\partial u}\left(D_u h_2 h_3\, dv\, dw\right)\, du$$

giving a total for these two faces of

$$\frac{\partial}{\partial u}\left(D_u h_2 h_3\, dv\, dw\right)\, du$$

Since u, v, and w are independent variables, this last expression may be written as

$$\frac{\partial}{\partial u}\left(h_2 h_3 D_u\right)\, du\, dv\, dw$$

and the other two corresponding expressions obtained by a simple permutation of the subscripts and of u, v, and w. Thus the total flux leaving the differential volume is

$$\left[\frac{\partial}{\partial u}\left(h_2 h_3 D_u\right) + \frac{\partial}{\partial v}\left(h_3 h_1 D_v\right) + \frac{\partial}{\partial w}\left(h_1 h_2 D_w\right)\right]\, du\, dv\, dw$$

and the divergence of $\mathbf{D}$ is found by dividing by the differential volume,

$$(1) \quad \nabla\cdot\mathbf{D} = \frac{1}{h_1 h_2 h_3}\left[\frac{\partial}{\partial u}\left(h_2 h_3 D_u\right) + \frac{\partial}{\partial v}\left(h_3 h_1 D_v\right) + \frac{\partial}{\partial w}\left(h_1 h_2 D_w\right)\right]$$

The components of the gradient of a scalar V may be obtained (following the methods of Sec. 4.6) by expressing $d\mathbf{L}$ in general curvilinear coordinates,

$$d\mathbf{L} = h_1\, du\, \mathbf{a}_u + h_2\, dv\, \mathbf{a}_v + h_3\, dw\, \mathbf{a}_w$$

dotting ∇V with $d\mathbf{L}$ to obtain the differential increase in V,

$$dV = (\nabla V)_u h_1\, du + (\nabla V)_v h_2\, dv + (\nabla V)_w h_3\, dw$$

keeping v and w constant,

$$dv = dw = 0$$

and obtaining

$$(\nabla V)_u = \left.\frac{dV}{h_1\, du}\right|_{v,w\ \text{const}} = \frac{\partial V}{h_1\, \partial u}$$

The remaining components are found in a similar manner, and the gradient is then

$$(2) \qquad \nabla V = \frac{\partial V}{h_1 \, \partial u} \mathbf{a}_u + \frac{\partial V}{h_2 \, \partial v} \mathbf{a}_v + \frac{\partial V}{h_3 \, \partial w} \mathbf{a}_w$$

The components of the curl of a vector $\mathbf{H}$ are obtained by considering a differential path first in a $u = $ constant surface and finding the circulation of $\mathbf{H}$ about that path, as discussed for cartesian coordinates in Sec. 8.3. The contribution along the segment in the $\mathbf{a}_v$ direction is

$$H_{v0} h_2 \, dv - \frac{1}{2} \frac{\partial}{\partial w} (H_v h_2 \, dv) \, dw$$

and that from the oppositely directed segment is

$$-H_{v0} h_2 \, dv - \frac{1}{2} \frac{\partial}{\partial w} (H_v h_2 \, dv) \, dw$$

The sum of these two parts is

$$-\frac{\partial}{\partial w} (H_v h_2 \, dv) \, dw$$

or

$$-\frac{\partial}{\partial w} (h_2 H_v) \, dv \, dw$$

and the sum of the contributions from the other two portions of the path is

$$\frac{\partial}{\partial v} (H_w h_3 \, dw) \, dv$$

or

$$\frac{\partial}{\partial v} (h_3 H_w) \, dv \, dw$$

The $\mathbf{a}_u$ component of curl $\mathbf{H}$ is therefore

$$(\nabla \times \mathbf{H})_u = \frac{1}{h_2 h_3} \left[\frac{\partial}{\partial v} (h_3 H_w) - \frac{\partial}{\partial w} (h_2 H_v) \right]$$

and the other two components may be obtained by cyclic permutation. The result is expressible as a determinant,

$$(3) \qquad \nabla \times \mathbf{H} = \begin{vmatrix} \dfrac{\mathbf{a}_u}{h_2 h_3} & \dfrac{\mathbf{a}_v}{h_3 h_1} & \dfrac{\mathbf{a}_w}{h_1 h_2} \\[2ex] \dfrac{\partial}{\partial u} & \dfrac{\partial}{\partial v} & \dfrac{\partial}{\partial w} \\[2ex] h_1 H_u & h_2 H_v & h_3 H_w \end{vmatrix}$$

The Laplacian of a scalar is found by using (1) and (2):

$$(4) \quad \nabla^2 V = \nabla \cdot \nabla V = \frac{1}{h_1 h_2 h_3} \left[\frac{\partial}{\partial u} \left(\frac{h_2 h_3}{h_1} \frac{\partial V}{\partial u} \right) + \frac{\partial}{\partial v} \left(\frac{h_3 h_1}{h_2} \frac{\partial V}{\partial v} \right) + \frac{\partial}{\partial w} \left(\frac{h_1 h_2}{h_3} \frac{\partial V}{\partial w} \right) \right]$$

Equations (1) to (4) may be used to find the divergence, gradient, curl, and Laplacian in any orthogonal coordinate system for which h_1, h_2, and h_3 are known.

A.3 VECTOR IDENTITIES

The vector identities listed below may be proved by expansion in cartesian (or general curvilinear) coordinates. The first two identities involve the scalar and vector triple products, the next three are concerned with operations on sums, the following three apply to operations when the argument is multiplied by a scalar function, the next three apply to operations on scalar or vector products, and the last four concern the second-order operations.

(1) $\quad (\mathbf{A} \times \mathbf{B}) \cdot \mathbf{C} \equiv (\mathbf{B} \times \mathbf{C}) \cdot \mathbf{A} \equiv (\mathbf{C} \times \mathbf{A}) \cdot \mathbf{B}$

(2) $\quad \mathbf{A} \times (\mathbf{B} \times \mathbf{C}) \equiv (\mathbf{A} \cdot \mathbf{C}) \mathbf{B} - (\mathbf{A} \cdot \mathbf{B}) \mathbf{C}$

(3) $\quad \nabla \cdot (\mathbf{A} + \mathbf{B}) \equiv \nabla \cdot \mathbf{A} + \nabla \cdot \mathbf{B}$

(4) $\quad \nabla (V + W) \equiv \nabla V + \nabla W$

(5) $\quad \nabla \times (\mathbf{A} + \mathbf{B}) \equiv \nabla \times \mathbf{A} + \nabla \times \mathbf{B}$

(6) $\quad \nabla \cdot (V \mathbf{A}) \equiv \mathbf{A} \cdot \nabla V + V \nabla \cdot \mathbf{A}$

(7) $\quad \nabla (V W) \equiv V \nabla W + W \nabla V$

(8) $\quad \nabla \times (V \mathbf{A}) \equiv \nabla V \times \mathbf{A} + V \nabla \times \mathbf{A}$

(9) $\quad \nabla \cdot (\mathbf{A} \times \mathbf{B}) \equiv \mathbf{B} \cdot \nabla \times \mathbf{A} - \mathbf{A} \cdot \nabla \times \mathbf{B}$

(10) $\quad \nabla (\mathbf{A} \cdot \mathbf{B}) \equiv (\mathbf{A} \cdot \nabla) \mathbf{B} + (\mathbf{B} \cdot \nabla) \mathbf{A} + \mathbf{A} \times (\nabla \times \mathbf{B}) + \mathbf{B} \times (\nabla \times \mathbf{A})$

(11) $\quad \nabla \times (\mathbf{A} \times \mathbf{B}) \equiv \mathbf{A} \nabla \cdot \mathbf{B} - \mathbf{B} \nabla \cdot \mathbf{A} + (\mathbf{B} \cdot \nabla) \mathbf{A} - (\mathbf{A} \cdot \nabla) \mathbf{B}$

(12) $\quad \nabla \cdot \nabla V \equiv \nabla^2 V$

(13) $\quad \nabla \cdot \nabla \times \mathbf{A} \equiv 0$

(14) $\quad \nabla \times \nabla V \equiv 0$

(15) $\quad \nabla \times \nabla \times \mathbf{A} \equiv \nabla (\nabla \cdot \mathbf{A}) - \nabla^2 \mathbf{A}$

APPENDIX B DIMENSIONS AND UNITS

The three fundamental dimensions of classical mechanics are mass, length, and time, symbolized by the dimensional symbols $[M]$, $[L]$, and $[T]$. It is then possible to determine the dimensions of the remaining mechanical quantities in terms of these fundamental dimensions, and we find that velocity has the dimensional symbol $[LT^{-1}]$, force has the symbol $[MLT^{-2}]$, and so forth. When the theory of heat is considered, a fourth fundamental dimension for temperature $[\theta]$ is customarily introduced, and the fifth fundamental dimension is associated with electromagnetic phenomena and is usually taken as charge $[Q]$.

It is not necessary that five fundamental dimensions be chosen;[1] either more or less may be used, and we shall later consider briefly one system in which no fundamental electromagnetic dimension is used. However, the five selected above are conventional and familiar.

The dimensional symbols of the other electrical quantities may be found by using the dimensional equation for Coulomb's law,

$$[\epsilon_0] = \left[\frac{Q^2}{FR^2}\right] = [M^{-1}L^{-3}T^2Q^2]$$

the definition of E,

$$[E] = \left[\frac{F}{Q}\right] = [MLT^{-2}Q^{-1}]$$

and so forth. The dimensional symbols of the magnetic terms begin with I,

$$[I] = \left[\frac{Q}{t}\right] = [QT^{-1}]$$

and the process continues with the force between current elements to determine $[\mu_0]$,

$$[\mu_0] = \left[\frac{FR^2}{I^2L^2}\right] = [MLQ^{-2}]$$

the magnetic field intensity,

$$[H] = \left[\frac{I}{L}\right] = [L^{-1}T^{-1}Q]$$

and so on. The dimensional symbols of the electromagnetic quantities appearing throughout this book are given in Table B.1, in the order in which they are introduced. The dashes indicate dimensionless quantities.

[1] See H. L. Langhaar, "Dimensional Analysis and Theory of Models," John Wiley & Sons, Inc., New York, 1951, p. 5, or W. K. H. Panofsky and M. Phillips, "Classical Electricity and Magnetism," Addison-Wesley Publishing Company, Reading, Mass., 1955, p. 375.

TABLE B.1   Dimensions and Units of the Electric and Magnetic Quantities in the International System

Symbol	Name	Dimension	Unit	Abbreviation
F	Force	MLT^{-2}	Newton	N
Q	Charge	Q	Coulomb	C
r	Distance	L	Meter	m
ϵ_0	Permittivity	$M^{-1}L^{-3}T^2Q^2$	Farad/meter	F/m
E	Electric field intensity	$MLT^{-2}Q^{-1}$	Volt/meter	V/m
ρ	Volume charge density	$L^{-3}Q$	Coulomb/meter^3	C/m^3
v	Volume	L^3	meter^3	m^3
ρ_L	Linear charge density	$L^{-1}Q$	Coulomb/meter	C/m
ρ_s	Surface charge density	$L^{-2}Q$	Coulomb/meter^2	C/m^2
Ψ	Electric flux	Q	Coulomb	C
D	Electric flux density	$L^{-2}Q$	Coulomb/meter^2	C/m^2
S	Area	L^2	meter^2	m^2
W	Work, energy	ML^2T^{-2}	Joule	J
V	Potential	$ML^2T^{-2}Q^{-1}$	Volt	V
p	Dipole moment	LQ	Coulomb-meter	C-m
I	Current	$T^{-1}Q$	Ampere	A
J	Current density	$L^{-2}T^{-1}Q$	Ampere/meter^2	A/m^2
$\mu_{e,h}$	Mobility	$M^{-1}TQ$	meter^2/volt-second	m^2/V-s
σ	Conductivity	$M^{-1}L^{-3}TQ^2$	Mho/meter	℧/m
R	Resistance	$ML^2T^{-1}Q^{-2}$	Ohm	Ω
P	Polarization	$L^{-2}Q$	Coulomb/meter^2	C/m^2
$\chi_{e,m}$	Susceptibility	———		
C	Capacitance	$M^{-1}L^{-2}T^2Q^2$	Farad	F
H	Magnetic field intensity	$L^{-1}T^{-1}Q$	Ampere/meter	A/m
K	Surface current density	$L^{-1}T^{-1}Q$	Ampere/meter	A/m
B	Magnetic flux density	$MT^{-1}Q^{-1}$	Weber/meter^2 (or tesla)	Wb/m^2 (or T)
μ_0	Permeability	MLQ^{-2}	Henry/meter	H/m
Φ	Magnetic flux	$ML^2T^{-1}Q^{-1}$	Weber	Wb
V_m	Magnetic scalar potential	$T^{-1}Q$	Ampere	A
A	Vector magnetic potential	$MLT^{-1}Q^{-1}$	Weber/meter	Wb/m
T	Torque	ML^2T^{-2}	Newton-meter	N-m
m	Magnetic moment	$L^2T^{-1}Q$	Ampere-meter^2	A-m^2
M	Magnetization	$L^{-1}T^{-1}Q$	Ampere/meter	A/m
$\mathcal{R}$	Reluctance	$M^{-1}L^{-3}Q^2$	Ampere-turn/weber	A-t/Wb
L	Inductance	ML^2Q^{-2}	Henry	H
ω	Radian frequency	T^{-1}	Radian/second	rad/s
λ	Wavelength	L	Meter	m

Symbol	Name	Dimension	Unit	Abbreviation
η	Intrinsic impedance	$ML^2T^{-1}Q^{-2}$	Ohm	Ω
γ	Propagation constant	L^{-1}	Complex neper/meter	m^{-1}
α	Attenuation constant	L^{-1}	Neper/meter	nep/m
β	Phase constant	L^{-1}	Radian/meter	rad/m
f	Frequency	T^{-1}	Hertz	Hz
$\mathcal{P}$	Poynting vector	MT^{-3}	Watt/meter^2	W/m^2
P	Power	ML^2T^{-3}	Watt	W
δ	Skin depth	L	Meter	m
Γ	Reflection coefficient	——		
s	Standing-wave ratio	——		
G	Conductance	$M^{-1}L^{-2}TQ^2$	Mho	$\mho$
Z	Impedance	$ML^2T^{-1}Q^{-2}$	Ohm	Ω
Y	Admittance	$M^{-1}L^{-2}TQ^2$	Mho	$\mho$
Q	Quality factor	——		

The information in this table may be used to check the dimensions of derived equations and thus to show algebraic mistakes. For instance, the total power radiated by a differential current element as found in Sec. 13.3 is shown to be dimensionally correct as follows:

$$P_{\text{av}} = \frac{\pi}{3}\sqrt{\frac{\mu_0}{\epsilon_0}}\left(\frac{I_0 d}{\lambda}\right)^2$$

$$P = \left[\left(\frac{MLQ^{-2}}{M^{-1}L^{-3}T^2Q^2}\right)^{1/2}\left(\frac{T^{-1}QL}{L}\right)^2\right] = [ML^2T^{-3}]$$

Dimensional analysis cannot provide any information about numerical factors, nor can it differentiate between such expressions as $\nabla \cdot \mathbf{D}$, $\nabla \times \mathbf{D}$, $d\mathbf{D}/dx$, and $\partial\mathbf{D}/\partial x$ (all are $[L^{-3}Q]$). It is evident that the dimensions of a single new quantity appearing in an equation can be found rapidly by writing the corresponding dimensional equation. As a simple example,

$$\mathbf{E} = \nabla \times \nabla \times \mathbf{\Pi}$$

shows that the dimensions of $\mathbf{\Pi}$ (called the *Hertz vector*) are $[ML^3T^{-2}Q^{-1}]$.

A system of units must next be defined. We shall first describe the International System (or the rationalized mks system) which is used in this book and is now standard in electrical engineering and much of physics. It has also been officially adopted as the international system of units by many countries, including the United States.[1] The fundamental unit of length is the meter, defined as 1,650,763.73 times the wavelength of the radiation in vacuum corresponding to the unperturbed transition between the levels $2p_{10}$ and $5d_5$ of krypton 86, the orange-red line.   The second is the fundamental unit of time and the international second is defined as 9,192,631,770 periods of the transition frequency between the hyperfine levels $F = 4$, $m_F = 0$, and $F = 3$, $m_F = 0$ of the ground state $^2s_{1/2}$ of the atom of cesium 133, unperturbed by external fields.   The standard mass of one kilogram is defined as the mass of an international standard in the form of a platinum-iridium cylinder at the International Bureau of Weights and Measures at Sèvres, France.   The unit of temperature is the Kelvin degree, defined by placing the triple-point temperature of water at 273.16 degrees Kelvin.   A fifth unit is the candela, defined so that the luminous intensity of an omnidirectional radiator at the freezing temperature of platinum is 0.006 candela per square meter.

The last of the fundamental units is the coulomb.   Before explicitly defining the coulomb, we must first define the newton and the ampere.   The mks unit of force is the newton, and it is defined in terms of the other fundamental units from Newton's third law as the force required to produce an acceleration of one meter per second per second on a one-kilogram mass.   We next define the ampere as the constant current present in two straight parallel conductors of infinite length and negligible cross section, separated one meter in vacuum, that produces a repulsive force of 2×10^{-7} newtons per meter length between the two conductors.   The coulomb is then defined as the charge transported in one second by a current of one ampere.

Returning to the definition of the ampere, the force between the two parallel conductors is known to be

$$ F = \mu_0 \frac{I^2}{2\pi d} \qquad [MLT^{-2}] $$

and thus

$$ 2 \times 10^{-7} = \mu_0 \frac{1}{2\pi} $$

or

$$ \mu_0 = 4\pi\ 10^{-7} \qquad [MLQ^{-2}] $$

We thus find that our definition of the coulomb and ampere has been formulated in such a way as to assign an exact simple numerical value to the permeability of free space.

---

[1] Although the United States recognizes the mks system or International System and has legally sanctioned the use of metric units since 1866, the so-called English system of units is also legally sanctioned, and it is the system in common usage.   It will probably be many years before odometers are calibrated in kilometers, potatoes are weighed in newtons, and Miss America is a 90–60–90. However, such agencies as the National Bureau of Standards and the National Aeronautics and Space Administration make extensive, but not exclusive, use of the International System.

Although the meter, the second, the kilogram, the Kelvin degree, and the candela have been defined by direct comparison with an international standard or by direct measurement, we see that the coulomb is defined indirectly. Moreover, although we do not say so, it is obvious that the fifth step in the definition sequence was the assignment of a value of $4\pi10^{-7}$ to μ_0. This indirect definition of the coulomb may be illustrated by considering a sequence of definitions in which we first define the standard mass as before, choose time as the next fundamental dimension, and then define the fundamental unit of time as the "jiffy," the time required to travel one meter at the velocity of light in free space. The velocity of light would then have the simple value of one meter per jiffy, but the value of the standard jiffy would depend upon a measurement analogous to our measurement of the velocity of light in the International System. Scientists would devise elaborate experiments, not to determine the velocity of light (one meter per jiffy, as every schoolboy knows), but to ascertain the number of periods of the cesium transition in a jiffy.[1]

Returning to the International System, the units in which the other electric and magnetic quantities are measured are given in the body of the text at the time each quantity is defined, and all of them can be related to the basic units already defined. For example, our work with the plane wave in Chap. 11 shows that the velocity with which an electromagnetic wave propagates in free space is

$$U_0 = \frac{1}{\sqrt{\mu_0\epsilon_0}}$$

and thus

$$\epsilon_0 = \frac{1}{\mu_0 U_0^2} = \frac{1}{4\pi10^{-7}U_0^2} \qquad [M^{-1}L^{-3}T^2Q^2]$$

Thus the numerical value of ϵ_0 depends upon the measured value of the velocity of light in vacuum, $(2.997925 \pm 0.000003) \times 10^8$ m/s.

The several units are also given in Table B.1 for easy reference.

Finally, other systems of fundamental dimensions have been used in electricity and magnetism. In the electrostatic system of units (esu), Coulomb's law is written for free space,

$$F = \frac{Q_1Q_2}{R^2} \qquad \text{(esu)}$$

and the dimensional symbol for charge is expressible in terms of the mechanical units as $[M^{1/2}L^{3/2}T^{-1}]$. Thus the number of fundamental dimensions is reduced by one. One of the undesirable consequences of this reduction is that less dimensional information is available for the electrostatic quantities. For example, D and E both have the esu dimensional symbol of $[M^{1/2}L^{-1/2}T^{-1}]$, and the possibility of their confusion is present. It is also evident that fractional exponents are necessary. The gram and centimeter are the fundamental units of mass and distance, and the esu system is therefore a cgs system.

---

[1] Given (correctly) in the latest Jiffyland scientific journals as $(3,066.331 \pm 0.003)$ periods/jiffy.

In a similar manner, the electromagnetic system of units (emu) is based on Coulomb's law for magnetic poles, and the dimensional symbol of the magnetic pole may be written as a function of only $[M]$, $[L]$, and $[T]$. When electric quantities are expressed in esu units, magnetic quantities in emu units, and both appear in the same equation (such as Maxwell's curl equations), the velocity of light appears explicitly. This follows from noting that in esu $\epsilon_0 = 1$, but $\mu_0\epsilon_0 = 1/U_0^2$, and therefore $\mu_0 = 1/U_0^2$, and in emu $\mu_0 = 1$, and hence $\epsilon_0 = 1/U_0^2$. Thus, in this intermixed system known as the Gaussian system of units,

$$\nabla \times \mathbf{H} = 4\pi\mathbf{J} + \frac{1}{U_0}\frac{\partial\mathbf{D}}{\partial t} \qquad \text{(Gaussian)}$$

Other systems include the factor 4π explicitly in Coulomb's law, and it then does not appear in Maxwell's equations. When this is done the system is said to be rationalized. Hence the Gaussian system is an unrationalized cgs system (when rationalized it is known as the Heaviside-Lorentz system), and the International System we have used throughout this book is a rationalized mks system.

Table B.2 gives the conversion factors between the more important units of the International System (or rationalized mks system) and the Gaussian system. The conversion factor X is used by setting one mks unit equal to X Gaussian units. For example, 1 C $= 3 \times 10^9$ statC. The velocity of light is to be used in cgs units; that is, $U_0 = (2.997925 \pm 0.000003)10^{10}$ cm/s $\doteq 3 \times 10^{10}$ cm/s.

TABLE B.2 **Conversion of mks or International Units to Gaussian Units**

Quantity	mks unit	X	Gaussian unit	
Q	C	$10^{-1}U_0$	StatC	(esu)
E	V/m	$10^6/U_0$	StatV/cm	(esu)
D	C/m^2	$4\pi \times 10^{-5}U_0$	Lines/cm^2	(esu)
ρ	C/m^3	$10^{-7}U_0$	StatC/cm^3	(esu)
V	V	$10^8/U_0$	StatV	(esu)
I	A	10^{-1}	AbA	(emu)
H	A/m	$4\pi \times 10^{-3}$	Oersted	(emu)
B	Wb/m^2	10^4	Gauss	(emu)
Φ	Wb	10^8	Maxwell	(emu)
L	H	10^9	AbH	(emu)
C	F	$10^{-9}U_0^2$	StatF	(esu)
R	Ω	10^9	AbΩ	(emu)
ϵ	F/m	$4\pi \times 10^{-11}U_0^2$		(esu)
μ	H/m	$10^7/4\pi$		(emu)
σ	$\mho$/m	10^{-11}	Ab$\mho$/cm	(emu)

C MATERIAL CONSTANTS

Table C.1 lists typical values of the relative dielectric constant ϵ_R for several common insulating or dielectric materials. The values should only be considered representative for each material, and they apply to normal temperature and humidity conditions and to very low audio frequencies.

TABLE C.1   **Relative Dielectric Constant**

Material	ϵ_R	Material	ϵ_R
Air	1.0006	Polyethylene	2.26
Bakelite	4.9	Polystyrene	2.53
Glass (Pyrex)	5	Porcelain	6
Glycerine	45	Quartz (fused)	3.8
Mica	6	Soil (sandy)	3
Mineral oil	2.4	Teflon	2.03
Neoprene	6.7	Vacuum	1
Nylon	3.7	Water (distilled)	80
Plexiglas	3.4	Wood (dry)	4

Table C.2 gives the conductivity σ for several good conductors and good insulators and for a few intermediate materials which cannot generally be classed as either. The values apply at zero frequency.

TABLE C.2   **Conductor and Insulator Conductivity**

Material	σ, $\mho/m$	Material	σ, $\mho/m$
Silver	6.17×10^7	Water (fresh)	10^{-3}
Copper	5.80×10^7	Water (distilled)	2×10^{-4}
Aluminum	3.72×10^7	Soil (sandy)	10^{-5}
Brass	1.5×10^7	Bakelite	10^{-9}
Solder	0.7×10^7	Porcelain	2×10^{-13}
Nichrome	0.089×10^7	Quartz	10^{-17}
Water (sea)	4		

INDEX